The Facility Guide to OBRA Regulations and the Long Term Care Survey Process

- Survey Protocols (SOM, Appendix P)
  - Guidance to Surveyors (SOM, Appendix PP)
    - CMS Survey Process Forms

D1451689

MED·PASS®
The Fine Art of Document Design

MED·PASS
Heaton™
RESOURCES

H50192

10800 Industry Lane
Miamisburg, OH 45342
800-438-8884 (phone)   800-230-8687 (fax)
www.heaton.org
www.med-pass.com

Published by

MED-PASS, Inc.

Printed in the United States of America

Revised December 2009

Editors: Terri Pate, Stacy Yale, RN, BSN

Product number
H50192

The Facility Guide to OBRA Regulations and the Long-Term Care Survey Process

Chapter 1
Survey Protocol for Long-Term Care Facilities (SOM, Appendix P)

This chapter contains instructions for surveyors on how to conduct the survey process. The seven survey tasks and some of the investigative protocols to the survey process are included.

Chapter 2
Guidance to Surveyors for Long-Term Care Facilities (SOM, Appendix PP)

This chapter contains current OBRA regulations, interpretive guidelines, survey procedures and probes, and investigative protocols as issued in CMS' Internet-only manual and the *Federal Register*.

Chapter 3
Exhibits — CMS Survey Process Forms for Long-Term Care Facilities

This chapter contains sample forms and documents (exhibits) that surveyors use when conducting facility surveys.

[This page intentionally left blank]

The Facility Guide to OBRA Regulations, and the Long Term Care Survey Process

- Survey Protocols (SOM, Appendix P)
  - Guidance to Surveyors (SOM, Appendix PP)
  - CMS Survey Process Forms

Chapter 1

Survey Protocol for Long-Term Care Facilities (SOM, Appendix P)

Sources

CMS Publication # 100-07, Appendix P, *State Operations Manual*, Transmittal # 42, dated April 24, 2009.

CMS Publication # 100-07, Appendix P, *State Operations Manual*, Transmittal # 41, dated April 10, 2009.

CMS Publication # 100-07, Appendix P, *State Operations Manual*, Transmittal # 31, dated January 4, 2008.

CMS Publication # 100-07, Appendix P, *State Operations Manual*, Transmittal # 26, dated August 17, 2007.

CMS Publication # 100-07, Appendix P, *State Operations Manual*, Transmittal # 22, dated December 15, 2006.

The Facility Guide to OBRA Regulations, and the Long-Term Care Survey Process

Chapter 1

Survey Protocol for Long-Term Care Facilities (SOM, Appendix P)

Index

(Rev. 42, 04-24-09)

I. Introduction

(Rev. 31, Issued: 01-04-08, Effective: 01-04-08, Implementation: 01-04-08)

Skilled nursing facilities (SNFs) and nursing facilities (NFs) are required to be in compliance with the requirements at 42 CFR Part 483, Subpart B, to receive payment under the Medicare or Medicaid programs. To certify a SNF or NF, complete at least a:

- Life Safety Code (LSC) survey; and

- Standard Survey. There are two types of Standard Surveys, the Traditional Survey and the Quality Indicator Survey (QIS). CMS deems both as surveys of record to evaluate compliance of nursing homes with the requirements at 42 CFR 483.5-483.75:

  o The Traditional Survey, which uses Forms CMS-670, CMS-671, CMS-672, CMS-677, and CMS-801 through CMS-807 (see Exhibits 85, 86, and 88 thru 95*); and *[**Editor's Note:** The exhibit numbers cited are incorrect. The correct exhibit numbers are: Exhibits 74, 85, 88, 89, 91, 92, 93, 94, 95, 96, 264, and 265.]

  o The QIS, which uses the QIS procedures and forms as contained in the QIS Surveyor Training Manual. CMS maintains the authority to identify those States that are permitted to use the QIS. Only CMS-approved training entities and training materials may be used by States to train their surveyors in the QIS. The QIS is used by a State Survey Agency only upon approval by CMS.

    NOTE: CMS is in the process of a staged implementation of the QIS as a replacement for the current (Traditional) survey process. The QIS is a two-staged, computer-assisted survey process with Stage 1 consisting of both computer analysis of offsite data as well as data collected by surveyors onsite from observations, interviews, and record reviews of large computer-selected resident samples. Stage 2 consists of systematic surveyor investigations of triggered issues and residents using the Guidance to Surveyors as well as a set of investigative tools known as critical elements protocols. In addition to the Stage 1 and Stage 2 sample-based investigations, the QIS also contains several facility-level tasks that are unstaged and are completed either on every survey or when triggered as areas of concern. reviews of large computer-selected resident samples. The information collected throughout Stage 1 is analyzed by computer to derive a set of approximately 160 Quality of Care Indicators (QCIs) that are used to compare the facility being surveyed to national norms. QCIs that score beyond a statistical threshold are computer-selected for Stage 2 review, and the relevant residents are also computer selected. Stage 2 consists of systematic surveyor investigations of triggered issues and residents using a set of detailed investigative tools known as critical elements protocols. In addition to the Stage 1 and Stage 2 sample-based investigations, the QIS also contains several facility-level tasks that are unstaged and are completed either on every survey or when triggered as areas of concern.

    During this period, as CMS conducts pilot implementation, CMS deems both the QIS and Traditional Survey as surveys-of-record to evaluate compliance of nursing homes with the requirements at 42 CFR 483.5-483.75.

Do not announce SNF/NF surveys to the facility. Conduct standard surveys and complete them on consecutive workdays, whenever possible. They may be conducted at any time including weekends, 24 hours a day. When standard surveys begin at times beyond the business hours of 8:00 a.m. to 6:00 p.m., or begin on a Saturday or Sunday, the entrance conference and initial tour should be modified in recognition of the residents' activity (e.g., sleep, religious services) and types and numbers of staff available upon entry.

Use the standard survey procedure discussed in this section for all standard surveys of SNFs and NFs, whether freestanding, distinct parts, or dually participating. For surveys of facilities predominantly serving short stay residents, modifications of offsite survey preparation and sampling procedures will be necessary.

> **NOTE:** Do not use this process for surveys of intermediate care facilities for the mentally retarded (ICFs/MR), swing-bed hospitals, or skilled nursing sections of hospitals that are not separately certified as SNF distinct parts. Survey Protocols and Interpretive Guidelines for these surveys are found in Appendix J* (ICFs/MR) and Appendix T* (swing-bed hospitals and hospitals with non-distinct part SNFs). *[**Editor's Note:** The references cited are referring to Appendix J and Appendix T of the *State Operations Manual*.]

When the survey team suspects substandard quality of care (SQC), expand the standard (or abbreviated) survey sample as necessary to determine scope. If the existence of SQC is verified, then inform the Administrator that the facility has SQC and an extended (or partial extended) survey will be conducted.

Surveys

If a possible noncompliant situation related to any requirement is identified while conducting the information gathering tasks of the survey, investigate the situation to determine whether the facility is in compliance with the requirements.

Standard Survey

The QIS Standard Survey is composed of Tasks 1 – 9 and the Traditional Standard Survey is composed of Tasks 1 – 7. Both versions of the survey process are resident-centered, outcome-oriented inspections that rely on a case-mix stratified sample of residents to gather information about the facility's compliance with participation requirements. Outcomes include both actual and potential negative outcomes, as well as failure of a facility to help residents achieve their highest practicable level of well-being. Based on the specific procedures detailed in this Appendix, a standard survey assesses:

- Compliance with residents' rights and quality of life requirements;

- The accuracy of residents' comprehensive assessments and the adequacy of care plans based on these assessments;

- The quality of care and services furnished, as measured by indicators of medical, nursing, rehabilitative care and drug therapy, dietary and nutrition services, activities and social participation, sanitation and infection control; and

- The effectiveness of the physical environment to empower residents, accommodate resident needs, and maintain resident safety, including whether requested room variances meet health, safety, and quality of life needs for the affected residents.

Extended Survey

The extended survey is conducted after substandard quality of care is determined during a standard survey. If, based on performing the resident-centered tasks of the standard survey it is determined that the facility has provided substandard quality of care in 42 CFR 483.13, Resident Behavior and Facility Practices; 42 CFR 483.15, Quality of Life; and/or 42 CFR 483.25, Quality of Care, conduct an extended survey within 14 days after completion of the standard survey. (See Section II.A.2. for further information about the QIS extended survey and Section III* for further information about the Traditional Extended Survey. *[**Editor's Note:** The section number cited is incorrect. The correct section number is II.B.2.]

Abbreviated Standard Survey

This survey focuses on particular tasks that relate, for example, to complaints received or a change of ownership, management or director of nursing. The abbreviated standard survey does not cover all aspects covered in the standard survey, but rather concentrates on a particular area of concern(s). For example, an abbreviated standard survey may be conducted to substantiate a complaint. The survey team can expand the abbreviated standard survey to cover additional areas, or to a Traditional Standard Survey if, during the Abbreviated Standard Survey, evidence is found that warrants a more extensive review. (See also Chapter 5* of this manual for additional administrative procedures related to complaints.) At this time, the QIS is not used to conduct an abbreviated standard survey. See §II.A.4. below for investigation of complaints during the QIS standard survey. *[**Editor's Note:** The reference cited is referring to Chapter 5 of the *State Operations Manual*.]

Partial Extended Survey

A partial extended survey is always conducted after substandard quality of care is found during an abbreviated standard survey or during a revisit, when substandard quality of care was not previously identified. If, based on performing the abbreviated standard survey or revisit it is determined that the facility has provided substandard quality of care in 42 CFR 483.13, Resident Behavior and Facility Practices; 42 CFR 483.15, Quality of Life; and/or 42 CFR 483.25, Quality of Care, conduct a partial extended survey. (See Section III* for further information about the partial extended survey. At this time, the QIS is not used for partial extended surveys.) *[**Editor's Note:** The section number cited is incorrect. The correct section number is II.B.2.]

Post-Survey Revisit (Follow-Up)

The post-survey revisit is an onsite visit intended to verify correction of deficiencies cited in a prior survey. See §2732 and Appendix P, Part I, Section VI*, "Writing the Statement of Deficiencies." *[**Editor's Note:** The section number cited is incorrect. The correct section number is III.] (See Section II.A.3*. for further information about the QIS revisit and Section VI. for further information about the Traditional revisit.) *[**Editor's Note:** The section number cited is incorrect. The correct section number is II.B.3.] If substandard quality of care is determined during a revisit, complete a partial extended survey, if a partial extended or extended survey had not been conducted as the result of the prior standard or abbreviated standard survey.

Initial Certification Survey

In a survey for initial certification of SNFs or NFs, perform the tasks of both the Traditional Standard and Extended Surveys. During the initial survey, focus both on residents and the structural requirements that relate to qualification standards and resident rights notification, whether or not problems are identified during the information gathering tasks. Gather additional information to verify compliance with every tag number. For example, during an initial survey, verify the qualifications of the social worker, dietitian, and activities professional. Also, review the rights notification statements on admissions contracts. Complete the "Statement of Deficiencies and Plan of Correction" (Form CMS-2567) in Exhibit 7.

Specialty Surveyors

All members of a survey team need not be onsite for the entire survey. Specialty surveyors participating in surveys (e.g., a pharmacist, physician, or registered dietitian) must be onsite during that portion of the survey dealing with their area of expertise. However, they must conduct that portion while the rest of the team is present. All members of the survey team should enter the facility at the same time, if possible. Before leaving the facility, at the completion of his/her portion of the survey, the specialty surveyor must meet with the team or team coordinator to discuss his/her findings and to provide supporting documentation. The specialty surveyor should also share any information he/she obtained that may be useful to other team members. If he/she is not present at the information analysis for deficiency determination, the specialty surveyor should be available by telephone at that time and during the exit conference.

Team Communication

Throughout the survey process, the team (including specialty surveyors onsite at the time) should discuss among themselves, on a daily basis, observations made and information obtained in order to focus on the concerns of each team member, to facilitate information gathering and to facilitate decision making at the completion of the standard survey.

II. The Survey Process

II.A. - The Quality Indicators Survey (QIS)

The QIS survey is used as the survey-of-record only for states that have received CMS approval, and only by surveyors who have completed QIS training. Sections II.A.1.-4. below describe the use of the QIS for standard surveys, extended surveys, post-survey revisits, and complaint investigations.

1. The QIS Standard Survey

The QIS standard survey consists of the following Tasks (details are contained in the QIS Surveyor Training Manual, which is incorporated by reference):

Introduction

Task 1: Offsite Survey Preparation:

- Offsite Survey Preparation and Initial Sampling

Task 2: Onsite Preparatory Activities and Entrance Conference

- Prior to the Entrance Conference
- Entrance Conference
- Possible Off Hours Activities

Task 3: Initial Tour

- Tour

Task 4: Stage I Survey Tasks

- Finalize Sample Selection

  o Stage I Sample Selection Procedures

- Stage I Team Meetings (first meeting)
- Stage I Information Gathering
- Stage I Admission Sample Review

  o Medical Record Review

- Stage I Census Sample Review

  o Resident Interviews
  o Resident Unavailable for Interviews
  o Resident Observations
  o Staff Interviews
  o Medical Record Review
  o Family Interviews

Task 5: Non-Staged Survey Tasks

- Resident Council President/Representative Interview
- Dining Observation
- Kitchen/Food Service Observation
- Infection Control Policies and Practices
- Demand Billing Review
- Abuse Prohibition Review
- Quality Assessment and Assurance (QA&A Review)

Task 6: Transition From Stage I to Stage II

- Update the Resident Pool
- Review Completion of Stage I
- Review Surveyor-Initiated Residents and/or Care Areas
- Import All Data into the Primary Laptop
- Review the Relevant Findings Report
- Review the QCI Results Report

Task 7: Stage II Survey Tasks

- Introduction
- Team Meetings
- Stage II Sample Selection

  o Substituting Residents
  o Supplementing the Sample

- Staff Assignments
- Stage II Information Gathering

  o Stage II Critical Element Pathways
  o Medication Administration Observation and Unnecessary Drug Review

- Facility-Level Investigations

  o Environmental Observation
  o Resident Funds
  o Admission, Transfer, and Discharge Review
  o Sufficient Staff

Task 8: Analysis and Decision-Making: Integration of Information

- Integration of Facility-Level Information
- Integration of Critical Element Pathways
- Analysis of Information Gained
- Analysis of Scope and Severity and Team Decision-Making

Task 9: Exit Conference

- Exit Conference

2. The QIS Extended Survey

When the survey team is conducting a QIS standard survey and they have determined there is substandard quality of care, they will conduct QIS extended survey procedures. Substandard quality of care is defined as one or more deficiencies with scope/severity levels of F, H, I, J, K, or L in any of the following regulatory groupings:

- 42 CFR 483.13, Resident Behavior and Facility Practices;
- 42 CFR 483.15, Quality of Life; and/or
- 42 CFR 483.25, Quality of Care.

The purpose of the QIS extended survey is to gather further information (unless already gathered during the standard survey) concerning the facility's nursing and medical services and administration, in order to evaluate systemic issues with the facility's provision of services and management that may be non-complaint with the long term care requirements, and may have contributed to problems cited in the substandard quality of care deficiency(ies). When conducting the QIS extended survey, the survey team coordinator will surveyor-initiate all Tags within the following regulatory groupings into the QIS survey software: 42 CFR 483.30, Nursing Services; 42 CFR 483.40, Physician Services; and 42 CFR 483.75, Administration. There are no specific QIS forms to assist this review. The survey team shall document their findings about these Tags on Surveyor Notes Worksheets (Form CMS-807) and shall input their findings into the QIS software. If the QIS Staffing Review protocol was not already completed during the standard survey, the survey team will complete this protocol.

At the discretion of the State Survey Agency, the QIS extended survey can be conducted either:

- Prior to the exit conference, in which case the facility will be provided with findings from the standard and extended survey; or

- Subsequent to the standard survey, but no longer than 2 weeks after the completion of the standard survey, if the survey team is unable to complete the extended survey prior to the exit conference.

3. The QIS Post-Survey Revisit (Follow-up)

A QIS post-survey revisit is conducted in accordance with §7317 to confirm that the facility is in compliance and has the ability to remain in compliance. The purpose of the revisit is to reevaluate the specific care and services that were cited as noncompliant during the QIS standard and/or extended survey. The specific procedures for each revisit depend on the deficiencies that were cited during the QIS standard survey. Detailed procedures are found in the QIS Surveyor Training Manual. For each QIS revisit, the surveyor(s) will use portions of the QIS standard survey, only as applicable to their need to evaluate the facility's return to compliance for requirements cited as deficiencies. For all QIS revisits, the surveyor(s) will review offsite the Statement of Deficiencies and conduct a focused review of the summary information from the QIS standard survey. Once onsite, the surveyor(s) will ask the facility to provide a roster of residents. The surveyor(s) will use the QIS software as well as information from the QIS standard survey (such as residents investigated) to surveyor-initiate the Care Areas and/or Tags and residents to be investigated. The surveyor(s) will use Stage 2 Critical Element Pathways (CEs) protocols as applicable to the Tags that have been cited, or the general CE for aspects of care not covered by the other CEs. For example, if deficiencies were cited for pressure ulcers and medication errors, the surveyor(s) would use the pressure ulcer CE and the QIS Medication Administration and Unnecessary Drug Review form to conduct these investigations. The surveyor(s) will input findings into the QIS software and proceed through QIS deficiency decision making, and scoring of scope and severity for any deficiencies that are cited.

4. The QIS Complaint Survey Procedures

The QIS is used for investigation of complaints during a QIS standard survey. The survey team coordinator will surveyor-select the complaint area(s) of concern and the resident(s) involved in the complaint and add them to the list of issues and residents evaluated during the QIS standard survey. The QIS Surveyor Training Manual contains further details concerning the manner in which these surveyor-selected concerns and issues are added to the standard survey for investigation, determination of whether they are substantiated or unsubstantiated, and conveying of findings into the CMS ASPEN data system.

At this time, the QIS is not used for investigation of complaints during an abbreviated standard survey. Surveyors should use the procedures contained in §VII.A.* below for these investigations. *[**Editor's Note:** The section number cited is incorrect. The correct section number is II.B.4.A.]

II.B. - The Traditional Survey

II.B.1 - Traditional Standard Survey Tasks

Task 1 - Offsite Survey Preparation

A. General Objectives

The objectives of offsite survey preparation are to analyze various sources of information available about the facility in order to:

- Identify and pre-select concerns for Phase 1 of the survey, based on the Facility Quality Measure/Indicator Report (see description below at B.3.a*.). *[**Editor's Note:** The section number cited is incorrect. The correct section number is B.1.] This pre-selection is subject to amendment based on the results of the tour;

- Pre-select potential residents for Phase I of the survey based on the Resident Level Quality Measure/Indicator Reports (see description below at B.3.a*.) *[**Editor's Note:** The section number cited is incorrect. The correct section number is B.1.] This pre-selection is subject to amendment based on the results gathered during the tour, entrance conference, and facility Roster/Sample Matrix;

- Note concerns based on other sources of information listed below and note other potential residents who could be selected for the sample; and

- Determine if the areas of potential concerns or special features of the facility require the addition to the team of any specialty surveyors.

B. Information Sources for Offsite Survey Preparation

The following sources of information (1-8) are used during the offsite team meeting to focus the survey.

1. Quality Measure/Indicator Reports

QM/QIs are to be used as indicators of potential problems or concerns that warrant further investigation. They are not determinations of facility compliance with the long term care requirements. There are three QM/QI reports which should be downloaded from the State database:

- Facility Characteristics Report (Exhibit 268)

  This report provides demographic information about the resident population (in percentages) for a selected facility compared to all the facilities in the State. It includes information in the following domains: Gender, age, payment source, diagnostic characteristics, type of assessment, stability of conditions, and discharge potential.

- Facility Quality Measure/Indicator Report (Exhibit 269)

  This report provides facility status for each of the MDS-based QM/QIs (quality measures and quality indicators) as compared to State and national averages. Listed are the individual QM/QIs (grouped by domains). This report begins with a set of 12 domains and a total of 31 QM/QIs for the chronic (long stay) resident population, followed by three additional QM/QIs for the post-acute care (PAC) resident population. For each QM/QI, (reading across a row from left to right) are:

  o The numerator - the number of residents in the facility who have the condition;

  o The denominator - the number of residents in the facility who could have the condition;

  o The facility observed percentage of residents who have the condition;

  o The facility adjusted percentage of residents who have the condition;

  o The State average percentage of residents who have the condition;

  o The national average percentage of residents who have the condition; and

  o The State percentile ranking of the facility on the QM/QI - a descriptor of how the facility compares (ranks) with other facilities in the state. The higher the percentile rank, the greater potential there is for a care concern in the facility.

  o An asterisk is present in any row in which the facility flagged on a QM/QI, which means that the facility is at or above the 90th percentile; and any of the three sentinel event rows if any resident has the condition (see D. below for more information on sentinel events).

- Resident Level Quality Measure/Indicator Reports (Exhibit 270)

  The resident level reports are divided into Chronic Care and PAC samples, to correspond to the division of residents in the Facility Quality Measure/Indicator Report described above. Both reports provide resident-specific information generated using current records from the CMS Minimum Data Set (MDS) data base. An X appears in a QM/QI column for a resident who has that condition. If a QM/QI is risk adjusted, this X is in either the high or low risk subcolumn, indicating whether this resident was at high or low risk to develop the condition. The Chronic Care version contains the following columns for each long-stay resident, reading from left to right:

  o Resident identification number;

  o Resident name in alphabetical order;

o   MDS type of assessment (1 = admission, 2 = annual, 3 = significant change, 4 = significant correction, and 5 = quarterly);

o   Columns for each QM/QI for the chronic care resident in the same order and under the same domains as on the Facility Quality Measure/Indicator Report; and

o   A column that counts how many QM/QIs the resident triggered.

The PAC version contains the following columns for each PAC resident, reading from left to right:

o   Resident identification number;

o   Resident name in alphabetical order;

o   Columns for the three PAC QM/QIs; and

o   A column that counts how many QM/QIs the resident triggered.

NOTE: Resident-specific information in the Resident Level reports must be kept confidential in accordance with the Privacy Act. These reports are only for the use of the State agency, CMS representatives, and the facility.

2.   **Statements of Deficiencies (CMS-2567) and Statements of Isolated Deficiencies Which Cause No Actual Harm With Only Potential For Minimal Harm (Form A)**

Statements of deficiencies from the previous survey should be reviewed, along with the sample resident identifiers list. Review the specific information under each deficiency and note any special areas of concern. For example, a deficiency was cited for comprehensive care planning last year. Share with the team the specific care planning problems that were listed as the reasons for this deficiency. For resident-centered requirements, determine if any residents identified in the deficiency might be good candidates for the sample. For example, a deficiency was cited for abuse partly based on surveyor observation of a staff member striking a resident who was combative. Identify this resident by name and add the name to the Offsite Preparation Worksheet. During the Initial Tour, evaluate this resident for inclusion in the sample.

3.   **OSCAR Report 3, History Facility Profile, and OSCAR Report 4, Full Facility Profile from CMS' OSCAR Computer System**

(Refer to Exhibit 96 for sample copies of Reports 3 and 4.) Report 3 contains the compliance history of the facility over the past 4 surveys. Use it to determine if the facility has patterns of repeat deficiencies in particular tags or related tags. This report also lists the dates of any complaint investigations and Federal monitoring surveys during the 4-year time period.

Report 4 contains information provided by the facility during the previous survey on the Resident Census (Form CMS-672). This report compares facility population characteristics with State, CMS region, and national averages.

4.   **Results of Complaint Investigations**

Review information from both complaints investigated since the previous standard survey and complaints filed with the survey agency, but not yet investigated. Note resident and staff names related to the complaints and note patterns of problems relating to specific wings or shifts.

5.   **Information about Waivers or Variances**

If the facility has, or has requested any staffing waiver or room variances, note these for onsite review. The team will determine onsite if these should be granted, continued, or revoked due to a negative effect on resident care or quality of life.

6. Information from the State Ombudsman Office

Note any potential areas of concern reported by the ombudsman office and note resident names reported as potential sample residents, residents for closed record review, or family members for family interviews and the reasons for their recommendation by the ombudsman.

7. Preadmission Screening and Resident Review Reports (PASRR)

Some States may have formal mechanisms to share with the survey agency the results of PASRR screens for residents with mental illness or mental retardation. If this information is available, evaluate if there are any potential concerns and note names of residents for possible inclusion in the sample.

8. Other Pertinent Information

At times, the survey agency may be aware of special potential areas of concern that were reported in the news media or through other sources. Evaluate this information to determine if there are potential areas of concern that should be investigated onsite.

C. Team Coordinator Responsibilities

The team coordinator and/or designee is responsible for completing the following tasks:

1. Contact the ombudsman office in accordance with the policy developed between the State survey agency and State ombudsman agency. The purposes of this contact are to notify the ombudsman of the proposed day of entrance into the facility and to obtain any information the ombudsman wishes to share with the survey team. Ascertain whether the ombudsman will be available if residents participating in the group or individual interviews wish her/him to be present.

2. Obtain all information sources listed in B. above for presentation at the offsite team meeting. (See Section B. for descriptive information about these reports.) They are as follows:

    *   Specified QI/QM Reports:

        o   Facility Characteristics Report;

        o   Facility Quality Measure/Indicator Report; and

        o   The two resident level reports:

            -   Resident Level Quality Measure/Indicator Report: Chronic Care Sample; and

            -   Resident Level Quality Measure/Indicator Report: Post Acute Care Sample

NOTE: It is important that the QM/QI reports be generated as close to the date of survey as possible, preferably no more than a few days prior to the survey.

    *   Form CMS-2567 and Statement of Isolated Deficiencies Which Cause No Actual Harm With Only Potential For Minimal Harm;

    *   Standard OSCAR Report 3 and 4;

    *   Results of complaint investigations;

    *   Information about waivers or variances;

    *   Information from the State Ombudsman office;

- Preadmission Screening and Resident Review Reports; and

- Other pertinent information.

3. Complete the following additional duties:

- Copy and distribute to the team the facility's floor plan if the team is unfamiliar with the facility's layout;

- Make extra copies of the OSCAR Reports 3 and 4, and the QM/QI reports to be given to the facility's administrator;

- Obtain an extra copy of the group interview worksheet (see Form CMS-806B, Exhibit 94) to give to the council president.

D. Offsite Survey Preparation Team Meeting

Present copies of the information obtained to the survey team members for review at a team meeting offsite. The team must prepare for the survey offsite, so that they are ready to begin the Entrance Conference and Initial Tour immediately after they enter the facility. The team should:

1. Review the Facility Characteristics Report to note the facility's demographics. This report can be used to identify whether the facility's population is unusual, e.g., high prevalence of young or male residents, high prevalence of residents with psychiatric diagnosis, high percentage of significant change assessments, etc.;

2. Use a copy of the Roster/Sample Matrix (Form CMS-802, Exhibit 90[*]) to highlight concerns the team identifies for Phase 1 of the survey, and to list residents pre-selected and the QM/QI conditions for which each was selected. Mark the offsite block on this form to distinguish it from the Phase 1 version that will be completed in Task 4, "Sample Selection;" [*][**Editor's Note:** The exhibit cited is incorrect. The correct numbers are: Exhibits 265, 266, and 267.]

The Facility Quality Measure/Indicator Report divides the QM/QIs into a set for the chronic care residents, followed by three post acute measures, which are based on MDS information for short-stay residents. The three PAC QM/QI items include two that are the same topics as the chronic care residents (13.2, Short-stay residents who had moderate to severe pain, and 13.3, Short-stay residents with pressure ulcers) and one unique item (13.1, Short-stay residents with delirium). Use this report to select concerns based on the following:

- Any sentinel health event QM/QI that is flagged. For the chronic care sample, a "sentinel health event" is a QM/QI that represents a significant occurrence that should be selected as a concern, even if it applies to only one or a few residents. The sentinel event QM/QIs are 5.4, Prevalence of fecal impaction, 7.3, Prevalence of dehydration, and 12.2, Low-risk residents with pressure ulcers. This means that even if one resident has any of these conditions, this QM/QI will flag and the care area must be selected as a concern and the resident with the problem must be selected for the sample. If there are multiple residents who flag on a sentinel event QM/QI, it is not necessary to select all of them;

- Any other QM/QI that is flagged at the 90th percentile; and

- Any unflagged QM/QI in which the facility is at the 75th percentile or greater.

For the items that are duplicated between the chronic care and PAC residents (pain and pressure ulcers), note whether the area of concern was selected based on only chronic or PAC samples, or both. The survey team may also wish to select as concerns any other QM/QIs that are of interest to them because they are related to QM/QIs that have been selected.

3. Begin selection of potential residents for the Phase 1 survey sample with the chronic care sample residents to represent the concerns that have been selected, including selecting residents who have sentinel event QM/QI conditions; if multiple residents have a sentinel event QM/QI condition, it is not necessary to select all of them. Use Table 1 in this section and the number of the total resident census to determine the sample size for the Phase 1 sample. Pre-select a few more residents (3-5) than the actual number that will be required for Phase 1 sample since

some selected residents may no longer be available. Most if not all residents from the PAC sample are likely to have been discharged. The survey team may use this sample of residents from which to select potential closed records for review. (If some PAC residents that triggered a selected QM/QI are still at the facility, the team may select some of these residents in order to investigate issues of concern).

- In any facility in which the team has noted concerns with weight loss, dehydration, and/or pressure sores, select approximately one-half of the pre-selected sample as residents who have one or more of these conditions.

  For the condition of hydration, select a resident who has flagged for the sentinel event QM/QI 7.3 (Prevalence of dehydration) and residents may be selected who have any of the following related QM/QI conditions: 5.4 – Prevalence of fecal impaction; 6.1, - Residents with a urinary tract infection; 7.1 – Residents who lose too much weight; 7.2 – Prevalence of tube feeding; and 9.1 – Residents whose need for help with daily activities has increased. The best residents to select will be those who also have multiple care areas that have been selected as concerns. For any facility in which these concerns were not identified, the team should still select some residents who have these QM/QI conditions, if any, on the Resident Level Quality Measure/Indicator Reports, but this need not be 50% of the Phase 1 sample size.

- For the remaining half of the Phase 1 preliminary sample, select residents to represent the remaining areas of concern.

NOTE: If there are no other QM/QIs that have been selected as concerns, the team may select residents based on other sources of information, e.g., complaints or a report from the ombudsman, or may wait to select the remaining Phase 1 residents based on Initial Tour findings.

If the average length of stay for the facility's population is less than 14 days, there may be little information available. Pre-selection of QM/QI-based concerns and/or the full sample may not be possible. Selection of some or all concerns and residents may need to be totally conducted onsite.

- The survey team should be alert to inconsistencies on the Facility Quality Measure/Indicator Report that may indicate facility error in completing and/or transmitting its Minimum Data Set (MDS) records, or a problem with State's software or CMS' database. The following are some possible indicators of data quality problems:

  o The denominator for QM/QIs that use "all residents" substantially exceeds or is substantially smaller than the facility bed size;

  o The number of residents with a QM/QI condition, i.e., the numerator, exceeds the resident population; or

  o The numerator for a particular QM/QI is zero although other information sources indicate otherwise. For example, the QM/QI report shows zero residents in restraints, but the ombudsman notified the team that she/he verified complaints about restraints. The most common reason for this type of inconsistency is incorrect MDS coding by the facility.

If these or other potential accuracy concerns are noted, the team should add resident assessment accuracy as a concern for the survey.

NOTE: This review need not be done for "short-stay" facilities, which will often have unusual values in the numerator and denominator due to rapid turnover of residents.

The Facility Quality Measure/Indicator Report is generated using the current MDS records in the State database at the time the report was generated. However, it excludes residents who have only an initial MDS record in the system. This was done so that the report reflects the care residents have received while residing in the facility, as opposed to the conditions of residents at the time of admission to the facility. The Resident Level reports are calculated using the most recently transmitted MDS record, e.g., annual, significant change, quarterly, or initial MDS record. Differences could be seen between the Facility Quality Measure/Indicator Report and the Resident Level reports since the former does not use the admission MDS data. For example, a Resident Level report may indicate a resident had a catheter but the Facility Quality Measure/Indicator Report might show a "0." This is not an accuracy problem, it only reflects the use of different data to generate each report.

4. Review the OSCAR reports after the review of the QM/QI reports to add corroborative information to the QM/QI information, e.g., a pattern of repeat deficiencies in a requirement related to a flagged QM/QI, and/or to point out areas of large discrepancies between the QM/QI numerators and the OSCAR Reports, e.g., the OSCAR 4 report lists the facility as having triple the average number of residents in restraints, but the QM/QI for restraints shows the facility has less restraints than most facilities). The team coordinator may wish to discuss such discrepancies with the administrator on entrance to determine the reason for them.

Relate information between Reports 3 and 4 such as a pattern of repeat deficiencies in range of motion and a lower than average percentage of residents receiving rehabilitative services. Also, note any special resident characteristics not contained in the QM/QI reports.

NOTE: Both the OSCAR reports and the QM/QI reports can alert surveyors to the acuity and characteristics of the facility's residents at the time the information for these reports was determined. This information may not represent the current condition of residents in the facility at the time of the survey. Keep in mind that the OSCAR information is approximately 1 year old, and the QM/QI information may be from 2-6 months old. Resident characteristics that were reported by the facility during the last survey may have changed significantly and may be the source of some discrepancies between OSCAR and QM/QI information.

5. Review all other sources of information and record additional information on the Offsite Preparation Worksheet (Form CMS-801, Exhibit 89), for example, residents' names for possible inclusion in the Phase 2 sample based on non-QM/QI sources of information (B.2 through 8 above), special features of the facility, or special resident populations. Identify any outstanding complaints needing investigation. At this meeting, establish preliminary surveyor assignments and projections of which days team members will enter early and/or stay late to make observations of resident care and quality of life.

Task 2 - Entrance Conference/Onsite Preparatory Activities

(Rev. 26; Issued: 08-17-07; Effective/Implementation Dates: 08-17-07)

A. Entrance Conference

1. The team coordinator informs the facility's administrator about the survey and introduces team members.

2. After the introduction to the administrator, the other team members should proceed to the initial tour (Task 3), while the team coordinator conducts the entrance conference.

3. The team coordinator should:

   - Request a copy of the actual working schedules for licensed and registered nursing staff for this time period by the end of the tour or earlier if possible.

   - Inform facility staff that the survey team will be communicating with them throughout the survey and will ask for facility assistance when needed. (See §2713.A for further information about facility staff accompanying surveyors.) Advise them that they have the opportunity to provide the team with any information that would clarify an issue brought to their attention.

   - Explain the survey process and answer any questions from facility staff.

   - Give the Administrator copies of the QM/QI reports and the OSCAR 3 and 4 reports that are being used for the survey. Briefly explain these reports and how they were used by the survey team in Task 1. If there are discrepancies between the OSCAR information and the QM/QI Facility Characteristics report, ask the administrator, or person designated by the administrator, to explain the discrepancies.

   - Ask the administrator to describe any special features of the facility's care and treatment programs, organization, and resident case-mix. For example, does the facility have a special care unit for residents with dementia? Are residents with heavy care needs placed in particular units? If so, which ones?

- Ask the administrator if the facility utilizes paid feeding assistants. If yes, request further information about how and where the paid feeding assistants receive their training. Determine whether the training for the paid feeding assistant was provided through a State-approved training program by qualified professionals as defined by State law, with a minimum of 8 hours of training.

- Request the names of staff (including agency staff) who have successfully completed training for paid feeding assistants, and who are currently assisting selected residents with eating meals and/or snacks;

  NOTE: Paid feeding assistants must work under the supervision of a registered nurse (RN) or licensed practical nurse (LPN). Therefore, if a facility has a nursing waiver, that facility cannot use paid feeding assistants when a licensed nurse is not available.

- Inform the administrator that there will be interviews with individual residents, groups of residents, family members, friends, and legal representatives, and that these interviews are conducted privately, unless the interviewees request the presence of a staff member. Ask the administrator to ensure that there are times during the survey when residents can contact the survey team without facility staff present and without having to ask facility staff to leave or to allow access to the team.

- Determine through interview with the administrator if the facility has a functioning QA&A committee. Determine:

  Which staff participate on the committee;

  o   Who leads the committee;

  o   How often the committee meets; and

  o   With whom should the survey team discuss QA&A concerns.

- Ask the administrator to provide the following information within 1 hour of the conclusion of the entrance conference (or later at the survey team's option):

  1.   List of key facility personnel and their locations, e.g., the Administrator; directors of finance, nursing services, social services, and activities; dietitian or food supervisor; rehabilitation services staff; charge nurses; pharmacy consultant; plant engineer; housekeeping supervisor; persons responsible for infection control and quality assurance; health information management professional; and the medical director;

  2.   A copy of the written information that is provided to residents regarding their rights;

  3.   Meal times, dining locations, copies of all menus, including therapeutic menus that will be served for the duration of the survey;

  4.   Medication pass times (by unit, if variable);

  5.   List of admissions during the past month, and a list of residents transferred or discharged during the past 3 months with destinations;

  6.   A copy of the facility's layout, indicating the location of nurses' stations, individual resident rooms, and common areas, if not obtained in Task 1;

  7.   A copy of the facility admission contract(s) for all residents, i.e., Medicare, Medicaid, other payment sources;

8. Facility policies and procedures to prohibit and investigate allegations of abuse and the name of a person the administrator designates to answer questions about what the facility does to prevent abuse. (See Task 5G, Abuse Prohibition Review, for further information);

9. Evidence that the facility, on a routine basis, monitors accidents and other incidents, records these in the clinical or other record; and has in place a system to prevent and/or minimize further accidents and incidents;

   NOTE: **At the discretion of the facility, this evidence could include or be a record of accident and incident reports.**

10. The names of any residents age 55 and under; and

11. The names of any residents who communicate with non-oral communication devices, sign language, or who speak a language other than the dominant language of the facility.

- Ask the facility to complete, to the best of their ability, the Roster/Sample Matrix (Form CMS-802), including all residents on bed-hold, by the end of the initial tour, or to provide this information in some other format, e.g., computer-generated list.

NOTE: This is an important source of resident information, which is crucial for the team to have for their sample selection meetings. Stress to the facility that this form should be completed first and given to the team coordinator by the end of the initial tour. After the Roster/Sample Matrix is delivered to the team, the facility may make modifications for accuracy or add additional information within 24 hours.

- Ask the facility to provide the following within 24 hours of the Entrance Conference:

1. A completed Long Term Care Facility Application for Medicare and Medicaid (Form CMS-671), (see Exhibit 85) and a Resident Census and Conditions of Residents (Form CMS-672), (See Exhibit 86[*]); and [*][**Editor's Note:** The exhibit number cited is incorrect. The correct number is Exhibit 264.]

2. A list of Medicare residents who requested demand bills in the last 6 months (SNFs or dually-participating SNF/NFs only).

- Also, ask the administrator the following questions:

1. Which, if any, rooms have less square footage than required? Do you have a variance in effect and are you prepared to continue to request a variance for any such rooms? (F458)

2. Which, if any, rooms are occupied by more than four residents? Do you have a variance in effect and are you prepared to continue to request a variance for any such rooms? (F457)

3. Is there at least one window to the outside in each room? (F461)

4. Which, if any, bedrooms are not at or above ground level? (F461)

5. Do all bedrooms have access to an exit corridor? (F459)

6. What are the procedures to ensure water is available to essential areas when there is a loss of normal supply? (F466)

NOTE: If the survey is commencing at times beyond the business hours of 8:00 a.m. to 6:00 p.m., or on a Saturday or Sunday, once onsite, announce the survey, ascertain who is in charge, ask the person to notify the administrator that a survey has begun. Modify the entrance conference in accordance with staff available and complete the task and the onsite preparatory activity as appropriate within the context of the survey.

4. For any survey conducted outside of the influenza season (October 1-March 31), obtain the name of the staff person who is responsible for coordinating and implementing the facility's immunization program to request a list of current residents who were in the facility during the previous influenza season, October 1 to March 31.

B. Onsite Preparatory Activities

1. In areas easily observable by residents and visitors, post, or ask the facility to post, signs announcing that a survey is being performed and that surveyors are available to meet with residents in private.

2. The team coordinator or designee should contact the resident council president after the Entrance Conference to introduce her/himself and to announce the survey. Provide the president with a copy of the group interview questions. Request the assistance of the president for arranging the group interview and to solicit any comments or concerns. Ask the council president for permission to review council minutes for the past 3 months (see Task 5D, Section 3B, for further information). If there is not an active resident council, or if the council does not have officers, ask for a list of residents who attend group meetings, if any, and select a resident representative to assist in arranging the group interview. If the ombudsman has indicated interest in attending the group interview, ask the president if that is acceptable to the group; if it is, notify the ombudsman of the time/place of the meeting.

3. The team coordinator, the surveyor assigned to conduct the group interview, or a designee should arrange for date, time and private meeting space for the interview. Advise the facility staff that non-interviewable residents are not part of this meeting. (See Task 5D for further guidance.)

Task 3 - Initial Tour

A. General Objectives

The Initial Tour is designed to:

- Provide an initial review of the facility, the residents, and the staff;

- Obtain an initial evaluation of the environment of the facility, including the facility kitchen; and

- Confirm or invalidate the pre-selected concerns, if any, and add concerns discovered onsite.

B. General Procedures

The initial tour is used to gather information about concerns which have been pre-selected; new concerns discovered onsite; and whether residents pre-selected for the Phase 1 sample offsite are still present in the facility. In addition, attempt to meet and talk with as many residents as possible during the tour in order to identify other candidates for the sample, to get an initial overview of facility care and services, to observe staff/resident interactions; and to evaluate the impact of the facility environment on the residents. The tour also includes a first brief look at the facility's kitchen.

Document tour information, on either the Roster/Sample Matrix (Form CMS-802 or the Surveyor Notes Worksheet (Form CMS-807). Document any concerns regarding the general environment on the General Observations of the Facility Worksheet, (Form CMS-803) or Surveyor Notes Worksheets, (Form CMS-807). (See Task 5A for further information.) Surveyors may also document notes on the facility's Roster/Sample Matrix or other list of residents provided by the facility. Document any concerns noted in the brief tour of the facility kitchen on the Kitchen/Food Service Observation worksheet (Form CMS-804, Exhibit 92). (See Task 5B for information regarding observations to make during this brief tour.)

C. Protocol

Surveyors should tour individually as assigned by the team coordinator. It is desirable for team members to have a facility staff person who is familiar with the residents accompany them during the tour to answer questions and provide introductions to residents or family. However, do not delay the beginning of the Initial Tour if facility staff are not available. Begin the tour as soon as possible after entering the facility.

NOTE: When standard surveys begin at times beyond the business hours of 8:00 a.m. to 6:00 p.m., or begin on a Saturday or Sunday, the initial tour will need to be modified in recognition of the residents' activity, e.g., sleep, religious services, and types and numbers of staff available upon entry. The tour may focus on specific care and quality of life issues, e.g., restraint use, meal service, use of foam or paper meal service products rather than regular dinnerware, adherence to the planned menu; sufficiency of staff; whether enteral/parenteral fluids are being administered as ordered; whether incontinent residents are being checked, toileted, changed; etc., as appropriate. The tour should not be delayed for lack of staff to accompany the surveyor and/or survey team.

Phase 1- Pre-selected Concerns and Potential Residents:

During the tour, determine whether each resident pre-selected offsite for the Phase 1 sample is still there. Determine which, if any, of the pre-selected Phase 1 sample residents are interviewable residents who can be selected to participate in a Quality of Life Assessment Resident Interview or Group Interview. (See Task 5D.) This can be accomplished by talking with residents and asking questions. Examples of questions that can be asked are: What is your name? What are you planning to do today?

NOTE: Do not rely solely on the information that the facility provides concerning which residents are interviewable. The survey team should determine the residents who are able to participate in a Quality of Life Assessment interview.

If possible, determine if there are family members of non-interviewable residents in the pre-selected Phase 1 sample who can be selected for a Quality of Life Assessment family interview. Also note other non-interviewable residents among the facility population whose family members could be selected for interviews;

Observations of All Residents During the Tour.

Ask staff to identify those residents who have no family or significant others. The team may include one or more of these residents in the Phase 2 sample for investigation of quality of life issues.

Have staff identify newly admitted residents, i.e., who have been admitted within the past 14 days, for possible inclusion in the sample for investigation of decline or deterioration that may have occurred before all MDS, other resident assessment information, and care planning is completed.

Have staff identify any residents for whom transfer or discharge is planned within the next 30 days.

Note residents who are interviewable or who have special factors, as listed in Task 4. When on the Initial Tour, observe and document possible quality of care and quality of life concerns in addition to those pre-selected offsite. If observed concerns involve specific residents, note the resident's name and room number on the worksheet, and the date/time when describing the observed concern. Include the details of the observation in documentation, including any effects on the residents involved.

Conduct a brief initial observation of the kitchen. (See Task 5B for further information).

While on tour, identify the licensed and registered nursing staff who are currently on duty. At the end of the tour, compare the observed staff with the duty roster the facility is to provide. If there are discrepancies between the duty roster and the staff observed onsite, ask the person in charge to explain the discrepancies. This information will be used in Task 6 to determine if the facility is compliant with the requirements for licensed and registered nursing staff at 42 CFR 483.30(a)(2), F353 and 42 CFR 483.30(b)(1), F354.

During the tour focus on the following:

- Quality of Life

    1. Resident grooming and dress, including appropriate footwear;

    2. Staff - resident interaction related to residents' dignity; privacy and care needs, including staff availability and responsiveness to residents' requests for assistance;

3. The way staff talk to residents, the nature and manner of interactions, and whether residents are spoken to when care is given; and

4. Scheduled activities taking place and appropriateness to the residents.

- Emotional and behavioral conduct of the residents and the reactions and interventions by the staff:

  1. Resident behaviors such as crying out, disrobing, agitation, rocking, pacing; and

  2. The manner in which these behaviors are being addressed by staff, including nature and manner of staff interactions, response time, staff availability, and staff means of dealing with residents who are experiencing catastrophic reactions. (See "Abuse Prohibition Investigative Protocol" in Task 5G for a definition of catastrophic reaction.)

- Care issues, how care is provided, and prevalence of special care needs

  1. Skin conditions, e.g., excessive dryness, wetness;

  2. Skin tears, bruising, or evidence of fractures that warrant investigation;

  3. Dehydration risk factors including availability of water for most residents, and other indicators or factors, e.g., the amount and color of urine in tubing and collection bags, dependence on staff, the presence of strong urinary odors, and resident complaints of dry mouth and lips;

  4. Clinical signs such as edema, emaciation and contractures;

  5. Functional risk factors such as poor positioning and use of physical restraints;

  6. Side effects of antipsychotic drug use such as tardive dyskinesia, e.g., lip, tongue or other involuntary abnormal movements;

  7. Presence or prevalence (numbers) of infections including antibiotic resistant strains of bacteria (e.g., Methicillin Resistant Staphylococcus Aureus (MRSA), Vancomycin Resistant Enterococcus (VRE), Clostridium Difficile (C-Diff) or other infections: Urinary tract infections, draining wounds, eye infections, skin rashes (especially if spreading, undiagnosed, and/or not responding to treatment), respiratory infections, gastroenteritis including diarrhea, etc.;

  8. Pressure sores, old scars from pressure sores or evidence of surgical repair of pressure sores;

  9. Amputation;

  10. Significant weight loss;

  11. Feeding tubes and/or improper positioning while feeding is infusing; and

  12. Ventilators, oxygen, or intravenous therapies.

- Impact of the facility environment and safety issues:

  1. Infection control practices, e.g., handwashing, glove use, and isolation procedures);

  2. Functional and clean equipment, including kitchen equipment;

  3. Presentation and maintenance of a homelike and clean environment; and

  4. Availability, use, and maintenance of assistive devices.

NOTE: If the initial tour is being conducted during a mealtime, include an initial brief observation of the dining areas. Note if there are any concerns with meal service, quality of life, positioning, sufficient space, etc.

Task 4 - Sample Selection

A. General Objective

The objective of this task is to select a case-mix stratified sample (see Special Factors to Consider in Sample Selection below for further information) of facility residents based on QM/QIs and other offsite and onsite sources of information in order to assess compliance with the resident-centered long term care requirements.

B. General Procedures

- The Phase 1 sample is pre-selected during Task 1, "Offsite Survey Preparation," based on QM/QIs and other areas of concern. The pre-selected sample is reviewed during the sample selection meeting and residents are retained for the sample unless they are discharged, or the survey team has another reason to substitute, e.g., to select interviewable residents. Each team member is assigned a certain number of residents, completing all facets of review that have been selected including any quality of life assessment protocols selected for these residents.

- The Phase 2 sample is selected onsite, part way through the survey when surveyors have collected enough information to determine the focus of the remainder of the survey. The Phase 2 sample residents are selected to represent new concerns and/or to continue further investigation of Phase 1 concerns when Phase 1 reviews proved inconclusive or when necessary to determine scope of a problem. It is statutorily required that the sample in each facility be case-mix stratified in order to capture both interviewable and non-interviewable residents as well as residents from both heavy and light care categories.

NOTE: If the team is conducting sample selection during meal time, delay or interrupt this task to conduct brief observations of the dining areas. Note if there are any concerns with meal service, quality of life, positioning, sufficient space, etc.

C. Definitions

- **Interviewable Resident** -This is a resident who has sufficient memory and comprehension to be able to answer coherently the majority of questions contained in the Resident Interview. These residents can make day-to-day decisions in a fairly consistent and organized manner.

- **Comprehensive Review** - For Task 5C, "Resident Review," this includes observations, interviews, and record reviews for all care areas for the sampled residents, as applicable.

- **Focused Review** - For Task 5C, "Resident Review," this includes the following:

  o For Phase 1: Observations, interviews and record reviews concerning all highlighted areas of concern and all unhighlighted areas pertinent to the resident; and

  o For Phase 2: Observations, interviews and record review for all highlighted areas of concern pertinent to the resident.

- **Closed Record Review** - For Task 5C, "Resident Review," this includes a record review of residents' care issues and transfer and discharge.

- **Roster/Sample Matrix** - This worksheet, (Exhibit 265, Form CMS-802), is used by the survey team during Offsite Survey Preparation, and at the Phase 1 and Phase 2 Sample Selection meetings to note areas of concern for the survey, and to select residents for the sample. There are separate sets of instructions for the use of this form by the survey team and the facility. (See these instructions at Exhibits 266 and 267.

D. Protocol

1. Phase 1 - Sample Selection

The Phase 1 sample is pre-selected during Task 1, Offsite Survey Preparation, based on the facility's QM/QIs of concern. (See Task 1 for further information.) Final Phase 1 sample selection occurs after the tour is completed and the facility has provided the completed Roster/Sample Matrix (Form CMS-802, Exhibit 265), or provided this information in some other format, e.g., computer-generated list. However, do not delay Phase 1 sample selection if the facility's Roster/Sample Matrix has not arrived. The team will complete the sample selection for Phase 1 by performing the following tasks:

NOTE: For facilities with a population of "short-stay" residents, the team may not have been able to pre-select concerns or potential sampled residents. In that instance, Phase 1 sample selection will occur during this task.

- First determine if any pre-selected concerns should be dropped due to the QM/QI data not representing the conditions of current residents. For example, there was a pre-selected QM/QI concern with residents with tube feedings, but the tour has verified there are no residents in the facility who are receiving tube feedings. Note new concerns and determine if some pre-selected residents can be evaluated for the new concerns as well as those originally selected.

- Review the Roster/Sample Matrix provided by the facility and compare it to the findings from the tour to determine if there is a reason to substitute another resident for any of the residents from the Offsite sample. A pre-selected resident who is no longer in the facility can be considered for the closed record review. The team may substitute other residents for those pre-selected, if necessary. They can select either from the QM/QI reports, the tour, or the facility's Roster/Sample Matrix.

If any resident is substituted for a pre-selected resident, record a short explanation on the Offsite Roster/Sample Matrix next to that person's name, e.g., "discharged."

- Check "Phase 1" on the copy of the Roster/Sample Matrix that will be used to denote the resident sample for Phase 1 of the survey.

  o Highlight the column for each identified concern for Phase 1.

  o Use Table 1 in this section and the number of the total resident census to determine the number of comprehensive and focused reviews, number of closed records, number of resident and family interviews, and the minimum number of residents who have conditions of weight loss, hydration risk and/or pressure sores, i.e., the WHP group. The number in the WHP column represents the minimum total of residents who must be selected for the Phase 1 sample to represent any or all of these conditions. For example, in a facility with 96 residents, out of 12 residents selected for the Phase 1 sample, a minimum of 6 will be those who have any of these conditions mentioned above, if any of these 3 QM/QIs were selected as concerns.

  o Use the unnumbered blocks to the right of Resident Name to fill in the total number of residents in each sub-sample for the entire survey as listed in Table 1. For example, in a facility with a census of 100, the total number of individual interviews is 5. Enter that number in the small block below that title.

  o All residents selected for comprehensive reviews are selected by the team during the Phase 1 sample selection. Residents selected for focused reviews, closed record reviews, individual and family interviews may be selected during Phase 1 or Phase 2 sample selection.

  o Each resident the team selects is entered on the worksheet. Note the following about each resident:

    - Resident number and room number;

    - Surveyor assigned to complete the resident review and any quality of life assessment protocols (Resident Interview or Family Interview) that are selected for the resident;

- Check any columns that pertain to this resident, whether or not they are highlighted as concerns for Phase 1. Each resident will be reviewed for each checked area, not just those that are highlighted; and

- If there is anything about this resident that the team decides to investigate that is not one of the numbered columns on the worksheet, use a blank column at the far right to write the item that will be assessed and check that column for that resident. For example, if the team wants to assess ventilator use for a particular resident, write "ventilator" in one of the blank columns and make a check mark in that column for that resident.

2. Phase 2 Sample Selection

Part way through the survey, after the team has obtained enough information to decide what concerns need further investigation, the team meets to determine the areas of concern, if any, for Phase 2 of the survey and to select the remaining sample. It is not necessary to complete all the reviews of all residents in Phase 1 before this meeting. Determine which Phase 1 concerns are ruled out as these do not need to be carried over into Phase 2 sample selection.

- Select concerns for Phase 2 based on the following:

   o Initial concerns noted during Offsite Survey Preparation or the Initial Tour that have not yet been reviewed;

   o Currently un-reviewed concerns that are related to those under investigation, e.g., adding residents who have had falls based on results of the Phase 1 discovery of a problem with use of psychoactive drugs; and

   o Current concerns for which the information gathered is inconclusive.

- Select residents for the Phase 2 sample based on the following:

   o The statute requires selection of a "case mix stratified" sample (but not for each phase of the sample selection, just for the total sample). This stratification is defined by CMS as including residents who are interviewable and non-interviewable, and as including residents who require heavy and light care. It is important that at least one resident in the sample represent each of these categories. The requirements of the sample selection procedures make it necessary for survey teams to select interviewable and non-interviewable residents in order to complete the Task 5D, Quality of Life Assessment Interviews, so those categories of case-mix stratification will be automatically filled by complying with the sample selection procedures. At the beginning of the Phase 2 sample selection meeting, the team should review the Phase 1 sample to determine if at least one heavy care and one light care resident has been selected to fulfill this portion of the case mix stratification requirement. If not, it is a priority to ensure that if either heavy or light care residents are missing from the Phase 1 sample, that at least one is selected from the missing category in Phase 2.

   o Select residents who represent one or more of the areas of concern the team has selected for Phase 2 of the survey.

   o If no residents have been selected for the Phase 1 sample for hydration, and if any residents are seen during Phase 1 of the survey who appear to have risk factors for dehydration, e.g., such as residents who are dependent on staff for activities of daily living, are immobile, receive tube feedings, or have dementias in which the resident no longer recognizes thirst, select at least one of these residents at risk and review the care area of dehydration.

- During Phase 2 sample selection, a clean copy of the Sample/Matrix worksheet is used as follows:

   o Check "Phase 2" on the copy of the Roster/Sample Matrix that will be used to denote the resident sample for Phase 2 of the survey;

   o Highlight the column for each identified concern for Phase 2;

o Each resident the team selects is entered on the worksheet. Note the following about each resident:

- Resident number and room number;

- Surveyor assigned to complete the resident review and any quality of life assessment protocols (Resident Interview, or Family Interview) that are selected for the resident;

- Checkmarks are made only in the highlighted columns and these residents will be reviewed for these concerns, and any other concerns that are discovered during this review;

- Be sure that residents are selected to complete the required number of resident interviews, family interviews, and closed record reviews.

- If there are no outstanding areas of concern and the team has already selected interviewable, non-interviewable, heavy care and light care residents, then select remaining residents to represent any of the following, in no particular order:

o An area of concern on the worksheet that has not been highlighted, but which the team has determined should be assessed;

o Living units that are unrepresented; and

o Special factors below that have not been reviewed.

NOTE: When selecting the sample in a facility in which there are no outstanding areas of concern, each resident will be reviewed for at least one area on the Roster/Sample Matrix that has not yet been reviewed.

3. Special Factors to Consider in Sample Selection

Residents must be selected for both the Phase 1 and Phase 2 samples as representatives of concerns to be investigated and to fulfill the case mix stratified sample requirement. If during sample selection, many more residents are identified than can be selected to represent the concerns of interest, consider the factors below in determining which residents to select:

- New admissions, especially if admitted during the previous 14 days. Even though the Resident Assessment Instrument (RAI) is not required to be completed for these residents, the facility must plan care from the first day of each resident's admission;

- Residents most at risk of neglect and abuse, i.e., residents who have dementia; no or infrequent visitors, psychosocial, interactive, and/or behavioral dysfunction; or residents who are bedfast and totally dependent on care;

- Residents in rooms in which variances have been granted for room size or number of beds in room;

- Residents receiving hospice services;

- Residents with end-stage renal disease;

- Residents under the age of 55;

- Residents with mental illness or mental retardation; and

- Residents who communicate with non-oral communication devices, sign language, or who speak a language other than the dominant language of the facility.

4.   Other Phase 2 Tasks

- If there are any concerns about residents' funds, check that the amount of the surety bond is at least equal to the amount of residents' funds the facility is managing as of the most recent quarter.

- If concerns have been identified in the area of infection control, review policies and procedures including a focus on what preventative infection control practices the facility has in place. For example, does the facility administer the influenza vaccine yearly to its residents, and administer pneumococcal vaccine to new residents as appropriate (does facility evaluate whether new residents have received the pneumococcal vaccine within the last 5 years)?

- Complete Task 5F Quality Assessment Assurance Review.

- If the group interview has not yet occurred, discuss what special concerns to ask of the group.

- If the facility has or has requested a nurse staffing waiver, review the requirements at 42 CFR 483.30.

- Review the Resident Census and Condition of Residents (Form CMS-672) that the facility has completed. Note any new areas of concern and determine if there appears to be large discrepancies between what is recorded by the facility and what the team has observed. For example, the team has noted 13 residents with pressure sores and the facility has listed 3. If there are large discrepancies, ask the facility to verify their totals. Answer questions F146 - F148 on the Resident Census.

- If the team has identified quality of care problems during Phase 1 of the survey, use the investigative protocol at Task 5C: Nursing Services, Sufficient Staffing to gather information and (at Task 6) to determine compliance with the following requirement: 42 CFR 483.30(a), F353 Nursing services, Sufficient Staff. If problems with staffing have been discovered early in Phase 1, this protocol can begin in Phase 1.

5.   Substituting Residents

If the team has found it necessary during the survey to remove a resident from the sample, e.g., a resident refused to complete the interview, replace this resident with another who best fulfills the reasons the first person was selected. For example, the resident who was removed had been selected because he/she was in restraints and had a pressure sore. Attempt to select another resident who meets both of these criteria. In Phase 1, the substituted resident should be selected from the pre-selected list of residents which was determined offsite, if possible, or from other information gained during the survey. Make the substitution as early in the survey as feasible. Note on the Roster/Sample Matrix that the new resident was substituted for resident #___, and briefly give the reason the first resident was dropped.

6.   Supplementary Sample

If sampled residents are found not to provide enough information to make deficiency determinations concerning specific requirements under review, or to determine if there is "substandard quality of care" (see Task 6 for further information), supplement the sample with residents who represent the areas of concern under investigation. Focus review for these residents only on the concern under investigation and any other concerns that are discovered during this review. Add the names of these residents to the Phase 2 Sample Matrix worksheet, checking the relevant categories. Use the Resident Review Worksheet to complete these investigations.

Table 1 - Survey Procedures for Long Term Care Facilities - Resident Sample Selection

Survey Procedures for Long Term Care Facilities
Resident Sample Selection

Resident Census	Phase 1/ Phase 2	Compre-hensive Reviews *	Focused Reviews *	Closed Rec. Reviews *	Res./ Family Interviews	W, H, P Group **
1 - 4	All / 0	2	2	0	1/1	All
5 - 10	3 / 2	2	2	1	1 / 1	2
11 - 20	5 / 3	2	5	1	2 / 2	3
21 - 40	6 / 4	2	7	1	3 / 2	3
41 - 44	7 / 4	2	8	1	3 / 2	4
45 - 48	7 / 5	2	9	1	3 / 2	4
49 - 52	8 / 5	3	9	1	4 / 2	4
53 - 56	8 / 6	3	9	2	4 / 2	4
57 - 75	9 / 6	4	9	2	4 / 2	5
76 / 80	10 / 6	4	9	3	4 / 2	5
81 - 85	10 / 7	4	10	3	4 / 2	5
86 - 90	11 / 7	4	11	3	4 / 2	6
91 - 95	11 / 8	4	12	3	4 / 2	6
96 - 100	12 / 8	5	12	3	5 / 2	6
101 - 105	13 / 8	5	13	3	5 / 2	7
106 - 110	13 / 9	5	14	3	5 / 2	7
111 - 115	14 / 9	5	15	3	5 / 2	7
116 - 160	14 / 10	5	16	3	5 / 2	7
161 - 166	15 / 10	5	17	3	5 / 2	8
167 - 173	16 / 10	5	18	3	5 / 2	8
174 - 180	16 / 11	5	19	3	5 / 2	8
181 - 186	17 / 11	5	20	3	5 / 2	9
187 - 193	17 / 12	5	21	3	5 / 2	9
194 - 299	18 / 12	5	22	3	5 / 2	9
300 - 400	18 / 12	5	22	3	6 / 3	9
401 -	18 / 12	5	22	3	7 / 3	9

*   Comprehensive reviews plus focused reviews plus closed record reviews added together equals the total sample size (Phase 1 plus Phase 2).

**   For any survey in which there are identified concerns in the areas of (W) unintended weight loss, (H) hydration, and/or (P) pressure sores, this is the minimum total of residents who must be selected for the Phase 1 sample to represent any or all of these conditions.

Task 5 - Information Gathering

(Rev. 22, Issued: 12-15-06, Effective/Implementation: 12-18-06)

Task 5 provides an organized, systematic, and consistent method of gathering information necessary to make decisions concerning whether the facility has met the requirements reviewed during the Standard Survey.

Task 5 includes the following sub-tasks:

5A General Observations of the Facility: Assessment of the environment of the facility affecting the resident's life, health and safety;

5B Kitchen/Food Service Observations: Assessment of the facility's food storage, preparation and service;

5C Resident Review: An integrated, holistic assessment of the sampled residents which includes the assessment of: drug therapies, the quality of life of the resident as affected by his/her room environment and daily interactions with staff, and assessment of those pertinent care concerns identified for each sampled resident by the survey team. Closed record reviews and dining observations are integrated into the resident review;

5D Quality of Life Assessment: Assessment of residents' quality of life through individual interviews, a group interview, family interviews, and observations of residents who are non-interviewable;

5E Medication Pass and Pharmacy Services: An assessment of the pharmaceutical services provided in the facility, including the provision of the medication pass observation; the application of the medication error detection methodology; the provision of services by a licensed pharmacist; and facility procedures and processes in place regarding the acquiring, receiving, dispensing and administering medications, use of controlled medications, and medication access and storage.

5F Quality Assessment and Assurance Review: An assessment of the facility's Quality Assessment and Assurance program to determine if the facility identifies and addresses specific care and quality issues and implements a program to resolve those issues; and

5G Abuse Prohibition Review: A determination of whether the facility has developed and operationalized policies and procedures designed to protect residents from abuse, neglect, involuntary seclusion, and misappropriation of their property. This includes policies and procedures for hiring practices, training and ongoing supervision for employees and volunteers who provide services, and the reporting and investigation of allegations and occurrences that may indicate abuse.

Use survey worksheets and Guidance to Surveyors, also known as the Interpretive Guidelines, for each of the sub-tasks and requirements reviewed in Task 5. While these sub-tasks are discrete information gathering activities, there are a number of things to take into consideration during Task 5.

A. General Procedures

As appropriate, use the interpretations, definitions, probes, and procedures provided in the Guidance to Surveyors to guide the investigation and to help determine whether, based on the investigation and findings, the facility has met the requirements.

Worksheet documentation should be resident-centered, as appropriate. For example, if the lack of a reading light near the resident's bedroom chair is being documented, also note that this resident has said he/she prefers to read in his/her chair, and that the light over the chair is inadequate.

Relate to the requirements and provide clear evidence, as appropriate, of the facility's failure to meet a requirement. As information is collected, keep in mind that the information written on the worksheet will be used by the team to determine if there are any deficiencies, and, if so, the degree of severity and scope. Make documentation specific enough so that these decisions can be made. Include information about how the faulty facility practice affected residents, the number of residents affected, and the number of residents at risk. This documentation will be used both to make deficiency determinations and to categorize deficiencies for severity and scope. The Guidance to Surveyors assists in gathering information in order to determine whether the facility has met the requirements. For example, the facility has care plan objectives which are measurable. If the resident does not meet her/his goals, does the documentation reflect how the lack of implementation of the care plan and/or lack of quarterly assessments prevents the resident from reaching her/his goals?

In conducting the survey, use the worksheets in conjunction with the survey procedures and Guidance to Surveyors. When investigating a concern, note the tag number listed on the worksheet for that requirement and use the Guidance to Surveyors for that tag to direct the investigation.

Devote as much time as possible during the survey to performing observations and conducting formal and informal interviews. Limit record reviews to obtaining specific information, i.e., look at what is needed, not the whole record.

The information gathering tasks are interrelated. Information acquired while doing observations and interviews will direct the record review. Likewise, information obtained while doing the record review may help direct what observations or interviews are needed. Acquire the information that is necessary to make deficiency decisions in Task 6 using the survey worksheets and corresponding Guidance to Surveyors for each of the sub-tasks in Task 5.

Regardless of the task, be alert at all times to the surrounding care environment and activities. For example, while conducting the dining observations of sampled residents and the medication pass observation, observe the environment and residents, e.g., care being given, staff interactions with residents, and infection control practices.

The team should meet on a daily basis to share information, e.g., findings to date, areas of concern, any changes needed in the focus of the survey. These meetings include discussions of concerns observed, possible requirements to which those problems relate, and strategies for gathering additional information to determine whether the facility is meeting the requirements.

Throughout the survey, discuss observations, as appropriate, with team members, facility staff, residents, family members, and the ombudsman. Maintain an open and ongoing dialogue with the facility throughout the survey process. This gives the facility the opportunity to provide additional information in considering any alternative explanations before making deficiency decisions. This, however, does not mean that every negative observation is reported on a daily basis, e.g., at a nightly conference. Moreover, if the negative observation relates to a routine that needs to be monitored over time to determine whether a deficiency exists, wait until a trend has been established before notifying the facility of the problem. If it has been verified through observation and record review that a resident's condition has declined, start the investigation to determine if this decline was avoidable or unavoidable by asking a knowledgeable facility staff member, such as the nurse or other professional staff member charged with responsibility for the resident's care, to provide documentation in the resident's chart that provides the reasons for why they believe this decline occurred. Use this information to guide the investigation, but use professional judgment and team approach to determine if a deficient practice has occurred.

In conducting the tasks of the Standard Survey, situations may be identified to indicate that the facility may not be meeting a requirement not routinely reviewed in the Standard Survey.

Investigate this further. For example, residents at the council meeting say that they have not had a visit from a physician (or extender) for several months. This would lead to an investigation of facility compliance with the requirements for frequency of physician visits.

Verify information and observations in terms of credibility and reliability. If the credibility or reliability of information is doubted, validate that information or gather additional information before using it to make a compliance decision.

B. Observations

The objectives of the observational portion of information gathering are to gather resident-specific information for the residents included in the sample, and also, to be alert to the provision of care, staff-resident interactions, and quality of life for all residents.

C. Informal and Formal Interviews

The objectives of interviews are to:

- Collect information;

- Verify and validate information obtained from other survey procedures; and

- Provide the opportunity for all interested parties to provide what they believe is pertinent information.

Interview residents, staff, family, ombudsman, family council representatives, and other appropriate persons. Informal interviews are conducted throughout the duration of the information gathering tasks of the survey. Formal structured interviews are also done as part of the Quality of Life Assessment protocols. Use the information obtained from interviews to assist in deciding what additional observations and record review information is necessary. Avoid asking leading questions, but use the Guidance to Surveyors for specific requirements to focus questions and determine the significance of the answers.

In general, the individual who provides information during an interview will not be identified as providing that information. However, it is possible that their identity may be revealed if a deficiency is cited based in whole or part on their information, and that deficiency citation is appealed.

If residents appear reticent in providing information or express concern about retaliation:

- Verify that residents have information on whom to contact in the event they become the objects of retaliation by the facility; and

- With the resident's permission, notify the ombudsman of the resident's concerns.

D. Record Review

The objectives of the record review are to:

- Acquire information to direct initial and/or additional observations and interviews;

- Provide a picture of the current status of the resident as assessed by the facility; and

- Evaluate assessments, plans of care, and outcomes of care interventions for residents included in the sample. Record review of RAI information, care planning, implementation of the care plan, and evaluation of care is one facet of the resident review which determines if there has been a decline, improvement, or maintenance in identified focus areas.

NOTE: Do not spend excessive time gathering and recording information from the record. Use the record review to obtain information necessary to validate and/or clarify information obtained through observation and interviews. Ask facility staff to assist in finding any information that has not been found or that requires validation.

E. Determining Citations of Past Noncompliance at the Time of the Current Survey

During information gathering, findings of past noncompliance may be identified. Before considering a citation of past noncompliance with a specific regulatory tag, surveyors must determine if current compliance with the specific regulatory tag exists. Similar to verifying correction of current noncompliance on a revisit, surveyors should use a variety of methods to determine whether correction of the past noncompliance occurred and continues. This may include, but is not limited to, the following:

- Interviews with facility staff, such as the administrator, nursing staff, social services staff, medical director, quality assessment and assurance committee members, and/or other facility staff, as indicated, to determine what procedures, systems, structures, and processes have been changed.

- Reviewing through observation, interview, and record review, how the facility identified and implemented interventions to address the noncompliance. Examples of interventions may include, but are not limited to:

  o The facility's review, revision, or development of policies and/or procedures to address the areas of concerns;

  o The provision and use of new equipment, as necessary;

  o The provision of staff training required to assure ongoing compliance for the implementation and use of new and/or revised policies, procedures, and/or equipment, especially with new and/or temporary staff;

  o The provision of additional staffing, changes in assignments or deployment of staff, as needed; and

  o The provision of a monitoring mechanism to assure that the changes made are being supervised, evaluated, and reinforced by responsible facility staff.

- Evaluating whether the facility has a functioning quality assessment and assurance committee, whose responsibilities include the identification of quality issues; providing timely response to ascertain the cause; implementing corrective action; implementing monitoring mechanisms in place to assure continued correction and revision of approaches as necessary to eliminate the potential risk of occurrence to other residents and to assure continued compliance.

A citation of past noncompliance must meet all of the criteria described in section H of Task 6 below.

Sub-Task 5A - General Observations of the Facility

(Rev. 22, Issued: 12-15-06, Effective/Implementation: 12-18-06)

A. General Objective

The general objective of this task is to observe physical features in the facility's environment that affect residents' quality of life, health, and safety. Use the General Observations of the Facility worksheet (Form CMS-803, Exhibit 91) to complete this task.

B. General Procedures

During the Initial Tour, each surveyor should note and document any concerns in resident rooms and the general environment. Any concerns should be investigated and followed up either through the resident review for sampled residents or during the General Observation task. During the remainder of the survey, one surveyor is assigned to complete the General Observation of the Facility worksheet (Form CMS-803). This surveyor assures that all items on this worksheet are completed. Each surveyor who completes a medication pass observation should review medication storage on the assigned units and provide information regarding that review to the assigned surveyor responsible for the completion of Form CMS-803. All surveyors should share any additional concerns regarding the environment with the surveyor assigned to complete the worksheet. Begin observations as soon as possible after entering the facility, normally after introductions at the entrance conference.

During Task 5A, review the condition of the environment, e.g., cleanliness, sanitation, presence or absence of pests, accident hazards, functioning of equipment, and the proper and safe storage of drugs, biologicals, housekeeping compounds and equipment. (See Form CMS-803 worksheet for specific areas to review.)

C. Making Observations

The focus in Task 5A is on quality of life and environmental health and safety indicators in areas of the facility that would be visited or used by residents. However, some non-resident areas should also be reviewed due to their potential negative effect on residents, e.g., utility rooms.

Document thoroughly at the time of observations. If additional documentation space is needed, use the Surveyor Notes Worksheet Form CMS-807.

Plan to observe the facility's environment at different times during the survey, e.g., first and second shift, common areas when in use by residents.

Share any concerns with the team coordinator and other team members to determine the possible need to gather additional information.

Sub-Task 5B - Kitchen/Food Service Observation

A. General Objective

The general objective of the Kitchen/Food Service Observation is to determine if the facility is storing, preparing, distributing, and serving food according to <u>42 CFR 483.35(h)(2)</u>[*] to prevent food borne illness. [*][**Editor's Note:** The reference cited should be 42 CFR 483.25(i)(2).]

B. General Procedures

One surveyor is assigned to conduct the Kitchen/Food service observation.

NOTE: The surveyor assigned to complete this task should begin the task with a brief visit to the kitchen as part of the initial tour, in order to observe the sanitation practices and cleanliness of the kitchen. Observe whether potentially hazardous foods have been left on counter tops or steam table and/or being prepared, the manner in which foods are being thawed, the cleanliness, sanitary practices, and appearance of kitchen staff, e.g., appropriate attire, hair restraints.

Use the Kitchen/Food Service Observation worksheet to direct observations of food storage, food preparation, and food service/sanitation. (See Kitchen/Food Service Observation worksheet (Form CMS-804, <u>Exhibit 92</u>) for specific areas to review).

In addition to completion of the Form CMS-804, also evaluate:

- The availability of food in relation to the number of residents; and

- Whether food being prepared is consistent with the written, planned menu.

NOTE: During team meetings, if surveyors, during the Dining Observation portion of the Resident Review, identified any concerns, such as the provision of meals that are not consistent in quality (such as color and texture of vegetables or meats, the preparation and presentation of mechanically altered foods); complaints regarding taste or texture of food and foods with an "off" or bad odor; or residents being at nutritional risk, including high prevalence of residents with unintended weight loss; then the surveyor assigned to Task 5(b) should review the following as appropriate.

Direct observations to the tray line and kitchen to determine:

- If recipes are available and consistent with the menu and followed by employees;

- If appropriate equipment is available and used to prepare and serve foods;

- If the food is being held for more than 30 minutes prior to food service, e.g., in the steam table, oven, refrigerator rather than freezer for frozen foods, etc.; and

- If cooked leftovers used during food preparation were stored and used within the appropriate time frames, and reheated to at least 165 degrees F.

Sub-Task 5C - Resident Review

(Rev. 42; Issued: 04-24-09; Effective/Implementation Dates: 04-24-09)

A. General Objectives

The general objectives of the Resident Review are to determine:

- How resident outcomes and the resident's quality of life are related to the provision of care by the facility;

- If the care provided by the facility has enabled residents to reach or maintain their highest practicable physical, mental, and psychosocial well-being;

- If residents are assisted to have the best quality of life that is possible. The review will include aspects of the environment, staff interactions, and provision of services that affect sampled residents in their daily lives;

- If the facility has properly assessed its residents through the completion of the Resident Assessment Instrument (RAI), including accurate coding and transmitting of the Minimum Data Set (MDS) and has properly assessed care needs, conducted proper care planning, implemented the plan and evaluated care provided to the residents; and

- If there are additional areas of concern that need to be investigated in Phase II of the survey.

B. General Procedures

The team coordinator assigns specific residents in the sample to surveyors.

One surveyor should conduct the entire Resident Review for an assigned resident. If the resident has been chosen for a Quality of Life Assessment protocol (Task 5D), this same surveyor should also complete that protocol. If a surveyor has not passed the Surveyor Minimum Qualifications Test (SMQT) or if the complexity of a resident's care requires expertise of more than one discipline, surveyors should work jointly to complete the review. A surveyor must successfully complete the SMQT to survey independently.

To facilitate the Resident Review, ask the charge nurse for schedules of the following, as appropriate:

1. Meals;

2. Medications;

3. Activities;

4. Tube feedings and special treatments;

5. Specialized rehabilitation therapies; and

6. Physician visits or visits of other health professionals such as dentists, podiatrists, or nurse practitioners.

For all sampled residents except closed records, parts A, B, and C (Resident Room Review, Daily Life Review, and Assessment of Drug Therapies) on the Resident Review Worksheet (Exhibit 93) are completed. The difference between the two reviews is that the focus of the part D Care Review is more extensive for Comprehensive Reviews. Determine, as appropriate, if there has been a decline, maintenance or improvement of the resident in the identified focused care areas and/or Activities of Daily Living (ADL) functioning. If there has been a lack of improvement or a decline, determine if the decline or lack of improvement was avoidable or unavoidable.

C. Comprehensive Care Review

A Comprehensive Review includes observations, interviews, and a record review. After observing and talking with the resident, the surveyor conducts a comprehensive review, which includes the following:

- A check of specific items on the MDS for accurate coding of the resident's condition. The specific items to be checked will be based on QM/QIs identified for the resident on the Resident Level Summary. At least 2 of the QM/QIs identified for the resident must be matched against the QM/QI definitions (see Exhibit 270) and against evidence other than the MDS to verify that the resident's condition is accurately recorded in the MDS. What is being verified is that the resident's condition was accurately assessed at the time the MDS was completed;

- An overall review of the facility's completion of the RAI process including their:

  o Use of the Resident Assessment Protocols (RAPs);

  o Evaluation of assessment information not covered by the RAPs;

  o Identification of risks and causes of resident conditions;

  o Completion of the RAP Summary;

  o Development of a care plan that meets the identified needs of the resident;

- A review of the implementation of the care plan and resident response;

- A review of the relationship of the resident's drug regimen to the resident's condition (see the description of procedures for completing part C below);

- A thorough review of any of the following conditions that apply to the resident: weight loss, dehydration, pressure sores. This review is completed using the investigative protocols found below as a guide. (NOTE: All the residents selected for comprehensive reviews should have one or more of these concerns checked on the QM/QI reports [unless there are no residents with these concerns in the facility]); and

- An evaluation of the resident's dining experience (see Dining Observation Protocol below).

D. Focused Care Review Phase 1

This focused review includes observations, interviews, and a record review. This review focuses on care areas that were checked for the resident on the Resident Level Summary and any additional care items checked by the team as pertinent to the resident, e.g., all areas that are checked on the Roster/Sample Matrix by the team for the resident are reviewed, whether or not they have been highlighted as concerns for the survey. The dining observation is done for a resident if the resident has any checkmarks related to dining or the investigating team member has any concerns about the resident related to dining, e.g., such as weight loss.

The Phase 1 focused care review includes all care areas the team has checked for the resident: a review of the MDS, the facility's use of the RAPs, care planning, implementation of the care plan, and the resident's response to the care provided.

E. Focused Care Review Phase 2

This focused review includes observations, interviews and a record review, which concentrates only on those areas of concern for which the team requires additional information. For example, if the team needs additional information concerning facility compliance with the requirements for tube feeding, review only those RAI areas related to tube feeding; make observations of nutritional status, complications, and techniques of tube feeding, and interview residents, family and staff concerning related areas.

F. Closed Record Review

This includes a record review of the resident's care issues and transfer and discharge requirements. It may be possible to select some or all of the closed records from the preselected list of residents for the Phase 1 sample, if any of these preselected residents were noted onsite to be discharged or deceased.

Assess quality of care and quality of life requirements that relate to the identified care areas for the sampled resident. While assessing these, note and investigate concerns with any other requirements.

G. Conducting the Resident Review

The Resident Review consists of 4 main sections: Resident Room Review, Daily Life Review, Assessment of Drug Therapies, and Care Review. See Resident Review Worksheet and instructions (Form CMS-805, Exhibit 93)) for specific areas to review.

1. Section A - The Resident Room Review assesses aspects of accommodation of needs, environmental quality, and quality of life in the resident's room. Through observations and interviews, evaluate how the resident's environment affects his/her quality of life.

3. Section B - The Daily Life Review is a review of the resident's daily quality of life, especially in the areas of staff responsiveness to resident grooming and other needs, staff interactions, choices, and activities. Through ongoing observations and interviews, evaluate the resident's daily life routines and interactions with staff.

4. Section C - The Assessment of Drug Therapies is a review of the medications the resident is receiving to evaluate whether the effectiveness of the therapeutic regimen, including all drugs that may play a significant role in the resident's everyday life, is being monitored and assessed. Record the information on the Resident Review Worksheet, Form CMS-805. Review and record, as pertinent, all non-prescription and prescription medications taken by the resident during the past 7 days. In addition follow the guidance in Appendix PP, Tag·F329 for the determination of unnecessary medications.

5. Section D -- The care review is an assessment of those quality of care areas (see 42 CFR 483.25) that are pertinent to the sampled resident. The survey team, through use of the Roster/Sample Matrix, determines what care areas will be reviewed for each sampled resident. Additional areas for evaluation may be identified during the review.

   There are a designated number of comprehensive, focused and closed record care reviews completed, depending on the size of the sample.

H. Care Observations and Interviews

Make resident observations and conduct interviews, which include those factors or care areas as determined by the Roster/Sample Matrix. For example, if the resident was chosen because he/she is receiving tube feedings, observe the care and the outcomes of the interventions, facility monitoring and assessment, and nutritional needs/adequacy related to tube feeding.

Complete the following tasks:

- Observe the resident and caregivers during care and treatments, at meals, and various times of the day, including early morning and evening, over the entire survey period. Observe residents in both informal and structured settings, e.g., receiving specialized rehabilitation services, participating in formal and informal activities. Also, observe staff-resident interactions;

- Gather resident-specific information, including information on the resident's functional ability, potential for increasing ability, and any complications concerning special care needs;

- Evaluate implementation of the care plan. Determine if the care plan is consistently implemented by all personnel at all times of the day, and if the care plan is working for the resident. If the care plan is not working, look for evidence that the facility has identified this and acted on it even if the care plan has not formally been revised;

- Determine if there is a significant difference between the facility's assessment of the resident and observations; and

- Evaluate the adequacy of care provided to the resident using the Guidance to Surveyors.

Do not continue to follow residents once enough information has been accrued to determine whether the resident has received care in accordance with the regulatory requirements.

If there are indicators to suggest the presence of a quality of care problem that is not readily observable, e.g., a leg ulcer covered with a dressing, or a sacral pressure sore, ask facility staff to assist in making observations by removing, for example, a dressing or bedclothes.

Resident care observations should be made by those persons who have the clinical knowledge and skills to evaluate compliance.

When observing residents, respect their right to privacy, including the privacy of their bodies. If the resident's genital or rectal area or female breast area must be observed in order to document and confirm suspicions of a care problem, a member of the nursing staff must be present at this observation, and the resident must give clear consent. If the resident is unable to give consent, e.g., is unresponsive, incompetent, and a legal surrogate (family member who can act on the resident's behalf or legal representative as provided by State law) is present, ask this individual to give consent.

An observation of a resident's rectal or genital area (and for females, the breast area) may be made without a resident's or legal surrogate's consent, under the following conditions:

1. It is determined that there is a strong possibility that the resident is receiving less than adequate care, which can only be confirmed by direct observation;

2. The resident is unable to give clear consent; and

3. A legal surrogate is not present in the facility.

Only a surveyor who is a licensed nurse, a physician's assistant or a physician may make an observation of a resident's genitals, rectal area, or, for females, the breast area.

I.   Record Review

Conduct a record review to provide a picture of the current status of the resident as assessed by the facility; information on changes in the resident's status over the last 12 months for those areas identified for review; and information on planned care, resident goals, and expected outcomes.

Use the record review to help determine whether the assessments accurately reflect the resident's status and are internally consistent. An example of inconsistency may be that the facility assessed the resident's ADLs as being independently performed yet had indicated that the resident requires task segmentation for performing ADLs.

For sampled residents selected for either a comprehensive or a focused review, conduct a review of the RAI information including:

- The face sheet of the MDS for background information including customary routines and demographic information to provide an understanding of the resident prior to admission. This assists in assessing the quality of life of the resident.

- The latest MDS to determine which RAPS were triggered. For a sampled resident receiving a comprehensive review, note all triggered areas. Also, review the facility's assessment of the resident's level of functioning and note particularly drug therapy and cognitive, behavior, and ADL function. For a resident receiving a focused review in Phase I of the survey, review both the areas of concern specific to the resident and the other care areas that have been identified with the Roster/Sample Matrix. For Phase 2 residents, review only those areas that have been identified by the team as areas of concern.

If the RAI is less than 9 months old, review and compare with the previous RAI and the most recent quarterly review. If the RAI is 9 months or older, compare the current RAI with the most recent quarterly review. Review the following:

- The RAP summary sheet to see where the assessment documentation is located for any RAP triggered;

- The information summarizing the assessments (RAPS) and decision to proceed or not to proceed to care planning. Determine if the assessments indicate that the facility used the RAPs and considered the nature of the problem, the causal and risk factors, the need for referrals, complications, and decisions for care planning. If this is a reassessment, review whether the facility determined if the care plan required revision or was effective in moving the resident toward his/her goals;

- The care plan to identify whether the facility used the RAI to make sound care planning decisions. Determine whether the facility identified resident strengths, needs, and problems which needed to be addressed to assist the resident to maintain or improve his/her current functional status. Determine whether the facility identified resident-centered, measurable goals and specific interventions to achieve those goals. With observations, interviews, and record review, determine if the facility implemented the interventions defined; and

- Determine whether the facility documentation and resident status as observed indicate the decision to proceed or not to proceed to care planning was appropriate. This information will assist in determining whether a resident's decline or failure to improve was avoidable or unavoidable.

- It is not necessary to review the entire resident record. Review only those sections that are necessary to verify and clarify the information necessary to make compliance decisions. These sections may include, for example, laboratory reports, progress notes, and drug regimen review reports.

- In any care area in which it is determined that there has been a lack of improvement, a decline, or failure to reach highest practicable well being, assess if the change for the resident was avoidable or unavoidable. Note both the faulty facility practice and its effect on resident(s). Determine if a reassessment based on significant change should have been conducted, and if the absence of reassessment contributed to the resident's decline or lack of improvement.

- Verify that the information needed has been obtained to determine if the facility fulfilled its obligation to provide care that allowed the resident to attain or maintain the highest practicable physical, mental, and psychosocial well-being.

NOTE: When conducting either a focused or comprehensive review, if there are areas of concern which fall outside the care areas identified, investigate these, as necessary.

The following are special investigative protocols which should be used in Task 5C to gather information and in Task 6, to determine facility compliance in the care areas of pressure sore/ulcer(s), hydration, unintended weight loss, sufficient nursing staffing, and dining and food services.

NOTE: "Although the RAI assessments discussed in the following [investigative protocols] must occur at specific times, by Federal regulation, a facility's obligation to meet each resident's needs through ongoing assessment is not neatly confined to these mandated time frames. Likewise, completion of the RAI in the prescribed time frame does not necessarily fulfill a facility's obligation to perform a comprehensive assessment. Facility's are responsible for assessing areas that are relevant to individual residents regardless of whether these areas are included in the RAI." ("CMS Long-Term Care Facility Resident Assessment Instrument User's Manual," Version 2.0.)

Investigative Protocol

Hydration

Objectives:

- To determine if the facility identified risk factors which lead to dehydration and developed an appropriate preventative care plan; and

- To determine if the facility provided the resident with sufficient fluid intake to maintain proper hydration and health.

Task 5C: Use:

Use this protocol for the following situations:

- A sampled resident who flagged for the sentinel event of dehydration (QM/QI 7.3);

- A sampled resident who has one or more of the following QM/QI conditions:

    o 5.4 – Prevalence of fecal impaction;

    o 6.1 – Residents with a urinary tract infection;

    o 7.1 – Residents who lose too much weight;

    o 7.2 – Prevalence of tube feeding;

    o 9.1 – Residents whose need for help with daily activities has increased; and

    o Any of the three pressure ulcer QM/QIs: 12.1, 12.2, or 13.3.

- A sampled resident who was discovered to have any of the following risk factors: vomiting/diarrhea resulting in fluid loss, elevated temperatures and/or infectious processes, dependence on staff for the provision of fluid intake, use of medications including diuretics, laxatives, and cardiovascular agents, renal disease, dysphagia, a history of refusing fluids, limited fluid intake or lacking the sensation of thirst.

Procedures:

- Observations/interviews conducted as part of this procedure should be recorded on the Forms CMS-805 and/or the Form CMS-807.

- Determine if the resident was assessed to identify risk factors that can lead to dehydration, such as those listed above and whether there were abnormal laboratory test values which may be an indicator of dehydration.

    NOTE: A general guideline for determining baseline daily fluid needs is to multiply the resident's body weight in kilograms (kg) x 30ml (2.2 lbs = 1 kg), except for residents with renal or cardiac distress, or other restrictions based on physician orders. An excess of fluids can be detrimental for these residents.

- Determine if an interdisciplinary care plan was developed utilizing the clinical conditions and risk factors identified, taking into account the amount of fluid that the resident requires. If the resident is receiving enteral nutritional support, determine if the tube feeding orders included a sufficient amount of free water, and whether the water and feeding are being administered in accordance with physician orders?

- Observe the care delivery to determine if the interventions identified in the care plan have been implemented as described.

  o What is the resident's response to the interventions? Does staff provide the necessary fluids as described in the plan? Do the fluids provided contribute to dehydration, e.g., caffeinated beverages, alcohol? Was the correct type of fluid provided with a resident with dysphagia?

  o Is the resident able to reach, pour and drink fluids without assistance and is the resident consuming sufficient fluids? If not, are staff providing the fluids according to the care plan?

  o Is the resident's room temperature (heating mechanism) contributing to dehydration? If so, how is the facility addressing this issue?

  o If the resident refuses water, are alternative fluids offered that are tolerable to the resident?

  o Are the resident's beverage preferences identified and honored at meals?

  o Does staff encourage the resident to drink? Are they aware of the resident's fluid needs? Are staff providing fluids during and between meals?

  o Determine how the facility monitors to assure that the resident maintains fluid parameters as planned. If the facility is monitoring the intake and output of the resident, review the record to determine if the fluid goals or calculated fluid needs were met consistently.

- Review all related information and documentation to look for evidence of identified causes of the condition or problem. This inquiry should include interviews with appropriate facility staff and health care practitioners, who by level of training and knowledge of the resident, should know of, or be able to provide information about the causes of a resident's condition or problem.

  NOTE: If a resident is at an end of life stage and has an advance directive, according to State law, (or a decision has been made by the resident's surrogate or representative, in accordance with State law) or the resident has reached an end of life stage in which minimal amounts of fluids are being consumed or intake has ceased, and all appropriate efforts have been made to encourage and provide intake, then dehydration may be an expected outcome and does not constitute noncompliance with the requirement for hydration. Conduct observations to verify that palliative interventions, as described in the plan of care, are being implemented and revised as necessary, to meet the needs/choices of the resident in order to maintain the resident's comfort and quality of life. If the facility has failed to provide the palliative care, cite noncompliance with 42 CFR 483.25, F309, Quality of Care.

- Determine if the care plan is evaluated and revised based on the response, outcomes, and needs of the resident.

Task 6: Determination of Compliance:

- Compliance with 42 CFR 483.25(j), F327, Hydration:

  o For this resident, the facility is compliant with this requirement to maintain proper hydration if they properly assessed, care planned, implemented the care plan, evaluated the resident outcome, and revised the care plan as needed. If not, cite at F327.

- Compliance with 42 CFR 483.20(b)(1) & (2), F272, Comprehensive Assessments:

  o For this resident in the area of hydration, the facility is compliant with this requirement if they assessed factors that put the resident at risk for dehydration, whether chronic or acute. If not, cite at F272.

- Compliance with 42 CFR 483.20(k)(1), F279, Comprehensive Care Plans:

  o   For this resident in the area of hydration, the facility is compliant with this requirement if they developed a care plan that includes measurable objectives and timetables to meet the resident's needs as identified in the resident's assessment. If not, cite at F279.

- Compliance with 42 CFR 483.20(k)(3)(ii), F 282, Provision of care in accordance with the care plan:

  o   For this resident in the area of hydration, the facility is compliant with this requirement if qualified persons implemented the resident's care plan. If not, cite at F282.

This page intentionally left blank. Next page is 39.

This page intentionally left blank.

Investigative Protocol

Dining and Food Service

Objectives:

- To determine if each resident is provided with nourishing, palatable, attractive meals that meet the resid~ nutritional and special dietary needs;

- To determine if each resident is provided services to maintain or improve eating skills; and

- To determine if the dining experience enhances the resident's quality of life and is supportive of including food service and staff support during dining.

Task 5C: Use

This protocol will be used for:

- All sampled residents identified with malnutrition, unintended weight loss, mechanically alte. sores/ulcers, and hydration concerns; and

- Food complaints received from residents, families and others.

General Considerations:

- Use this protocol at two meals during the survey, preferably the noon and evening meals.

- Record information on the Form CMS-805 if it pertains to a specific sampled resident, or on the Form CMS-807 if it relates to the general observations of the dining service/dining room.

    o Discretely observe all residents, including sampled residents, during meals keeping questions to a minimum to prevent disruption in the meal service.

- For each sampled resident being observed, identify any special needs and the interventions planned to meet their needs. Using the facility's menu, record in writing what is planned in writing to be served to the resident at the meal observed.

- Conduct observations of food preparation and quality of meals.

Procedures:

1. During the meal service, observe the dining room and/or resident's room for the following:

    - Comfortable sound levels;

    - Adequate illumination, furnishings, ventilation; absence of odors; and sufficient space;

    - Tables adjusted to accommodate wheelchairs, etc.; and

    - Appropriate hygiene provided prior to meals.

2. Observe whether each resident is properly prepared for meals. For example:

    - Resident's eyeglasses, dentures, and/or hearing aids are in place;

- Proper positioning in chair, wheelchair, gerichair, etc., at an appropriate distance from the table (tray table and bed at appropriate height and position); and

- Assistive devices/utensils identified in care plans provided and used as planned.

3. Observe the food service for:

- Appropriateness of dishes and flatware for each resident. Single use disposable dining ware is not used except in an emergency and, other appropriate dining activities. Except those with fluid restriction, each resident has an appropriate place setting with water and napkin;

- Whether meals are attractive, palatable, served at appropriate temperatures and are delivered to residents in a timely fashion.

  o Did the meals arrive 30 minutes or more past the scheduled mealtime?

  o If a substitute was needed, did it arrive more than 15 minutes after the request for a substitute?

- Are diet cards, portion sizes, preferences, and condiment requests being honored?

4. Determine whether residents are being promptly assisted to eat or provided necessary assistance/cueing in a timely manner after their meal is served.

- Note whether residents at the same table or in resident rooms, are being served and assisted concurrently.

- If you observe a resident who is being assisted by a staff member to eat or drink, and the resident is having problems with eating or drinking, inquire if the staff member who is assisting them is a paid feeding assistant. If so, follow the procedures at tag F373.

5. Determine if the meals served were palatable, attractive, nutritious and met the needs of the resident. Note the following:

- Whether the resident voiced concerns regarding the taste, temperature, quality, quantity and appearance of the meal served;

- Whether mechanically altered diets, such as pureed, were prepared and served as separate entree items (except when combined food, e.g., stews, casseroles, etc.);

- Whether attempts to determine the reason(s) for the refusal and a substitute of equal nutritive value was provided, if the resident refused/rejected food served; and

- Whether food placement, colors, and textures were in keeping with the resident's needs or deficits, e.g., residents with vision or swallowing deficits.

Sample Tray Procedure

If residents complain about the palatability/temperature of food served, the survey team coordinator may request a test meal to obtain quantitative data to assess the complaints. Send the meal to the unit that is the greatest distance from the kitchen or to the affected unit or dining room. Check food temperature and palatability of the test meal at about the time the last resident on the unit is served and begins eating.

6. Observe for institutional medication pass practices that interfere with the quality of the residents' dining experience. This does not prohibit the administration of medications during meal service for medications that are necessary to be given at a meal, nor does this prohibit a medication to be given during a meal upon request of a resident who is accustomed to taking the medication with the meal, as long as it has been determined that this practice does not interfere with the effectiveness of the medication.

   • Has the facility attempted to provide medications at times and in a manner to support the dining experience of the resident, such as:

     o Pain medications being given prior to meals so that meals could be eaten in comfort;

     o Foods served are not routinely or unnecessarily used as a vehicle to administer medications (mixing the medications with potatoes or other entrees).

7. Determine if the sampled resident consumed adequate amounts of food as planned.

   • Determine if the facility is monitoring the foods/fluids consumed. Procedures used by the facility may be used to determine percentage of food consumed, if available; otherwise, determine the percentage of food consumed using the following point system:

     o Each food item served except for water, coffee, tea, or condiments equals one point. Example: Breakfast: juice, cereal, milk, bread and butter, coffee (no points) equals four points. If the resident consumes all four items in the amount served, the resident consumes 100% of breakfast. If the resident consumes two of the four food items served, then 50% of the breakfast would have been consumed. If three-quarters of a food item is consumed, give one point; for one-half consumed, give .5 points; for one- fourth or less, give no points. Total the points consumed x 100 and divide by the number of points given for that meal to give the percentage of meal consumed. Use these measurements when determining the amount of liquids consumed: Liquid measurements: 8 oz. cup = 240 cc, 6 oz. cup = 180 cc, 4 oz. cup = 120 cc, 1 oz. cup = 30 cc. [**Editor's Note:** The Joint Commission has added the abbreviation "cc" to a list of additional abbreviations, acronyms, and symbols list posted on there website. While no additions were made to the "do not use" list at this time, the list will be reviewed annually for possible inclusion as part of the development of future Joint Commission NPSGs. For more information pertaining to the official "do not use" list see www.jcaho.org/accredited+organizations/06_goal2_faqs.pdf.

     o Compare these findings with the facility's documentation to determine if the facility has accurately recorded the intake. Ask the staff if these findings are consistent with the resident's usual intake; and

     o Note whether plates are being returned to the kitchen with 75% or more of food not eaten.

8. If concerns are noted with meal service, preparation, quality of meals, etc., interview the person(s) responsible for dietary services to determine how the staff are assigned and monitored to assure meals are prepared according to the menu, that the meals are delivered to residents in a timely fashion, and at proper temperature, both in the dining rooms/areas and in resident rooms.

   NOTE: If concerns are identified in providing monitoring by supervisory staff during dining or concerns with assistance for residents to eat, evaluate nursing staffing in accord with 42 CFR 483.30(a), F353, and quality of care at 42 CFR 483.25(a)(2) and (3).

Task 6: Determination of Compliance:

   • Compliance with 42 CFR 483.35(d)(1)(2), F364, Food

     o The facility is compliant with this requirement when each resident receives food prepared by methods that conserve nutritive value, palatable, attractive and at the proper temperatures. If not, cite F364.

- Compliance with 42 CFR 483.35(b), F362, Dietary services, sufficient staff

  o The facility is compliant with this requirement if they have sufficient staff to prepare and serve palatable and attractive, nutritionally adequate meals at proper temperatures. If not, cite F362.

  NOTE: If serving food is a function of the nursing service rather than dietary, refer to 42 CFR 483.30(a), F353.

- Compliance with 42 CFR 483.15(h)(1), F252, Environment

  o The facility is compliant with this requirement if they provide a homelike environment during the dining services that enhances the resident's quality of life. If not, cite F252.

- Compliance with 42 CFR 483.70(g)(1)(2)(3)(4), F464, Dining and Resident Activities

  o The facility is compliant with this requirement if they provide adequate lighting, ventilation, furnishings and space during the dining services. If not, cite F464.

Investigative Protocol

Nursing Services, Sufficient Staffing

Objectives:

- To determine if the facility has sufficient nursing staff available to meet the residents' needs.

- To determine if the facility has licensed registered nurses and licensed nursing staff available to provide and monitor the delivery of resident care.

Task 5C: Use:

NOTE: This protocol is not required during the standard survey, unless it is triggered in the event of care concerns/problems which may be associated with sufficiency of nursing staff. It is required to be completed for an extended survey.

This protocol is to be used when:

- Quality of care problems have been identified, e.g., residents not receiving the care and services to prevent pressure sore/ulcer(s), unintended weight loss and dehydration, and to prevent declines in their condition as described in their comprehensive plans of care, such as bathing, dressing, grooming, transferring, ambulation, toileting, and eating; and

- Complaints have been received from residents, families or other resident representatives concerning services, e.g., care not being provided, call lights not being answered in a timely fashion, and residents not being assisted to eat.

Procedures:

- Determine if the registered/licensed nursing staff are available to:

  o Supervise and monitor the delivery of care by nursing assistants according to residents' care plans;

  o Assess resident condition changes;

  o Monitor dining activities to identify concerns or changes in residents' needs;

  o Respond to nursing assistants' requests for assistance; o Correct inappropriate or unsafe nursing assistants techniques; and

  o Identify training needs for the nursing assistants.

- If problems were identified with care plans/services not provided as needed by the resident, focus the discussion with supervisory staff on the situations which led to using the protocol: how do they assure that there are adequate staff to meet the needs of the residents; how do they assure that staff are knowledgeable about the needs of the residents and are capable of delivering the care as planned; how do they assure that staff are appropriately deployed to meet the needs of the residents; how do they provide orientation for new or temporary staff regarding the resident needs and the interventions to meet those needs; and how do they assure that staff are advised of changes in the care plan?

- Determine if nursing assistants and other nursing staff are knowledgeable regarding the residents' care needs, e.g., the provision of fluids and foods for residents who are unable to provide these services for themselves; the provision of turning, positioning and skin care for those residents identified at risk for pressure sore/ulcers; and the provision of incontinence care as needed;

- If necessary, review nursing assistant assignments in relation to the care and or services the resident requires to meet his/her needs;

- In interviews with residents, families and/or other resident representatives, inquire about the staff's response to requests for assistance, and the timeliness of call lights being answered; and

- Determine if the problems are facility-wide, cover all shifts or if they are limited to certain units or shifts, or days of the week. This can be based on information already gathered by the team with additional interviews of residents, families, and staff, as necessary.

Task 6: Determination of Compliance:

NOTE: Meeting the State-mandated staffing ratio, if any, does not preclude a deficiency of insufficient staff if the facility is not providing needed care and services to residents.

- Compliance with 42 CFR 483.30(a), F353, Sufficient Staff:

    o The facility is compliant with this requirement if the facility has provided a sufficient number of licensed nurses and other nursing personnel to meet the needs of the residents on a 24-hour basis. If not, cite F353.

J.   Closed Record Reviews

Closed records are included in the total resident sample. If possible, select closed records of residents who have been identified through the use of offsite information concerning a particular care issue. If there is a care area that is an identified concern, try to obtain the closed records of residents who had the same care needs before death, discharge, or transfer. Document information on the Form CMS-805, Sections C and D, as appropriate.

Look for information to determine compliance with quality of care and other requirements such as:

- Assessment and care of infections;

- Pressure sores;

- Significant weight loss;

- Restraints;

- Multiple falls or injuries;

- Discharge planning; and

- Transfer and discharge requirements.

Unless there is a reason to review the entire record, focus the review on the appropriateness of care and treatment surrounding the resident's discharge or transfer, and the events leading up to that discharge or transfer. For example, if the survey team has identified a concern with inadequate identification and care of residents with infections, and several residents have recently been hospitalized with serious infections, the review would be a focused review on the care and assessment these residents received before they were hospitalized. In addition:

- Look for documentation related to transfer, discharge, and bed-hold, including facility's discharge planning, notices, and reasons for facility-initiated moves, e.g., proper planning and transferring subsequent to a change in payor or care needs; and

- Determine if within 30 days of the death of a resident, the facility conveyed the deceased resident's personal funds and a final accounting to the individual or probate jurisdiction administering the individual's estate as provided by State law (see 42 CFR 483.10(c)(6), F160).

[**Editor's Note:** Appendix P, II. The Survey Process, B. The Traditional Standard Survey, Subtask 5C Resident Review: deleted current sections K (Review of a Resident Receiving Hospice Care) and L (Review of a Resident Receiving Dialysis Services), renumbered current section M (Review of Influenza and Pneumococcal Immunizations) as K and added new section L (Liability Notices and Beneficiary Appeal Rights). These changes are reflected in S&C Letter 09-22, dated January 23, 2009 and Transmittal 41, dated April 10, 2009.]

K. Review of Influenza and Pneumococcal Immunizations

Use the Investigative Protocol contained at Tag F334 to complete a review of the implementation of the facility's immunization policies and procedures.

L. Liability Notices and Beneficiary Appeal Rights

Medicare-participating long term care facilities are obligated to inform Medicare Part A and B beneficiaries about specific rights related to billing, and to submit bills to the Fiscal Intermediary (FI) or Medicare Administrative Contractor (MAC) when requested by the beneficiary. In a Medicare-participating long term care facility, verify compliance with these requirements.

Listed below are the requirements of the Skilled Nursing Facility (SNF).

1. If a SNF provider believes on admission or during a resident's stay that Medicare will not pay for skilled nursing or specialized rehabilitative services, and that an otherwise covered item or service may be denied as not reasonable and necessary, the facility must notify the resident or his/her legal representative in writing and explain:

    - Why these specific services may not be covered;

    - The beneficiary's potential liability for payment for the non-covered services;

    - The beneficiary right to have a claim submitted to Medicare; and

    - The beneficiary's standard claim appeal rights that apply if the claim is denied by Medicare.

This notice requirement may be fulfilled by use of either the Skilled Nursing Facility Advanced Beneficiary Notice (SNFABN) (Form CMS-10055) **or** one of the five uniform Denial Letters. The SNFABN and the Denial Letters inform the beneficiary of his/her right to have a claim submitted to Medicare and advises them of the standard claim appeal rights that apply if the claim is denied by Medicare. These claims are often referred to as "demand bills" and are reviewed by the FI or MAC. (See Chapter 1, §60.3 of the Medicare Claims Processing Manual, Pub. 100-04 for detailed instructions on submitting institutional demand bills.) The SNF:

    - Must keep a copy of the SNFABN or Denial Notice on file;

    - Must file a claim when requested by the beneficiary; and

    - May not charge the resident for Medicare covered Part A services while a decision is pending.

2. The SNF must issue the Notice of Medicare Provider Non-coverage (Form CMS-10123) when there is a termination of all Medicare Part A services for coverage reasons. The Notice of Medicare Provider Non-coverage informs the beneficiary of his/her right to an expedited review of a service termination by the Quality Improvement Organization (QIO). The Notice to Medicare Provider Non-coverage is sometimes referred to as an "Expedited Appeal Notice" or a "Generic Notice." The SNF should not issue this notice if the beneficiary exhausts the Medicare covered days as the number of SNF benefit days is set in law and the QIO cannot extend the benefit period. Thus, a service termination due to the exhaustion of benefits is not considered a termination for "coverage" reasons. The SNF:

    - Must keep a copy of the Notice of Medicare Provider Non-coverage on file;

    - Must file a claim when requested by the beneficiary; and

    - May not charge the resident for Medicare covered Part A services while a decision is pending.

Failure to provide written liability of payment and/or appeal notice(s), to submit the bill (if requested by a resident), or to charge the resident for Medicare covered Part A services while a decision is pending may constitute a violation of the facility's provider agreement. Refer to S&C-09-20 or go to http://www.cms.hhs.gov/bni/ for more details about liability notices and resident appeal rights.

Procedure to Determine Compliance

1. During the entrance conference, obtain a list of Medicare beneficiaries who requested demand bills in the past 6 months. From the list, randomly select one resident's file to determine if the facility submitted the bill to the FI or MAC. In general, Medicare claims must be filed within one full calendar year following the year in which the services were provided. (For more information, refer to 42 CFR 424.44 and the Medicare Claims Processing Manual, Pub. 100-04, Chapter 1, General Billing Requirements, §70.1.) If the facility failed to submit the bill to the FI or MAC within the required time frame or charged the resident while the decision was pending, the facility is in violation of the provider agreement with respect to resident billing requirements. Cite Tag F492, 42 CFR 483.75(b), Compliance with Federal, State and local laws and professional standards, and refer to 42 CFR 489.21, Specific limitations on charges.

   NOTE: If no Medicare beneficiaries requested a demand bill in the past 6 months, this portion of the review is complete, and the surveyor should continue with the closed record review.

2. During closed record review, review three charts of discharged Medicare beneficiaries from the SNF. If the current closed record review sample does not include three Medicare beneficiaries discharged from the SNF, expand the sample. Look for a copy of appropriate liability and appeal notice(s). If the facility failed to provide the resident the appropriate liability and/or appeal notice(s), the facility is in violation of the notice requirements. Cite Tag F156, 42 CFR 483.10, Resident Rights.

   If the record indicates the resident requested the facility submit the bill for appeal, determine if the facility submitted the bill to the FI or MAC within the required time frame. In general, Medicare claims must be filed within one full calendar year following the year in which the services were provided. (For more information refer to 42 CFR 424.44 and the Medicare Claims Processing Manual, Pub. 100-04, Chapter 1, General Billing Requirements, §70.1.) If the facility failed to submit the bill to the FI or MAC within the required timeframe or charged the resident while the decision was pending, the facility is in violation of the provider agreement with respect to resident billing requirements. Cite Tag F492, 42 CFR 483.75(b), Compliance with Federal, State and local laws and professional standards, and refer to 42 CFR 489.21, Specific Limitations on Charges.

Sub-Task 5D - Quality of Life Assessment

A. Introduction

The assessment of the quality of life and rights of residents incorporates review of selected tags within the following requirements:

- 42 CFR 483.10, Resident Rights;

- 42 CFR 483.12, Admission, Transfer and Discharge Rights;

- 42 CFR 483.13, Resident Behavior and Facility Practices;

- 42 CFR 483.15, Quality of Life; and

- 42 CFR 483.70, Physical Environment.

Since quality of life and quality of care are closely interrelated concepts, the survey process holistically integrates the quality of life assessment into the following tasks or sub-tasks:

- Task 5A, General Observations of the Facility (see Task 5A for further description);

- Task 5C, Resident Review, Sections A and B (see Task 5C for further description); and

- Task 5D, Quality of Life Assessment.

B. General Objectives

The general objectives of the quality of life assessment are:

- To determine if the facility protects and promotes the rights of residents;

- To assess the impact of the facility's environment, facility schedules and policies, and staff interactions with residents on the quality of residents' lives;

- To determine if the facility is assisting residents to achieve and maintain their highest practicable well-being; and

[This page intentionally left blank]

• To determine if the facility provides equal access to quality care for all residents, regardless of payment source.

C. Quality of Life Protocols

Task 5D includes the following sub-tasks: interviews of interviewable residents, a meeting with the resident group or council, family interviews of residents who are not interviewable, and observations of these same non-interviewable residents. These are each described below.

1. Resident Interview

These interviews are conducted with a subsample of interviewable residents from the resident sample. Refer to Table 1 in Task 4 to determine how many residents to interview. For example, in a facility with a census of 100, Table 1 directs the team to select 5 residents to interview.

It is helpful to divide the interview into two or more short segments. Seeing the resident more than once helps to establish rapport and gives the resident a chance to think over the questions and provide more information later. Surveyors are encouraged to have several short conversations with interviewable residents during the course of the survey.

Locate a private place for the interview, and arrange interview times at the resident's convenience. Resident interviews should be conducted privately unless the resident expresses a preference to have a family member, staff member or the ombudsman present.

Prior to the interview, complete question 11 by writing any concerns that have been discovered about this resident or about the facility that you would like to discuss with the resident. Issues that are already covered in the other questions of the interview need not be listed.

For example, during Offsite Survey Preparation, the team has noted that the facility has had repeated deficiencies for pest control of roaches. On the Initial Tour, it may have been noticed the resident and her roommate were speaking angrily to each other. During the survey, the team has discovered disagreeable smells in this resident's unit, low levels of lighting in the dining room and some residents who go into others' rooms and rummage through drawers. Also, add items discovered in the Resident Review about any of this resident's special needs and preferences that the facility should be taking into account. For example, a preference for a shower instead of a bath, or a need to have extra strong lighting because of a vision deficit. Add all these items to Question 11.

At the beginning of the first interview segment, use the probes on the first page of the interview to guide the explanation to the resident of the purpose of the interview. Discuss with the resident that some of his/her answers may be written down, and ask if that is all right. Then take a few minutes to establish rapport by letting the resident direct the conversation. For residents who are uncommunicative at first, use cues from their surroundings or from what is known about this resident to begin the conversation. Try to seek some commonality that will allow the resident to develop some ease in talking. For example, remark on family pictures and other personal items seen in the resident's room, or bring up a past occupation or hobby or a current activity preference of the resident that is of mutual interest. Share a little about yourself, as appropriate.

Use the resident interview protocol to guide the conversation with the resident, but bring up topics in an order that is sensible to the conversation. Probe for further information if the answer the resident is giving is incomplete or unclear. After the interview, follow-up on the concerns the resident has raised. Include in the documentation both the facility practice in question and its effect on the resident. Share these concerns with team members so that they can pursue them during the remainder of the survey. (See the tag numbers in parentheses after particular questions for interpretive guidance on following up on resident comments.)

NOTE: There are some problems that a resident will express that are not within the scope of the long-term care requirements. For example, a resident is complaining during an interview that he/she is displeased that he/she does not have a private room. This facility does not have private rooms, nor do the requirements mandate private rooms. If there is no issue related to one of the requirements, further investigation is not needed.

2. Group Interview

This interview is conducted with members of the resident council if one exists, or with an informal group of residents if there is no council. Staff members and residents' family members are not to be present at this interview unless the group specifically requests a certain person's presence. The group need not be restricted to officers of the resident council. The survey team members should feel free to invite other residents they encounter who are able to converse and provide information. The resident council should also be encouraged to invite other residents at their discretion. It is preferable to keep the group size manageable, e.g., usually no more than 12, to facilitate communication. Residents who are not able to participate should not be included in this interview.

Prior to the meeting, review council minutes if they were provided by the council. Determine if there are any particular concerns you would like to discuss. Write in Question 13 these concerns and any other special concerns the team has learned about this facility during Offsite Survey Preparation, the Initial Tour, or during other observations and interviews. Concerns that are already covered in other questions of the interview need not be written.)

During the meeting, it may be helpful to have one surveyor conduct the interview while another takes notes. At the beginning of the meeting, use the probes on the first page of the protocol to guide introductions and describing the purpose of the interview. Spend a few minutes establishing rapport with the group by letting them direct the conversation. If residents have nothing to say at this time, use a general question such as, "Tell me what life is like in this facility," or "What makes a good day for you here?" Then continue with the protocol questions, probing for more information where necessary and presenting questions in an order that is sensible to the conversation. Get residents to talk in terms of actual situations or examples, using open-ended probes such as: "Can you tell me more about that? Can you give me an example?" or "How does that work here?"

After the meeting, follow-up on any concerns the residents have raised that are within the scope of the long-term care requirements. Share these concerns with the team to focus their investigations.

3. Interview With Family Member or Friend of Non-Interviewable Resident

The family interview is the first part of a two-part protocol. The purpose of this interview is to obtain information about the prior and current preferences of a subsample of non-interviewable residents to help assess whether the facility is individualizing daily life activities, care and services to the highest practicable level. The information gained through the interview will be used to complete Part D. below, the Observation of Non-Interviewable Resident. Follow-up on any concerns raised by the family member about the resident's treatment by the facility.

Use Table 1 in Task 4, to determine how many residents will receive the family interview and resident observation. For example, in a facility with a census of 100, 2 residents are selected.

Prior to the interview, review the relevant sections of the Minimum Data Set about past activities and preferences, and the resident's social history and activities assessment, if any. Begin completing this worksheet with information from the chart, and then use the interview to fill in missing information.

Information about a resident's past lifestyle and preferences may be more or less relevant, depending on the resident's condition and on the length of time spent in the nursing home. However, even after years of institutionalization, some features of a resident's prior life may still be relevant, even if the resident is now debilitated and uncommunicative. Collect information about how the resident's current cognitive status and physical condition have changed his/her past preferences.

Family members do not always know the prior history of a nursing home resident. Therefore, Question 1 of this interview serves to obtain information about the family member's knowledge of the resident. If the family member's answers to Question 1 show that he/she has little or no knowledge of the resident's past history, this interview may be discontinued. If discontinued, end the interview with a general question such as, "What would you like to tell me about this facility and how your relative is treated?" This resident can still remain as part of the survey sample. Select another non-interviewable resident from the sample for a family interview and observation of non-interviewable resident protocol.

If the family member has partial knowledge, the interview may be partially completed with whatever information is obtained in answer to the protocol questions.

Be aware that family members may have strong emotions about their relative's decline and institutionalization. Allow them to express their feelings, but gently direct them back to the questions of the protocol.

The interview may be conducted in person with a family member who was met on tour or by telephone, if necessary.

The second part of this protocol is the Observation of Non-Interviewable Resident. The purpose of this protocol is to obtain information through direct observation about the quality of life of the non-interviewable residents who have received family interviews.

Combine the information gained during the interview with what has been learned about the resident during the Resident Review to write any special items to observe in item 1. What special needs and preferences does this resident have that the nursing home should be taking into account? For example, a resident is ambulatory with Alzheimer's Disease. Her prior life included meeting the school bus at 3 p.m. every day to pick up her children. Now she attempts to leave the facility around that time. What is the facility doing to accommodate this agenda of the resident? Another resident enjoyed being outdoors, and the family member stated she believes this resident would still like the opportunity to go outdoors. Is the facility responding to this preference? Another resident preferred tea to coffee. Is this preference taken into account? A resident preferred to be addressed as Mrs. Hernandez. How does staff address this resident? A resident liked to ski, but can no longer do so due to her condition. However, she may like to see a movie on skiing, have a skiing picture in her room, or go outside in the snow. Has the facility noted this preference? A resident always watched a certain soap opera every day. The family member says that even though she is now confused, this show may still attract her interest. Is this show being made available to the resident?

Use this protocol to complete approximately 1 hour of observations per resident, divided into short segments in at least three settings, at different times of the day. This need not be dedicated time - surveyors can complete other tasks while conducting this observation. Part of the time should be spent in a location in which what is happening as staff interact with the resident in his/her room can be observed. The remainder of the time should be divided among other locations frequented by the resident, including the dining room, activities rooms, other common areas, and therapy rooms. Some observations of this resident may have already been completed prior to the interview, as part of the Resident Review. Continue making observations until all probes on the worksheet are covered, including the special items noted for observation. When making observations of the resident in particular settings, e.g., an activity or physical therapy, observations need not be for the entire duration of the activity or therapy session.

Use the probes in this protocol to guide observations. Note the areas of concern on the Resident Review Worksheet. For each concern, be specific in noting time, location, and exact observations. Record what is seen and heard, rather than a judgment of the situation. Instead of writing that the resident's dignity was violated by some interaction, simply record the interaction.

NOTE: During the individual, group and family interviews, ask questions regarding their awareness of to whom and how to report allegations, incidents and/or complaints. Share this information with the surveyor assigned to complete Task 5G.

Follow-up on areas of concern observed. For example, at lunch it was observed that the resident was given only one food item at a time. The resident was reaching out for other food and his/her drink. Determine through staff interview and chart review if this method of feeding this resident has a therapeutic purpose or if it is an unnecessary restriction on his/her freedom to select the food he/she wishes to eat.

Share observations with the team to assist them in their investigations of quality of life of other residents.

D. Follow-Up on Concerns Raised Through Interviews

Whenever information is obtained about areas of concern through resident interviews, attempt to investigate these areas through whatever means are appropriate. These might include interviews with other residents, staff, and families, and reviews of written facility information such as policies and procedures, and the admission rights information given to residents.

Sometimes these other sources will provide no other corroborating information. If that is the case, the team will determine during decision-making if the requirement is met or not met through the information obtained in resident interviews.

E. Confidentiality

If residents or family members have stated during interviews that they do not want certain information they have shared in confidence to be shared with the facility, respect their wishes. However, the issue can still be investigated. During the survey, discuss the issue with the team and make the topic the subject of other interviews and observations. For example, a resident has said that certain staff "make fun" of him/her, but he/she asks you to keep that in confidence. The resident's comment may not be referred to in the statement of deficiencies. However, discuss this with the team and decide how best to pursue the matter while respecting the resident's wishes. Team members may want to address this topic with other residents, family members or the resident group. When aware of which staff are involved, attempt to observe these staff interacting with residents.

If other residents have complained about the same problem, their comments may be referred to generally as a group. For example, "Three out of five residents interviewed reported that…" Use judgment to determine if the statement would compromise the resident's confidentiality.

Sub-Task 5E - Medication Pass and Pharmacy Services

(Rev. 22, Issued: 12-15-06, Effective/Implementation: 12-18-06)

A. Objectives

- To determine whether the facility safely administers medications including:

    o   Accuracy of medication administration (including preparation and technique);

    o   Labeling that contains at least the name and strength/concentration of the medication, as well as expiration date when applicable, and

    o   Security of medications;

- To determine whether medications are stored and handled in accordance with manufacturers' recommendations and/or state or federal requirements;

- To determine whether the facility reconciles controlled medications, as appropriate;

- To determine whether the facility obtains the services of a licensed pharmacist; and

- To determine whether the facility provides or obtains pharmaceutical services, including routine and emergency medications, to meet the needs of each resident.

B. Use

- The medication pass (C.1) and a review of storage and access to medications (C.2) must be conducted on every Initial and Standard survey; and on Partial Extended, Abbreviated Standard and Revisit, as necessary;

- Review for the provision of licensed pharmacist consultation (C.5) on the initial survey and on any other survey type, if the survey team has identified concerns that indicate:

    o   That the facility does not have a licensed pharmacist; and/or

    o   That the licensed pharmacist may not have performed his/her functions related to the provision of pharmaceutical services;

- Review for the development and implementation of pharmaceutical procedures (C.4) if, during the course of the survey, concerns have been identified regarding the availability of medications; accurate and timely medication acquisition; receiving, dispensing, administering, labeling, and storage of medications; reconciliation of controlled medications (C.3); and the use of qualified, authorized personnel to handle and dispense medications.

Survey Protocol for Long-Term Care Facilities (SOM, Appendix P)

C. General Procedures

1. Medication Pass (includes labeling)

See Guidance to Surveyors at 483.25(m) for information on conducting the medication pass and for the identification of medication errors. Use the Medication Pass Worksheet (Form CMS-677, Exhibit 88) to record observations. On Form CMS-677, the column marked "Record" is for the purpose of recording the prescriber's actual order if different than what was observed as administered.

When observing the medication pass:

- Be as neutral and unobtrusive as possible;

- Observe different routes and/or forms of medications such as intravenous (IV), intramuscular (IM), or subcutaneous (SQ) injections; transdermal patches; inhaler medications; eye drops; and medications provided through enteral tubes;

- Initially observe the administration at least 20-25 medications, observing as many staff administering medications as possible to facilitate a review of the facility's entire medication distribution system;

- Record, from the medication label, the name and dose/concentration of each medication administered. Also record the route of administration (if other than oral) and the expiration date, if expired;

- Record all multiples, such as 2 drops or 2 tablets. For liquids, record actual volume, or in the case of items such as psyllium, record number of "rounded teaspoonfuls" and the amount of liquid. In the absence of a number, it is assumed to be one;

- Observe whether staff confirmed the resident's identity prior to giving medications and whether the medications were identified up to the point of administration. Note any concerns;

- Record the techniques and procedures that staff used to handle and administer medications, such as proper hand hygiene, checking pulses, flushing gastric tubes, crushing medications, route and location of administration (e.g., sub-Q or IM injection, eye, ear, inhalation, or skin patch), shaking and/or rotating medication, giving medications with or between food or meals, whether medications are under the direct control/observation of the authorized staff; and

- Observe whether staff immediately documented the administration and/or refusal of the medication after the administration or the attempt. Note any concerns.

After the medication pass, compare your observations with the prescriber's orders. Review to assure that medication records, including prescriber's orders and the Medication Administration Record (MAR) are accurate and complete. Determine whether there was an error(s) in medication administration. A medication error is the preparation or administration of medications or biologicals that is not in accordance with any of the following:

- The prescriber's order (whether given incorrectly or omitting an ordered dosage);

- Manufacturer's specifications (not recommendations) regarding the preparation and administration of the medication or biological;

- Accepted professional standards and principles that apply to professionals providing services;

    NOTE: If no errors are found after reconciliation of the pass with the prescriber's orders, the medication pass observation is complete.

- If one or more errors are found, observe the administration of another 20-25 medications.

After completion of the observations and reconciliations, calculate the facility's medication error rate, if one or more errors are found. Add the number of significant and non-significant errors (see guidance at F332/333) and divide by the opportunities for error (doses given plus the doses ordered but not given). Multiply this by 100.

If it is determined that the facility's overall error rate (including significant and non-significant errors) is 5 percent or more, a medication error deficiency exists at F332.

If one or more significant errors were identified, a medication error deficiency exists at F333.

NOTE: If a **significant** medication error has been identified during the course of a Resident Review, including a complaint investigation, it is not necessary to have observed a medication pass in order to cite a deficiency at F333.

2. Medication Storage (includes labeling)

Review medication storage (Use CMS Form 803 for documentation) in order to determine whether:

- Medications and biologicals are accessible only to authorized staff and are locked when not under the direct observation of the authorized staff;

- Controlled medications are stored in a manner to limit access and to facilitate reconciliation in accordance with the facility policies;

- Medications are stored to maintain their integrity and to support safe administration of the correct medication to the correct resident, by the correct route and in the correct dose, such as:

  o Temperature, light, and humidity controls meet specifications for the medication;

  o Medications available for use are not expired, contaminated, or unusable;

  o Medication labels are legible; intact; contain the name and dose/concentration of the medication, appropriate cautionary/accessory instructions such as "do not crush," expiration date when applicable; and support the safe administration of the medication; and

  o Multi-dose vials are labeled per facility policy and manufacturer's specifications once use of the vial has been initiated.

3. Controlled Medications

If a concern regarding controlled medications was identified during the survey process or during the medication pass, interview facility staff, such as the director of nursing, and the licensed pharmacist regarding the concern. If a potential problem has been identified regarding lack of reconciliation or loss of controlled medications:

- Determine whether Scheduled II controlled medications are in separately locked, permanently affixed compartments (or are a minimal amount of unit dose packages);

- Review the facility procedure and a sample of the reconciliation records, and compare the amount of medication available with the amount the records indicate should be available; and

- Interview the director of nursing and/or licensed pharmacist regarding:

  o Actual frequency of the reconciliation;

  o How the facility investigates loss or inability to reconcile controlled medications; and o   How the licensed pharmacist has been involved in recognizing the situation and collaborating with the facility to review and update its practices and procedures.

4. Pharmaceutical Services

If concerns have been identified regarding pharmaceutical services (such as: any of the required components related to safe medication use, storage, labeling; the use of authorized staff to administer medications; emergency medication issues; licensed pharmacist consultation), review the facility's evidence (e.g., licensed pharmacist's reports to the facility) that they have been receiving ongoing pharmacy consultation regarding all aspects of the provision of pharmaceutical services in the facility, including identification of problems and recommendations for corrective actions. Determine whether the licensed pharmacist is available during the survey or identify how to contact the licensed pharmacist in order to respond to surveyor questions about pharmaceutical services. Review procedures and interview staff and/or the licensed pharmacist regarding the areas of concern.

For example, the following steps might be used, if a concern has been identified regarding medications not being administered in a timely manner:

- Identify the types of medications (such as antibiotics, pain medications) that are not being passed on a timely basis,

- Interview the director of nursing and/or the staff responsible for passing medications regarding:

  o   A delay in obtaining or administering a medication(s);

  o   The potential causes of the delay; and

  o   Facility procedures for scheduled times of administration;

- Interview the licensed pharmacist to determine if he/she identified the concern regarding timely medication administration and had made recommendations to facility staff in order to address the concern;

- Interview facility staff regarding the response to recommendations made by the licensed pharmacist; and

- As necessary, if concerns are identified regarding sufficient authorized staff to pass medications, interview the director of nursing regarding staff assignments and work allocation in relation to medication passes in order to meet the needs of the residents.

5. Provision of a Licensed Pharmacist

If there is no licensed pharmacist providing services in the facility, interview the administrator and others, as appropriate, regarding:

- The length of time the facility has been without the services of a licensed pharmacist; and

- Current efforts underway to obtain the services of a licensed pharmacist.

If the facility has a licensed pharmacist, and concerns have been identified regarding the provision of services related to his/her functions, interview the licensed pharmacist, administrator, and, as necessary, the director of nurses and/or medical director regarding the processes to provide and oversee pharmaceutical services consultation.

Sub-Task 5F - Quality Assessment and Assurance (QA&A) Review

A. General Objectives—The QA&A review protocol is designed to determine if:

- A QA&A committee exists and meets in accordance with the regulatory requirements of 42 CFR 483.75 (o); and

- The QA&A committee is functional, i.e., it identifies, develops, plans, implements, monitors, and ensures correction of deviations from quality.

B. General Procedures—to complete Sub-Task 5F, follow the Investigative Protocol contained in the Guidance to Surveyors at F520.

NOTE: The surveyor(s) completing Sub-Task 5F should not conduct a review of the minutes of the QA&A committee, as the regulation does not require the facility to disclose the records of the QA&A committee.

Sub-Task 5G - Abuse Prohibition Review

A. General Objective

To determine if the facility has developed and operationalized policies and procedures that prohibit abuse, neglect, involuntary seclusion and misappropriation of property for all residents. The review includes components of the facility's policies and procedures as contained in the Guidance to Surveyors at 42 CFR 483.13(c), F226. (See Guidance to Surveyors for further information.)

These include policies and procedures for the following:

- Screening of potential hirees;

- Training of employees (both for new employees, and ongoing training for all employees);

- Prevention policies and procedures;

- Identification of possible incidents or allegations which need investigation;

- Investigation of incidents and allegations;

- Protection of residents during investigations; and

- Reporting of incidents, investigations, and facility response to the results of their investigations.

B. General Procedures:

• Utilize the Abuse Prohibition Investigative Protocol to complete this task.

Investigative Protocol

Abuse Prohibition

Objective:

To determine if the facility has developed and operationalized policies and procedures that prohibit abuse, neglect, involuntary seclusion and misappropriation of property for all residents.

Use:

Use this protocol on every standard survey.

Task 5G Procedures:

- Obtain and review the facility's abuse prohibition policies and procedures to determine that they include the key components, i.e. screening, training, prevention, identification, investigation, protection and reporting/response. (See Guidance to Surveyors at F226.) It is not necessary for these items to be collected in one document or manual.

- Interview the individual(s) identified by the facility as responsible for coordinating the policies and procedures to evaluate how each component of the policies and procedures is operationalized, if not obvious from the policies. How do you monitor the staff providing and/or supervising the delivery of resident care and services to assure that care service is provided as needed to assure that neglect of care does not occur? How do you determine which injuries of unknown origin should be investigated as alleged occurrences of abuse? How are you ensuring that residents, families, and staff feel free to communicate concerns without fear of reprisal?

- Request written evidence of how the facility has handled alleged violations. Select 2-3 alleged violations (if the facility has this many) since the previous standard survey or the previous time this review has been done by the State.

  o Determine if the facility implemented adequate procedures:

  - For reporting and investigating;

  - For protection of the resident during the investigation;

  - For the provision of corrective action;

  NOTE: The reporting requirements at 483.13(c) specify both a report of the alleged violation and a report of the results of the investigation to the State survey agency.

  o Determine if the facility reevaluated and revised applicable procedures as necessary.

- Interview several residents and families regarding their awareness of to whom and how to report allegations, incidents and/or complaints. This information can be obtained through the resident, group, and family interviews at Task 5D.

- Interview at least five direct care staff, representing all three shifts, including activity staff and nursing assistants, to determine the following:

  o If staff are trained in and are knowledgeable about how to appropriately intervene in situations involving residents who have aggressive or catastrophic reactions.

NOTE: Catastrophic reactions are extraordinary reactions of residents to ordinary stimuli, such as the attempt to provide care. One definition in current literature is: ". . . catastrophic reactions [are] defined as reactions or mood changes of the resident in response to what may seem to be minimal stimuli (e.g., bathing, dressing, having to go to the bathroom, a question asked of the person) that can be characterized by weeping, blushing, anger, agitation, or stubbornness. "Catastrophic reactions and other behaviors of Alzheimer residents: Special unit compared to traditional units." Elizabeth A Swanson, Meridean L. Maas, and Cathleen Buckwalter. Archives of Psychiatric Nursing. Vol. VII No. 5 (October 1993). Pp. 292-299.

  o If staff are knowledgeable regarding what, when and to whom to report according to the facility policies.

- Interview at least three front line supervisors of staff who interact with residents (Nursing, Dietary, Housekeeping, Activities, Social Services). Determine how they monitor the provision of care/services, the staff/resident interactions, deployment of staff to meet the residents' needs, and the potential for staff burnout which could lead to resident abuse.

- Obtain a list of all employees hired within the previous 4 months, and select five from this list. Ask the facility to provide written evidence that the facility conducted pre-screening based on the regulatory requirements at 42 CFR 483.13(c).

Task 6 Determination of Compliance:

Take account of all the information gained during this review as well as all other information gained during the survey. When a deficiency exists, determine if F225 or F226 provides the best regulatory support for the deficiency.

- 483.13(c), F226, Staff Treatment of Residents:

  o The facility is compliant with this requirement if they have developed and implemented written policies and procedures that prohibit mistreatment, neglect, and abuse of residents and misappropriation of resident property. If not, cite at F226.

- 483.13(c)(1)(2)(3)and (4), F225, Staff Treatment of Residents:

  o The facility is compliant with this requirement if they took appropriate actions in the areas of screening, reporting, protecting, investigating and taking appropriate corrective actions. If not, cite at F225.

Task 6 - Information Analysis for Deficiency Determination

A. General Objectives

The objectives of information analysis for deficiency determination are:

- To review and analyze all information collected and to determine whether or not the facility has failed to meet one or more of the regulatory requirements; and

- To determine whether to conduct an extended survey.

B. Overview

The worksheets and procedures are designed to assist the surveyor in gathering, investigating, organizing, and analyzing information about the quality of services provided by the facility in order to determine whether the facility has failed to meet long-term care requirements.

The information gathering portions of the survey have focused on the resident and the delivery of services by the facility using observation, interview and record review as sources of information. The information analysis and decision-making portion of the survey focuses on making determinations about whether the facility meets requirements.

Information analysis and decision Making builds on discussions of the daily team meetings, which should include discussions of observed problems, areas of concern, and possible failure to meet requirements.

Decisions about deficiencies are to be team decisions with each member of the team, including specialty surveyors (see Section I.C.), having input into the decisions. The team coordinator or designee should document the deficiency decisions and the substance of the evidence on the Form CMS-807.

For initial surveys, a determination must be made regarding whether the facility meets every long-term care requirement.

C. Decision-Making Process

Each member of the team should review his/her worksheets to identify concerns and specific evidence relating to requirements that the facility has potentially failed to meet. In order to identify the facility's deficient practices and to enable collating and evaluating the evidence, worksheets should reflect the source of the evidence and should summarize the concerns on relevant data tags.

- Begin the decision-making task by taking into account the daily discussions, the findings documented on the worksheets, discussions with the facility, observations over the course of the survey, and the discussions regarding definitions of deficiencies in the following section. At a minimum, focus on the regulatory groupings 42 CFR 483.10, Resident Rights; 42 CFR 483.13, Resident Behavior and Facility Practice; 42 CFR 483.15, Quality of Life; 42 CFR 483.20, Resident Assessment' and 42 CFR 483.25, Quality of Care. Gather information from all worksheets pertinent to the particular requirements being reviewed (e.g., documentation from all worksheets concerning resident rights). In general, what is the facility's performance in meeting these requirements? Does the facility protect and promote resident rights? Discuss results of the information-gathering phase in the context of facility conformance with these resident-centered requirements and the examples of resident-facility interactions that cause you to believe there may be deficiencies.

- Prioritize the review of worksheets so that the first information the team discusses relates to those requirements that the facility has potentially failed to meet. For example, what documentation on the Quality of Life Assessment worksheet supports the belief that the facility does not protect and promote resident rights? What information on other worksheets supports or does not support the team's assessment of Resident Rights? Evaluate the specifics of the regulatory language and the specific data collected (e.g., observation, resident, family and staff interview information) with respect to the facility's performance in each requirement. Review the worksheets on an individual tag-by-tag basis. If data indicate that the facility has not met a specific requirement (see Task 6, Section D), document that deficiency.

- In order to ensure that no requirements are missed, proceed through the requirements sequentially as they appear in the interpretive guidelines, preferably section by section. Findings/evidence within each section should be shared by each team member during this discussion. Consider all aspects of the requirements within the tag/section being discussed and evaluate how the information gathered relates to the specifics of the regulatory language and to the facility's performance in each requirement. The team should come to consensus on each requirement for which problems have been raised by any member. If no problems are identified for a particular tag number during the information gathering process, then no deficiency exists for that tag number.

- The team coordinator, or a designee, collates all information and records the substance of the decision-making discussion on the Form CMS-807. (See Exhibit 95.)

- Determine if there is substandard quality of care.

- If substandard quality of care exists, conduct an extended survey.

D. Deficiency Criteria

To determine if a deficiency exists, use the following definitions and guidance:

- A "deficiency" is defined as a facility's failure to meet a participation requirement specified in the Social Security Act or in Part 483, Subpart B (i.e., 42 CFR 483.5 - 42 CFR 483.75).

- To help determine if a deficiency exists, look at the language of the requirement. Some requirements need to be met for each resident. Any violation of these requirements, even for one resident, is a deficiency.

- Other requirements focus on facility systems.

For some requirements, especially those in the regulatory grouping of Quality of Life (42 CFR 483.15), the team will evaluate the sum of the staff actions and/or decisions for an individual resident to determine if the requirement is met for that individual. Quality of Life requirements are best evaluated comprehensively, rather than in terms of a single incident. However, a single incident which is considered severe enough may result in a deficiency.

Certain facility systems requirements must be met in an absolute sense, e.g., a facility must have a RN on duty 7 days a week unless it has received a waiver. Other facility system requirements are best evaluated comprehensively, rather than in terms of a single incident. In evaluating these requirements, the team will examine both the individual parts of the system, e.g., the adequacy of the infection control protocol, the adequacy of facility policy on hand washing, as well as the actual implementation of that system.

E. Evidence Evaluation

The survey team must evaluate the evidence documented during the survey to determine if a deficiency exists due to a failure to meet a requirement and if there are any negative resident outcomes due to the failure. Failure to meet requirements related to quality of care, resident rights, and quality of life generally fall into two categories:

1. Potential or Actual Physical, Mental or Psychosocial Injury or Deterioration to A Resident Including Violation of Residents' Rights.

   Some situations which illustrate this level of harm could be:

   a. Development of, or worsening of, a pressure sore;

   b. Loss of dignity due to lying in a urine-saturated bed for a prolonged period; and

   c. Social isolation caused by staff failure to assist the resident in participating in scheduled activities.

   This category of negative outcome may be identified when an identified facility practice is so divergent from accepted principles of practice that harm has occurred or a future negative outcome or harm is probable. An example would be nurse aides in a facility who often fail to wash their hands between caring for residents. In this example, there is a strong potential for harm although there has been no evidence of a high facility infection rate, or of infections spreading from one resident to another. Should a resident contract an infection or become colonized with a highly contagious bacteria, there is a high potential for a major outbreak of nosocomial infection.

2. Lack of (or the Potential for Lack of) Reaching the Highest Practicable Level of Physical, Mental or Psychosocial Well-Being.

   No deterioration occurred, but the facility failed to provide necessary care for resident improvement. For example:

   a. The facility identified the resident's desire to reach a higher level of ability, e.g., improvement in ambulation, and care was planned accordingly. However, the facility failed to implement, or failed to consistently implement the plan of care, and the resident failed to improve, i.e., did not reach his/her highest practicable well-being;

b. The facility identified a need in the comprehensive assessment, e.g., the resident was withdrawn/depressed, but the facility did not develop a care plan or prioritize this need of the resident, planning to address it at a later time. The resident received no care or treatment to address the need and did not improve, i.e., remained withdrawn/depressed. Therefore, the resident was not given the opportunity to reach his/her highest practicable well-being;

c. The facility failed to identify the resident's need/problem/ability to improve, e.g., the ability to eat independently if given assistive devices, and, therefore, did not plan care appropriately. As a result, the resident failed to reach his/her highest practicable well-being, i.e., eat independently.

d. A facility's written procedures or oral explanations do not provide information about which residents are supposed to be fully informed, e.g., the resident is provided treatment which they may have wished to refuse.

If the resident is the primary source of information, the team should conduct further information gathering and analysis. This may include additional interviews with family and staff or record reviews to supplement or corroborate the resident's report. If additional sources of information are not available, determine if the interviewees are reliable sources of information and if the information received is accurate. If so, citation of a deficiency may be based on resident information alone.

In cases where residents are unable to speak for themselves, the survey team should assess how most people would react to the situation in question. For example, a female resident who is unable to express herself is wheeled down the hall in a wheelchair on the way to her shower with only a towel partially covering her body. The team will decide if this incident is inappropriate because the resident is unable to express herself. Quality of life and Residents' Rights requirements are most often evaluated using this type of analysis.

F. Determination of Substandard Quality of Care

The team must determine if substandard quality of care exists. Substandard quality of care is defined as one or more deficiencies related to participation requirements under 42 CFR 483.13, Resident Behavior and Facility Practices, Quality of Life, or 42 CFR 483.25, Quality of Care which, constitute either immediate jeopardy to resident health or safety, pattern or widespread deficiencies at severity level 3, or widespread deficiencies at severity level 2. (See Section V*., Deficiency Categorization.) *[**Editor's Note:** The section number cited is incorrect. The correct section number is IV.]

G. Special Circumstances

Substandard quality of care and immediate jeopardy determinations trigger additional survey tasks and must be determined during the information gathering tasks of the survey and/or during information analysis and decision-making.

Immediate jeopardy is defined as a situation in which the facility's failure to meet one or more requirements of participation has caused, or is likely to cause, serious injury, harm, impairment, or death to a resident. At any time during the survey, if one or more team members identifies possible immediate jeopardy, the team should meet immediately to confer. The guiding principles to determine immediate jeopardy and serious threat make it clear that the threat can be related to mental, as well as physical well-being, and that the situation in question need not be a widespread problem. If the team concurs, the team coordinator must consult immediately with his/her supervisor. If the supervisor concurs that the situation constitutes immediate jeopardy, the team coordinator informs the facility Administrator or designee that the immediate jeopardy termination procedures are being invoked. The team coordinator should explain the nature of the immediate jeopardy to the Administrator or designee. The survey team should complete the entire survey. See Appendix Q [**Editor's Note:** The reference cited is located in the *State Operations Manual*.] for guidance regarding determination of immediate jeopardy, and §3010 for procedures to follow if the immediate jeopardy termination procedures are invoked.

When surveyors suspect substandard quality of care (SQC), they expand the standard (or abbreviated) survey sample as necessary to determine scope (Refer to Task 4, Supplementary Sample for further information). If there is no deficiency(ies) classified as substandard quality of care and there is a deficiency under the regulatory Groupings of 42 CFR 483.13, 42 CFR 483.15 and/or 42 CFR 483.25, that are classified as an isolated incident of severity level 3, or, as a pattern of severity level 2, then determine if there is sufficient evidence to make the decision that there is not substandard quality of care.

If the evidence is not adequate and the number of observations only allowed for isolated scope when there is a severity level 3, or pattern for scope when there is a severity level 2, then expand the sample to include additional reviews of that requirement. For example, if residents in the facility are receiving care for a colostomy, and for the one resident with a colostomy in the sample, it is determined that care provided caused actual harm to the resident, there would be a deficiency of isolated actual harm, but there would not be sufficient evidence to determine that there was substandard quality of care. Thus, the sample would need to be expanded before determining that substandard quality of care did or did not exist. On the other hand, if the number of individuals with a colostomy in the facility was the same (6), and 4 residents with colostomies were included in the sample and only one had deficient care, there would be no need to expand the sample. If the team verifies the existence of SQC, the Administrator should be informed that the facility is in SQC and an extended (or partial extended) survey will be conducted. If expanding the sample determines that SQC does not exist, no extended or partial extended survey will be conducted.

H. Determining Citations of Past Noncompliance at the Time of the Current Survey

Past noncompliance may be identified during any survey of a nursing home. To cite past noncompliance with a specific survey data tag (F-tag or K-tag), all of the following three criteria must be met:

1. The facility was not in compliance with the specific regulatory requirement(s) (as referenced by the specific F-tag or K-tag) at the time the situation occurred;

2. The noncompliance occurred after the exit date of the last standard recertification survey and before the survey (standard, complaint, or revisit) currently being conducted; and

3. There is sufficient evidence that the facility corrected the noncompliance and is in substantial compliance at the time of the current survey for the specific regulatory requirement(s), as referenced by the specific F-tag or K-tag.

Task 7 - Exit Conference

A. General Objective

The general objective of the exit conference is to inform the facility of the survey team's observations and preliminary findings.

B. Conduct of Exit Conference

Conduct the exit conference with facility personnel. Invite the ombudsman and an officer of the organized residents group, if one exists, to the exit conference. Also, invite one or two residents to attend. The team may provide an abbreviated exit conference specifically for residents after completion of the normal facility exit conference. If two exit conferences are held, notify the ombudsman and invite the ombudsman to attend either or both conferences.

Do not discuss survey results in a manner that reveals the identity of an individual resident. Provide information in a manner that is understandable to those present, e.g., say the deficiency "relates to development of pressure sores," not "Tag F314."

Describe the team's preliminary deficiency findings to the facility and let them know they will receive a report of the survey which will contain any deficiencies that have been cited (Form CMS-2567). If requested, provide the facility with a list of residents included in the standard survey sample. Do not give the team's Roster/Sample Matrixes to the facility, because they contain confidential information.

If an extended survey is required and the survey team cannot complete all or part of the extended survey prior to the exit conference, inform the Administrator that the deficiencies, as discussed in the conference, may be amended upon completion of the extended survey. (See §2724 for additional information concerning exit conferences.)

During the exit conference, provide the facility with the opportunity to discuss and supply additional information that they believe is pertinent to the identified findings. Because of the ongoing dialogue between surveyors and facility staff during the survey, there should be few instances where the facility is not aware of surveyor concerns or has not had an opportunity to present additional information prior to the exit conference.

II.B.2. - The Traditional Extended and/or Partial Extended Survey

Conduct an extended survey subsequent to a standard survey and conduct a partial extended survey subsequent to an abbreviated survey when you have determined that there is a substandard quality of care in:

- 42 CFR 483.13, Resident behavior and facility practices;

- 42 CFR 483.15, Quality of life; and/or

- 42 CFR 483.25, Quality of care.

When conducting the extended/partial extended survey, at a minimum, fully review and verify compliance with each tag number within 42 CFR 483.30, Nursing Services; 42 CFR 483.40, Physician Services; and 42 CFR 483.75, Administration. Focus on the facility's policies and procedures that may have produced the substandard quality of care. As appropriate, include a review of staffing, inservice training and the infection control program. An extended/partial extended survey explores the extent to which structure and process factors such as written policies and procedures, staff qualifications and functional responsibilities, and specific agreements and contracts of the facility may have contributed to the outcomes. If the extended/partial extended survey was triggered by a deficiency in quality of care, conduct a detailed review of the accuracy of resident assessment. During the partial extended survey, consider expanding the scope of the review to include a more comprehensive evaluation of the requirements at 42 CFR 483.13, 42 CFR 483.15, and/or 42 CFR 483.25 in which substandard quality of care was found.

Document the observations from the extended or partial extended survey on the Form CMS-805, (see Exhibit 93) or the Form CMS-807 (see Exhibit 95).

Review of the Accuracy of Resident Assessments During an Extended/Partial Extended Survey

The objective of this review is to determine if resident assessments are accurate.

If an extended/partial extended survey is conducted based on substandard quality of care in Quality of Care (42 CFR 483.25), review the accuracy of resident assessments by:

- Reviewing a sample of comprehensive resident assessments completed no more than 30 days prior to conducting the survey;

- Comparing observations of the resident with the facility's assessment;

- Conducting the number of assessment reviews needed to make a decision concerning the accuracy of the facility's resident assessments; and

- Determining if observations of the resident, and interviews with resident/staff/family, "match" the facility's assessment (or specific portions of the assessment) of the resident. If observations and interviews do not "match," investigate further.

Record the indepth review of the accuracy of resident assessments on page 3 of the Form CMS-805. (See Exhibit 93.)

Timing for Conducting the Extended Survey and Partial Extended Survey

Conduct the extended or partial extended survey:

- Prior to the exit conference, in which case the facility will be provided with information from the standard, abbreviated standard, partial extended or extended surveys; or

- Not later than 2 weeks after the standard/abbreviated survey is completed, if the team is unable to conduct the extended survey or partial extended survey concurrent with the standard survey or the abbreviated survey. Advise the facility's Administrator that there will be an extended or partial extended survey conducted and that an exit conference will be held at the completion of the survey.

II.B.3 - The Traditional Post Survey Revisit (Follow-Up)

In accordance with §7317, the State agency conducts a revisit, as applicable, to confirm that the facility is in compliance and has the ability to remain in compliance. The purpose of the post-survey revisit (follow-up) is to re-evaluate the specific care and services that were cited as noncompliant during the original standard, abbreviated standard, extended or partial extended survey(s). Ascertain the status of corrective actions being taken on all requirements not in substantial compliance. Section 7304 contains the 5 elements a facility must address in developing an acceptable plan of correction. One of these elements is what continuous quality improvement system(s) a facility has in place to monitor its performance in identifying the deficient practice/care and assuring that it does not recur.

Because this survey process focuses on the care of the resident, revisits are generally necessary to ascertain whether the deficient practices have been corrected. The nature of the noncompliance dictates the scope of the revisit. For example, do not perform another drug pass if no drug distribution related deficiencies were cited on the initial survey. Do interviews and closed record reviews, as appropriate. Prior to the revisit, review appropriate documents, including the plan of correction, to focus the revisit review.

Conduct as many survey tasks as needed to determine compliance status. Always conduct Sub-Task 5F. However, the team is not prohibited from gathering information related to any requirement during a post-survey revisit.

When selecting the resident sample for the revisit survey, determine the sample size using 60% of the sample size for a standard survey as described in Table 1, Resident Sample Selection. (Phase 1 sample size is 60%.) The follow-up survey does not require a 2 Phase sample selection.

Focus on selecting residents who are most likely to have those conditions/needs/problems cited in the original survey. If possible, include some residents identified as receiving substandard quality of care during the prior survey. If, after completing the revisit activities, you determine that the cited incidence(s) of noncompliance was not corrected, initiate enforcement action, as appropriate. (See §7400 for specific guidance concerning initiation of enforcement action.)

Use appropriate CMS forms during this survey. However, if the need for documentation is minimal, use the Surveyor Notes Worksheet (Form CMS-808). (See Exhibit 95 to record the results of the revisit.)

II.B.4 - The Traditional Abbreviated Standard Survey

A. Complaint Investigations

(See also Chapter 5[*]) [*]**[Editor's Note:** The reference cited is referring to Chapter 5 of the *State Operations Manual*.]

B. Substantial Changes in a Facility's Organization and Management

If a facility notifies the survey agency of a change in organization or management, review the change to ensure compliance with the regulations. Request copies of the appropriate documents, e.g., written policies and procedures, personnel qualifications and agreements. If changes in a facility's organization and management are significant and raise questions of its continued compliance, determine, through a survey, whether certain changes have caused a decline in quality of care furnished by a SNF or NF.

III. Writing the Statement of Deficiencies

A. General Objective

The general objective of this section is to write the statement of deficiencies in terms specific enough to allow a reasonably knowledgeable person to understand the aspect(s) of the requirement(s) that is (are) not met. For findings of past noncompliance and or current noncompliance indicate the data prefix tag and regulatory citation, followed by a summary of the evidence and supporting observations using resident identifiers. This documentation must be written in language specific enough to use to identify levels of severity and scope at the completion of the survey. If information was identified during confidential resident interviews, do not include a resident identifier when recording the source of the evidence. List the data tags in the order specified in the Code of Federal Regulations.

When a citation of past noncompliance is written, a nursing home does not provide a plan of correction as the deficiency is already corrected; however, the survey team documents the facility's corrective actions on Form CMS-2567. (Additional information about citations of past noncompliance is found at Chapter 7[*].) [*][**Editor's Note**: The reference cited is referring to Chapter 7 of the *State Operations Manual*.]

When a facility is in substantial compliance, but has deficiencies which are isolated with no actual harm and potential for only minimal harm, the deficiencies are recorded on the "Notice of Isolated Deficiencies" instead of on the Form CMS-2567. A plan of correction is not required but a facility is expected to correct all deficiencies.

The statement of deficiencies should:

- Specifically reflect the content of each requirement that is not met;

- Clearly identify the specific deficient entity practices and the objective evidence concerning these practices;

- Identify the extent of the deficient practice, including systemic practices, where appropriate; and

- Identify the source(s) of the evidence, e.g., interview, observation, or record review.

Following deficiency categorization (Section V[*]), enter on Form CMS-2567L the letter corresponding to the box of the scope and severity grid (Chapter 7, §7400.E.) for at least any deficiency which constitutes substandard quality of care and any deficiency which drives the choice of a required remedy category. Enter these letters in ID prefix tag column immediately below the tag number of the Form CMS-2567L. [*][**Editor's Note**: The section cited is incorrect. The correct section is Section IV., Deficiency Categorization.]

IV. Deficiency Categorization

A. General Objective

After the survey team determines that a deficiency (ies) exists, assess the effect on resident outcome (severity level) and determine the number of residents potentially or actually affected (scope level). Use the results of this assessment to determine whether or not the facility is in substantial compliance or is noncompliant. When a facility is noncompliant, consider how the deficient practice is classified according to severity and scope levels in selecting an appropriate remedy. (See §7400 for discussion of remedies.)

Scope and severity determinations are also applicable to deficiencies at §483.70(a), Life Safety from Fire.

B. Guidance on Severity Levels

There are four severity levels. Level 1, no actual harm with potential for minimal harm; Level 2, no actual harm with potential for more than minimal harm that is not immediate jeopardy; Level 3, actual harm that is not immediate jeopardy; Level 4, immediate jeopardy to resident health or safety. These four levels are defined accordingly:

1. Level 1 is a deficiency that has the potential for causing no more than a minor negative impact on the resident(s).

2. Level 2 is noncompliance that results in no more than minimal physical, mental and/or psychosocial discomfort to the resident and/or has the potential (not yet realized) to compromise the resident's ability to maintain and/or reach his/her highest practicable physical, mental and/or psychosocial well-being as defined by an accurate and comprehensive resident assessment, plan of care, and provision of services.

3. Level 3 is noncompliance that results in a negative outcome that has compromised the resident's ability to maintain and/or reach his/her highest practicable physical, mental and psychosocial well-being as defined by an accurate and comprehensive resident assessment, plan of care, and provision of services. This does not include a deficient practice that only could or has caused limited consequence to the resident.

4. Level 4 is immediate jeopardy, a situation in which immediate corrective action is necessary because the facility's noncompliance with one or more requirements of participation has caused, or is likely to cause, serious injury, harm, impairment, or death to a resident receiving care in a facility. (See Appendix Q.) [**Editor's Note:** The section cited is referring to Appendix Q of the *State Operations Manual*.]

C. Guidance on Scope Levels

Scope has three levels: isolated; pattern; and widespread. The scope levels are defined accordingly:

1. Scope is isolated when one or a very limited number of residents are affected and/or one or a very limited number of staff are involved, and/or the situation has occurred only occasionally or in a very limited number of locations.

2. Scope is a pattern when more than a very limited number of residents are affected, and/or more than a very limited number of staff are involved, and/or the situation has occurred in several locations, and/or the same resident(s) have been affected by repeated occurrences of the same deficient practice. The effect of the deficient practice is not found to be pervasive throughout the facility.

3. . Scope is widespread when the problems causing the deficiencies are pervasive in the facility and/or represent systemic failure that affected or has the potential to affect a large portion or all of the facility's residents. Widespread scope refers to the entire facility population, not a subset of residents or one unit of a facility. In addition, widespread scope may be identified if a systemic failure in the facility (e.g., failure to maintain food at safe temperatures) would be likely to affect a large number of residents and is, therefore, pervasive in the facility.

D. General Procedures

After the team makes a decision to cite a deficiency(ies), evaluate the deficient practice's impact on the resident(s) and the prevalence of the deficient practice. Review deficiency statements, worksheets, and results of team discussions for evidence on which to base these determinations. The team may base evidence of the impact or prevalence for residents of the deficient practices on record reviews, interviews and/or observations. Whatever the source, the evidence must be credible.

After determining the severity level of a deficient practice, determine scope. When determining scope, evaluate the cause of the deficiency. If the facility lacks a system/policy (or has an inadequate system) to meet the requirements and this failure has the potential to affect a large number of residents in the facility, then the deficient practice is likely to be widespread. If an adequate system/policy is in place but is being inadequately implemented in certain instances, or if there is an inadequate system with the potential to impact only a subset of the facility's population, then the deficient practice is likely to be pattern. If the deficiency affects or has the potential to affect one or a very limited number of residents, then the scope is isolated.

If the evidence gathered during the survey for a particular requirement includes examples of various severity or scope levels, surveyors should generally classify the deficiency at the highest level of severity, even if most of the evidence corresponds to a lower severity level. For example, if there is a deficiency in which one resident suffered a severity 3 while there were widespread findings of the same deficiency at severity 2, then the deficiency would be generally classified as severity 3, isolated.

E. Psychosocial Outcome Severity Guide

Purpose

The purpose of the Psychosocial Outcome Severity Guide is to help surveyors determine the severity of psychosocial outcomes resulting from the identified noncompliance at a specific F tag. The Guide is used to determine the severity of a deficiency in any regulatory grouping (e.g., Quality of Care, Quality of Life) that resulted in a negative psychosocial outcome.

This Guide is not intended to replace the current scope and severity grid. It is to be used in conjunction with the scope and severity grid to determine the severity of outcomes to each resident involved in a deficiency that has resulted in a psychosocial outcome. The team should select the level of severity for the deficiency based on the highest level of physical or psychosocial outcome. For example, a resident who was slapped by a staff member may experience only a minor physical outcome from the slap but suffer a greater psychosocial outcome. In this case the severity level based on the psychosocial outcome would be used as the level of severity for the deficiency.

Overview

Psychosocial outcomes (i.e., mood and behavior) may result from a facility's noncompliance with any regulatory requirement. Although a resident may experience either a negative physical outcome or a negative psychosocial outcome, some may experience or have the potential to experience both types of negative outcomes. Psychosocial outcomes and physical outcomes are equally important in determining the severity of noncompliance, and both need to be considered before assigning a severity level. The severity level assigned should reflect the most significant negative outcome or highest level of harm/potential harm.

The presence of a given affect (i.e., behavioral manifestation of mood demonstrated by the resident) does not necessarily indicate a psychosocial outcome that is the direct result of noncompliance. A resident's reactions and responses (or lack thereof) also may be affected by pre-existing psychosocial issues, illnesses, medication side effects, and/or other factors. Because many nursing home residents have sadness, anger, loss of self-esteem, etc. in reaction to normal life experiences, the survey team must have determined that the psychosocial outcome is a result of the noncompliance.

Psychosocial outcomes of interest to surveyors are those caused by the facility's noncompliance with any regulation. This also includes psychosocial outcomes resulting from facility failure to assess and develop an adequate care plan to address a resident's pre-existing psychosocial issues, which led to continuation or worsening of the condition.

Instructions

This Guide is designed to be used separately for each resident included in the deficiency. Each resident's psychosocial response to the noncompliance is the basis for determining psychosocial severity of a deficiency. To determine severity, use the information gathered through the investigative process (Task 5). Compare the resident's behavior (e.g., their routine, activity, and responses to staff or to everyday situations) and mood before and after the noncompliance.

If the survey team determines that a facility's noncompliance has resulted in a negative psychosocial outcome to one or more residents, the team should use this Guide to evaluate the severity of the outcome for each resident identified in the deficiency (in accordance with the instructions at Task 6). The team should determine severity based on the resident's response in the following circumstances:

- If the resident can communicate a psychosocial reaction to the deficient practice, compare this response to the Guide; or

- If the resident is unable to express her/himself verbally but shows a noticeable non-verbal response that is related to the deficient practice, compare the non-verbal response to the Guide.

Application of the Reasonable Person Concept

There are circumstances in which the survey team may apply the "reasonable person concept" to determine severity of the deficiency. To apply the reasonable person concept, the survey team should determine the severity of the psychosocial outcome or potential outcome the deficiency may have had on a reasonable person in the resident's position (i.e., what degree of actual or potential harm would one expect a reasonable person in a similar situation to suffer as a result of the noncompliance).

NOTE: The reasonable person concept described in this Guide is merely a tool to assist the survey team's assessment of the severity level of negative psychosocial outcomes. Although the reasonable person concept is used in many areas of the law, the application of common law defenses to the assessment of severity pursuant to this Guide would be inappropriate and is expressly precluded.

The survey team should use the reasonable person concept when the resident's psychosocial outcome may not be readily determined through the investigative process:

- When there is no discernable response or when circumstances obstruct the direct evaluation of the resident's psychosocial outcome. Such circumstances may include, but are not limited to, the resident's death, subsequent injury, cognitive impairments, physical impairments, or insufficient documentation by the facility. In this situation, the survey team may use the reasonable person concept to evaluate the severity (Level 2, Level 3, or Level 4) of the deficient practice; or

- When the resident's reaction to a deficient practice is markedly incongruent with the level of reaction the reasonable person would have to the deficient practice. In this situation, the survey team may use the reasonable person concept to evaluate the potential severity (Level 2 or Level 4) of the deficient practice.

Clarification Of Terms

"Anger" refers to an emotion caused by the frustrated attempts to attain a goal, or in response to hostile or disturbing actions such as insults, injuries, or threats that do not come from a feared source.[1]

"Apathy" refers to a marked indifference to the environment; lack of a response to a situation; lack of interest in or concern for things that others find moving or exciting; absence or suppression of passion, emotion, or excitement.[2]

"Anxiety" refers to the apprehensive anticipation of future danger or misfortune accompanied by a feeling of distress, sadness, or somatic symptoms of tension. Somatic symptoms of tension may include, but are not limited to, restlessness, irritability, hyper-vigilance, an exaggerated startle response, increased muscle tone, and teeth grinding. The focus of anticipated danger may be internal or external.[3]

"Dehumanization" refers to the deprivation of human qualities or attributes such as individuality, compassion, or civility. Dehumanization is the outcome resulting from having been treated as an inanimate object or as having no emotions, feelings, or sensations.[4]

"Depressed mood" (which does not necessarily constitute clinical depression) is indicated by negative statements; self-deprecation; sad facial expressions; crying and tearfulness; withdrawal from activities of interest; and/or reduced social interactions. Some residents such as those with moderate or severe cognitive impairment may be more likely to demonstrate nonverbal symptoms of depression.[5]

"Humiliation" refers to a feeling of shame due to being embarrassed, disgraced, or depreciated. Some individuals lose so much self-esteem through humiliation that they become depressed.[6]

PSYCHOSOCIAL OUTCOME SEVERITY GUIDE

The following are levels of negative psychosocial outcomes that developed, continued, or worsened as a result of the facility's noncompliance. This Guide is only to be used once the survey team has determined noncompliance at a regulatory requirement. The survey team must have established a connection between the noncompliance and a negative psychosocial outcome to the resident as evidenced by observations, record review, and/or interviews with residents, their representatives, and/or staff.

Severity Level 4 Considerations: Immediate Jeopardy to Resident Health or Safety

Immediate Jeopardy is a situation in which the facility's noncompliance with one or more requirements of participation:

- Has allowed/caused/resulted in, or is likely to allow/cause /result in serious injury, harm, impairment, or death to a resident; and

- Requires immediate correction, as the facility either created the situation or allowed the situation to continue by failing to implement preventative or corrective measures.

Examples of negative psychosocial outcomes as a result of the facility's noncompliance may include but are not limited to:

- Suicidal ideation/thoughts and preoccupation (with a plan) or suicidal attempt (active or passive) such as trying to jump from a high place, throwing oneself down a flight of stairs, refusing to eat or drink in order to kill oneself.

- Engaging in self-injurious behavior that is likely to cause serious injury, harm, impairment, or death to the resident (e.g., banging head against wall).

- Sustained and intense crying, moaning, screaming, or combative behavior.

- Expressions (verbal and/or non-verbal) of severe, unrelenting, excruciating, and unrelieved pain; pain has become all-consuming and overwhelms the resident.

- Recurrent (i.e., more than isolated or fleeting) debilitating fear/anxiety that may be manifested as panic, immobilization, screaming, and/or extremely aggressive or agitated behavior(s) (e.g., trembling, cowering) in response to an identifiable situation (e.g., approach of a specific staff member).

- Ongoing, persistent expression of dehumanization or humiliation in response to an identifiable situation, that persists regardless of whether the precipitating event(s) has ceased and has resulted in a potentially life-threatening consequence.

- Expressions of anger at an intense and sustained level that has caused or is likely to cause serious injury, harm, impairment, or death to self or others.

Severity Level 3 Considerations: Actual Harm that is not Immediate Jeopardy

Severity Level 3 indicates noncompliance that results in actual harm, and can include but may not be limited to clinical compromise, decline, or the resident's inability to maintain and/or reach his/her highest practicable well-being.

Examples of negative psychosocial outcomes as a result of the facility's noncompliance may include but are not limited to:

- Significant decline in former social patterns that does not rise to a level of immediate jeopardy.

- Persistent depressed mood[7,8,9] that may be manifested by verbal and nonverbal symptoms such as:

  o Social withdrawal; irritability; anxiety; hopelessness; tearfulness; crying; moaning;

  o Loss of interest or ability to experience or feel pleasure nearly every day for much of the day;

  o Psychomotor agitation[10] (e.g., inability to sit still, pacing, hand-wringing, or pulling or rubbing of the skin, clothing, or other objects), accompanied by a bothered or sad expression;

  o Psychomotor retardation (e.g., slowed speech, thinking, and body movements; increased pauses before answering);

  o Verbal agitation[11] (e.g., repeated requests for help, groaning, sighing, or other repeated verbalizations), accompanied by sad facial expressions;

  o Expressions of feelings of worthlessness or excessive guilt nearly every day (not merely self-reproach or guilt about being sick or needing care);

  o Markedly diminished ability to think or concentrate;

  o Recurrent thoughts of death (not just fear of dying) or statements without an intent to act (e.g., "I wish I were dead" or "my family would be better off without me").

- Expressions (verbal and/or non-verbal) of persistent pain or physical distress (e.g., itching, thirst) that has compromised the resident's functioning such as diminished level of participation in social interactions and/or ADLs, intermittent crying and moaning, weight loss and/or diminished appetite. Pain or physical distress has become a central focus of the resident's attention, but it is not all-consuming or overwhelming (as in Severity Level 4).

- Chronic or recurrent fear/anxiety that has compromised the resident's well-being and that may be manifested as avoidance of the fear-inducing situation(s) or person(s); preoccupation with fear; resistance to care and/or social interaction; moderate aggressive or agitated behavior(s) related to fear; sleeplessness due to fear; and/or verbal expressions of fear. Expressions of fear/anxiety are not to the level of panic and immobilization (as in Severity Level 4).

- Ongoing, persistent feeling and/or expression of dehumanization or humiliation that persists regardless of whether the precipitating, dehumanizing event(s) or situation(s) has ceased. The feelings of dehumanization and humiliation have not resulted in a life-threatening consequence.

- Apathy and social disengagement such as listlessness; slowness of response and thought (psychomotor retardation); lack of interest or concern especially in matters of general importance and appeal, resulting from facility noncompliance.

- Sustained distress (e.g., agitation indicative of understimulation as manifested by fidgeting; restlessness; repetitive verbalization of not knowing what to do, needing to go to work, and/or needing to find something).

- Anger that has caused aggression that could lead to injuring self or others. Verbal aggression can be manifested by threatening, screaming, or cursing; physical aggression can be manifested by self-directed responses or hitting, shoving, biting, and scratching others.

Severity Level 2 Considerations: No Actual Harm with Potential for More Than Minimal Harm that is Not Immediate Jeopardy

Severity Level 2 indicates noncompliance that results in a resident outcome of no more than minimal discomfort and/or has the potential to compromise the resident's ability to maintain or reach his or her highest practicable level of well being. The potential exists for greater harm to occur if interventions are not provided.

Examples of negative psychosocial outcomes as a result of the facility's noncompliance may include but are not limited to:

- Intermittent sadness, as reflected in facial expression and/or demeanor, tearfulness, crying, or verbal/vocal agitation (e.g., repeated requests for help, moaning, and sighing).

- Feelings and/or complaints of discomfort or moderate pain. The resident may be irritable and/or express discomfort.

- Fear/anxiety that may be manifested as expressions or signs of minimal discomfort (e.g., verbal expressions of fear/anxiety; pulling away from a feared object or situation) or has the potential, not yet realized, to compromise the resident's well-being.

- Feeling of shame or embarrassment without a loss of interest in the environment and the self.

- Complaints of boredom and/or reports that there is nothing to do, accompanied by expressions of periodic distress that do not result in maladaptive behaviors (e.g., verbal or physical aggression).

- Verbal or nonverbal expressions of anger that did not lead to harm to self or others.

Severity Level 1 Considerations: No Actual Harm with Potential for Minimal Harm

Severity Level 1 is not an option because any facility practice that results in a reduction of psychosocial well-being diminishes the resident's quality of life. The deficiency is, therefore, at least a Severity Level 2 because it has the potential for more than minimal harm.

V. Confidentiality and Respect for Resident Privacy

Conduct the survey in a manner that allows for the greatest degree of confidentiality for residents, particularly regarding the information gathered during the in-depth interviews. Use the resident identifier (e.g., a code number the survey team has assigned to each resident in the sample) on the Form CMS-2567 in place of the resident's name, which should never be used on the Form CMS-2567.

When communicating to the facility about substandard quality of care, fully identify the resident(s) by name if the situation was identified through observation or record review. Improperly applied restraints, medication error, cold food, gloves not worn for a sterile procedure, and diet inconsistent with order are examples of practices that can be identified to the facility by resident name. Information about injuries due to broken equipment, prolonged use of restraints, and opened mail is more likely to be obtained through resident and family interviews. Do not identify residents or family members providing this information without their permission.

Notes and worksheets contain pre-decisional information and are, therefore, not required to be disclosed to the facility at the time of the survey. However, once the Form CMS-2567 has been written, portions of the worksheets explaining the findings reported on the Form CMS-2567 may become subject to release under the Freedom of Information Act (FOIA). Information on the worksheets that was not subsequently used as a basis for writing a deficiency remains pre-decisional and is exempt from disclosure. That information would have to be deleted, according to FOIA guidelines, before the worksheets could be released.

The requirements of the FOIA apply only to those documents held by the Federal government. They do not apply to State or local governments. Therefore, surveyor worksheets held by the State are subject to State disclosure laws only.

VI. Information Transfer

In conjunction with conducting surveys, the State should provide information to the facility about care and regulatory topics that would be useful to the facility for understanding and applying best practices in the care and treatment of long term care residents.

This information exchange is not a consultation with the facility, but is a means of disseminating information that may be of assistance to the facility in meeting long term care requirements. States are not liable, nor are they to be held accountable if training which occurs during information transfer does not "correct" problems at the facility.

Performance of the function is at the discretion of the State and can be performed at various times, including during the standard survey, during follow-up or complaint surveys, during other conferences or workshops or at another time mutually agreeable to the survey agency and the facility. The time allotted for this information transfer should not usually exceed one hour. In no instance should the information transfer delay the survey process.

The Centers for Medicare & Medicaid Services, in cooperation with State survey agencies and consumer and provider groups, will develop and provide packages of training materials suitable for use in this activity.

ENDNOTES

[1] Gall, S., Beins, B., & Feldman, J. (1996). The Gale Encyclopedia of Psychology. Detroit, MI: Gale Research.

[2] Random House. (1981). The Random House Dictionary of the English Language. New York: Author.

[3] American Psychiatric Association (1994). Diagnostic and statistical manual of mental disorders (Fourth Edition). Washington, DC: Author.

[4] Random House. (1981).

[5] Minimum Data Set Version 2.0, Section E.

[6] Corsini, R. (1999). The Dictionary of Psychology. Ann Arbor, MI: Taylor and Francis.

[7] Alexopolous, G., Abrams, R., Young, R., & Shamoian, C. (1988). Cornell scale for depression in dementia. Biological Psychiatry, 23, 271-284.

[8] Brink, T.L., Yesavage, J.A., Lum, O., Heersema, P., Adey, M., & Rose, T.L. (1982). Screening tools for geriatric depression. Clinical Gerontologist, 1, 37-43.

[9] Warren, W.L. (1994). Revised Hamilton Rating Scale for Depression (RHRSD). Los Angeles, CA: Western Psychological Services.

[10] Cohen-Mansfield, J. (2003). Agitation in the elderly: Definitional and theoretical conceptualizations. In D.P. Hay, D. Klein, L. Hay, G. Grossberg, & J.S. Kennedy (Eds.) Agitation in Patients with Dementia: A Practical Guide to Diagnosis and Management (pp. 1-22). Washington, DC: American Psychiatric Publishing Inc.

[11] Cohen-Mansfield, J. (2003). Agitation in the elderly: Definitional and theoretical conceptualizations.

[This page intentionally left blank]

The Facility Guide to OBRA Regulations, and the Long Term Care Survey Process

- Survey Protocols (SOM, Appendix P)
  - Guidance to Surveyors (SOM, Appendix PP)
  - CMS Survey Process Forms

Chapter 1

Attachment A

Medicare/Medicaid State Operations Manual
Provider Certification

Source

CMS Publication # 100-07, Appendix P, *State Operations Manual*, Transmittal # 1, dated May 21, 2004

Editor's Note

Information in this Attachment contains excerpts from Chapters 2, 3, and 7 of the *State Operations Manual* referenced in Appendix P – Survey Protocol for Long-Term Care Facilities. (*See Chapter 1 of this manual*).

Chapter 2

The Certification Process

2713A - Accompanying Surveyors

(Rev. 1, 05-21-04)

The surveyors may allow, or refuse to allow, facility personnel to accompany them during a survey. Each case is at the SA and the surveyor's discretion and is to be worked out with facility management. Facility personnel may be helpful. They may answer questions or point out certain concerns to the survey team, thus making the entire process easier. Conversely, facility personnel may hinder the surveyor, argue about observed problems, and make the survey more difficult. This is not to be tolerated. The surveyors may refuse to allow facility staff to accompany the team if such behavior occurs. The surveyors should make a decision based on the circumstances at the time of the survey. However, the surveyors will always conduct interviews with patients/residents in strict privacy and with prior permission of the individuals.

2724 - Exit Conference

(Rev. 1, 05-21-04)

Subsequent to the pre-exit conference held to allow team members to exchange and formulate survey findings, the surveyors conduct an exit conference ("an exit") with the entity's administrator, designee, and other invited staff. The purpose of the exit conference is to informally communicate preliminary survey team findings and provide an opportunity for the interchange of information, especially if there are differences of opinion. Although it is CMS' general policy to conduct an exit conference, be aware of situations that would justify refusal to continue an exit conference. For example:

- If the provider is represented by counsel (all participants in the exit conference should identify themselves), surveyors may refuse to continue the conference if the entity's attorney attempts to turn it into a evidentiary hearing; or

- Any time the provider creates an environment that is hostile, overly intimidating, or inconsistent with the informal and preliminary nature of an exit conference, surveyors may refuse to conduct or continue the conference.

Additionally, as discussed in §2714, if the entity wishes to audio tape the conference, it must tape the entire meeting and provide the surveyors with a copy of the tape at the conclusion of the conference. Videotaping is also permitted if it is not disruptive to the conference, and a copy is provided at the conclusion of the conference. It is at the sole discretion of the surveyor(s) to determine if videotaping is permitted.

It is critical that the surveyors establish and maintain control throughout the exit conference. Surveyors should present their findings but refrain from arguing with the provider. Be mindful that providers are likely to react defensively to surveyor findings. The provider has a right to disagree with the findings and present arguments to refute them. Surveyors should be receptive to such disagreements. If the provider presents information to negate any of the findings, surveyors should indicate their willingness to reevaluate the findings before leaving the facility. The survey team's reasonableness demonstrates their fairness and professionalism. The degree of receptivity displayed by providers during the exit conference often depends upon the attitudes and survey style of the survey team.

If the LSC survey is conducted independently of the health survey, the fire authority conducts a separate exit conference.

The following guidelines are helpful to surveyors in performing an exit conference:

2724A - Introductory Remarks

(Rev. 1, 05-21-04)

Introduce yourself to those present. Restate why the survey was conducted. Express the team's appreciation for anything the provider has done to facilitate the survey. Explain that the exit conference is an informal meeting to discuss preliminary survey findings and thereby assist the provider or supplier in developing an acceptable PoC, if appropriate and required. Indicate that official findings are presented in writing on Form CMS-2567 and will be forwarded to the provider within 10 working days. Indicate that the provider will, in turn, have 10 calendar days to submit a PoC. (See §2728.)

2724B - Ground Rules

(Rev. 1, 05-21-04)

Explain how you will conduct the exit conference and how the team's findings will be presented; for example, each surveyor may present a portion of the total findings. Inform the provider that where there are disagreements between the team and the provider about the findings that cannot be resolved during the conference or before the team leaves the facility, the provider will have the opportunity to submit additional evidence to the team, the State, and/or the RO after the conference. (See §2728.B. concerning provider attempts to refute survey findings on the Form CMS-2567.)

2724C - Presentation of Findings

(Rev. 1, 05-21-04)

In presenting findings, avoid reading your findings or referring to them by their data tag number. Explain why the findings are a violation of Medicare requirements. If the provider asks for the regulatory basis, provide it. Under no circumstances should you make general statements such as, "Overall the facility is very good." Stick to the facts. Do not rank requirements. Treat requirements as equally as possible. Cite problems that clearly violate regulatory requirements. Avoid statements such as, "The condition was not met," or "The standard was not met."

2724D - Closure

(Rev. 1, 05-21-04)

When you have completed the exit conference, explain the process to the provider. Inform the provider that you will send a formal statement of deficiencies, unless your procedures call for Form CMS-2567 to be left with the provider following the exit conference. Explain the due date for submitting a PoC and how the rest of the certification process works. If you have identified an immediate and serious threat to patient health and safety, explain the significance of that finding and the need for immediate corrective action. In this or any other instance when adverse action is anticipated, explain the implications. Make it clear that only compliance will stop the adverse action.

In an initial survey, the surveyor tells the provider or supplier to expect notification of initial approval or denial of Medicare participation from the RO, and notification by the SMA concerning Medicaid participation, if appropriate. The surveyor explains that the RO establishes the effective date of participation and notifies the provider or supplier in writing and that Medicare payment will not be made before the effective date.

Notices of Medicare recertification from the RO are not necessarily sent unless there are changes in approved services or in sizes of distinct parts certified. Notices of reapproval of NFs and ICFs/MR are made according to State policy.

2732 - Follow-Up on PoCS

(Rev. 1, 05-21-04)

2732A - Post-Survey Revisit

(Rev. 1, 05-21-04)

The SA follows up on all deficiencies cited in PoCs. In some cases, the cited deficiencies may be of a nature that a mail or telephone contact will suffice in lieu of an onsite visit (e.g., the facility agreed to amend its bylaws or written policies). A mail or telephone contact is acceptable as long as the SA has no reason to question the validity of the reported corrections. However, an onsite visit is generally required for deficiencies concerning quality of care. Because the LTC survey process focuses on the care of the resident, revisits are almost always necessary to ascertain whether the deficiencies have indeed been corrected. (See Appendix P for further instructions about follow-up surveys in SNFs and NFs.) If documentation or onsite verification is warranted, the SA obtains appropriate verification before reporting a deficiency as corrected. The revisit (or the mail or telephone contact) requires that the SA complete a Post-Certification Revisit Report (Form CMS-2567B).

2732B - Form CMS-2567B (See Exhibit 8) *[of the SOM]*

(Rev. 1, 05-21-04)

At the time of the follow-up visit to verify corrections of deficiencies previously cited on Form CMS-2567 and/or when corrections are verifiable by telephone contact or mail, the SA completes Form CMS-2567B for the corrections that have been completed. The SA enters:

1. Provider or supplier identification information;

2. Date of the revisit or date of verification;

3. Prefix tag;

4. Corresponding regulatory reference cited on the original Form CMS-2567; and

5. Date the correction was accomplished.

If possible, the revisit is to be conducted by a member(s) of the survey team who cited the original findings. The SA has the completed form initialed by the reviewing official and signed by the surveyor and retains the fourth copy for its provider file, mails a copy to the provider or supplier, and forwards a copy to the RO or SMA, as appropriate.

If, at the time of the revisit, some deficiencies have not been corrected, the SA completes another Form CMS-2567 summarizing the deficiencies not corrected by data prefix tag number. The SA asks the provider or supplier to provide a revised PoC with new completion dates. The SA annotate under the heading "Statement of Deficiencies and Plan of Correction," "Summary of Deficiencies Not Corrected on a Follow-Up Visit," and enters the date of the revisit beneath the date of the survey.

The SA associates the fourth copy of the revised Form CMS-2567 with Form CMS-2567B, retains a copy for its provider file, sends a copy to the provider or supplier, and forwards the remaining copies to the RO or SMA, as appropriate. The SA considers whether the uncorrected deficiencies affect the ability of the provider or supplier to meet the CoPs or Requirements. If they do, the SA documents noncompliance and initiates a termination action.

2732C - Notifying Governing Bodies of Continuing Deficiencies

(Rev. 1, 05-21-04)

Generally, the SA deals directly with the administrator or director on a routine basis. However, the SA may notify the governing body if an administrator or director has been ineffective in correcting deficiencies. If the SA does so, it advises the administrator or director.

Chapter 3

Additional Program Activities

3010 - Termination Procedures - Immediate Jeopardy to Patient Health and Safety (Medicare)

(Rev. 1, 05-21-04)

(See §§7307 - 7309 [of the *State Operations Manual*] for SNFs/NFs.)

3010A - Substantial Noncompliance With Program Requirements Which Poses Immediate Jeopardy to Patient Health or Safety

(Rev. 1, 05-21-04)

"Immediate Jeopardy" is interpreted as a crisis situation in which the health and safety of patients is at risk. Generally, it is a deficient practice that indicates the operator's inability to furnish safe care and services, although it may not have resulted in actual harm. The threat of probable harm is real and important and could be perceived as something that will result in potentially severe temporary or permanent injury, disability, or death. Therefore, it must be perceived as something that is likely to occur in the very near future. If the patients are not protected effectively from the threat, or if the threat is not removed, there is a high probability that serious harm or injury could occur at any time or already has occurred and may occur again.

A list of operational definitions of what can constitute an immediate jeopardy to patient health and safety is presented as a guide to be used by all surveyors. (See Appendix Q. [of the *State Operations Manual*]) Generally, the criteria applies to most providers and suppliers, although some criteria may apply to only certain types of providers or suppliers. The operational definitions are not intended to be all-inclusive, nor are they intended to inhibit the professional judgment of the surveyors. Surveyors may find that an immediate jeopardy does not exist when the definitions seem to apply or that such a threat does exist even though the definitions do not address the situation or condition observed by the surveyors.

The key factor in the use of the immediate jeopardy termination authority is, as the name implies, limited to immediate and serious. The threat must be present when you are onsite and must be of such magnitude as to seriously jeopardize a patient's health and safety. There should be no other application of immediate jeopardy terminations. Do not use these procedures to enforce compliance quickly on more routine deficiencies.

3010B - Processing of Immediate Jeopardy Terminations

(Rev. 1, 05-21-04)

When an immediate jeopardy to patient health or safety is documented, the SA and RO complete termination procedures within 23 calendar days. Processing times given here are the maximum allowed. Do not postpone or stop the procedure unless compliance is achieved and documented through onsite verification. If there is a credible allegation that the threat or deficiency has been corrected, the SA conducts a revisit prior to termination if possible. Do not use this procedure if there is an ICF/MR time-limited provider agreement that is subject to cancellation or nonrenewal within 23 calendar days after the survey. In such a case, process the cancellation or nonrenewal. (See §3007 [of the *State Operations Manual*].)

Special Procedures for IJ in Psychiatric Hospitals

It is the RO that makes the determination of non-compliance when an immediate jeopardy to patient health or safety exists, not the CMS' contract surveyors. The CMS' contract surveyors will notify the RO when onsite during survey an immediate jeopardy to patient health or safety exists, the RO completes the termination procedures within 23 calendar days. On the last day of the survey, CMS' contract surveyors telephone Central Office (CO) to certify noncompliance and that an immediate jeopardy exists. CO immediately notifies the RO of the surveyors' findings. The CMS contract surveyors discuss their findings with the provider and tell the providers that they are mailing the RO by overnight express mail completed Forms CMS-1537A and CMS-2567. A copy is also mailed to CO for review. The RO reviews the survey package (Forms CMS-1537A and CMS-2567), and if it determines noncompliance, it mails Form CMS-2567 to the provider. After doing so, the RO follows the 23 calendar day termination procedure as outlined below beginning with the fifth working day.

23-Day Termination Procedures

1. **Date of Survey** - The date of the survey is the date on which the entire survey is completed, regardless of when the exit conference is held.

2. **Second Working Day** - No later than 2 working days following the survey date. The SA:

   • Telephones the RO that it is certifying noncompliance and that an immediate jeopardy exists; and

   • Notifies the provider/supplier (by telegram or overnight express mail or FAX) of its deficiencies and inform the provider/supplier that it is recommending termination to the RO, which will issue a formal notice. The notice advises the provider/supplier of its right to due process, the expected schedule for termination action, and that the deficiency must be corrected and verified by the SA to halt the termination. If the provider also participates in Medicaid, the SA notifies the SMA of its certification of noncompliance.

3. **Third Working Day** - The SA forwards all supporting documentation to the RO (e.g., statement of deficiencies, correspondence, contact reports, Form CMS-1539). The SA forwards the information by overnight mail to assure that the RO receives it in time to meet the 5-working-day deadline. Upon receipt of the SA information, the RO reviews the documents and makes its determination of noncompliance.

4. **Fifth Working Day** - The provider/supplier and the public are then notified by the RO of the proposed termination action by the most expeditious means available. A press release to the radio and television stations serving the area in which the provider/supplier or institution is located is acceptable if a newspaper notice cannot be arranged in the time allotted. Notice must be made at least 2 calendar days prior to the effective date of termination. (See 42 CFR 488.456(c).)

5. **Tenth Working Day** - If the SA only sent notification of the IJ deficiencies on the second working day to the provider/supplier and RO, and there are other, non-IJ deficiencies, (non-IJ condition and standard level), then the SA must write up another 2567 with the non-IJ deficiencies and forward copies to the provider/supplier, the RO and SMA within ten working days. The SA retains a copy for its records.

6. **Twenty-Third Calendar Day** - The termination takes effect unless compliance is achieved or threat is removed. If the threat has been removed, but deficiencies still exist at the Condition level, the SA gives the provider/supplier up to 67 more calendar days, or 90 calendar days total (23 plus 67). These dates are maximum times, and participation may be terminated earlier if processing allows. However, the RO must adhere to both the provider/supplier and public notice timeframes.

If the RO disagrees based upon its review of the documentation, the RO discusses the results of the review with the SA and solicits further evidence to support the SA's recommendation. The RO confers with the SA as to the appropriate action to be taken. Should the RO and the SA fail to agree that an immediate jeopardy exists, a revisit will be conducted by the RO and the SA together to ascertain whether or not immediate jeopardy to the patient's health and safety exists or has been removed. If the RO and SA agree that an immediate jeopardy exists, no revisit is necessary by the RO. Under no circumstances should the RO reverse a SA recommendation that an immediate jeopardy has been removed or not removed unless the determination is made on the basis of an onsite determination by Federal surveyors.

Medicaid agreements with facilities that concurrently participate in Medicare should be terminated on the same date the Medicare agreement is terminated. Where State law permits, Medicaid-only facilities should be terminated by the State within the above time limits. For NFs that also participate as SNFs, the State's timing of termination shall control. (See 42 CFR 488.452.)

Chapter 7

Administrative Guidelines to the Enforcement Procedures

7304 - Certification-Related Terms

An opportunity to correct deficiencies before remedies are imposed is not assured. The CMS or the State has no obligation to give a facility an opportunity to correct deficiencies prior to imposing remedies, and must only meet the minimum notice requirements that are applicable to the imposition of remedies. CMS' policy about when facilities with deficiencies are given an opportunity to correct them before remedies are imposed follows:

7304A - Opportunity to Correct Deficiencies Before Remedies Are Imposed

(Rev. 1, 05-21-04)

At CMS' or the State's discretion, facilities may be given an opportunity to correct their deficiencies before remedies are imposed when they do not meet the criteria in this section for no opportunity to correct.

7304B - No Opportunity to Correct Deficiencies Before Remedies Are Imposed

(Rev. 1, 05-21-04)

7304B1 - Mandatory Criteria for Having No Opportunity to Correct

(Rev. 1, 05-21-04)

- Facilities having deficiencies of actual harm or above (level G or above) on the current survey as well as having deficiencies of actual harm or above on the previous standard survey.*

- Facilities having deficiencies of actual harm or above (level G or above) on the current survey as well as having deficiencies of actual harm or above on any type of survey between the current survey and the last standard survey.*

> ***NOTES PERTAINING TO THE TWO BULLETS ABOVE** - The "current" survey is whatever survey is currently being performed, i.e., standard, revisit, complaint.
>
> The two G level deficiencies must be separated by a certification of compliance, i.e., from different noncompliance cycles. In other words, level G deficiencies from multiple surveys within the same noncompliance cycle will not be combined to make the "double G" determination.
>
> Facilities being given an opportunity to correct that: (1) subsequently have a survey during the same noncompliance cycle and, (2) it cites a G level deficiency and, (3) this G level deficiency causes the facility to now meet the criteria for no opportunity to correct), then the resulting immediate sanction(s) are imposed prospectively from the specific survey that caused the facility to meet the no opportunity to correct criteria. The immediate sanctions should not be imposed retroactively to supersede the opportunity to correct period from the earlier survey. In other words, do not revoke a previously offered opportunity to correct.
>
> If the most recent standard survey is within the currently running noncompliance cycle, then look back to the most recent standard survey that is not in the currently running noncompliance cycle in making "double G" determinations.

Since "G" level (or above) deficiencies are especially significant for enforcement purposes, it is necessary to officially record this deficiency history in the Online Survey, Certification and Reporting System when revisits find that deficiencies, originally below the "G" level, have worsened to the "G" level or above. In other words, the original scope and severity rating of a deficiency will only be changed in the current data system by a revisit if that same deficiency remains at revisit but has worsened to a "G" level of above.

- Previously terminated facilities having deficiencies causing actual harm on the first survey after re-entry into the program.

- Facilities having immediate jeopardy noncompliance. Removal of immediate jeopardy may, at CMS' discretion, result in rescission of termination but it will not result in rescission of alternative remedies such as civil money penalties or denial of payment for new admissions.

- Facilities having noncompliance against which a per instance civil money penalty was imposed. While the facility will not be given an opportunity to correct the noncompliance associated with the per instance civil money penalty (i.e., each tag for which the per instance civil money penalty is used), the State will determine whether to provide an opportunity to correct for the remaining noncompliance before remedies are imposed (see §7511 [of the *State Operations Manual*]).

7304B2 - Additional State Discretion

(Rev. 1, 05-21-04)

States have the discretion to establish additional guidelines for determining when facilities will be subject to immediate remedies with no opportunity to correct.

7304C - Other Times When Facilities May Not be Given an Opportunity to Correct Deficiencies

(Rev. 1, 05-21-04)

At CMS' or the State's discretion, other facilities having noncompliance on the current survey may also be subject to immediate sanctions even when they do not meet the above mandatory criteria for no opportunity to correct. These facilities may not be provided an opportunity to correct after consideration of the following minimum factors by CMS or the State:

- Scope and severity of the deficiency;

- Unwillingness and inability of the facility to correct the deficiency; and

- The effectiveness of the facility's quality assurance and monitoring system to prevent recurrence of the deficiency.

7304D - Acceptable Plan of Correction

(Rev. 1, 05-21-04)

Except in cases of past noncompliance, facilities having deficiencies (other than those at scope and severity level A) must submit an acceptable plan of correction before substantial compliance can be determined. An acceptable plan of correction must:

- Address how corrective action will be accomplished for those residents found to have been affected by the deficient practice;

- Address how the facility will identify other residents having the potential to be affected by the same deficient practice;

- Address what measures will be put into place or systemic changes made to ensure that the deficient practice will not recur;

- Indicate how the facility plans to monitor its performance to make sure that solutions are sustained. The facility must develop a plan for ensuring that correction is achieved and sustained. This plan must be implemented, and the corrective action evaluated for its effectiveness. The plan of correction is integrated into the quality assurance system; and

- Include dates when corrective action will be completed. The corrective action completion dates must be acceptable to the State. If the plan of correction is unacceptable for any reason, the State will notify the facility in writing. If the plan of correction is acceptable, the State will notify the facility by phone, e-mail, etc. Facilities should be cautioned that they are ultimately accountable for their own compliance, and that responsibility is not alleviated in cases where notification about the acceptability of their plan of correction is not made timely. The plan of correction will serve as the facility's allegation of compliance.

In cases of -nonimmediate jeopardy, a plan of correction must be submitted within 10 calendar days from the date the facility receives its Form CMS-2567. If an acceptable plan of correction is not received within 10 calendar days from the date the facility received its Form CMS-2567, the State notifies the facility that it is recommending to the regional office and/or the State Medicaid agency that remedies be imposed effective as soon as notice requirements are met. This is because, in nonimmediate jeopardy cases, the plan of correction serves as the facility's allegation of compliance and, without it, CMS and the State have no basis on which to verify compliance.

In most cases of immediate jeopardy, the facility submits an allegation of removal of the immediate jeopardy and defers submission of a plan of correction until the immediate jeopardy has been removed. The allegation of removal of the immediate jeopardy must include the date the immediate jeopardy was removed, and sufficient detail demonstrating that the immediate jeopardy has been addressed. Once the removal of the immediate jeopardy is verified, the surveying entity will provide a Form CMS-2567 to the facility, including the noncompliance which constituted immediate jeopardy, and request that a plan of correction be submitted within 10 calendar days.

7304E - Last Day of Survey

(Rev. 1, 05-21-04)

For purposes of computing 3 months or 6 months from the finding of noncompliance when the health and life safety code portions of the survey are on the same enforcement track (see §7410 [*of the State Operations Manual*]), use the last day of onsite observations of the standard health survey on which the noncompliance was identified, regardless of which survey preceded the other. If the life safety code was the second of the two surveys to be performed on the same enforcement track, and it was the survey that found the noncompliance, the clock still starts on the last day of the standard health survey. For purposes of the first notice of noncompliance, use the last day of the survey that found the noncompliance.

When two separate enforcement tracks are being used (one for the health portion and one for the life safety code portion), the mandatory denial of payment for new admissions and termination time frames would be 3 months and 6 months, respectively, for each separate portion.

EXCEPTION: For purposes of sending notices, in immediate jeopardy situations, the last day of the survey begins with the survey that found the immediate jeopardy.

7304F - Setting the Mandatory 3-Month and 6-Month Sanction Time Fames

(Rev. 1, 05-21-04)

These dates should be set based on full months rather than on a number of days. With few exceptions, these dates should be set by simply going to the same numerical date in the 3rd or 6th month following the survey date. For example, if a survey ended on January 15, the 3-month effective date for the mandatory denial of payment for new admissions remedy is April 15, and the 6-month mandatory termination date is July 15.

Exceptions to this rule involve those cases for which a 3-month or 6-month numerical date is not on the calendar. In these cases, move ahead a day or two to the beginning of the next month. For example, if a survey ended on January 31, the 3-month effective date for the mandatory denial of payment for new admissions remedy would be April 31 if there was a 31st day in April - but since there is not, the 3-month effective date is May 1 and the 6-month mandatory termination date is July 31.

7317 - Response to the Plan of Correction

(Rev. 1, 05-21-04)

7317A - Verifying Facility Compliance

(Rev. 1, 05-21-04)

While the plan of correction serves as the facility's allegation of compliance in nonimmediate jeopardy cases, substantial compliance cannot be certified and any remedies imposed cannot be lifted until facility compliance has been verified. The chart that follows at B2 of this section provides a course of action for certifying compliance based on the seriousness of the noncompliance and the number of revisits that have already occurred. It represents a continuum, ranging from accepting the latest correction date on the facility's approved plan of correction as the date of compliance without an onsite revisit, to conducting an onsite revisit to establish that date.

The chart that follows at B2 of this section indicates the circumstances under which revisits must occur and remedies must be imposed, as well as provides policy for conducting revisits, lifting remedies, and certifying compliance. It is important to remember that: revisits may be conducted anytime for any level of noncompliance subject to the allowed number of revisits (see §7317.B, below); remedies may be imposed anytime for any level of noncompliance; and revisits are not assured before termination can occur. Also, it should be noted that this guidance applies to prospective, as well as currently participating, facilities.

7317B - Revisits

(Rev. 1, 05-21-04)

While both paper reviews and onsite reviews are considered to be revisits, only onsite revisits are considered in the revisit count for purposes of the revisit policy.

1. **No guarantee of revisit.** A facility is not entitled to any revisits; revisits are performed at the discretion of CMS or the State. When conducted, however, one revisit will normally be conducted after a survey which found noncompliance and another before the expiration of the 6-month period by which a facility must be in substantial compliance to avoid termination of its provider agreement. Authorization must be obtained from the regional office for more than 2 revisits for Medicare-only and dually participating facilities.

   The following chart provides the course of action for certifying substantial compliance and for conducting revisits:

Revisit/Date of Compliance Policy

Revisit #	Substantial Compliance	Old deficiencies corrected but continuing noncompliance at F (no SQC) or below	Old deficiencies corrected but continuing noncompliance at F (SQC), harm or IJ	Noncompliance continues	Any noncompliance
1st revisit	Compliance is certified as of the latest correction date on the approved PoC, unless it is determined that either correction actually occurred between the latest correction date on the PoC and the date of the 1st revisit, or correction occurred sooner than the latest correction date on the PoC.	1. A 2nd revisit is discretionary if acceptable evidence is provided. When evidence is accepted with no 2nd revisit, compliance is certified as of the date confirmed by the evidence. 2. When a 2nd revisit is conducted, acceptable evidence is required if the facility wants a date earlier than that of the 2nd revisit to be considered for the compliance date.	1. A 2nd revisit is required. 2. Acceptable evidence is required if the facility wants a date earlier than that of the 2nd revisit to be considered for the compliance date.	1. A 2nd revisit is required. 2. Acceptable evidence is required if the facility wants a date earlier than that of the 2nd revisit to be considered as the compliance date. 3. A remedy **must be** imposed.	
2nd revisit	Compliance is certified as of the date of the 2nd revisit or the date confirmed by the acceptable evidence, whichever is sooner.				1. A remedy must be imposed if not already imposed. 2. Either conduct a 3rd revisit or proceed to termination.
A 3rd REVISIT IS NOT ASSURED AND MUST BE APPROVED BY THE RO					
3rd revisit	Compliance is certified as of the date of the 3rd revisit.				Proceed to termination.

Examples of acceptable evidence may include, but are not limited to:

∧ An invoice or receipt verifying purchases, repairs, etc.
∧ Sign-in sheets verifying attendance of staff at in-services training.
∧ Interviews with more than 1 training participant about training.
∧ Contact with resident council, e.g., when dignity issues are involved.

Givens:

∧ An approved PoC is required whenever there is noncompliance;
∧ Remedies can be imposed anytime for any level of noncompliance;
∧ Revisits can be conducted anytime for any level of noncompliance;

Survey Protocol for Long-Term Care Facilities (SOM, Appendix P)

2. **Purpose of Revisit**. The purpose of a revisit is to determine whether substantial compliance has been achieved.

3. **Number of revisits**. Two revisits are permitted, at the State's discretion, without prior approval from the regional office; a third revisit may be approved only at the discretion of the regional office. Regional offices are limited to approving only this one additional revisit. While CMS cannot require States to get regional office approval for the third revisit to a non-State operated Medicaid-only facility and also cannot required them to get such approval from the State Medicaid agency, States should consult with the Medicaid agency prior to conducting a third revisit so that the programs are run consistently.

The effect of specific survey activities on the revisit count follows:

- **Complaint surveys**. Initial complaint investigation visits, whether substantiated or not, are not included in the revisit count. However, when the complaint survey is conducted at the same time as the revisit, the revisit is included in the revisit count. And, although the complaint survey itself is not considered a revisit, any revisits associated with it count toward the revisit count. This also applies to Federal complaint guidelines.

  When a complaint is received and the complaint survey is conducted **after** the third revisit but **before** the 6-month termination date, any deficiencies identified by the complaint survey should be cited and would provide additional evidence in support of the termination action. Since three revisits have already been conducted, another revisit cannot be conducted without consultation with the regional office and central office. Situations such as this should be discussed with the regional office since it may have already sent a termination letter. In addition, States should not use this complaint survey as an opportunity to determine if deficiencies from the third revisit have been corrected.

- **Life safety code surveys**. When the revisit is for the sole purpose of **either** the health survey or the life safety code survey, **but not both**, there are separate revisit counts toward each survey, regardless of the timing of the two surveys and regardless of whether the same entity is performing the surveys and revisits. When the revisit is for both the health survey and the life safety code survey, both surveys are covered by the same revisit count.

- **Visits to determine removal of immediate jeopardy**. A visit to determine if immediate jeopardy has been removed will be included in the revisit count. (See §7308 for documentation requirements [*of the SOM*].)

- **Visits to special focus facilities**. The revisit policy applies to Special Focus Facilities as it does to all other facilities, but the extra drop-by visits to these facilities do not count against the revisit count.

- **State monitoring**. Monitoring visits are not included in the revisit count because no survey is being performed. State monitoring is a remedy to oversee the correction of cited deficiencies and ensure that residents are protected from harm; revisits are onsite visits specifically intended to verify correction of deficiencies cited in a previous survey.

4. **Timing of Revisit**. When conducted, revisits occur any time between the last correction date on the plan of correction and the 60th day from the survey date to confirm that the facility is in substantial compliance and, in certain cases, has the ability to remain in substantial compliance. Conducting a revisit before the 60th day allows time for a notice of a mandatory denial of payment for new admissions at the 3rd month, if necessary. If the facility is found to be in substantial compliance, the State will certify compliance.

5. **Correction of Level A, B, and C Deficiencies**. While facilities are expected to correct deficiencies at levels A, B, and C, deficiencies at these levels are within the substantial compliance range and, therefore, need not be reviewed for correction during subsequent revisits within the same noncompliance cycle.

6. **Revisits for Substandard Quality of Care , Harm, and Immediate Jeopardy**. When substandard quality of care, actual harm, or immediate jeopardy is cited and the first revisit determines that the facility has achieved substantial compliance with those affected tags, no continued revisits are necessary for any other tags that are at or below Level F (no substandard quality of care). However, if a revisit is not conducted for these other tags, the facility must provide evidence that they are corrected and are now in substantial compliance. Revisits must continue to verify substantial compliance with the original or subsequent substandard quality of care, actual harm, or immediate jeopardy deficiencies, even if they improve to lower levels of noncompliance.

7. **New Owner**. If a new operator assumes the existing provider agreement, he or she is responsible for assuring that corrections are made within the revisit policy.

7317C - Noncompliance Cycles

(Rev. 1, 05-21-04)

A noncompliance cycle begins with a recertification or complaint survey that finds noncompliance and ends when substantial compliance is achieved or the facility is terminated from the Medicare or Medicaid program. The noncompliance cycle cannot exceed 6 months. Once a remedy is imposed, it continues until the facility is in substantial compliance (and in some cases, until it can demonstrate that it can remain in substantial compliance), or is terminated from the programs.

Enforcement Process

7400 - Enforcement Remedies for Skilled Nursing Facilities and Nursing Facilities

(Rev. 1, 05-21-04)

7400A - Introduction

(Rev. 1, 05-21-04)

Sections 1819(h) and 1919(h) of the Act, as well as 42 CFR 488.404, 488.406, and 488.408, provide that CMS or the State may impose one or more remedies in addition to, or instead of, termination of the provider agreement when the State or CMS finds that a facility is out of compliance with participation requirements. The remedies available to the regional office, the State Medicaid Agency, or both, as appropriate, are listed in subsection C.

7400B - General

(Rev. 1, 05-21-04)

The nursing home enforcement protocol/procedures are based on the premise that all requirements must be met and enforced, and requirements take on greater or lesser significance depending on the specific circumstances and resident outcomes in each facility.

A skilled nursing facility, nursing facility, or dually participating facility will be subject to one or more enforcement remedies for noncompliance with one or more participation requirements. Each facility that has deficiencies (other than those isolated deficiencies that have been determined to constitute no actual harm with potential for only minimal harm) must submit an acceptable plan of correction. CMS' requirement about submittal of plans of correction can be found in §7304. A plan of correction **is not** an enforcement remedy.

It is important to note that §1919(h)(3)(A)&(B) provides CMS with authority to take enforcement action against **any** nursing facility when it finds that the nursing facility is no longer in compliance with participation requirements.

7400C - Listing of Remedies

(Rev. 1, 05-21-04)

7400C1 - Available Enforcement Remedies

(Rev. 1, 05-21-04)

In accordance with 42 CFR 488.406, the following remedies are available:

- Termination of the provider agreement;

- Temporary management;

- Denial of payment for all Medicare and/or Medicaid residents by CMS;

- Denial of payment for all new Medicare and/or Medicaid admissions;

- Civil money penalties;

- State monitoring;

- Transfer of residents;

- Transfer of residents with closure of facility;

- Directed plan of correction;

- Directed in-service training; and

- Alternative or additional State remedies approved by CMS.

7400C2 - Mandatory Enforcement Remedies

(Rev. 1, 05-21-04)

Regardless of what other remedies the State Medicaid Agency may want to establish in addition to the remedy of termination of the provider agreement, it must establish, at a minimum, the following statutorily-specified remedies or an approved alternative to these specified remedies:

- Temporary management;

- Denial of payment for all new admissions;

- Civil money penalties;

- Transfer of residents;

- Transfer of residents with closure of facility; and

- State monitoring.

The State Medicaid Agency may establish additional or alternative remedies as long as the State has been authorized by CMS to do so under its State plan. Guidance on the review and approval (or disapproval) of State Plan amendment requests for alternative or additional remedies can be found in §7805 [*of the SOM*].

7400C3 - Availability of State Medicaid Agency Remedies to the Regional Office in Dually Participating Facilities

(Rev. 1, 05-21-04)

Whenever a State Medicaid Agency's remedy is unique to its State plan and has been approved by CMS, then that remedy may also be imposed by the regional office against the Medicare provider agreement of a dually participating facility in that State. For example, where CMS has approved a State's ban on admissions remedy as an alternative remedy under the State plan, CMS may impose this remedy but only against Medicare and Medicaid residents; only the State can ban the admission of private pay residents.

7400D - Measuring Seriousness of Deficiencies

(Rev. 1, 05-21-04)

Measuring the seriousness of deficiencies is **only** for the purpose of determining the enforcement response most appropriate for specific degrees of noncompliance. The scope and severity system by which the seriousness of deficiencies is rated, is a national system to be used by States and CMS. Immediate jeopardy has historically been determined by guidance provided in Appendix Q and will continue to be determined using that guidance. Appendix P provides guidance about how to determine the seriousness of nonimmediate jeopardy deficiencies.

7400E - Selection of Remedies

(Rev. 1, 05-21-04)

7400E1 - Factors That Must Be Considered When Selecting Remedies

(Rev. 1, 05-21-04)

In order to select the appropriate remedy(ies) for a facility's noncompliance, the seriousness of the deficiencies must first be assessed, because specific levels of seriousness correlate with specific categories of enforcement responses. The assessment factors that must be used to determine the seriousness of deficiencies are presented on the visual matrix that follows in this subsection. These factors are also listed below. They relate to whether the deficiencies constitute:

- No actual harm with a potential for minimal harm;

- No actual harm with a potential for more than minimal harm but not immediate jeopardy;

- Actual harm that is not immediate jeopardy; or

- Immediate jeopardy to resident health or safety.

AND, whether deficiencies:

- Are isolated;

- Constitute a pattern; or

- Are widespread.

ASSESSMENT FACTORS USED TO DETERMINE
THE SERIOUSNESS OF DEFICIENCIES MATRIX

	Isolated	Pattern	Widespread
Immediate jeopardy to resident health or safety	J⬚PoC⬚ Required: Cat. 3 Optional: Cat. 1 Optional: Cat. 2	K⬚PoC⬚ Required: Cat. 3 Optional: Cat. 1 Optional: Cat. 2	L⬚PoC⬚ Required: Cat. 3 Optional: Cat. 2 Optional: Cat. 1
Actual harm that is not immediate	G PoC Required* Cat. 2 Optional: Cat. 1	H PoC Required* Cat. 2 Optional: Cat. 1	I⬚PoC⬚ Required* Cat. 2 Optional: Cat. 1 Optional: Temporary Mgmt.
No actual harm with potential for more than minimal harm that is not immediate jeopardy	D PoC Required* Cat. 1 Optional: Cat. 2	E PoC Required* Cat. 1 Optional: Cat. 2	F⬚PoC⬚ Required* Cat. 2 Optional: Cat. 1
No actual harm with potential for minimal harm	A ▮No PoC▮ No remedies ▮ ▮Commitment to ▮Correct ▮ Not on CMS-2567	B ▮PoC▮	C ▮PoC▮

⬚ Substandard quality of care is any deficiency in 42 CFR 483.13, Resident Behavior and Facility Practices, 42 CFR 483.15 Quality of Life, or 42 CFR 483.25, Quality of Care, that constitutes immediate jeopardy to resident health or safety; or a pattern of or widespread actual harm that is not immediate jeopardy; or a widespread potential for more than minimal harm that is not immediate jeopardy, with no actual harm.

▮ Substantial compliance

REMEDY CATEGORIES

Category 1 (Cat.1)

Directed Plan of Correction
State Monitor; and/or
Directed In-Service
Training

Category 2 (Cat.2)

Denial of Payment for New
 Admissions
Denial of Payment for All Individuals
 imposed by CMS; and/or
Civil money penalties:
$50 - $3,000/day
$1,000 - $10,000/instance

Category 3 (Cat.3)

Temp. Mgmt.
Termination
Optional:
Civil money penalties
3,050-$10,000/day
$1,000 - $10,000/instance

Denial of payment for new admissions must be imposed when a facility is not in substantial compliance within 3 months after being found out of compliance.

Survey Protocol for Long-Term Care Facilities (SOM, Appendix P)

(Rev. 1, 05-21-04)

Denial of payment and State monitoring must be imposed when a facility has been found to have provided substandard quality of care on three consecutive standard surveys.

NOTE: Termination may be imposed by the State or CMS at any time.

* This is required only when a decision is made to impose alternative remedies instead of or in addition to termination.

Once the seriousness of the deficiencies is determined, and the decision is made to impose remedies **instead of, or in addition to**, termination, the regional office, or the State Medicaid Agency, or both, as determined in accordance with §7300 [*of the SOM*], must select one or more remedies from the remedy category (or a CMS approved alternative or additional State remedy) associated with the specific level of noncompliance in accordance with the visual matrix above. The remedy category to be applied against facility noncompliance will be determined by the most serious deficiencies identified, i.e., the deficiencies falling into the box closest to Level L. Additional factors may be considered, including but not limited to, those provided in subsection 2 below.

7400E2 - Other Factors That May Be Considered in Selecting Enforcement Remedy Within a Remedy Category

(Rev. 1, 05-21-04)

Additional factors that may be considered to assist in determining which and/or how many remedies to impose within the available remedy categories for particular levels of noncompliance, include but are not limited to:

- The relationship of one deficiency to other deficiencies;

- The facility's prior history of noncompliance in general, and specifically with reference to the cited deficiencies; and

- The likelihood that the selected remedy(ies) will achieve correction and continued compliance.

EXAMPLE:

If failure to spend money is the root cause of the facility's noncompliance, then any civil money penalty that is imposed should at least exceed the amount saved by the facility by not maintaining compliance.

7400E3 - Requirement for Facility to Submit Plan of Correction

(Rev. 1, 05-21-04)

Except when a facility has isolated deficiencies that constitute no actual harm with potential for no more than minimal harm, each facility that has a deficiency must submit an acceptable plan of correction. For a plan of correction to be acceptable, it must address all of the required elements provided in §7304. Those facilities having isolated deficiencies that constitute no actual harm with potential for minimal harm need not submit a plan of correction. The regional office approves plans of corrections for State-operated facilities and for validation surveys; the State approves all others. The process and timetable for CMS' approval of plans of corrections under the continuation of payment provision is in accordance with §7600 [*of the SOM*]. The requirement that facilities submit a plan of correction can be found in §7304.

7400F - When To Select Remedy From Specific Remedy Category

(Rev. 1, 05-21-04)

7400F1 - Category 1

(Rev. 1, 05-21-04)

Select at least one remedy from category 1 when there:

- are isolated deficiencies that constitute no actual harm with a potential for more than minimal harm but not immediate jeopardy; or

- is a pattern of deficiencies that constitutes no actual harm with a potential for more than minimal harm but not immediate jeopardy.

EXCEPT when the facility is in substantial compliance, one or more of the remedies in category 1 may be applied to any deficiency.

CATEGORY 1 remedies include:

- Directed plan of correction (see §7500) [of the *State Operations Manual*];

- State monitoring (see §7504) [of the *State Operations Manual*]; and

- Directed in-service training (see §7502) [of the *State Operations Manual*].

NOTE: As an agent of CMS or the State Medicaid Agency, the State may impose one or more category 1 remedies, as authorized by CMS or the State Medicaid Agency, in accordance with §7314 [of the *State Operations Manual*].

7400F2 - Category 2

(Rev. 1, 05-21-04)

Select at least one remedy from category 2 when there are:

- Widespread deficiencies that constitute no actual harm with a potential for more than minimal harm but not immediate jeopardy; or

- One or more deficiencies (regardless of scope) that constitute actual harm that is not immediate jeopardy.

EXCEPT when the facility is in substantial compliance, one or more of the remedies in category 2 may be applied to any deficiency.

NOTE: The State Medicaid Agency does not have the statutory authority to impose the remedy of denial of payment for all Medicare and/or Medicaid residents. As an agent of CMS or the State Medicaid Agency, the State may provide notice of imposition of denial of payment for new admissions, as authorized by CMS and/or the State Medicaid Agency, in accordance with §7314 [of the *State Operations Manual*].

CATEGORY 2 remedies include:

- Denial of payment for all new Medicare and/or Medicaid admissions (see §7506) [of the *State Operations Manual*];

- Denial of payment for all Medicare and/or Medicaid residents, imposed by the regional office (see §7508) [of the *State Operations Manual*];

- Civil money penalties of $50 - $3,000 per day of noncompliance (see §7510); and

- Civil money penalties of $1,000 - $10,000 per instance of noncompliance (see §7510).

7400F3 - Selection from Category 3

(Rev. 1, 05-21-04)

Termination or temporary management, or both, must be selected when there are one or more deficiencies that constitute immediate jeopardy to resident health or safety. A civil monetary penalty of $3,050 - $10,000 per day or a civil money penalty of $1,000 - $10,000 per instance may be imposed in addition to the remedies of termination and/or temporary management. Temporary management is also an option when there are widespread deficiencies constituting actual harm that is not immediate jeopardy.

CATEGORY 3 remedies include:

- Temporary management (see §7550) [of the *State Operations Manual*];

- Termination (see §7556) [of the *State Operations Manual*];

- Civil money penalties of $3,050 - $10,000 per day of noncompliance optional, in addition to the remedies of termination and/or temporary management (See §7510); or

- Civil money penalties of $1,000 - $10,000 per instance of noncompliance optional (see §7510).

NOTE: Termination may be imposed by the State Medicaid Agency or the regional office at any time. Transfer of residents or transfer of residents with closure of the facility will be imposed by the State, as appropriate. Although temporary management must be imposed when there is a finding of immediate jeopardy (and termination is not sought), temporary management may be imposed for lesser levels of noncompliance.

[This page intentionally left blank]

The Facility Guide to OBRA Regulations, and the Long Term Care Survey Process

- Survey Protocols (SOM, Appendix P)
  - Guidance to Surveyors (SOM, Appendix PP)
    - CMS Survey Process Forms

Chapter 2

Guidance to Surveyors for Long-Term Care Facilities (SOM, Appendix PP)

Sources

CMS Publication # 100-07, Appendix PP, *State Operations Manual*, Transmittal # 55, dated December 2, 2009

CMS Publication # 100-07, Appendix PP, *State Operations Manual*, Transmittal # 48, dated June 12, 2009

CMS Publication # 100-07, Appendix PP, *State Operations Manual*, Transmittal # 41, dated April 10, 2009

Federal Register, Volume 73, Number 157, pages 47075 through 47092, dated Wednesday, August 13, 2008

CMS Publication # 100-07, Appendix PP, *State Operations Manual*, Transmittal # 36, dated August 1, 2008

CMS Publication # 100-07, Appendix PP, *State Operations Manual*, Transmittal # 27, dated August 17, 2007

CMS Publication # 100-07, Appendix PP, *State Operations Manual*, Transmittal # 26, dated August 17, 2007

CMS Publication # 100-07, Appendix PP, *State Operations Manual*, Transmittal # 22, dated December 15, 2006

CMS Publication # 100-07, Appendix PP, *State Operations Manual*, Transmittal # 21, dated October 20, 2006

Federal Register, Volume 71, Number 184, page 55340, dated Friday, September 22, 2006

Federal Register, Volume 71, Number 133, page 39229, dated Wednesday, July 12, 2006

CMS Publication # 100-07, Appendix PP, *State Operations Manual*, Transmittal # 19, dated June 1, 2006

CMS Publication # 100-07, Appendix PP, *State Operations Manual*, Transmittal # 15, dated November 28, 2005

CMS Publication # 100-07, Appendix PP, *State Operations Manual*, Transmittal # 12, dated October 14, 2005

CMS Publication # 100-07, Appendix PP, *State Operations Manual*, Transmittal # 8, dated June 28, 2005

CMS Publication # 100-07, Appendix PP, *State Operations Manual*, Transmittal # 5, dated November 19, 2004

CMS Publication # 100-07, Appendix PP, *State Operations Manual*, Transmittal # 4, dated November 12, 2004

CMS Publication # 100-07, Appendix PP, *State Operations Manual*, Transmittal # 1, dated May 21, 2004

Federal Register, Volume 68, Number 187, page 55239, dated Friday September 26, 2003

Federal Register, Volume 68, Number 149, pages 46071 and 46072, dated Monday August 4, 2003

Federal Register, Volume 60, Number 123, page 33293, dated Tuesday June 27, 1995

State Operations Manual

Appendix PP – Guidance to Surveyors for Long Term Care Facilities

---

Table of Contents

(Rev. 55, 12-02-09)

CFR Number	F Tag	Starting Page #

[This page intentionally left blank]

F150

§483.5 — Definitions

[**Editor's Note:** §483.5(a) through (c) was amended by *Federal Register*, Volume 68, Number 149, dated Monday, August 4, 2003. §483.5(a) was amended by *Federal Register*, Volume 71, Number 133, dated Wednesday, July 12, 2006. The changes are reflected in the text below.]

F150

§483.5 Definitions

(a) *Facility defined.* For purposes of this subpart, "*facility*" means a skilled nursing facility (SNF) that meets the requirements of sections 1819(a), (b), (c), and (d) of the Act, or a nursing facility (NF) that meets the requirements of sections 1919(a), (b), (c), and (d) of the Act. "Facility" may include a distinct part of an institution (as defined in paragraph (b) of this section and specified in §440.40 and §440.155 of this chapter), but does not include an institution for the mentally retarded or persons with related conditions described in §440.150 of this chapter. For Medicare and Medicaid purposes (including eligibility, coverage, certification, and payment), the "facility" is always the entity that participates in the program, whether that entity is comprised of all of, or a distinct part of, a larger institution. For Medicare, an SNF (see section 1819(a)(1) of the Act), and for Medicaid, an NF (see section 1919(a)(1) of the Act) may not be an institution for mental diseases as defined in §435.1010 of this chapter.

(b) *Distinct part* — (1) *Definition.* A distinct part SNF or NF is physically distinguishable from the larger institution or institutional complex that houses it, meets the requirements of this paragraph and of paragraph (b)(2) of this section, and meets the applicable statutory requirements for SNFs or NFs in sections 1819 or 1919 of the Act, respectively. A distinct part SNF or NF may be comprised of one or more buildings or designated parts of buildings (that is, wings, wards, or floors) that are: In the same physical area immediately adjacent to the institution's main buildings; other areas and structures that are not strictly contiguous to the main buildings but are located within close proximity of the main buildings; and any other areas that CMS determines on an individual basis, to be part of the institution's campus. A distinct part must include all of the beds within the designated area, and cannot consist of a random collection of individual rooms or beds that are scattered throughout the physical plant. The term "distinct part" also includes a composite distinct part that meets the additional requirements of paragraph (c) of this section.

(2) *Requirements.* In addition to meeting the participation requirements for long-term care facilities set forth elsewhere in this subpart, a distinct part SNF or NF must meet all of the following requirements:

(i) The SNF or NF must be operated under common ownership and control (that is, common governance) by the institution of which it is a distinct part, as evidenced by the following:

(A) The SNF or NF is wholly owned by the institution of which it is a distinct part.

(B) The SNF or NF is subject to the by-laws and operating decisions of a common governing body.

(C) The institution of which the SNF or NF is a distinct part has final responsibility for the distinct part's administrative decisions and personnel policies, and final approval for the distinct part's personnel actions.

(D) The SNF or NF functions as an integral and subordinate part of the institution of which it is a distinct part, with significant common resource usage of buildings, equipment, personnel, and services.

(ii) The administrator of the SNF or NF reports to and is directly accountable to the management of the institution of which the SNF or NF is a distinct part.

(iii) The SNF or NF must have a designated medical director who is responsible for implementing care policies and coordinating medical care, and who is directly accountable to the management of the institution of which it is a distinct part.

(iv) The SNF or NF is financially integrated with the institution of which it is a distinct part, as evidenced by the sharing of income and expenses with that institution, and the reporting of its costs on that institution's cost report.

(v) A single institution can have a maximum of only one distinct part SNF and one distinct part NF.

(vi)(A) An institution cannot designate a distinct part SNF or NF, but instead must submit a written request with documentation that demonstrates it meets the criteria set forth above to CMS to determine if it may be considered a distinct part.

(B) The effective date of approval of a distinct part is the date that CMS determines all requirements (including enrollment with the fiscal intermediary (FI)) are met for approval, and cannot be made retroactive.

(C) The institution must request approval from CMS for all proposed changes in the number of beds in the approved distinct part.

(c) *Composite distinct part* — **(1)** *Definition.* A composite distinct part is a distinct part consisting of two or more noncontiguous components that are not located within the same campus, as defined in §413.65(a)(2) of this chapter.

(2) Requirements. In addition to meeting the requirements of paragraph (b) of this section, a composite distinct part must meet all of the following requirements:

(i) A SNF or NF that is a composite of more than one location will be treated as a single distinct part of the institution of which it is a distinct part. As such, the composite distinct part will have only one provider agreement and only one provider number.

(ii) If two or more institutions (each with a distinct part SNF or NF) undergo a change of ownership, CMS must approve the existing SNFs or NFs as meeting the requirements before they are considered a composite distinct part of a single institution. In making such a determination, CMS considers whether its approval or disapproval of a composite distinct part promotes the effective and efficient use of public monies without sacrificing the quality of care.

(iii) If there is a change of ownership of a composite distinct part SNF or NF, the assignment of the provider agreement to the new owner will apply to all of the approved locations that comprise the composite distinct part SNF or NF.

(iv) To ensure quality of care and quality of life for all residents, the various components of a composite distinct part must meet all of the requirements for participation independently in each location.

[**Editor's Note:** CMS has not updated the information in the Interpretive Guidelines for §483.5 to reflect the changes made by *Federal Register*, Volume 68, Number 149, dated Monday, August 4, 2003.]

Interpretive Guidelines §483.5

The following are the statutory definitions at §§1819(a) and 1919(a) of the Act for a SNF and a NF:

"Skilled nursing facility" is defined as an institution (or a distinct part of an institution) which is primarily engaged in providing skilled nursing care and related services for residents who require medical or nursing care, or rehabilitation services for the rehabilitation of injured, disabled, or sick persons, and is not primarily for the care and treatment of mental diseases; has in effect a transfer agreement (meeting the requirements of §1861(1)) with one or more hospitals having agreements in effect under §1866; and meets the requirements for a SNF described in subsections (b), (c), and (d) of this section.

"Nursing facility" is defined as an institution (or a distinct part of an institution) which is primarily engaged in providing skilled nursing care and related services for residents who require medical or nursing care, rehabilitation services for the rehabilitation of injured, disabled, or sick persons, or on a regular basis, health-related care and services to individuals who because of their mental or physical condition require care and services (above the level of room and board) which can be made available to them only through institutional facilities, and is not primarily for the care and treatment of mental diseases; has in effect a transfer agreement (meeting the requirements of §1861(1)) with one or more hospitals having agreements in effect under §1866; and meets the requirements for a NF described in subsections (b), (c), and (d) of this section.

If a provider does not meet one of these definitions, it cannot be certified for participation in the Medicare and/or Medicaid programs.

NOTE: If the survey team finds substandard care in §§483.13, 483.15, or 483.25, follow the instructions for partial extended or extended surveys.

[**Editor's Note**: §483.5(d) through (e) was added by *Federal Register*, Volume 71, Number 184, dated Friday, September 22, 2006. The changes are reflected in the text below.]

§483.5(d) *Common area.* **Common areas are dining rooms, activity rooms, meeting rooms where residents are located on a regular basis, and other areas in the facility where residents may gather together with other residents, visitors, and staff.**

§483.5(e) *Fully sprinklered.* **A fully sprinklered long term care facility is one that has all areas sprinklered in accordance with National Fire Protection Association 13 "Standard for the Installation of Sprinkler Systems" without the use of waivers or the Fire Safety Evaluation System.**

[This page intentionally left blank]

F151 – F177
§483.10 — Resident Rights

§483.10 Resident Rights

The resident has a right to a dignified existence, self-determination, and communication with and access to persons and services inside and outside the facility. A facility must protect and promote the rights of each resident, including each of the following rights.

Interpretive Guidelines §483.10

All residents in long term care facilities have rights guaranteed to them under Federal and State law. Requirements concerning resident rights are specified in §§483.10, 483.12, 483.13, and 483.15. Section 483.10 is intended to lay the foundation for the remaining resident's rights requirements which cover more specific areas. These rights include the resident's right to:

- Exercise his or her rights (§483.10(a));

- Be informed about what rights and responsibilities he or she has (§483.10(b));

- If he or she wishes, have the facility manage his personal funds (§483.10(c));

- Choose a physician and treatment and participate in decisions and care planning (§483.10(d));

- Privacy and confidentiality (§483.10(e));

- Voice grievances and have the facility respond to those grievances (§483.10(f));

- Examine survey results (§483.10(g));

- Work or not work (§483.10(h));

- Privacy in sending and receiving mail (§483.10(i));

- Visit and be visited by others from outside the facility (§483.10(j));

- Use a telephone in privacy (§483.10(k));

- Retain and use personal possessions (§483.10(1)) to the maximum extent that space and safety permit;

- Share a room with a spouse, if that is mutually agreeable (§483.10(m));

- Self-administer medication, if the interdisciplinary care planning team determines it is safe (§483.10(n)); and

- Refuse a transfer from a distinct part, within the institution (§483.10(o)).

A facility must promote the exercise of rights for each resident, including any who face barriers (such as communication problems, hearing problems and cognition limits) in the exercise of these rights. A resident, even though determined to be incompetent, should be able to assert these rights based on his or her degree of capability.

F151

§483.10(a) Exercise of Rights

§483.10(a)(1) The resident has the right to exercise his or her rights as a resident of the facility and as a citizen or resident of the United States.

§483.10(a)(2) The resident has the right to be free of interference, coercion, discrimination, and reprisal from the facility in exercising his or her rights.

Interpretive Guidelines §483.10(a)(1)

Exercising rights means that residents have autonomy and choice, to the maximum extent possible, about how they wish to live their everyday lives and receive care, subject to the facility's rules, as long as those rules do not violate a regulatory requirement.

Intent §483.10(a)(2)

This regulation is intended to protect each resident in the exercise of his or her rights.

Interpretive Guidelines §483.10(a)(2)

The facility must not hamper, compel, treat differentially, or retaliate against a resident for exercising his/her rights. Facility behaviors designed to support and encourage resident participation in meeting care planning goals as documented in the resident assessment and care plan are not interference or coercion.

Examples of facility practices that may limit autonomy or choice in exercising rights include reducing the group activity time of a resident trying to organize a residents' group; requiring residents to seek prior approval to distribute information about the facility; discouraging a resident from hanging a religious ornament above his or her bed; singling out residents for prejudicial treatment such as isolating residents in activities; or purposefully assigning inexperienced aides to a resident with heavy care needs because the resident and/or his/her representative, exercised his/her rights.

Procedures §483.10(a)(2)

Pay close attention to resident or staff remarks and staff behavior that may represent deliberate actions to promote or to limit a resident's autonomy or choice, particularly in ways that affect independent functioning. Because reprisals may indicate abuse, if the team determines that a facility has violated this requirement through reprisals taken against residents, then further determine if the facility has an effective system to prevent the neglect and abuse of residents. (§483.13(c), F224-F225.)

F152

§483.10(a)(3) -- In the case of a resident adjudged incompetent under the laws of a State by a court of competent jurisdiction, the rights of the resident are exercised by the person appointed under State law to act on the resident's behalf.

§483.10(a)(4) -- In the case of a resident who has not been adjudged incompetent by the State court, any legal-surrogate designated in accordance with State law may exercise the resident's rights to the extent provided by State law.

Interpretive Guidelines §483.10(a)(3) and (4)

When reference is made to "resident" in the Guidelines, it also refers to any person who may, under State law, act on the resident's behalf when the resident is unable to act for himself or herself. That person is referred to as the resident's surrogate or representative. If the resident has been formally declared incompetent by a court, the surrogate or representative is whoever was appointed by the court - a guardian, conservator, or committee. The facility should verify that a surrogate or representative has the necessary authority. For example, a court-appointed conservator might have the power to make financial decisions, but not health care decisions.

A resident may wish to delegate decision-making to specific persons, or the resident and family may have agreed among themselves on a decision-making process. To the degree permitted by State law, and to the maximum extent practicable, the facility must respect the resident's wishes and follow that process.

The rights of the resident that may be exercised by the surrogate or representative include the right to make health care decisions. However, the facility may seek a health care decision (or any other decision or authorization) from a surrogate or representative only when the resident is unable to make the decision. If there is a question as to whether the resident is able to make a health care decision, staff should discuss the matter with the resident at a suitable time and judge how well the resident understands the information. In the case of a resident who has been formally declared incompetent by a court, lack of capacity is presumed. Notwithstanding the above, if such a resident can understand the situation and express a preference, the resident should be informed and his/her wishes respected to the degree practicable. Any violations with respect to the resident's exercise of rights should be cited under the applicable tag number.

The involvement of a surrogate or representative does not automatically relieve a facility of its duty to protect and promote the resident's interests. For example, a surrogate or representative does not have the right to insist that a treatment be performed that is not medically appropriate, and the right of a surrogate or representative to reject treatment may be subject to State law limits.

Procedures §483.10(a)(3) and (4)

Determine as appropriate if the rights of a resident who has been adjudged incompetent or who has a representative acting on his/her behalf to help exercise his/her rights are exercised by the legally appointed individual.

§483.10(b) Notice of Rights and Services

[**Editor's Note:** §483.10(b)(1) was moved by CMS in Transmittal 5, dated November 19, 2004. See Tag F156.]

F153

§483.10(b)(2) -- The resident or his or her legal representative has the right--

(i) **Upon an oral or written request, to access all records pertaining to himself or herself including current clinical records within 24 hours (excluding weekends and holidays); and**

(ii) **After receipt of his or her records for inspection, to purchase at a cost not to exceed the community standard photocopies of the records or any portions of them upon request and 2 working days advance notice to the facility.**

Interpretive Guidelines §483.10(b)(2)

An oral request is sufficient to produce the current record for review.

In addition to clinical records, the term "records" includes all records pertaining to the resident, such as trust fund ledgers pertinent to the resident and contracts between the resident and the facility.

"Purchase" is defined as a charge to the resident for photocopying. If State statute has defined the "community standard" rate, facilities should follow that rate. In the absence of State statute, the "cost not to exceed the community standard" is that rate charged per copy by organizations such as the public library, the Post Office or a commercial copy center, which would be selected by a prudent buyer in addition to the cost of the clerical time needed to photocopy the records. Additional fees for locating the records or typing forms/envelopes may not be assessed.

F154

§483.10(b)(3) -- The resident has the right to be fully informed in language that he or she can understand of his or her total health status, including but not limited to, his or her medical condition;
Interpretive Guidelines §483.10(b)(3)

"Total health status" includes functional status, medical care, nursing care, nutritional status, rehabilitation and restorative potential, activities potential, cognitive status, oral health status, psychosocial status, and sensory and physical impairments. Information on health status must be presented in language that the resident can understand. This includes minimizing use of technical jargon in communicating with the resident, having the ability to communicate in a foreign language and the use of sign language or other aids, as necessary. (See §483.10(d)(3), F175*, for the right of the resident to plan care and treatment.) *[**Editor's Note**: The tag number cited should be F280.]

Procedures §483.10(b)(3)

Look, particularly during observations and record reviews, for on-going efforts on the part of facility staff to keep residents informed. Look for evidence that information is communicated in a manner that is understandable to residents and communicated at times it could be most useful to residents, such as when they are expressing concerns, or raising questions, as well as on an on-going basis.

§483.10(d)(2) – The resident has the right to be fully informed in advance about care and treatment and of any changes in that care or treatment that may affect the resident's well-being;

Interpretive Guidelines §483.10(d)(2)

"Informed in advance" means that the resident receives information necessary to make a health care decision, including information about his/her medical condition and changes in medical condition, about the benefits and reasonable risks of the treatment, and about reasonable available alternatives.

F155

§483.10(b)(4) -- The resident has the right to refuse treatment, to refuse to participate in experimental research, and to formulate an advance directive as specified in paragraph (8) of this section; and

Interpretive Guidelines §483.10(b)(4)

"Treatment" is defined as care provided for purposes of maintaining/restoring health, improving functional level, or relieving symptoms.

"Experimental research" is defined as development and testing of clinical treatments, such as an investigational drug or therapy, that involve treatment and/or control groups. For example, a clinical trial of an investigational drug would be experimental research.

"Advance directive" means a written instruction, such as a living will or durable power of attorney for health care, recognized under State law relating to the provision of health care when the individual is incapacitated.

As provided under State law, a resident who has the capacity to make a health care decision and who withholds consent to treatment or makes an explicit refusal of treatment either directly or through an advance directive, may not be treated against his/her wishes.

A facility may not transfer or discharge a resident for refusing treatment unless the criteria for transfer or discharge are met. (See §483.12(a)(1) and (2).)

If the resident is unable to make a health care decision, a decision by the resident's surrogate or representative to forego treatment may, subject to State law, be equally binding on the facility. The facility should determine exactly what the resident is refusing and why. To the extent the facility is able, it should address the resident's concern. For example, a resident requires physical therapy to learn to walk again after sustaining a fractured hip. The resident refuses therapy. The facility is expected to assess the reasons for this resident's refusal, clarify and educate the resident as to the consequences of refusal, offer alternative treatments, and continue to provide all other services.

If a resident's refusal of treatment brings about a significant change, the facility should reassess the resident and institute care planning changes. A resident's refusal of treatment does not absolve a facility from providing a resident with care that allows him/her to attain or maintain his/her highest practicable physical, mental and psychosocial well-being in the context of making that refusal.

The resident has the right to refuse to participate in experimental research. A resident being considered for participation in experimental research must be fully informed of the nature of the experiment (e.g., medication, treatment) and understand the possible consequences of participating. The opportunity to refuse to participate in experimental research must occur prior to the start of the research. Aggregated resident statistics that do not identify individual residents may be used for studies without obtaining residents' permission.

Procedures §483.10(b)(4)

If the facility participates in any experimental research involving residents, does it have an Institutional Review Board or other committee that reviews and approves research protocols? In this regard, §483.75(c), Relationship to Other HHS Regulations applies (i.e., the facility must adhere to 45 CFR Part 46, Protection of Human Subjects of Research).

See §483.10(b)(8), F156 with respect to the advance directive requirement.

F156

§483.10(b)(1) -- The facility must inform the resident both orally and in writing in a language that the resident understands of his or her rights and all rules and regulations governing resident conduct and responsibilities during the stay in the facility. The facility must also provide the resident with the notice (if any) of the State developed under §1919(e)(6) of the Act. Such notification must be made prior to or upon admission and during the resident's stay. Receipt of such information, and any amendments to it, must be acknowledged in writing;

Intent §483.10(b)(1)

This requirement is intended to assure that each resident know his or her rights and responsibilities and that the facility communicates this information prior to or upon admission, as appropriate during the resident's stay, and when the facility's rules change.

Interpretive Guidelines §483.10(b)(1)

"In a language that the resident understands" is defined as communication of information concerning rights and responsibilities that is clear and understandable to each resident, to the extent possible considering impediments which may be created by the resident's health and mental status. If the resident's knowledge of English or the predominant language of the facility is inadequate for comprehension, a means to communicate the information concerning rights and responsibilities in a language familiar to the resident must be available and implemented. For foreign languages commonly encountered in the facility locale, the facility should have written translations of its statements of rights and responsibilities, and should make the services of an interpreter available. In the case of less commonly encountered foreign languages, however, a representative of the resident may sign that he or she has explained the statement of rights to the resident prior to his/her acknowledgement of receipt. For hearing impaired residents who communicate by signing, the facility is expected to provide an interpreter. Large print texts of the facility's statement of resident rights and responsibilities should also be available.

"Both orally and in writing" means if a resident can read and understand written materials without assistance, an oral summary, along with the written document, is acceptable.

Any time State or Federal laws relating to resident rights or facility rules change during the resident's stay in the facility, he/she must promptly be informed of these changes.

"All rules and regulations" relates to facility policies governing resident conduct. A facility cannot reasonably expect a resident to abide by rules he or she has never been told about. Whatever rules the facility has formalized, and by which it expects residents to abide, should be included in the statement of rights and responsibilities.

§483.10(b)(5) -- The facility must--

   (i)   **Inform each resident who is entitled to Medicaid benefits, in writing, at the time of admission to the nursing facility or, when the resident becomes eligible for Medicaid of--**

        (A) **The items and services that are included in nursing facility services under the State plan and for which the resident may not be charged;**

        (B) **Those other items and services that the facility offers and for which the resident may be charged, and the amount of charges for those services; and**

   (ii) **Inform each resident when changes are made to the items and services specified in paragraphs (5)(i)(A) and (B) of this section.**

§483.10(b)(6) -- The facility must inform each resident before, or at the time of admission, and periodically during the resident's stay, of services available in the facility and of charges for those services, including any charges for services not covered under Medicare or by the facility's per diem rate.

Interpretive Guidelines §483.10(b)(5) and (6)

Residents should be told in advance when changes will occur in their bills. Providers must fully inform the resident of services and related changes.

"Periodically" means that whenever changes are being introduced that will affect the residents liability and whenever there are changes in services.

A Medicare beneficiary who requires services upon admission that are not covered under Medicare may be required to submit a deposit provided the notice provisions of §483.10(b)(6), if applicable, are met.

Procedures §483.10(b)(5) and (6)

See §483.10(c)(8) for those items and services that must be included in payment under skilled nursing and nursing facility benefits.

§483.10(b)(7) -- The facility must furnish a written description of legal rights which includes--

   (i)   **A description of the manner of protecting personal funds, under paragraph (c) of this section;**

   (ii) **A description of the requirements and procedures for establishing eligibility for Medicaid, including the right to request an assessment under section 1924(c) which determines the extent of a couple's non-exempt resources at the time of institutionalization and attributes to the community spouse an equitable share of resources which cannot be considered available for payment toward the cost of the institutionalized spouse's medical care in his or her process of spending down to Medicaid eligibility levels;**

   (iii) **A posting of names, addresses, and telephone numbers of all pertinent State client advocacy groups such as the State survey and certification agency, the State licensure office, the State ombudsman program, the protection and advocacy network, and the Medicaid fraud control unit; and**

(iv) **A statement that the resident may file a complaint with the State survey and certification agency concerning resident abuse, neglect, and misappropriation of resident property in the facility, and non-compliance with the advance directives requirements.**

Interpretive Guidelines §483.10(b)(7)

"The protection and advocacy network" refers to the system established to protect and advocate the rights of individuals with developmental disabilities specified in the Developmental Disabilities Assistance and Bill of Rights Act, and the protection and advocacy system established under the Protection and Advocacy for Mentally Ill Individuals Act.

Procedures §483.10(b)(7)

At the Entrance Conference, request a copy of the written information that is provided to residents regarding their rights and review it to determine if it addresses the specified requirements. Additional requirements that address the implementation of these rights are cross-referenced below.

§483.10(b)(8) -- The facility must comply with the requirements specified in subpart I of part 489 of this chapter relating to maintaining written policies and procedures regarding advance directives. These requirements include provisions to inform and provide written information to all adult residents concerning the right to accept or refuse medical or surgical treatment and, at the individual's option, formulate an advance directive. This includes a written description of the facility's policies to implement advance directives and applicable State law. Facilities are permitted to contract with other entities to furnish this information but are still legally responsible for ensuring that the requirements of this section are met. If an adult individual is incapacitated at the time of admission and is unable to receive information (due to the incapacitating condition or a mental disorder) or articulate whether or not he or she has executed an advance directive, the facility may give advance directive information to the individual's family or surrogate in the same manner that it issues other materials about policies and procedures to the family of the incapacitated individual or to a surrogate or other concerned persons in accordance with State law. The facility is not relieved of its obligation to provide this information to the individual once he or she is no longer incapacitated or unable to receive such information. Follow-up procedures must be in place to provide the information to the individual directly at the appropriate time. [Editor's Note: §483.10(b)(8) was amended by *Federal Register*, Volume 60, Number 123, dated Tuesday, June 27, 1995. The changes are reflected in the text above.]

Interpretive Guidelines §483.10(b)(8)

This provision applies to residents admitted on or after December 1, 1991. 42 CFR 489.102 specifies that at the time of admission of an adult resident, the facility must:

- Provide written information concerning his/her rights under State law (whether or not statutory or recognized by the courts of the State) to make decisions concerning medical care, including the right to accept or refuse medical or surgical treatment, and the right to formulate advance directives;

- Document in the resident's medical record whether or not the individual has executed an advance directive;

- Not condition the provision of care or discriminate against an individual based on whether or not the individual has executed an advance directive;

- Ensure compliance with requirements of State law regarding advance directives;

- Provide for educating staff regarding the facility's policies and procedures on advance directives; and

- Provide for community education regarding the right under State law (whether or not recognized by the courts of the State) to formulate an advance directive and the facility's written policies and procedures regarding the implementation of these rights, including any limitations the facility may have with respect to implementing this right on the basis of conscience.

The facility is not required to provide care that conflicts with an advance directive. In addition, the facility is not required to implement an advance directive if, as a matter of conscience, the provider cannot implement an advance directive and State law allows the provider to conscientiously object. (See §483.10(b)(4), F155.)

The sum total of the community education efforts must include a summary of the State law, the rights of residents to formulate advance directives, and the facility's implementation policies regarding advance directives. Video and audio tapes may be used in conducting the community education effort. Individual education programs do not have to address all the requirements if it would be inappropriate for a particular audience.

Procedures §483.10(b)(8)

During Resident Review, review the records of two selected sampled residents admitted on or after December 1, 1991, for facility compliance with advance directive notice requirements.

- Determine to what extent the facility educates its staff regarding advance directives.

- Determine to what extent the facility provides education for the community regarding one's rights under State law to formulate advance directives.

§483.10(b)(9) -- The facility must inform each resident of the name, specialty, and way of contacting the physician responsible for his or her care.

Interpretive Guidelines §483.10(b)(9)

"Physician responsible for his or her care" is defined as the attending or primary physician or clinic, whichever is responsible for managing the resident's medical care, and excludes other physicians whom the resident may see from time to time. When a resident has selected an attending physician, it is appropriate for the facility to confirm that choice when complying with this requirement. When a resident has no attending physician, it is appropriate for the facility to assist residents to obtain one in consultation with the resident and subject to the resident's right to choose. (See §483.10(d)(1), F163.)

If a facility uses the services of a clinic or similar arrangement, it may be sufficient for residents to have the name and contact information for the primary physician and/or a central number for the clinic itself.

§483.10(b)(10) -- The facility must prominently display in the facility written information, and provide to residents and applicants for admission oral and written information about how to apply for and use Medicare and Medicaid benefits, and how to receive refunds for previous payments covered by such benefits.

Interpretive Guidelines §483.10(b)(10)

To fulfill this requirement, the facility may use written materials issued by the State Medicaid agency and the Federal government relating to these benefits. Facilities may fulfill their obligation to orally inform residents or applicants for admission about how to apply for Medicaid or Medicare by assisting them in contacting the local Social Security Office or the local unit of the State Medicaid agency. Nursing facilities are not responsible for orally providing detailed information about Medicare and Medicaid eligibility rules.

"Refunds for previous payments" refers to refunds due as a result of Medicaid and Medicare payments when eligibility has been determined retroactively.

As part of determining Medicaid eligibility, at the time of admission, a married couple has the right to request and have the appropriate State agency assess the couple's resources.

F157

§483.10(b)(11) -- Notification of changes.

(i) **A facility must immediately inform the resident; consult with the resident's physician; and if known, notify the resident's legal representative or an interested family member when there is--**

(A) **An accident involving the resident which results in injury and has the potential for requiring physician intervention;**

(B) **A significant change in the resident's physical, mental, or psychosocial status (i.e., a deterioration in health, mental, or psychosocial status in either life-threatening conditions or clinical complications);**

(C) **A need to alter treatment significantly (i.e., a need to discontinue an existing form of treatment due to adverse consequences, or to commence a new form of treatment); or**

(D) **A decision to transfer or discharge the resident from the facility as specified in §483.12(a).**

(ii) **The facility must also promptly notify the resident and, if known, the resident's legal representative or interested family member when there is--**

(A) **A change in room or roommate assignment as specified in §483.15(e)(2); or**

(B) **A change in resident rights under Federal or State law or regulations as specified in paragraph (b)(1) of this section.**

(iii) **The facility must record and periodically update the address and phone number of the resident's legal representative or interested family member.**

Interpretive Guidelines §483.10(b)(11)

For purposes of §483.10(b)(11)(i)(B), life-threatening conditions are such things as a heart attack or stroke. Clinical complications are such things as development of a stage II pressure sore, onset or recurrent periods of delirium, recurrent urinary tract infection, or onset of depression. A need to alter treatment "significantly" means a need to stop a form of treatment because of adverse consequences (e.g., an adverse drug reaction), or commence a new form of treatment to deal with a problem (e.g., the use of any medical procedure, or therapy that has not been used on that resident before).

In the case of a competent individual, the facility must still contact the resident's physician and notify interested family members, if known. That is, a family that wishes to be informed would designate a member to receive calls. Even when a resident is mentally competent, such a designated family member should be notified of significant changes in the resident's health status because the resident may not be able to notify them personally, especially in the case of sudden illness or accident.

The requirements at §483.10(b)(1) require the facility to inform the resident of his/her rights upon admission and during the resident's stay. This includes the resident's right to privacy (§483.10(e), F164). If, after being informed of the right to privacy, a resident specifies that he/she wishes to exercise this right and not notify family members in the event of a significant change as specified at this requirement, the facility should respect this request, which would obviate the need to notify the resident's interested family member or legal representative, if known. If a resident specifies that he/she does not wish to exercise the right to privacy, then the facility is required to comply with the notice of change requirements.

In the case of a resident who is incapable of making decisions, the representative would make any decisions that have to be made, but the resident should still be told what is happening to him or her.

In the case of the death of a resident, the resident's physician is to be notified immediately in accordance with State law.

The failure to provide notice of room changes could result in an avoidable decline in physical, mental, or psychosocial well-being.

§483.10(b)(12) *Admission to a composite distinct part.* A facility that is a composite distinct part (as defined in §483.5(c) of this subpart) must disclose in its admission agreement its physical configuration, including the various locations that comprise the composite distinct part, and must specify the policies that apply to room changes between its different locations under §483.12(a)(8). [**Editor's Note**: §483.10(b)(12) was amended by *Federal Register*, Volume 68, Number 149, dated Monday, August 4, 2003. The changes are reflected in the text above.]

---

§483.10(c) Protection of Resident Funds

F158

§483.10(c)(1) Protection of Resident Funds

The resident has the right to manage his or her financial affairs, and the facility may not require residents to deposit their personal funds with the facility.

F159

§483.10(c)(2) Management of Personal Funds

Upon written authorization of a resident, the facility must hold, safeguard, manage, and account for the personal funds of the resident deposited with the facility, as specified in paragraphs (c)(3)-(8) of this section.

§483.10(c)(3) Deposit of Funds

    (i)   Funds in excess of $50. The facility must deposit any residents' personal funds in excess of $50 in an interest bearing account (or accounts) that is separate from any of the facility's operating accounts, and that credits all interest earned on resident's funds to that account. (In pooled accounts, there must be a separate accounting for each resident's share.)

    (ii)   Funds less than $50. The facility must maintain a resident's personal funds that do not exceed $50 in a non-interest bearing account, interest-bearing account, or petty cash fund.

NOTE: The Social Security Amendments of 1994 amended §1819(c)(6)(B)(i) to raise the limit from $50.00 to $100.00 for the minimum amount of resident funds that facilities must entrust to an interest bearing account. This increase applies only to Medicare SNF residents. While a facility may continue to follow a minimum of $50.00, the regulations do not require it.

Interpretive Guidelines §483.10(c)(1) through (3)

This requirement is intended to assure that residents who have authorized the facility in writing to manage any personal funds have ready and reasonable access to those funds. If residents choose to have the facility manage their funds, the facility may not refuse to handle these funds, but is not responsible for knowing about assets not on deposit with it.

Placement of residents' personal funds of less than $50.00 ($100.00 for Medicare residents) in an interest bearing account **is** permitted. Thus, a facility may place the total amount of a resident's funds, including funds of $50.00 ($100.00 for Medicare residents) or less, into an interest-bearing account. The law and regulations are intended to assure that residents have access to $50.00 ($100.00 for Medicare residents) in cash within a reasonable period of time, when requested. Requests for less than $50.00 ($100.00 for Medicare residents) should be honored within the same day. Requests for $50.00 ($100.00 for Medicare residents) or more should be honored within three banking days. Although the facility need not maintain $50.00 ($100.00 for Medicare residents) per resident on its premises, it is expected to maintain amounts of petty cash on hand that may be required by residents.

If pooled accounts are used, interest must be prorated per individual on the basis of actual earnings or end-of quarter balance.

Residents should have access to petty cash on an ongoing basis and be able to arrange for access to larger funds.

"Hold, safeguard, manage and account for" means that the facility must act as fiduciary of the resident's funds and report at least quarterly on the status of these funds in a clear and understandable manner. Managing the resident's financial affairs includes money that an individual gives to the facility for the sake of providing a resident with a noncovered service (such as a permanent wave). It is expected that in these instances, the facility will provide a receipt to the gift giver and retain a copy.

"Interest bearing" means a rate of return equal to or above the passbook savings rate at local banking institutions in the area.

Although the requirements are silent about oral requests by residents to have a facility hold personal funds, under the provisions regarding personal property (§483.10(l)), and misappropriation of property (§483.13(c)), residents may make oral requests that the facility temporarily place their funds in a safe place, without authorizing the facility to manage those funds. The facility has the responsibility to implement written procedures to prevent the misappropriation of these funds.

If you determine potential problems with funds through interviews, follow-up using the following procedures as appropriate:

If the facility does not have written authorization to handle resident's funds, but is holding funds for more than a few days, determine if the facility is managing these funds without written authorization. There must be written authorization for the facility to be in compliance with this requirement.

To assure that facilities are not using oral requests by residents as a way to avoid obtaining written authorization to hold, manage, safeguard and account for resident's funds, make sure that:

- There is a written declaration by the resident that the funds are being held for no more than a few days by the facility at the resident's request;

- These funds are not held for more than a few days; and

- The facility provides the resident a receipt for these funds and retains a copy for its records.

Review the administrative or business file and the bookkeeping accounts of residents selected for a comprehensive review who have authorized the facility to handle their personal funds.

- Are residents' funds over $50.00 ($100.00 for Medicare residents) or, at the facility's option, all resident funds, in an interest bearing account(s)?

- What procedure was followed when residents requested their funds?

- How long does it take for residents to receive: (a) petty cash allotments; (b) funds needing to be withdrawn from bank accounts?

- Were limits placed on amounts that could be withdrawn? If yes, was the reason based on resident care needs or facility convenience?

- Are funds records treated with privacy as required at F164?

NOTE: Banks may charge the resident a fee for handling their funds. Facilities may not charge residents for managing residents' funds because the services are covered by Medicare or Medicaid.

If problems are identified, review also §483.10(b)(7), Tag F156.

Monies due residents should be credited to their respective bank accounts within a few business days.

§483.10(c)(4) Accounting and Records

The facility must establish and maintain a system that assures a full and complete and separate accounting, according to generally accepted accounting principles, of each resident's personal funds entrusted to the facility on the resident's behalf.

(i) **The system must preclude any commingling of resident funds with facility funds or with the funds of any person other than another resident.**

(ii) **The individual financial record must be available through quarterly statements and on request to the resident or his or her legal representative.**

Interpretive Guidelines §483.10(c)(4)

This requirement constitutes the overall response of the facility to the resident's right to have the facility manage the resident's funds.

"Generally accepted accounting principles" means that the facility employs proper bookkeeping techniques, by which it can determine, upon request, the amount of individual resident funds and, in the case of an interest bearing account, how much interest these funds have earned for each resident, as last reported by the banking institution to the facility.

Proper bookkeeping techniques would include an individual ledger card, ledger sheet or equivalent established for each resident on which only those transactions involving his or her personal funds are recorded and maintained. The record should have information on when transactions occurred, what they were, as well as maintain the ongoing balance for every resident.

Anytime there is a transaction the resident should be given a receipt and the facility retains a copy.

Monies due residents should be credited to their respective bank accounts within a few business days.

"Quarterly statements" are to be provided in writing to the resident or the resident's representative within 30 days after the end of the quarter.

§483.10(c)(5) Notice of Certain Balances

The facility must notify each resident that receives Medicaid benefits--

(i) **When the amount in the resident's account reaches $200 less than the SSI resource limit for one person, specified in section 1611(a)(3)(B) of the Act; and**

(ii) **That, if the amount in the account, in addition to the value of the resident's other nonexempt resources, reaches the SSI resource limit for one person, the resident may lose eligibility for Medicaid or SSI.**

Interpretive Guidelines §483.10(c)(5)

The Social Security District Office can provide you with information concerning current SSI resource limits.

Procedures §483.10(c)(5)

If problems are identified for sampled residents who are Medicaid recipients, review financial records to determine if their accounts are within $200.00 of the SSI limit. If there are sampled residents in this situation, ask them or their representatives if they have received notice.

F160

483.10(c)(6) Conveyance upon death

Upon the death of a resident with a personal fund deposited with the facility, the facility must convey within 30 days the resident's funds, and a final accounting of those funds, to the individual or probate jurisdiction administering the resident's estate.

Procedures §483.10(c)(6)

As part of closed records review, determine if within 30 days of death, the facility conveyed the deceased resident's personal funds and a final accounting to the individual or probate jurisdiction administering the individual's estate as provided by State law.

F161

483.10(c)(7) Assurance of Financial Security

The facility must purchase a surety bond, or otherwise provide assurance satisfactory to the Secretary, to assure the security of all personal funds of residents deposited with the facility.

Interpretive Guidelines §483.10(c)(7)

A surety bond is an agreement between the principal (the facility), the surety (the insurance company), and the obligee (depending on State law, either the resident or the State acting on behalf of the resident), wherein the facility and the insurance company agree to compensate the resident (or the State on behalf of the resident) for any loss of residents' funds that the facility holds, safeguards, manages, and accounts for.

The purpose of the surety bond is to guarantee that the facility will pay the resident (or the State on behalf of the resident) for losses occurring from any failure by the facility to hold, safeguard, manage, and account for the residents' funds, i.e., losses occurring as a result of acts or errors of negligence, incompetence or dishonesty.

Unlike other types of insurance, the surety bond protects the obligee (the resident or the State), not the principal (the facility), from loss. The surety bond differs from a fidelity bond, which covers no acts or errors of negligence, incompetence or dishonesty.

The surety bond is the commitment of the facility in an objective manner to meet the standard of conduct specified in §483.10(c)(2), that the facility will hold, safeguard, manage and account for the funds residents have entrusted to the facility. The facility assumes the responsibility to compensate the obligee for the amount of the loss up to the entire amount of the surety bond.

Reasonable alternatives to a surety bond must:

- Designate the obligee (depending on State law, the resident individually or in aggregate, or the State on behalf of each resident) who can collect in case of a loss;

- Specify that the obligee may collect due to any failure by the facility, whether by commission, bankruptcy, or omission, to hold, safeguard, manage, and account for the residents' funds; and

- Be managed by a third party unrelated in any way to the facility or its management.

The facility cannot be named as a beneficiary.

Self-insurance is not an acceptable alternative to a surety bond. Likewise, funds deposited in bank accounts protected by the Federal Deposit Insurance Corporation, or similar entity, also are not acceptable alternatives.

Procedures §483.10(c)(7)

As part of Phase 2, if your team has any concerns about residents' funds, check the amount of the surety bond to make sure it is at least equal to the total amount of residents' funds, as of the most recent quarter.

If the State survey agency determines that individual circumstances associated with a facility's surety bond or its alternative are such that the survey agency cannot determine whether or not the facility is in compliance with the requirements at §483.10(c)(7), then it would be appropriate to make the referral to the State's fiscal department.

If a corporation has a surety bond that covers all of its facilities, there should be a separate review of the corporation's surety bond by the appropriate State agency, such as the State's fiscal department, to ensure that all the residents in the corporation's facilities within the State are covered against any losses due to acts or errors by the corporation or any of its facilities. The focus of the review should be to ensure that if the corporation were to go bankrupt or otherwise cease to operate, the funds of the residents in the corporation's facilities would be protected.

F162

§483.10(c)(8) Limitation on Charges to Personal Funds

The facility may not impose a charge against the personal funds of a resident for any item or services for which payment is made under Medicaid or Medicare (except for applicable deductible and coinsurance amounts).

The facility may charge the resident for requested services that are more expensive than or in excess of covered services in accordance with §489.32 of this chapter. (This does not affect the prohibition on facility charges for items and services for which Medicaid has paid. See §447.15, which limits participation in the Medicaid program to providers who accept, as payment in full, Medicaid payment plus any deductible, coinsurance, or copayment required by the plan to be paid by the individual.)

(i) Services included in Medicare or Medicaid payment. During the course of a covered Medicare or Medicaid stay, facilities may not charge a resident for the following categories of items and services:

(A) Nursing services as required at §483.30 of this subpart.

(B) Dietary services as required at §483.35 of this subpart.

(C) An activities program as required at §483.15(f) of this subpart.

(D) Room/bed maintenance services.

(E) Routine personal hygiene items and services as required to meet the needs of residents, including, but not limited to, hair hygiene supplies, comb, brush, bath soap, disinfecting soaps or specialized cleansing agents when indicated to treat special skin problems or to fight infection, razor, shaving cream, toothbrush, toothpaste, denture adhesive, denture cleaner, dental floss, moisturizing lotion, tissues, cotton balls, cotton swabs, deodorant, incontinence care and supplies, sanitary napkins and related supplies, towels, washcloths, hospital gowns, over the counter drugs, hair and nail hygiene services, bathing, and basic personal laundry.

(F) Medically-related social services as required at §483.15(g) of this subpart.

(ii) Items and services that may be charged to residents' funds. Listed below are general categories and examples of items and services that the facility may charge to residents' funds if they are requested by a resident, if the facility informs the resident that there will be a charge, and if payment is not made by Medicare or Medicaid:

(A) Telephone;

(B) Television/radio for personal use;

(C) **Personal comfort items, including smoking materials, notions and novelties, and confections;**

(D) **Cosmetic and grooming items and services in excess of those for which payment is made under Medicaid or Medicare;**

(E) **Personal clothing;**

(F) **Personal reading matter;**

(G) **Gifts purchased on behalf of a resident;**

(H) **Flowers and plants; and**

(I) **Social events and entertainment offered outside the scope of the activities program, provided under §483.15(f) of this subpart.**

(J) **Noncovered special care services such as privately hired nurses or aides.**

(K) **Private room, except when therapeutically required (for example, isolation for infection control).**

(L) **Specially prepared or alternative food requested instead of the food generally prepared by the facility, as required by §483.35 of this subpart.**

Intent §483.10(c)(8)

The intent of this requirement is to specify that facilities not charge residents for items and services for which payment is made under Medicare or Medicaid.

Interpretive Guidelines §483.10(c)(8)

The facility may charge the resident the difference for requested services that are more expensive than or in excess of covered services in accordance with §489.32 of this chapter. (This does not affect the prohibition on facility charges for items and services for which Medicaid has paid. See §447.15, which limits participation in the Medicaid program to providers who accept, as payment in full, Medicaid payment plus any deductible, coinsurance, or co-payment required by the plan to be paid by the individual.) If a State plan does not cover an item or service, such as eyeglasses, the resident may purchase that item or service out of his/her funds. See §483.15(g), F250 for the facility's responsibility to assist the resident in obtaining those services.

Procedures §483.10(c)(8)

As appropriate during Phase 2 of the survey, review the written information given to Medicare/Medicaid eligible residents and family members on admission that notifies them of the items and services that are covered under Medicare or the State plan. Review a sample of residents' monthly statements to ensure that personal funds are not used to pay for covered services. If charges found on monthly statements indicate that residents may have paid for covered items or services, determine if these items or services are over and above what is paid by Medicare or Medicaid.

If, through observations or interviews of residents selected for comprehensive or focused review, the team determines that families or residents hire sitters, and/or that a large number of residents or families are paying for outside food, determine if these practices reflect inadequate staffing and/or food.

Interpretive Guidelines §483.10(c)(8)(i)(E)

Prescription drugs are part of the pharmaceutical services that facilities are required to provide. (See §483.25(l) and (m), and §483.60.) However, at times, a resident needs a medical service that is recognized by State law, but not covered by the State plan. Such a medical service includes a prescription drug that is not on the State's formulary or that exceeds the number of medications covered by Medicaid. It may also include prescription eyeglasses or dentures. If a resident needs a recognized medical service over what is allowed by the State plan, the resident has the right under the Medicaid statute to spend his/her income on that service. If the service is more than what Medicaid pays, the resident may deduct the actual cost of the service from the Medicaid share of the cost. The facility must assist the resident in exercising his or her right to the uncovered medical expense deduction and may not charge the resident for such services.

"Hair hygiene supplies" refers to comb, brush, shampoos, trims and simple hair cuts provided by facility staff as part of routine grooming care. Hair cuts, permanent waves, hair coloring, and relaxing performed by barbers and beauticians not employed by a facility are chargeable.

"Nail hygiene services" refers to routine trimming, cleaning, filing, but not polishing of undamaged nails, and on an individual basis, care for ingrown or damaged nails.

"Basic personal laundry" does not include dry cleaning, mending, washing by hand, or other specialty services that need not be provided. A resident may be charged for these specialty services if he or she requests and receives them.

Interpretive Guidelines §483.10(c)(8)(ii)(I) Social Events

Facilities are required by §483.15(f) to provide an ongoing program of activities designed to meet, in accordance with the comprehensive assessment, the interests and physical, mental, and psychosocial well-being of each resident, and cannot charge residents for these services, whether they occur at the facility or off-site. Resident funds should not be charged for universal items such as bookmobile services or local newspaper subscriptions intended for use by more than one resident. However, if a resident requests and attends a social event or entertainment that is not part of the activities assessment and care plan for that resident, a facility may charge that resident's account only for actual expenses. Further, because of expenses associated with transportation, escorts and other related costs, a resident may be charged for actual expenses for an event or entertainment he or she requests and attends that may be free to the public.

Interpretive Guidelines §483.10(c)(8)(ii)(L) Specially Prepared Foods

A resident may refuse food usually prepared and food substitutions of similar nutritive value because of personal, religious, cultural, or ethnic preference. If the resident requests and receives food that is either not commonly purchased by the facility or easily prepared, then the facility may charge the resident. For example, the facility may charge the resident's account for specially prepared food if the facility has a restricted diet policy and notified the resident on admission of the fact, in accordance with §483.10(b). The facility may not charge the resident's account for specially prepared foods that are required by the physician's order of a therapeutic diet. If a facility changes its menu so that the menu no longer reflects the food preferences of residents, see F165, F242, and F243 to determine compliance with these requirements.

(iii) Requests for items and services.

    (A) The facility must not charge a resident (or his or her representative) for any item or service not requested by the resident.

    (B) The facility must not require a resident (or his or her representative) to request any item or service as a condition of admission or continued stay.

    (C) The facility must inform the resident (or his or her representative) requesting an item or service for which a charge will be made that there will be a charge for the item or service and what the charge will be.

Interpretive Guidelines §483.10(c)(8)(iii) Requests for Items and Services

A facility may not charge a resident or the resident's representative for items and services that are not requested by the resident or representative, whether or not the item or services is requested by a physician. The item or service ordered by the physician should fit in with the resident's care plan.

---

§483.10(d) Free Choice

The resident has the right to—

F163

§483.10(d)(1) -- Choose a personal attending physician

Interpretive Guidelines §483.10(d)(1)

The right to choose a personal physician does not mean that the physician must or will serve the resident, or that a resident must designate a personal physician. If a physician of the resident's choosing fails to fulfill a given requirement, such as §483.25(l)(1), Unnecessary drugs; §483.25(l)(2), Antipsychotic drugs; or §483.40, frequency of physician visits, the facility will have the right, after informing the resident, to seek alternate physician participation to assure provision of appropriate and adequate care and treatment. A facility may not place barriers in the way of residents choosing their own physicians. For example, if a resident does not have a physician, or if the resident's physician becomes unable or unwilling to continue providing care to the resident, the facility must assist the resident in exercising his or her choice in finding another physician.

Before consulting an alternate physician, one mechanism to alleviate a possible problem could involve the facility's utilization of a peer review process for cases which cannot be satisfactorily resolved by discussion between the medical director and the attending physician. Only after a failed attempt to work with the attending physician or mediate differences in delivery of care should the facility request an alternate physician when requested to do so by the resident or when the physician will not adhere to the regulations.

If it is a condition for admission to a continuing care retirement center, the requirement for free choice is met if a resident is allowed to choose a personal physician from among those who have practice privileges at the retirement center.

A resident in a distinct part of a general acute care hospital can choose his/her own physician, unless the hospital requires that physicians with residents in the distinct part have hospital admitting privileges. If this is so, the resident can choose his/her own physician, but cannot have a physician who does not have hospital admitting privileges.

If residents appear to have problems in choosing physicians, determine how the facility makes physician services available to residents.

[**Editor's Note:** §483.10(d)(2) was moved by CMS in Transmittal 5, dated November 19, 2004. See Tag F154.]

[**Editor's Note:** §483.10(d)(3) was moved by CMS in Transmittal 5, dated November 19, 2004. See Tag F280.]

F164

§483.10(e) Privacy and Confidentiality

The resident has the right to personal privacy and confidentiality of his or her personal and clinical records.

(1) Personal privacy includes accommodations, medical treatment, written and telephone communications, personal care, visits, and meetings of family and resident groups, but this does not require the facility to provide a private room for each resident;

(2) Except as provided in paragraph (e)(3) of this section, the resident may approve or refuse the release of personal and clinical records to any individual outside the facility;

(3) The resident's right to refuse release of personal and clinical records does not apply when—

(i) The resident is transferred to another health care institution; or

(ii) Record release is required by law

Interpretive Guidelines §483.10(e)

"Right to privacy" means that the resident has the right to privacy with whomever the resident wishes to be private and that this privacy should include full visual, and, to the extent desired, for visits or other activities, auditory privacy. Private space may be created flexibly and need not be dedicated solely for visitation purposes.

For example, privacy for visitation or meetings might be arranged by using a dining area between meals, a vacant chapel, office or room; or an activities area when activities are not in progress. Arrangements for private space could be accomplished through cooperation between the facility's administration and resident or family groups so that private space is provided for those requesting it without infringement on the rights of other residents.

With the exception of the explicit requirement for privacy curtains in all initially certified facilities (see §483.70(d)(1)(v)), the facility is free to innovate to provide privacy for its residents, as exemplified in the preceding paragraph. This may, but need not, be through the provision of a private room.

Facility staff must examine and treat residents in a manner that maintains the privacy of their bodies. A resident must be granted privacy when going to the bathroom and in other activities of personal hygiene. If an individual requires assistance, authorized staff should respect the individual's need for privacy. Only authorized staff directly involved in treatment should be present when treatments are given. People not involved in the care of the individual should not be present without the individual's consent while he/she is being examined or treated. Staff should pull privacy curtains, close doors, or otherwise remove residents from public view and provide clothing or draping to prevent unnecessary exposure of body parts during the provision of personal care and services.

Personal and clinical records include all types of records the facility might keep on a resident, whether they are medical, social, fund accounts, automated or other.

Additional guidelines on mail, visitation rights and telephone communication are addressed in §483.10(i), (j) and (k). See §483.70(d)(1)(iv) for full visual privacy around beds.

Procedures §483.10(e)(1) - (3)

Document **any** instances where you **observe** a resident's privacy being violated. Completely document how the resident's privacy was violated (e.g., Resident #12 left without gown or bed covers and unattended), and where and when this occurred (e.g., 2B Corridor, 3:30 pm, February 25). If possible, identify the responsible party.

§483.75(l)(4) The facility must keep confidential all information contained in the resident's records, regardless of the form or storage method of the records, except when release is required by--

(i) **Transfer to another health care institution;**

(ii) **Law;**

(iii) **Third party payment contract; or**

(iv) **The resident.**

Interpretive Guidelines §483.75(l)(4)

"**Keep confidential**" is defined as safeguarding the content of information including video, audio, or other computer stored information from unauthorized disclosure without the consent of the individual and/or the individual's surrogate or representative.

If there is information considered too confidential to place in the record used by all staff, such as the family's financial assets or sensitive medical data, it may be retained in a secure place in the facility, such as a locked cabinet in the administrator's office. The record should show the location of this confidential information.

§483.10(f) Grievances

A resident has the right to--

F165

A resident has the right to –

§483.10(f)(1) --Voice grievances without discrimination or reprisal. Such grievances include those with respect to treatment which has been furnished as well as that which has not been furnished; and

(SEE TAG F166 FOR GUIDANCE)

F166

A resident has the right to--

§483.10(f)(2) -- Prompt efforts by the facility to resolve grievances the resident may have, including those with respect to the behavior of other residents.

Intent §483.10(f)

The intent of the regulation is to support each resident's right to voice grievances (e.g., those about treatment, care, management of funds, lost clothing, or violation of rights) and to assure that after receiving a complaint/grievance, the facility actively seeks a resolution and keeps the resident appropriately apprised of its progress toward resolution.

Interpretive Guidelines §483.10(f)

"Voice grievances" is not limited to a formal, written grievance process but may include a resident's verbalized complaint to facility staff.

"Prompt efforts...to resolve" include facility acknowledgment of complaint/grievances and actively working toward resolution of that complaint/grievance.

If residents' responses indicate problems in voicing grievances and getting grievances resolved, determine how the facility deals with and makes prompt efforts to resolve resident complaints and grievances.

- With permission, review resident council minutes.

- Interview staff about how grievances are handled.

- Interview staff about communication (to resident) of progress toward resolution of complaint/grievance.

If problems are identified, also investigate compliance with §483.10(b)(7)(iii).

---

§483.10(g) Examination of Survey Results

F167

A resident has the right to--

(1) **Examine the results of the most recent survey of the facility conducted by Federal or State surveyors and any plan of correction in effect with respect to the facility. The facility must make the results available for examination in a place readily accessible to residents and must post a notice of their availability; and**

SEE GUIDANCE UNDER TAG F168

F168

A resident has the right to:

§483.10(g)(2) -- Receive information from agencies acting as client advocates, and be afforded the opportunity to contact these agencies.

Interpretive Guidelines §483.10(g)(1)-(2)

"Results of the most recent survey" means the Statement of Deficiencies (Form CMS-2567) and the Statement of Isolated Deficiencies generated by the most recent standard survey and any subsequent extended surveys, and any deficiencies resulting from any subsequent complaint investigation(s).

"Made available for examination" means that survey results and approved plan of correction, if applicable, are available in a readable form, such as a binder, large print, or are provided with a magnifying glass, have not been altered by the facility unless authorized by the State agency, and are available to residents without having to ask a staff person.

"Place readily accessible to residents" is a place (such as a lobby or other area frequented by most residents) where individuals wishing to examine survey results do not have to ask to see them.

F169

§483.10(h) Work

The resident has the right to--

(1) Refuse to perform services for the facility;

(2) Perform services for the facility, if he or she chooses, when--

 (i) The facility has documented the need or desire for work in the plan of care;

 (ii) The plan specifies the nature of the services performed and whether the services are voluntary or paid;

 (iii) Compensation for paid services is at or above prevailing rates; and

 (iv) The resident agrees to the work arrangement described in the plan of care

Interpretive Guidelines §483.10(h)(1)-(2)

"Prevailing rate" is the wage paid to workers in the community surrounding the facility for essentially the same type, quality, and quantity of work requiring comparable skills.

All resident work, whether of a voluntary or paid nature, must be part of the plan of care. A resident's desire for work is subject to discussion of medical appropriateness. As part of the plan of care, a therapeutic work assignment must be agreed to by the resident. The resident also has the right to refuse such treatment at any time that he or she wishes. At the time of development or review of the plan, voluntary or paid work can be negotiated.

Procedures §483.10(h)(1)-(2)

Are residents engaged in what may be paid or volunteer work (e.g., doing housekeeping, doing laundry, preparing meals)? Pay special attention to the possible work activities of residents with mental retardation or mental illness. If you observe such a situation, determine if the resident is in fact performing work and, if so, is this work, whether voluntary or paid, described in the plan of care?

§483.10(i) Mail

The resident has the right to privacy in written communications, including the right to--

F170

§483.10(i)(1) Send and promptly receive mail that is unopened; and

SEE GUIDANCE UNDER TAG F171

F171

§483.10(i)(2) Have access to stationery, postage, and writing implements at the resident's own expense.

Interpretive Guidelines §483.10(i)(1)-(2)

"Promptly" means delivery of mail or other materials to the resident within 24 hours of delivery by the postal service (including a post office box) and delivery of outgoing mail to the postal service within 24 hours, except when there is no regularly scheduled postal delivery and pick-up service.

F172

(Rev. 48; Issued: 06-12-09; Effective/Implementation Date: 06-12-09)

§483.10(j) Access and Visitation Rights

§483.10(j)(1) The resident has the right and the facility must provide immediate access to any resident by the following:

(i)   Any representative of the Secretary;

(ii) Any representative of the State;

(iii) The resident's individual physician;

(iv) The State long term care ombudsman (established under section 307 (a)(12) of the Older Americans Act of 1965);

(v)   The agency responsible for the protection and advocacy system for developmentally disabled individuals (established under part C of the Developmental Disabilities Assistance and Bill of Rights Act);

(vi) The agency responsible for the protection and advocacy system for mentally ill individuals (established under the Protection and Advocacy for Mentally Ill Individuals Act);

(vii) Subject to the resident's right to deny or withdraw consent at any time, immediate family or other relatives of the resident; and

(viii) Subject to reasonable restrictions and the resident's right to deny or withdraw consent at any time, others who are visiting with the consent of the resident.

§483.10(j)(2) The facility must provide reasonable access to any resident by any entity or individual that provides health, social, legal, or other services to the resident, subject to the resident's right to deny or withdraw consent at any time.

Interpretive Guidelines §483.10(j)(1) and (2)

The facility must provide immediate access to any representative of the Secretary of the Department of Health and Human Services, the State, the resident's individual physician, the State long term care ombudsman, or the agencies responsible for the protection and advocacy of individuals with developmental disabilities or mental illness. The facility cannot refuse to permit residents to talk with surveyors. Representatives of the Department of Health and Human Services, the State, the State long term care ombudsman system, and protection and advocacy agencies for individuals with developmental disabilities or mental illness are not subject to visiting hour limitations.

Immediate family or other relatives are not subject to visiting hour limitations or other restrictions not imposed by the resident. Likewise, facilities must provide 24-hour access to other non-relative visitors who are visiting with the consent of the resident. These other visitors are subject to "reasonable restrictions" according to the regulatory language. "Reasonable restrictions" are those imposed by the facility that protect the security of all the facility's residents, such as keeping the facility locked at night; denying access or providing limited and supervised access to a visitor if that individual has been found to be abusing, exploiting, or coercing a resident; denying access to a visitor who has been found to have been committing criminal acts such as theft; or denying access to visitors who are inebriated and disruptive. The facility may change the location of visits to assist care giving or protect the privacy of other residents, if these visitation rights infringe upon the rights of other residents in the facility. For example, a resident's family visits in the late evening, which prevents the resident's roommate from sleeping.

An individual or representative of an agency that provides health, social, legal, or other services to the resident has the right of "reasonable access" to the resident, which means that the facility may establish guidelines regarding the circumstances of the visit, such as location. If there are problems with the facility's provision of reasonable privacy for resident to meet with these representatives, refer to §483.10(e), Privacy and Confidentiality, Tag F164.

Procedures §483.10(j)(1) and (2)

Do residents and family members know that they are able to visit 24-hours a day? Do non-relative visitors know they are also able to visit 24-hours a day, but subject to reasonable restrictions as defined above? If you identify problems during resident, family, or group interviews, determine how the facility ensures 24-hour access to:

- Representatives of the State;

- Representatives of the U.S. Department of Health and Human Services;

- The resident's individual physician;

- Representatives of the State long-term care ombudsman;

- Representatives of agencies responsible for protecting and advocating rights of persons with mental illness or developmental disabilities;

- Immediate family or other relatives; and

- Other visitors, subject to reasonable restrictions as defined above.

F173

§483.10(j)(3) -- The facility must allow representatives of the State Ombudsman, described in paragraph (j)(1)(iv) of this section, to examine a resident's clinical records with the permission of the resident or the resident's legal representative, and consistent with State law.

Procedures §483.10(j)(3)

Ask the ombudsman if the facility allows him/her to examine residents' clinical records with the permission of the resident, and to the extent allowed by State law.

F174

§483.10(k) Telephone

The resident has the right to have reasonable access to the use of a telephone where calls can be made without being overheard.

Interpretive Guidelines §483.10(k)

Telephones in staff offices or at nurses' stations do not meet the provisions of this requirement. Examples of facility accommodations to provide reasonable access to the use of a telephone without being overheard include providing cordless telephones or having telephone jacks in residents' rooms.

"Reasonable access" includes placing telephones at a height accessible to residents who use wheelchairs and adapting telephones for use by the residents with impaired hearing.

§483.10(l) Personal Property

The resident has the right to retain and use personal possessions, including some furnishings, and appropriate clothing, as space permits, unless to do so would infringe upon the rights or health and safety of other residents.

Intent §483.10(l)

The intent of this regulation is to encourage residents to bring personal possessions into the facility, as space, safety considerations and fire code permits.

Interpretive Guidelines §483.10(l)

All residents' possessions, regardless of their apparent value to others, must be treated with respect, for what they are and for what they may represent to the resident. The right to retain and use personal possessions assures that the residents' environment be as homelike as possible and that residents retain as much control over their lives as possible. The facility has the right to limit the resident's exercise of this right on grounds of space and health or safety.

Procedures §483.10(l)

If residents' rooms have few personal possessions, ask residents, families and the local ombudsman if:

- Residents are encouraged to have and to use them;

- The facility informs residents not to bring in certain items and for what reason; and

- Personal property is safe in the facility.

Ask staff if the facility sets limits on the value of the property that residents may have in their possession or requires that residents put personal property in the facility's safe.

F175

(Rev. 48; Issued: 06-12-09; Effective/Implementation Date: 06-12-09)

§483.10(m) Married Couples

The resident has the right to share a room with his or her spouse when married residents live in the same facility and both spouses consent to the arrangement.

Interpretive Guidelines §483.10(m)

The right of residents who are married to each other to share a room does not give a resident the right, or the facility the responsibility, to compel another resident to relocate to accommodate a spouse. The requirement means that when a room is available for a married couple to share, the facility must permit them to share it if they choose. If a married resident's spouse is admitted to the facility later and the couple want to share a room, the facility must provide a shared room as quickly as possible. However, a couple is not able to share a room if one of the spouses has a different payment source for which the facility is not certified (if the room is in a distinct part, unless one of the spouses elects to pay for his or her care). This regulation does not prohibit the facility from accommodating residents who wish to room with another nursing home resident of their choice. For issues of residents being prohibited from rooming with persons of their choice, use §483.15(b)(3), Self-determination and Participation, Tag F242: "The resident has the right to make choices about aspects of his or her life in the facility that are significant to the resident."

F176

§483.10(n) Self-Administration of Drugs

An individual resident may self-administer drugs if the interdisciplinary team, as defined by §483.20(d)(2)(ii),[*] has determined that this practice is safe. [*][Editor's Note: The reference cited should be §483.20(k)(2)(ii).]

Interpretive Guidelines §483.10(n)

If a resident requests to self-administer drugs, it is the responsibility of the interdisciplinary team to determine that it is safe for the resident to self-administer drugs before the resident may exercise that right. The interdisciplinary team must also determine who will be responsible (the resident or the nursing staff) for storage and documentation of the administration of drugs, as well as the location of the drug administration (e.g., resident's room, nurses' station, or activities room). Appropriate notation of these determinations should be placed in the resident's care plan.

The decision that a resident has the ability to self-administer medication(s) is subject to periodic re-evaluation based on change in the resident's status. The facility may require that drugs be administered by the nurse or medication aide, if allowed by State law, until the care planning team has the opportunity to obtain information necessary to make an assessment of the resident's ability to safely self-administer medications. If the resident chooses to self-administer drugs, this decision should be made at least by the time the care plan is completed within seven days after completion of the comprehensive assessment.

Medication errors occurring with residents who self-administer drugs should not be counted in the facility's medication error rate (see Guidelines for §483.25(m)), but should call into question the judgment made by the facility in allowing self-administration for those residents.

Probes §483.10(n)

For residents selected for a comprehensive review or a focused review, as appropriate:

- Does resident self-administer drugs? Which ones? How much? How often?

- Does the care plan reflect self-administration?

F177

§483.10(o) Refusal of Certain Transfers

(1) **An individual has the right to refuse a transfer to another room within the institution, if the purpose of the transfer is to relocate--**

   (i) **A resident of a SNF, from the distinct part of the institution that is a SNF to a part of the institution that is not a SNF, or**

   (ii) **A resident of a NF, from the distinct part of the institution that is a NF to a distinct part of the institution that is a SNF.**

(2) **A resident's exercise of the right to refuse transfer under paragraph (o)(1) of this section does not affect the individual's eligibility or entitlement to Medicare or Medicaid benefits.**

Interpretive Guidelines §483.10(o)

This requirement applies to transfer within a physical plant.

These provisions allow a resident to refuse transfer from a room in one distinct part of an institution to a room in another distinct part of the institution for purposes of obtaining Medicare or Medicaid eligibility. If a resident refuses to transfer from a portion of the institution that is not Medicare certified, the resident forgoes the possibility of Medicare coverage for the care received there. If that portion of the institution is Medicaid certified and the resident is Medicaid-eligible, then Medicaid covered services would be paid by Medicaid. If the resident is Medicaid-eligible, but that portion of the institution is not Medicaid certified, then the resident would assume responsibility for payment for the services. If the resident is unable to pay for those services, then the facility may, after giving the resident a 30-day notice, transfer the resident under the provisions of §483.12(a).

When a resident occupies a bed in a distinct part NF that participates in Medicaid and not in Medicare, he or she may not be moved involuntarily to another part of the institution by the facility (or required to be moved by the State) solely for the purpose of assuring Medicare eligibility for payment. Such moves are only appropriate when they occur at the request of a resident (for example, when a privately paying Medicare beneficiary believes that admission to a bed in a Medicare-participating distinct part of the institution may result in Medicare payment).

See Guidelines, §483.12, for further discussion regarding transfers.

For transfers of residents between Medicare or Medicaid approved distinct parts:

- Is there a documented medical reason for the transfer?

- Was the resident transferred because of a change in payment source?

- If a Medicare or Medicaid resident is notified that he/she is no longer eligible, does the facility transfer the resident? Did the facility give the resident the opportunity to refuse the transfer? How? What happened?

- Ask the local ombudsman about facility compliance with transfer requirements. See also §483.12, Criteria for Transfer.

F201 – F208

§483.12 — Admission, Transfer, and Discharge Rights

§483.12 Admission, Transfer, and Discharge Rights

§483.12(a) Transfer, and Discharge

(1) Definition

Transfer and discharge includes movement of a resident to a bed outside of the certified facility whether that bed is in the same physical plant or not. Transfer and discharge does not refer to movement of a resident to a bed within the same certified facility.

Guidelines §483.12

This requirement applies to transfers or discharges that are initiated by the facility, not by the resident. Whether or not a resident agrees to the facility's decision, these requirements apply whenever a facility initiates the transfer or discharge. "Transfer" is moving the resident from the facility to another legally responsible institutional setting, while "discharge" is moving the resident to a non-institutional setting when the releasing facility ceases to be responsible for the resident's care.

If a resident is living in an institution participating in both Medicare and Medicaid (SNF/NF) under separate provider agreements, a move from either the SNF or NF would constitute a transfer.

Transfer and discharge provisions significantly restrict a facility's ability to transfer or discharge a resident once that resident has been admitted to the facility. The facility may not transfer or discharge the resident unless:

1. The transfer or discharge is necessary to meet the resident's welfare and the resident's welfare cannot be met in the facility;

2. The transfer or discharge is appropriate because the resident's health has improved sufficiently so the resident no longer needs the services provided by the facility;

3. The safety of individuals in the facility is endangered;

4. The health of individuals in the facility would otherwise be endangered;

5. The resident has failed, after reasonable and appropriate notice, to pay for a stay at the facility; or

6. The facility ceases to operate.

To demonstrate that any of the events specified in 1 - 5 have occurred, the law requires documentation in the resident's clinical record. To demonstrate situations 1 and 2, the **resident's** physician must provide the documentation. In situation 4, the documentation must be provided by **any** physician. (See §483.12(a)(2).)

Moreover, before the transfer or discharge occurs, the law requires that the facility notify the resident and, if known, the family member, surrogate, or representative of the transfer and the reasons for the transfer, and record the reasons in the clinical record. The facility's notice must include an explanation of the right to appeal the transfer to the State as well as the name, address, and phone number of the State long-term care ombudsman. In the case of a developmentally disabled individual, the notice must include the name, address and phone number of the agency responsible for advocating for the developmentally disabled, and in the case of a mentally ill individual, the name, address and phone number of the agency responsible for advocating for mentally ill individuals. (See §483.12(a)(3) and (5).)

Generally, this notice must be provided at least 30 days prior to the transfer. Exceptions to the 30-day requirement apply when the transfer is effected because of:

- Endangerment to the health or safety of others in the facility;

- When a resident's health has improved to allow a more immediate transfer or discharge;

- When a resident's urgent medical needs require more immediate transfer; and

- When a resident has not resided in the facility for 30 days.

In these cases, the notice must be provided as soon as practicable before the discharge. (See §483.12(a)(4).)

Finally, the facility is required to provide sufficient preparation and orientation to residents to ensure safe and orderly discharge from the facility. (See §483.12(a)(6).)

Under Medicaid, a participating facility is also required to provide notice to its residents of the facility's bed-hold policies and readmission policies prior to transfer of a resident for hospitalization or therapeutic leave. Upon such transfer, the facility must provide written notice to the resident and an immediate family member, surrogate or representative of the duration of any bed-hold. With respect to readmission in a Medicaid participating facility, the facility must develop policies that permit residents eligible for Medicaid, who were transferred for hospitalization or therapeutic leave, and whose absence exceeds the bed-hold period as defined by the State plan, to return to the facility in the first available bed. (See §483.12(b).)

A resident cannot be transferred for non-payment if he or she has submitted to a third party payor all the paperwork necessary for the bill to be paid. Non-payment would occur if a third party payor, including Medicare or Medicaid, denies the claim and the resident refused to pay for his or her stay.

§483.10(o), Tag F177, addresses the right of residents to refuse certain transfers within an institution on the basis of payment status.

F201

§483.12(a)(2) Transfer and Discharge Requirements

The facility must permit each resident to remain in the facility, and not transfer or discharge the resident from the facility unless--

(i)   **The transfer or discharge is necessary for the resident's welfare and the resident's needs cannot be met in the facility;**

(ii) **The transfer or discharge is appropriate because the resident's health has improved sufficiently so the resident no longer needs the services provided by the facility;**

(iii) **The safety of individuals in the facility is endangered;**

(iv) **The health of individuals in the facility would otherwise be endangered;**

(v)   **The resident has failed, after reasonable and appropriate notice, to pay for (or to have paid under Medicare or Medicaid) a stay at the facility. For a resident who becomes eligible for Medicaid after admission to a nursing facility, the nursing facility may charge a resident only allowable charges under Medicaid; or**

(vi) **The facility ceases to operate.**

SEE GUIDANCE UNDER TAG F202

F202

§483.12(a)(3) Documentation

When the facility transfers or discharges a resident under any of the circumstances specified in paragraphs (a)(2)(i) through (v) of this section, the resident's clinical record must be documented. The documentation must be made by--

    (i) **The resident's physician when transfer or discharge is necessary under paragraph (a)(2)(i) or paragraph (a)(2)(ii) of this section; and**

    (ii) **A physician when transfer or discharge is necessary under paragraph (a)(2)(iv) of this section.**

Interpretive Guidelines §483.12(a)(2) and (3)

If transfer is due to a significant change in the resident's condition, but not an emergency requiring an immediate transfer, then prior to any action, the facility must conduct the appropriate assessment to determine if a new care plan would allow the facility to meet the resident's needs. (See §483.20(b)(4)(iv),[*] F274, for information concerning assessment upon significant change.) [*][**Editor's Note**: The reference cited should be §483.20(b)(2)(ii).]

Conversion from a private pay rate to payment at the Medicaid rate does not constitute non-payment.

Refusal of treatment would not constitute grounds for transfer, unless the facility is unable to meet the needs of the resident or protect the health and safety of others.

Documentation of the transfer/discharge may be completed by a physician extender unless prohibited by State law or facility policy.

Procedures §483.12(a)(2) and (3)

During closed record review, determine the reasons for transfer/discharge.

- Do records document accurate assessments and attempts through care planning to address resident's needs through multi-disciplinary interventions, accommodation of individual needs and attention to the resident's customary routines?

- Did the resident's physician document the record if:

    o The resident was transferred/discharged for the sake of the resident's welfare and the resident's needs could not be met in the facility (e.g., a resident develops an acute condition requiring hospitalization)? or

    o The resident's health improved to the extent that the transferred/discharged resident no longer needed the services of the facility.

- Did a physician document the record if residents were transferred because the health of individuals in the facility is endangered?

- Do the records of residents transferred/discharged due to safety reasons reflect the process by which the facility concluded that in each instance transfer or discharge was necessary? Did the survey team observe residents with similar safety concerns in the facility? If so, determine differences between these residents and those who were transferred or discharged.

- Look for changes in source of payment coinciding with transfer. If you find such transfer, determine if the transfers were triggered by one of the criteria specified in §483.12(a)(2).

- Ask the ombudsman if there were any complaints regarding transfer and/or discharge. If there were, what was the result of the ombudsman's investigation?

- If the entity to which the resident was discharged is another long term care facility, evaluate the extent to which the discharge summary and the resident's physician justify why the facility could not meet the needs of this resident.

F203

§483.12(a)(4) Notice Before Transfer

Before a facility transfers or discharges a resident, the facility must--

(i) **Notify the resident and, if known, a family member or legal representative of the resident of the transfer or discharge and the reasons for the move in writing and in a language and manner they understand.**

(ii) **Record the reasons in the resident's clinical record; and**

(iii) **Include in the notice the items described in paragraph (a)(6) of this section.**

§483.12(a)(5) Timing of the notice.

(i) **Except when specified in paragraph (a)(5)(ii) of this section, the notice of transfer or discharge required under paragraph (a)(4) of this section must be made by the facility at least 30 days before the resident is transferred or discharged.**

(ii) **Notice may be made as soon as practicable before transfer or discharge when--**

   (A) **The safety of the individuals in the facility would be endangered under paragraph (a)(2)(iii) of this section;**

   (B) **The health of individuals in the facility would be endangered, under paragraph (a)(2)(iv) of this section;**

   (C) **The resident's health improves sufficiently to allow a more immediate transfer or discharge, under paragraph (a)(2)(ii) of this section;**

   (D) **An immediate transfer or discharge is required by the resident's urgent medical needs, under paragraph (a)(2)(i) of this section; or**

   (E) **A resident has not resided in the facility for 30 days.**

§483.12(a)(6) Contents of the notice

The written notice specified in paragraph (a)(4) of this section must include the following:

(i) **The reason for transfer or discharge;**

(ii) **The effective date of transfer or discharge;**

(iii) **The location to which the resident is transferred or discharged;**

(iv) **A statement that the resident has the right to appeal the action to the State;**

(v) **The name, address and telephone number of the State long term care ombudsman;**

(vi) **For nursing facility residents with developmental disabilities, the mailing address and telephone number of the agency responsible for the protection and advocacy of developmentally disabled individuals established under Part C of the Developmental Disabilities Assistance and Bill of Rights Act; and**

(vii) For nursing facility residents who are mentally ill, the mailing address and telephone number of the agency responsible for the protection and advocacy of mentally ill individuals established under the Protection and Advocacy for Mentally Ill Individuals Act.

Procedures §483.12(a)(4)-(6)

If the team determines that there are concerns about the facility's transfer and discharge actions, during closed record review, look at notices to determine if the notice requirements are met, including:

- Advance notice (either 30 days or, as soon as practicable, depending on the reason for transfer/discharge);

- Reason for transfer/discharge;

- The effective date of the transfer or discharge;

- The location to which the resident was transferred or discharged;

- Right of appeal;

- How to notify the ombudsman (name, address, and telephone number); and

- How to notify the appropriate protection and advocacy agency for residents with mental illness or mental retardation (mailing address and telephone numbers).

- Determine whether the facility notified a family member or legal representative of the proposed transfer or discharge.

F204

§483.12(a)(7) Orientation for Transfer or Discharge

A facility must provide sufficient preparation and orientation to residents to ensure safe and orderly transfer or discharge from the facility.

Interpretive Guidelines §483.12(a)(7)

"Sufficient preparation" means the facility informs the resident where he or she is going and takes steps under its control to assure safe transportation. The facility should actively involve, to the extent possible, the resident and the resident's family in selecting the new residence. Some examples of orientation may include trial visits, if possible, by the resident to a new location; working with family to ask their assistance in assuring the resident that valued possessions are not left behind or lost; orienting staff in the receiving facility to resident's daily patterns; and reviewing with staff routines for handling transfers and discharges in a manner that minimizes unnecessary and avoidable anxiety or depression and recognizes characteristic resident reactions identified by the resident assessment and care plan.

Procedures §483.12(a)(7)

During Resident Review, check social service notes to see if appropriate referrals have been made and, if necessary, if resident counseling has occurred.

§483.12(a)(8) Room changes in a composite distinct part.

Room changes in a facility that is a composite distinct part (as defined in §483.5(c)) must be limited to moves within the particular building in which the resident resides, unless the resident voluntarily agrees to move to another of the composite distinct part's locations. [Editor's Note: §483.12(a)(8) was amended by *Federal Register*, Volume 68, Number 149, dated Monday, August 4, 2003. The changes are reflected in the text above.]

F205

§483.12(b) Notice of Bed-Hold Policy and Readmission

§483.12(b)(1) Notice before transfer. Before a nursing facility transfers a resident to a hospital or allows a resident to go on therapeutic leave, the nursing facility must provide written information to the resident and a family member or legal representative that specifies--

(i)   The duration of the bed-hold policy under the State plan, if any, during which the resident is permitted to return and resume residence in the nursing facility; and

(ii)   The nursing facility's policies regarding bed-hold periods, which must be consistent with paragraph (b)(3) of this section, permitting a resident to return.

§483.12(b)(2) Bed-hold notice upon transfer. At the time of transfer of a resident for hospitalization or therapeutic leave, a nursing facility must provide to the resident and a family member or legal representative written notice which specifies the duration of the bed-hold policy described in paragraph (b)(1) of this section.

Interpretive Guidelines §483.12(b)(1) and (2)

The nursing facility's bed-hold policies apply to all residents.

These sections require two notices related to the facility's bed-hold policies to be issued. The first notice of bed-hold policies could be given well in advance of any transfer. However, reissuance of the first notice would be required if the bed-hold policy under the State plan or the facility's policy were to change. The second notice, which specifies the duration of the bed-hold policy, must be issued at the time of transfer.

In cases of emergency transfer, notice "at the time of transfer" means that the family, surrogate, or representative are provided with written notification within 24 hours of the transfer. The requirement is met if the resident's copy of the notice is sent with other papers accompanying the resident to the hospital.

Bed-hold for days of absence in excess of the State's bed-hold limit are considered non-covered services which means that the resident could use his/her own income to pay for the bed-hold. However, if such a resident does not elect to pay to hold the bed, readmission rights to the next available bed are specified at §483.12(b)(3). Non-Medicaid residents may be requested to pay for all days of bed-hold.

If residents (or their representatives in the case of residents who are unable to understand their rights) are unsure or unclear about their bed-hold rights, **review** facility bed-hold policies.

- Do policies specify the duration of the bed-hold?

- Is this time period consistent with that specified in the State plan?

- During closed record review, look at records of residents transferred to a hospital or on therapeutic leave to determine if bed-hold requirements were followed. Was notice given before and at the time of transfer?

F206

§483.12(b)(3) Permitting Resident to Return to Facility

A nursing facility must establish and follow a written policy under which a resident whose hospitalization or therapeutic leave exceeds the bed-hold period under the State plan, is readmitted to the facility immediately upon the first availability of a bed in a semi-private room if the resident--

(i)   **Requires the services provided by the facility; and**

(ii)   **Is eligible for Medicaid nursing facility services.**

Interpretive Guidelines §483.12(b)(3)

"First available bed in a semi-private room" means a bed in a room shared with another resident of the same sex. (see §483.10(m) for the right of spouses to share a room.)

Medicaid-eligible residents who are on therapeutic leave or are hospitalized beyond the State's bed-hold policy must be readmitted to the first available bed even if the residents have outstanding Medicaid balances. Once readmitted, however, these residents may be transferred if the facility can demonstrate that non-payment of charges exists and documentation and notice requirements are followed. The right to readmission is applicable to individuals seeking to return from a transfer or discharge as long as all of the specific qualifications set out in §483.12(b)(3) are met.

Procedures §483.12(b)(3)

For Medicaid recipients whose hospitalization or therapeutic leave exceeds the bed-hold period, do facility policies specify readmission rights?

Refer to the Minimum Data Set (MDS), section A.10, Discharge Planned; MDS 2.0, section Q, Discharge Potential and Overall Status.

Review the facility's written bed-hold policy to determine if it specifies legal readmission rights. Ask the local ombudsman if there are any problems with residents being readmitted to the facility following hospitalization. In closed record review, determine why the resident did not return to the facility.

Ask the social worker or other appropriate staff what he/she tells Medicaid-eligible residents about the facility's bed-hold policies and the right to return and how Medicaid-eligible residents are assisted in returning to the facility.

If potential problems are identified, talk to discharge planners at the hospital to which residents are transferred to determine their experience with residents returning to the facility.

§483.12(b)(4) Readmission to a composite distinct part.

When the nursing facility to which a resident is readmitted is a composite distinct part (as defined in §483.5(c) of this subpart), the resident must be permitted to return to an available bed in the particular location of the composite distinct part in which he or she resided previously. If a bed is not available in that location at the time of readmission, the resident must be given the option to return to that location upon the first availability of a bed there. [Editor's Note: §483.12(b)(4) was amended by *Federal Register*, Volume 68, Number 149, dated Monday, August 4, 2003. The changes are reflected in the text above.]

F207

§483.12(c) Equal Access to Quality Care

§483.12(c)(1) A facility must establish and maintain identical policies and practices regarding transfer, discharge, and the provision of services under the State plan for all individuals regardless of source of payment;

§483.12(c)(2) The facility may charge any amount for services furnished to non-Medicaid residents consistent with the notice requirement in §483.10(b)(5)(i) and (b)(6) describing the charges; and

§483.12(c)(3) The State is not required to offer additional services on behalf of a resident other than services provided in the State plan.

Interpretive Guidelines §483.12(c)

Facilities must treat all residents alike when making transfer and discharge decisions. "Identical policies and practices" concerning services means that facilities must not distinguish between residents based on their source of payment when providing services that are required to be provided under the law. All nursing services, specialized rehabilitative services, social services, dietary services, pharmaceutical services, or activities that are mandated by the law must be provided to residents according to residents' individual needs, as determined by assessments and care plans.

Procedures §483.12(c)

Determine if residents are grouped in separate wings or floors for reasons other than care needs.

F208

§483.12(d) Admissions Policy

(1) The facility must--

    (i)   Not require residents or potential residents to waive their rights to Medicare or Medicaid; and

    (ii)   Not require oral or written assurance that residents or potential residents are not eligible for, or will not apply for, Medicare or Medicaid benefits.

Interpretive Guidelines §483.12(d)(1)

This provision prohibits both direct and indirect request for waiver of rights to Medicare or Medicaid. A direct request for waiver, for example, requires residents to sign admissions documents explicitly promising or agreeing not to apply for Medicare or Medicaid. An indirect request for waiver includes requiring the resident to pay private rates for a specified period of time, such as two years ("private pay duration of stay contract") before Medicaid will be accepted as a payment source for the resident. Facilities must not seek or receive any kind of assurances that residents are not eligible for, or will not apply for, Medicare or Medicaid benefits.

Procedures §483.12(d)(1)

If concerns regarding admissions procedures arise during interviews, review admissions packages and contracts to determine if they contain prohibited requirements (e.g., "side agreements" for the resident to be private pay or to supplement the Medicaid rate).

Ask staff what factors lead to decisions to place residents in different wings or floors. Note if factors other than medical and nursing needs affect these decisions. Do staff know the source of payment for the residents they take care of?

Ask the ombudsman if the facility treats residents differently in transfer, discharge and covered services based on source of payment.

With respect to transfer and discharge, if the facility appears to be sending residents to hospitals at the time (or shortly before) their payment source changes from private-pay or Medicare to Medicaid, call the hospitals and ask their discharge planners if they have detected any pattern of dumping. Also, ask discharge planners if the facility readmits Medicaid recipients who are ready to return to the facility. During the tour, observe possible differences in services.

    •   Observe if there are separate dining rooms. If so, are different foods served in these dining rooms? For what reasons? Are residents excluded from some dining rooms because of source of payment?

- Observe the placement of residents in rooms in the facility. If residents are segregated on floors or wings by source of payment, determine if the facility is providing different services based on source of payment. Be particularly alert to differences in treatment and services. For example, determine whether less experienced aides and nursing staff are assigned to Medicaid portions of the facility. Notice the condition of the rooms (e.g., carpeted in private-pay wings, tile in Medicaid wings, proximity to the nurses' station, quality of food served as evening snacks).

As part of closed record review, determine if residents have been treated differently in transfers or discharges because of payment status. For example, determine if the facility is sending residents to acute care hospitals shortly before they become eligible for Medicaid as a way of getting rid of Medicaid recipients.

Ask social services staff to describe the facility's policy and practice on providing services, such as rehabilitative services. Determine if services are provided based on source of payment, rather than on need for services to attain or maintain functioning.

§483.12(d)(2) The facility must not require a third party guarantee of payment to the facility as a condition of admission or expedited admission, or continued stay in the facility. However, the facility may require an individual who has legal access to a resident's income or resources available to pay for facility care to sign a contract, without incurring personal financial liability, to provide facility payment from the resident's income or resources.

Interpretive Guidelines §483.12(d)(2)

The facility may not require a third person to accept personal responsibility for paying the facility bill out of his or her own funds. However, he or she may use the resident's money to pay for care. A third party guarantee is not the same as a third party payor, e.g., an insurance company; and this provision does not preclude the facility from obtaining information about Medicare or Medicaid eligibility or the availability of private insurance. The prohibition against third-party guarantees applies to all residents and prospective residents in all certified long term care facilities, regardless of payment source.

§483.12(d)(3) In the case of a person eligible for Medicaid, a nursing facility must not charge, solicit, accept, or receive, in addition to any amount otherwise required to be paid under the State plan, any gift, money, donation, or other consideration as a precondition of admission, expedited admission or continued stay in the facility. However,--

(i) **A nursing facility may charge a resident who is eligible for Medicaid for items and services the resident has requested and received, and that are not specified in the State plan as included in the term "nursing facility services" so long as the facility gives proper notice of the availability and cost of these services to residents and does not condition the resident's admission or continued stay on the request for and receipt of such additional services; and**

(ii) **A nursing facility may solicit, accept, or receive a charitable, religious, or philanthropic contribution from an organization or from a person unrelated to a Medicaid eligible resident or potential resident, but only to the extent that the contribution is not a condition of admission, expedited admission, or continued stay in the facility for a Medicaid eligible resident.**

Interpretive Guidelines §483.12(d)(3)

This requirement applies only to Medicaid certified nursing facilities.

Facilities may not charge for any service that is included in the definition of "nursing facility services" and, therefore, required to be provided as part of the daily rate. Facilities may not accept additional payment from residents or their families as a prerequisite to admission or to continued stay in the facility. Additional payment includes deposits from Medicaid-eligible residents or their families, or any promise to pay private rates for a specified period of time.

A nursing facility may charge a Medicaid beneficiary for a service the beneficiary has requested and received, **only** if:

- That service is not defined in the State plan as a "nursing facility" service;

- The facility informs the resident and the resident's representative in advance that this is not a covered service to allow them to make an informed choice regarding the fee; and

- The resident's admission or continued stay is not conditioned on the resident's requesting and receiving that service.

Procedures §483.12(d)(3)

Review State covered services. Compare with the list of items for which the facility charges to determine if the facility is charging for covered services.

Determine if the facility requires deposits from residents. If you identify potential problems with discrimination, review the files of one or more residents selected for a focused or comprehensive review to determine if the facility requires residents to submit deposits as a precondition of admission besides what may be paid under the State plan.

If interviews with residents suggest that the facility may have required deposits from Medicaid recipients at admission, except those admitted when Medicaid eligibility is pending, corroborate by, for example, reviewing the facility's admissions documents or interviewing family members.

§483.12(d)(4) States or political subdivisions may apply stricter admissions standards under State or local laws than are specified in this section, to prohibit discrimination against individuals entitled to Medicaid.

F221 – F226

§483.13 — Resident Behavior and Facility Practices

§483.13 Resident Behavior and Facility Practices

F221

Use Tag F221 for deficiencies concerning **physical** restraints.

USE GUIDANCE UNDER TAG F222

F222

Use Tag F222 for deficiencies concerning **chemical** restraints.

§483.13(a) Restraints

The resident has the right to be free from any physical or chemical restraints imposed for purposes of discipline or convenience, and not required to treat the resident's medical symptoms.

Intent §483.13(a)

The intent of this requirement is for each person to attain and maintain his/her highest practicable well-being in an environment that prohibits the use of restraints for discipline or convenience and limits restraint use to circumstances in which the resident has medical symptoms that warrant the use of restraints.

Interpretive Guidelines §483.13(a)

Definitions of Terms

"Physical Restraints" are defined as any manual method or physical or mechanical device, material, or equipment attached or adjacent to the resident's body that the individual cannot remove easily which restricts freedom of movement or normal access to one's body.

"Chemical Restraints" is defined as any drug that is used for discipline or convenience and not required to treat medical symptoms.

"Discipline" is defined as any action taken by the facility for the purpose of punishing or penalizing residents.

"Convenience" is defined as any action taken by the facility to control a resident's behavior or manage a resident's behavior with a lesser amount of effort by the facility and not in the resident's best interest.

"Medical Symptom" is defined as an indication or characteristic of a physical or psychological condition.

"Convenience" is defined as any action taken by the facility to control a resident's behavior or manage a resident's behavior with a lesser amount of effort by the facility and not in the resident's best interest.

Restraints may not be used for staff convenience. However, if the resident needs emergency care, restraints may be used for brief periods to permit medical treatment to proceed unless the facility has a notice indicating that the resident has previously made a valid refusal of the treatment in question. If a resident's unanticipated violent or aggressive behavior places him/her or others in imminent danger, the resident does not have the right to refuse the use of restraints. In this situation, the use of restraints is a measure of last resort to protect the safety of the resident or others and must not extend beyond the immediate episode. The resident's right to participate in care planning and the right to refuse treatment are addressed at §§483.20(k)(2)(ii) and 483.10(b)(4), respectively, and include the right to accept or refuse restraints.

Physical Restraints are defined as any manual method or physical or mechanical device, material, or equipment attached or adjacent to the resident's body that the individual cannot remove easily which restricts freedom of movement or normal access to one's body.

"Physical restraints" include, but are not limited to, leg restraints, arm restraints, hand mitts, soft ties or vests, lap cushions, and lap trays the resident cannot remove easily. Also included as restraints are facility practices that meet the definition of a restraint, such as:

- Using side rails that keep a resident from voluntarily getting out of bed;

- Tucking in or using velcro to hold a sheet, fabric, or clothing tightly so that a resident's movement is restricted;

- Using devices in conjunction with a chair, such as trays, tables, bars or belts, that the resident can not remove easily, that prevent the resident from rising;

- Placing a resident in a chair that prevents a resident from rising; and

- Placing a chair or bed so close to a wall that the wall prevents the resident from rising out of the chair or voluntarily getting out of bed.

Side rails sometimes restrain residents. The use of side rails as restraints is prohibited unless they are necessary to treat a resident's medical symptoms. Residents who attempt to exit a bed through, between, over or around side rails are at risk of injury or death. The potential for serious injury is more likely from a fall from a bed with raised side rails than from a fall from a bed where side rails are not used. They also potentially increase the likelihood that the resident will spend more time in bed and fall when attempting to transfer from the bed.

As with other restraints, for residents who are restrained by side rails, it is expected that the process facilities employ to reduce the use of side rails as restraints is systematic and gradual to ensure the resident's safety while treating the resident's medical symptom.

The same device may have the effect of restraining one individual but not another, depending on the individual resident's condition and circumstances. For example, partial rails may assist one resident to enter and exit the bed independently while acting as a restraint for another.

Orthotic body devices may be used solely for therapeutic purposes to improve the overall functional capacity of the resident.

An enclosed framed wheeled walker, with or without a posterior seat, would not meet the definition of a restraint if the resident could easily open the front gate and exit the device. If the resident cannot open the front gate (due to cognitive or physical limitations that prevent him or her from exiting the device or because the device has been altered to prevent the resident from exiting the device), the enclosed framed wheeled walker would meet the definition of a restraint since the device would restrict the resident's freedom of movement (e.g. transferring to another chair, to the commode, or into the bed). The decision on whether framed wheeled walkers are a restraint must be made on an individual basis.

"Medical Symptom" is defined as an indication or characteristic of a physical or psychological condition.

The resident's medical symptoms should not be viewed in isolation, rather the symptoms should be viewed in the context of the resident's condition, circumstances and environment. Objective findings derived from clinical evaluation and the resident's subjective symptoms should be considered to determine the presence of the medical symptom. The resident's subjective symptoms may not be used as the sole basis for using a restraint. Before a resident is restrained, the facility must determine the presence of a specific medical symptom that would require the use of restraints, and how the use of restraints would treat the medical symptom, protect the resident's safety, and assist the resident in attaining or maintaining his or her highest practicable level of physical and psychosocial well-being.

Medical symptoms that warrant the use of restraints must be documented in the resident's medical record, ongoing assessments, and care plans. While there must be a physician's order reflecting the presence of a medical symptom, CMS will hold the facility ultimately accountable for the appropriateness of that determination. The physician's order alone is not sufficient to warrant the use of the restraint. It is further expected, for those residents whose care plans indicate the need for restraints, that the facility engage in a systematic and gradual process toward reducing restraints (e.g., gradually increasing the time for ambulation and muscle strengthening activities). This systematic process would also apply to recently admitted residents for whom restraints were used in the previous setting.

Consideration of Treatment Plan

In order for the resident to be fully informed, the facility must explain, in the context of the individual resident's condition and circumstances, the potential risks and benefits of all options under consideration including using a restraint, not using a restraint, and alternatives to restraint use. Whenever restraint use is considered, the facility must explain to the resident how the use of restraints would treat the resident's medical symptoms and assist the resident in attaining or maintaining his/her highest practicable level of physical or psychological well-being. In addition, the facility must also explain the potential negative outcomes of restraint use which include, but are not limited to, declines in the resident's physical functioning (e.g., ability to ambulate) and muscle condition, contractures, increased incidence of infections and development of pressure sores/ulcers, delirium, agitation, and incontinence. Moreover, restraint use may constitute an accident hazard. Restraints have been found in some cases to increase the incidence of falls or head trauma due to falls and other accidents (e.g., strangulation, entrapment). Finally, residents who are restrained may face a loss of autonomy, dignity and self respect, and may show symptoms of withdrawal, depression, or reduced social contact. In effect, restraint use can reduce independence, functional capacity, and quality of life. Alternatives to restraint use should be considered and discussed with the resident. Alternatives to restraint use might include modifying the resident's environment and/or routine.

In the case of a resident who is incapable of making a decision, the legal surrogate or representative may exercise this right based on the same information that would have been provided to the resident. (See §483.10(a)(3) and (4).) However, the legal surrogate or representative cannot give permission to use restraints for the sake of discipline or staff convenience or when the restraint is not necessary to treat the resident's medical symptoms. That is, the facility may not use restraints in violation of the regulation solely based on a legal surrogate or representative's request or approval.

Assessment and Care Planning for Restraint Use

There are instances where, after assessment and care planning, a least restrictive restraint may be deemed appropriate for an individual resident to attain or maintain his or her highest practicable physical and psychosocial well-being. This does not alter the facility's responsibility to assess and care plan restraint use on an ongoing basis.

Before using a device for mobility or transfer, assessment should include a review of the resident's:

- Bed mobility (e.g., would the use of a device assist the resident to turn from side to side? Is the resident totally immobile and unable to change position without assistance?); and

- Ability to transfer between positions, to and from bed or chair, to stand and toilet (e.g., does the raised side rail add risk to the resident's ability to transfer?).

The facility must design its interventions not only to minimize or eliminate the medical symptom, but also to identify and address any underlying problems causing the medical symptom.

- Interventions that the facility might incorporate in care planning include:

  o Providing restorative care to enhance abilities to stand, transfer, and walk safely;

  o Providing a device such as a trapeze to increase a resident's mobility in bed;

  o Placing the bed lower to the floor and surrounding the bed with a soft mat;

  o Equipping the resident with a device that monitors his/her attempts to arise;

o Providing frequent monitoring by staff with periodic assisted toileting for residents who attempt to arise to use the bathroom;

o Furnishing visual and verbal reminders to use the call bell for residents who are able to comprehend this information and are able to use the call bell device; and/or

o Providing exercise and therapeutic interventions, based on individual assessment and care planning, that may assist the resident in achieving proper body position, balance and alignment, without the potential negative effects associated with restraint use.

Procedures §483.13(a)

Determine if the facility follows a systematic process of evaluation and care planning prior to using restraints. Since continued restraint use is associated with a potential for a decline in functioning if the risk is not addressed, determine if the interdisciplinary team addressed the risk of decline at the time restraint use was initiated and that the care plan reflected measures to minimize a decline. Also determine if the plan of care was consistently implemented. Determine whether the decline can be attributed to a disease progression or inappropriate use of restraints.

For sampled residents observed as physically restrained during the survey or whose clinical records show the use of physical restraints within 30 days of the survey, determine whether the facility used the restraint for convenience or discipline, or a therapeutic intervention for specific periods to attain and maintain the resident's highest practicable physical, mental, or psychosocial well-being.

Probes §483.13(a)

This systematic approach should answer these questions:

1. What are the medical symptoms that led to the consideration of the use of restraints?

2. Are these symptoms caused by failure to:

    a. Meet individual needs in accordance with the resident assessments including, but not limited to, section III of the MDS, Customary Daily Routines (MDS Version 2.0, section AC), in the context of relevant information in sections I and II of the MDS (MDS Version 2.0, sections AA and AB)?

    b. Use rehabilitative/restorative care?

    c. Provide meaningful activities?

    d. Manipulate the resident's environment, including seating?

3. Can the cause(s) of the medical symptoms be eliminated or reduced?

4. If the cause(s) cannot be eliminated or reduced, then has the facility attempted to use alternatives in order to avoid a decline in physical functioning associated with restraint use? (See Physical Restraints Resident Assessment Protocol (RAP), paragraph I).

5. If alternatives have been tried and deemed unsuccessful, does the facility use the least restrictive restraint for the least amount of time? Does the facility monitor and adjust care to reduce the potential for negative outcomes while continually trying to find and use less restrictive alternatives?

6. Did the resident or legal surrogate make an informed choice about the use of restraints? Were risks, benefits, and alternatives explained?

7. Does the facility use the Physical Restraints RAP to evaluate the appropriateness of restraint use?

8. Has the facility re-evaluated the need for the restraint, made efforts to eliminate its use and maintained residents' strength and mobility?

F223

§483.13(b) Abuse

The resident has the right to be free from verbal, sexual, physical, and mental abuse, corporal punishment, and involuntary seclusion.

Intent §483.13(b)

Each resident has the right to be free from abuse, corporal punishment, and involuntary seclusion. Residents must not be subjected to abuse by anyone, including, but not limited to, facility staff, other residents, consultants or volunteers, staff of other agencies serving the resident, family members or legal guardians, friends, or other individuals.

Interpretive Guidelines §483.13(b) and (c)

"Abuse" means the willful infliction of injury, unreasonable confinement, intimidation, or punishment with resulting physical harm, pain or mental anguish." (42 CFR §488.301)

This also includes the deprivation by an individual, including a caretaker, of goods or services that are necessary to attain or maintain physical, mental, and psychosocial well-being. This presumes that instances of abuse of all residents, even those in a coma, cause physical harm, or pain or mental anguish.

"Verbal abuse" is defined as the use of oral, written or gestured language that willfully includes disparaging and derogatory terms to residents or their families, or within their hearing distance, regardless of their age, ability to comprehend, or disability. Examples of verbal abuse include, but are not limited to: threats of harm; saying things to frighten a resident, such as telling a resident that he/she will never be able to see his/her family again.

"Sexual abuse" includes, but is not limited to, sexual harassment, sexual coercion, or sexual assault.

"Physical abuse" includes hitting, slapping, pinching and kicking. It also includes controlling behavior through corporal punishment.

"Mental abuse" includes, but is not limited to, humiliation, harassment, threats of punishment or deprivation.

"Involuntary seclusion" is defined as separation of a resident from other residents or from her/his room or confinement to her/his room (with or without roommates) against the resident's will, or the will of the resident's legal representative. Emergency or short term monitored separation from other Residents will not be considered involuntary seclusion and may be permitted if used for a limited period of time as a therapeutic intervention to reduce agitation until professional staff can develop a plan of care to meet the resident's needs.

Investigation of possible involuntary seclusion, may involve one of two types of situations: that in which residents are living in an area of the facility that restricts their freedom of movement throughout the facility, or that in which a resident is temporarily separated from other residents.

- If the stated purpose of a unit which prevents residents from free movement throughout the facility is to provide specialized care for residents who are cognitively impaired, then placement in the unit is not considered involuntary seclusion, as long as care and services are provided in accordance with each resident's individual needs and preferences rather than for staff convenience, and as long as the resident, surrogate, or representative (if any) participates in the placement decision, and is involved in continuing care planning to assure placement continues to meet resident needs and preferences.

- If a resident is receiving emergency short-term monitored separation due to temporary behavioral symptoms (such as brief catastrophic reactions or combative or aggressive behaviors which pose a threat to the resident, other residents, staff or others in the facility), this is not considered involuntary seclusion as long as this is the least restrictive approach for the minimum amount of time, and is being done according to resident needs and not for staff convenience.

If a resident is being temporarily separated from other residents, i.e., for less than 24 hours, as an emergency short-term intervention, answer these questions:

1. What are the symptoms that led to the consideration of the separation?

2. Are these symptoms caused by failure to:

   a. Meet individual needs?

   b. Provide meaningful activities?

   c. Manipulate the resident's environment?

3. Can the cause(s) be removed?

4. If the cause(s) cannot be removed, has the facility attempted to use alternatives short of separation?

5. If these alternatives have been tried and found ineffective, does the facility use separation for the least amount of time?

6. To what extent has the resident, surrogate or representative (if any) participated in care planning and made an informed choice about separation?

7. Does the facility monitor and adjust care to reduce negative outcomes, while continually trying to find and use less restrictive alternatives?

If, during the course of the survey, you identify the possibility of abuse according to the definitions above, investigate through interviews, observations, and record review. (For investigative options, refer to the Guidelines for Complaint Investigation which outlines the steps of investigations for various types of suspected abuse and misappropriation of property.)

Report and record any instances where the survey team observes an abusive incident. Completely document who committed the abusive act, the nature of the abuse and where and when it occurred. Ensure that the facility addresses the incident immediately.

Properly trained staff should be able to respond appropriately to resident behavior. The CMS does not consider striking a combative resident an appropriate response in any situation. Retaliation by staff is abuse and should be cited as such.

§483.13(c) Staff Treatment of Residents (F224* and F226**)

The facility must develop and implement written policies and procedures that prohibit mistreatment, neglect, and abuse of residents and misappropriation of resident property.

§483.13(c)(1)(i) Staff Treatment of Residents

(1) The facility must--

(i) Not use verbal, mental, sexual, or physical abuse, corporal punishment, or involuntary seclusion;

F224 *

* Intent §483.13(c), F224

Each resident has the right to be free from mistreatment, neglect and misappropriation of property. This includes the facility's identification of residents whose personal histories render them at risk for abusing other residents, and development of intervention strategies to prevent occurrences, monitoring for changes that would trigger abusive behavior, and reassessment of the interventions on a regular basis.

* Use tag F224 for deficiencies concerning mistreatment, neglect, or misappropriation of resident property.

* Guidelines §483.13(c), F224

"Neglect" means failure to provide goods and services necessary to avoid physical harm, mental anguish, or mental illness. (42 CFR 488.301)

"Misappropriation of resident property" means the deliberate misplacement, exploitation, or wrongful, temporary or permanent use of a resident's belongings or money without the resident's consent. (42 CFR 488.301)

F226 **

** Intent §483.13(c), F226

The facility must develop and operationalize policies and procedures for screening and training employees, protection of residents and for the prevention, identification, investigation, and reporting of abuse, neglect, mistreatment, and misappropriation of property. The purpose is to assure that the facility is doing all that is within its control to prevent occurrences.

** Use tag F226 for deficiencies concerning the facility's development and implementation of policies and procedures.

** Guidelines §483.13(c), F226

The facility must develop and implement policies and procedures that include the seven components: screening, training, prevention, identification, investigation, protection and reporting/response. The items under each component listed below are examples of ways in which the facility could operationalize each component.

I. Screening (483.13(c)(1)(ii)(A)&(B): Have procedures to:

- Screen potential employees for a history of abuse, neglect or mistreating residents as defined by the applicable requirements at 483.13(c)(1)(ii)(A) and (B). This includes attempting to obtain information from previous employers and/or current employers, and checking with the appropriate licensing boards and registries.

II. Training (42 CFR 483.74(e)): [Editor's Note: The reference cited should be §483.75(e).] **Have procedures to:**

- Train employees, through orientation and on-going sessions on issues related to abuse prohibition practices such as:

  o Appropriate interventions to deal with aggressive and/or catastrophic reactions of residents;

  o How staff should report their knowledge related to allegations without fear of reprisal;

  o How to recognize signs of burnout, frustration and stress that may lead to abuse; and

  o What constitutes abuse, neglect and misappropriation of resident property.

III. Prevention (483.13(b) and 483.13(c)): Have procedures to:

- Provide residents, families and staff information on how and to whom they may report concerns, incidents and grievances without the fear of retribution; and provide feedback regarding the concerns that have been expressed. (See 483.10(f) for further information regarding grievances.)

- Identify, correct and intervene in situations in which abuse, neglect and/or misappropriation of resident property is more likely to occur.

- This includes an analysis of:

  o Features of the physical environment that may make abuse and/or neglect more likely to occur, such as secluded areas of the facility;

  o The deployment of staff on each shift in sufficient numbers to meet the needs of the residents, and assure that the staff assigned have knowledge of the individual residents' care needs;

  o The supervision of staff to identify inappropriate behaviors, such as using derogatory language, rough handling, ignoring residents while giving care, directing residents who need toileting assistance to urinate or defecate in their beds; and

  o The assessment, care planning, and monitoring of residents with needs and behaviors which might lead to conflict or neglect, such as residents with a history of aggressive behaviors, residents who have behaviors such as entering other residents' rooms, residents with self-injurious behaviors, residents with communication disorders, those that require heavy nursing care and/or are totally dependent on staff.

IV. Identification (483.13(c)(2)): Have procedures to:

- Identify events, such as suspicious bruising of residents, occurrences, patterns, and trends that may constitute abuse; and to determine the direction of the investigation.

V. Investigation (483.13(c)(3)): Have procedures to:

- Investigate different types of incidents; and

- Identify the staff member responsible for the initial reporting, investigation of alleged violations and reporting of results to the proper authorities. (See §483.13(c)(2), (3), and (4).)

VI. Protection (483.13(c)(3)): Have procedures to:

- Protect residents from harm during an investigation.

VII. Reporting/Response (483.13(c)(1)(iii), 483.13(c)(2) and 483.13(c)(4)): Have procedures to:

- Report all alleged violations and all substantiated incidents to the state agency and to all other agencies as required, and take all necessary corrective actions depending on the results of the investigation;

- Report to the State nurse aide registry or licensing authorities any knowledge it has of any actions by a court of law which would indicate an employee is unfit for service; and

- Analyze the occurrences to determine what changes are needed, if any, to policies and procedures to prevent further occurrences.

F225

The facility must—

§483.13(c)(1)(ii) Not employ individuals who have been--

(A) Found guilty of abusing, neglecting, or mistreating residents by a court of law; or

(B) Have had a finding entered into the State nurse aide registry concerning abuse, neglect, mistreatment of residents or misappropriation of their property; and

(iii) Report any knowledge it has of actions by a court of law against an employee, which would indicate unfitness for service as a nurse aide or other facility staff to the State nurse aide registry or licensing authorities.

§483.13(c)(2) The facility must ensure that all alleged violations involving mistreatment, neglect, or abuse, including injuries of unknown source and misappropriation of resident property are reported immediately to the administrator of the facility and to other officials in accordance with State law through established procedures (including to the State survey and certification agency).

§483.13(c)(3) The facility must have evidence that all alleged violations are thoroughly investigated, and must prevent further potential abuse while the investigation is in progress.

§483.13(c)(4) The results of all investigations must be reported to the administrator or his designated representative and to other officials in accordance with State law (including to the State survey and certification agency) within 5 working days of the incident, and if the alleged violation is verified appropriate corrective action must be taken.

Intent §483.13(c)(1)(ii) and (iii)

The facility must not hire a potential employee with a history of abuse, if that information is known to the facility. The facility must report knowledge of actions by a court of law against an employee that indicates the employee is unfit for duty. The facility must report alleged violations, conduct an investigation of all alleged violations, report the results to proper authorities, and take necessary corrective actions.

Interpretive Guidelines §483.13(c)(1)(ii) and (iii)

Facilities must be thorough in their investigations of the past histories of individuals they are considering hiring. In addition to inquiry of the State nurse aide registry or licensing authorities, the facility should check information from previous and/or current employers and make reasonable efforts to uncover information about any past criminal prosecutions.

"Found guilty ... by a court of law" applies to situations where the defendant pleads guilty, is found guilty, or pleads *nolo contendere*.

"Finding" is defined as a determination made by the State that validates allegations of abuse, neglect, mistreatment of residents, or misappropriation of their property.

A certified nurse aide found guilty of neglect, abuse, or mistreating residents or misappropriation of property by a court of law, must have her/his name entered into the nurse aide registry. A licensed staff member found guilty of the above must be reported to their licensing board. Further, if a facility determines that actions by a court of law against an employee are such that they indicate that the individual is unsuited to work in a nursing home (e.g., felony conviction of child abuse, sexual assault, or assault with a deadly weapon), then the facility must report that individual to the nurse aide registry (if a nurse aide) or to the State licensing authorities (if a licensed staff member). Such a determination by the facility is not limited to mistreatment, neglect and abuse of residents and misappropriation of their property, but to any treatment of residents or others inside or outside the facility which the facility determines to be such that the individual should not work in a nursing home environment.

A State must not make a finding that an individual has neglected a resident if the individual demonstrates that such neglect was caused by factors beyond the control of the individual.

Interpretive Guidelines §483.13(c)(2) and (4)

The facility's reporting requirements under 483.13(c)(2) and (4) include reporting both alleged violations and the results of investigations to the State survey agency.

"**Injuries of unknown source**" – An injury should be classified as an "injury of unknown source" when both of the following conditions are met:

- The source of the injury was not observed by any person **or** the source of the injury could not be explained by the resident; **and**

- The injury is suspicious because of the extent of the injury **or** the location of the injury (e.g., the injury is located in an area not generally vulnerable to trauma) **or** the number of injuries observed at one particular point in time **or** the incidence of injuries over time.

"**Immediately**" means as soon as possible, but ought not exceed 24 hours after discovery of the incident, in the absence of a shorter State time frame requirement. Conformance with this definition requires that each State has a means to collect reports, even on off-duty hours (e.g., answering machine, voice mail, fax).

The phrase "**in accordance with State law**" modifies the word "officials" only. As such, State law may stipulate that alleged violations and the results of the investigations be reported to additional State officials beyond those specified in Federal regulations. This phrase does not modify what **types** of alleged violations must be reported or the time frames in which the reports are to be made. As such, States may not eliminate the obligation for any of the alleged violations (i.e., mistreatment, neglect, abuse, injuries of unknown source, and misappropriation of resident property) to be reported, nor can the State establish longer time frames for reporting than mandated in the regulations at §§483.13(c)(2) and (4). No State can override the obligation of the nursing home to fulfill the requirements under §483.13(c), so long as the Medicare/Medicaid certification is in place.

F240 – F258
§483.15 — Quality of Life

F240

§483.15 Quality of Life

A facility must care for its residents in a manner and in an environment that promotes maintenance or enhancement of each resident's quality of life.

Interpretive Guidelines §483.15

The intention of the quality of life requirements is to specify the facility's responsibilities toward creating and sustaining an environment that humanizes and individualizes each resident. Compliance decisions here are driven by the quality of life each resident experiences.

F241

(Rev. 48; Issued: 06-12-09; Effective/Implementation Date: 06-12-09)

§483.15(a) Dignity

The facility must promote care for residents in a manner and in an environment that maintains or enhances each resident's dignity and respect in full recognition of his or her individuality.

Interpretive Guidelines §483.15(a)

"Dignity" means that in their interactions with residents, staff carries out activities that assist the resident to maintain and enhance his/her self-esteem and self-worth. Some examples include (but are not limited to):

- Grooming residents as they wish to be groomed (e.g., hair combed and styled, beards shaved/trimmed, nails clean and clipped);

- Encouraging and assisting residents to dress in their own clothes appropriate to the time of day and individual preferences rather than hospital-type gowns;

- Assisting residents to attend activities of their own choosing;

- Labeling each resident's clothing in a way that respects his or her dignity (e.g., placing labeling on the inside of shoes and clothing);

- Promoting resident independence and dignity in dining such as avoidance of:

  o Day-to-day use of plastic cutlery and paper/plastic dishware;

  o Bibs (also known as clothing protectors) instead of napkins (except by resident choice);

  o Staff standing over residents while assisting them to eat;

  o Staff interacting/conversing only with each other rather than with residents while assisting residents.

- Respecting residents' private space and property (e.g., not changing radio or television station without resident's permission, knocking on doors and requesting permission to enter, closing doors as requested by the resident, not moving or inspecting resident's personal possessions without permission);

- Respecting residents by speaking respectfully, addressing the resident with a name of the resident's choice, avoiding use of labels for residents such as "feeders," not excluding residents from conversations or discussing residents in community settings in which others can overhear private information;

- Focusing on residents as individuals when they talk to them and addressing residents as individuals when providing care and services;

- Maintaining an environment in which there are no signs posted in residents' rooms or in staff work areas able to be seen by other residents and/or visitors that include confidential clinical or personal information (such as information about incontinence, cognitive status). It is allowable to post signs with this type of information in more private locations such as the inside of a closet or in staff locations that are not viewable by the public. An exception can be made in an individual case if a resident or responsible family member insists on the posting of care information at the bedside (e.g., do not take blood pressure in right arm). This does not prohibit the display of resident names on their doors nor does it prohibit display of resident memorabilia and/or biographical information in or outside their rooms with their consent or the consent of the responsible party if the resident is unable to give consent. (This restriction does not include the CDC isolation precaution transmission-based signage for reasons of public health protection, as long as the sign does not reveal the type of infection);

- Grooming residents as they wish to be groomed (e.g., removal of facial hair for women, maintaining the resident's personal preferences regarding hair length/style, facial hair for men, and clothing style). **NOTE:** For issues of failure to keep dependent residents' faces, hands, fingernails, hair, and clothing clean, refer to Activities of Daily Living (ADLs), Tag F312;

- Maintaining resident privacy of body including keeping residents sufficiently covered, such as with a robe, while being taken to areas outside their room, such as the bathing area (one method of ensuring resident privacy and dignity is to transport residents while they are dressed and assist them to dress and undress in the bathing room). **NOTE:** For issues of lack of visual privacy for a resident while that resident is receiving ADL care from staff in the bedroom, bathroom, or bathing room, refer to§483.10(e), Privacy and Confidentiality, Tag F164. Use Dignity F241 for issues of visual privacy while residents are being transported through common areas or are uncovered in their rooms and in view of others when not receiving care; and

- Refraining from practices demeaning to residents such as keeping urinary catheter bags uncovered, refusing to comply with a resident's request for toileting assistance during meal times, and restricting residents from use of common areas open to the general public such as lobbies and restrooms, unless they are on transmission-based isolation precautions or are restricted according to their care planned needs. An exception can be made for certain restrooms that are not equipped with call cords for safety.

Procedures §483.15(a)

For a sampled resident, use resident and family interviews as well as information from the Resident Assessment Instrument (RAI) to consider the resident's former life style and personal choices made while in the facility to obtain a picture of the resident's individual needs and preferences.

Throughout the survey, observe: Do staff show respect for residents? When staff interact with a resident, do staff pay attention to the resident as an individual? Do staff respond in a timely manner to the resident's requests for assistance? Do they explain to the resident what care they are doing or where they are taking the resident? Do staff groom residents as they wish to be groomed?

In group activities, do staff members focus attention on the group of residents? Or, do staff members appear distracted when they interact with residents? For example, do they continue to talk with each other while doing a "task" for a resident(s) as if the resident were not present?

Are residents restricted from using common areas open to the public such as the lobby or common area restrooms? If so, determine if the particular area is restricted to the resident for the resident's safety. For example, does the restroom lack a call cord for safety? If so, that restroom may be restricted from resident use. Are there signs regarding care information posted in view in residents' rooms? If these are observed, determine if such signs are there by resident or family direction. If so, these signs are allowable. If a particular resident has been restricted from common areas by the care team, confer with staff to determine the reason for the restriction.

Do staff members communicate personal information about residents in a way that protects the confidentiality of the information and the dignity of residents? This includes both verbal and written communications such as signage in resident rooms and lists of residents with certain conditions such as incontinence and pressure ulcers (or verbal staff reports of these confidential matters) at nursing stations in view or in hearing of residents and visitors. This does not include clinical information written in a resident's record.

Determine if staff members respond in a dignified manner to residents with cognitive impairments, such as not contradicting what residents are saying, and addressing what residents are trying to express (the agenda) behind their behavior. For example, a resident with dementia may be attempting to exit the building in the afternoon, but the actual intent is a desire to meet her children at the school bus, as she did when a young mother. Allowing the behavior under supervision such as walking with the resident without challenging or disputing the resident's intent and conversing with the resident about the desire (tell me about your children) may assist the behavior to dissipate, and the staff member can then invite the resident to come along to have a drink or snack or participate in a task or activity. For more information about "agenda" behavior, see Rader, J., Tornquist, E, Individualized Dementia Care: Creative, Compassionate Approaches, 1995, New York: Springer Publishing Company, or Fazio, S. Seman, D., Stansell, J., Rethinking Alzheimer's Care. Baltimore: Health Professions Press, 1999.

If the survey team identifies potential compliance issues regarding the privacy of residents during treatment, refer to §483.10(e), Privacy and Confidentiality, Tag F164.

F242

(Rev. 48; Issued: 06-12-09; Effective/Implementation Date: 06-12-09)

§483.15(b) Self-Determination and Participation

The resident has the right to--

(1) Choose activities, schedules, and health care consistent with his or her interests, assessments, and plans of care;

(2) Interact with members of the community both inside and outside the facility; and

(3) Make choices about aspects of his or her life in the facility that are significant to the resident.

Intent §483.15(b)

The intent of this requirement is to specify that the facility must create an environment that is respectful of the right of each resident to exercise his or her autonomy regarding what the resident considers to be important facets of his or her life. This includes actively seeking information from the resident regarding significant interests and preferences in order to provide necessary assistance to help residents fulfill their choices over aspects of their lives in the facility.

Interpretive Guidelines §483.15(b)

Many types of choices are mentioned in this regulatory requirement. The first of these is choice over "activities." It is an important right for a resident to have choices to participate in preferred activities, whether they are part of the formal activities program or self-directed. However, the regulation at §483.15(f) Activities, F248 covers both formal and self-directed activities. For issues concerning choices over activities, use Tag F248.

The second listed choice is "schedules." Residents have the right to have a choice over their schedules, consistent with their interests, assessments and plans of care. Choice over "schedules" includes (but is not limited to) choices over the schedules that are important to the resident, such as daily waking, eating, bathing, and the time for going to bed at night. Residents have the right to choose health care schedules consistent with their interests and preferences, and the facility should gather this information in order to be proactive in assisting residents to fulfill their choices. For example, if a resident mentions that her therapy is scheduled at the time of her favorite television program, the facility should accommodate the resident to the extent that it can.

If the resident refuses a bath because he or she prefers a shower or a different bathing method such as in-bed bathing, prefers it at a different time of day or on a different day, does not feel well that day, is uneasy about the aide assigned to help or is worried about falling, the staff member should make the necessary adjustments realizing the resident is not refusing to be clean but refusing the bath under the circumstance provided. The facility staff should meet with the resident to make adjustments in the care plan to accommodate his or her preferences.

NOTE: For issues regarding choice over arrangement of furniture and adaptations to the resident's bedroom and bathroom, see §483.15(e)(1), Accommodation of Needs, Tag F246.

According to this requirement at §483.15(b)(3), residents have the right to make choices about aspects of their lives that are significant to them. One example includes the right to choose to room with a person of the resident's choice if both parties are residents of the facility, and both consent to the choice.

If a facility changes its policy to prohibit smoking, it must allow current residents who smoke to continue smoking in an area that maintains the quality of life for these residents. Weather permitting, this may be an outside area. Residents admitted after the facility changes its policy must be informed of this policy at admission. (See §483.10(b)(1)).

Procedures §483.15(b)

During resident and family interviews, determine if the resident is able to exercise her/his choices regarding personal activities, including whether the facility provides assistance as needed to the resident to be able to engage in their preferred activities on a routine basis.

During resident and family interviews, determine what time the resident awakens and goes to sleep, and whether this is the resident's preferred time. Also determine whether the facility is honoring the resident's preferences regarding the timing (morning, afternoon, evening and how many times a week) for bathing and also the method (shower, bath, in-bed bathing). Obtain further information as necessary from observations and staff interviews. If the resident is unaware of the right to make such choices, determine whether the facility has actively sought information from the resident and/or family (for a resident unable to express choices) regarding preferences and whether these choices have been made known to caregivers.

F243

§483.15(c) Participation in Resident and Family Groups

(1) A resident has the right to organize and participate in resident groups in the facility;

(2) A resident's family has the right to meet in the facility with the families of other residents in the facility;

(3) The facility must provide a resident or family group, if one exists, with private space;

(4) Staff or visitors may attend meetings at the group's invitation;

(5) The facility must provide a designated staff person responsible for providing assistance and responding to written requests that result form group meetings;

SEE INTERPRETIVE GUIDANCE FOR §483.15(C) AT TAG F244

F244

§483.15(c)(6) When a resident or family group exists, the facility must listen to the views and act upon the grievances and recommendations of residents and families concerning proposed policy and operational decisions affecting resident care and life in the facility.

Interpretive Guidelines §483.15(c)

This requirement does not require that residents' organize a residents or family group. However, whenever residents or their families wish to organize, facilities must allow them to do so without interference. The facility must provide the group with space, privacy for meetings, and staff support. Normally, the designated staff person responsible for assistance and liaison between the group and the facility's administration and any other staff members attend the meeting only if requested.

- "A resident's or family group" is defined as a group that meets regularly to:

    o Discuss and offer suggestions about facility policies and procedures affecting residents' care, treatment, and quality of life;

    o Support each other;

    o Plan resident and family activities;

    o Participate in educational activities; or

    o For any other purpose.

The facility is required to listen to resident and family group recommendations and grievances. Acting upon these issues does not mean that the facility must accede to all group recommendations, but the facility must seriously consider the group's recommendations and must attempt to accommodate those recommendations, to the extent practicable, in developing and changing facility policies affecting resident care and life in the facility. The facility should communicate its decisions to the resident and/or family group.

Procedures §483.15(c)

If no organized group exists, determine if residents have attempted to form one and have been unsuccessful, and, if so, why.

F245

§483.15(d) Participation in Other Activities

A resident has the right to participate in social, religious, and community activities that do not interfere with the rights of other residents in the facility.

Interpretive Guidelines §483.15(d)

The facility, to the extent possible, should accommodate an individual's needs and choices for how he/she spends time, both inside and outside the facility.

Ask the social worker or other appropriate staff how they help residents pursue activities outside the facility.

F246

(Rev. 48; Issued: 06-12-09; Effective/Implementation Date: 06-12-09)

§483.15(e) Accommodation of Needs

A resident has a right to --

§483.15(e)(1) Reside and receive services in the facility with reasonable accommodation of individual needs and preferences, except when the health or safety of the individual or other residents would be endangered; and

Interpretive Guidelines §483.15(e)(1)

"Reasonable accommodations of individual needs and preferences," means the facility's efforts to individualize the resident's physical environment. This includes the physical environment of the resident's bedroom and bathroom, as well as individualizing as much as feasible the facility's common living areas. The facility's physical environment and staff behaviors should be directed toward assisting the resident in maintaining and/or achieving independent functioning, dignity, and well-being to the extent possible in accordance with the resident's own needs and preferences.

NOTE: For issues regarding the psychosocial environment experienced by the resident, such as being ignored by staff, being made to feel unwelcome or that their care needs are burdensome to staff, refer to §483.15(a), Tag F241, Dignity.

The facility is responsible for evaluating each resident's unique needs and preferences and ensuring that the environment accommodates the resident to the extent reasonable and does not endanger the health or safety of individuals or other residents. This includes making adaptations of the resident's bedroom and bathroom furniture and fixtures, as necessary to ensure that the resident can (if able):

- Open and close drawers and turn faucets on and off;

- See her/himself in a mirror and have toiletry articles easily within reach while using the sink;

- Open and close bedroom and bathroom doors, easily access areas of their room and bath, and operate room lighting;

- Use bathroom facilities as independently as possible with access to assistive devices (such as grab bars within reach) if needed; and

- Perform other desired tasks such as turning a table light on and off, using the call bell; etc.

NOTE: If a resident cannot reach her/his clothing in the closet, if the resident does not have private closet space, or if the resident does not have needed furniture (such as a chair) refer to §483.15(h)(4) and §483.70(d)(2)(iv), Tag F461.

The facility should strive to provide reasonably sufficient electric outlets to accommodate the resident's need to safely use her/his electronic personal items, as long as caution is maintained to not overload circuits. The bedroom should include comfortable seating for the resident and task lighting that is sufficient and appropriate for the resident's chosen activities. The facility should accommodate the resident's preferences for arrangement of furniture to the extent space allows, including facilitating resident choice about where to place their bed in their room (as long as the roommate, if any, concurs). There may be some limitations on furniture arrangement, such as not placing a bed over a heat register, or not placing a bed far from the call cord so as to make it unreachable from the bedside.

The facility should also ensure that furniture and fixtures in common areas frequented by residents are accommodating of physical limitations of residents. Furnishings in common areas should enhance residents' abilities to maintain their independence, such as being able to arise from living room furniture. The facility should provide seating with appropriate seat height, depth, firmness, and with arms that assist residents to arise to a standing position. One method of accommodating residents of different heights and differing types of needs in common areas is through the use of different sizes and types of furniture.

NOTE: If residents are prohibited from using common area restrooms, the lobby, or dining rooms outside of meal times, refer to §483.15(a), Tag F241, Dignity. For issues of sufficient lighting, refer to §483.15(h)(5), Tag F256, Adequate and Comfortable Lighting.

Staff should strive to reasonably accommodate the resident's needs and preferences as the resident makes use of the physical environment. This includes ensuring that items the resident needs to use are available and accessible to encourage confidence and independence (such as grooming supplies reachable near the bathroom sink), needed adaptive equipment (such as door handle grippers) are maintained in place, and functional furniture is arranged to accommodate the resident's needs and preferences, etc. This does not apply to residents who need extensive staff assistance and are incapable of using these room adaptations.

Staff should interact with the resident in a way that takes into account the physical limitations of the resident, assures communication, and maintains respect; for example, getting down to eye level with a resident who is sitting, speaking so a resident with limited hearing who reads lips can see their mouth when they speak, utilizing a hearing amplification device such as a pocket-talker if the resident has such a device, etc. Residents who use glasses, hearing aids, or similar devices should have them in use (except when the resident refuses), clean, and functional.

Procedures §483.15(e)(1)

Observe the resident using her/his room and common areas and interview the resident if possible to determine if the environment has been adapted as necessary to accommodate the resident's needs and preferences, as described above. Observe staff/resident interactions to determine if staff members adapt their interactions so that a resident with limited sight or hearing can see and hear them. Are hearing aids and glasses in use, clean, and functional? Determine if staff keep needed items within the resident's reach and provide necessary assistance (set up) to help maintain the resident's independent use of their environment to the maximum extent possible for the resident. Determine if the resident has the call system within reach and is able to use it if desired. (This does not include a resident who is too severely impaired to comprehend or is comatose.) Some residents need adaptations for limited hand dexterity or other physical limitations, such as larger buttons that can be pushed by a fist or bright colors to accommodate visual limitations.

Review the extent to which the facility adapts the physical environment to enable residents to maintain unassisted functioning. These adaptations include, but are not limited to:

- Furniture and adaptive equipment that enable residents to stand independently, transfer without assistance (e.g., arm supports, correct chair height and depth, firm support), maintain body symmetry, participate in resident-preferred activities, and promote mobility and independence for residents in going to the bathroom (e.g., grab bars, elevated toilet seats).

- Easily useable fixtures, drawer handles, faucets, etc.;

- Personal items kept within reach for independent use in the bathroom; and

- Bedroom furniture arranged to the residents' preferences as much as possible.

Determine if staff use appropriate measures to facilitate communication with residents who have difficulty communicating. For example, do staff communicate at eye level, and do they remove a resident from noisy surroundings if that resident is having difficulty hearing what is said?

If the facility has outdoor smoking areas, how have they accommodated residents when the weather is inclement?

F247

(Rev. 48; Issued: 06-12-09; Effective/Implementation Date: 06-12-09)

A resident has a right to—

§483.15(e)(2) Receive notice before the resident's room or roommate in the facility is changed.

Interpretive Guidelines §483.15(e)(2)

The facility should be sensitive to the trauma a move or change of roommate causes some residents, and should attempt to be as accommodating as possible. This includes learning the resident's preferences and taking them into account when discussing changes of rooms or roommates and the timing of such changes. For a resident who is being moved at the facility's request, a staff member should explain to the resident the reason for the move and support the resident by providing the opportunity to see the new location and meet the new roommate, and to ask questions about the move. For a resident who is receiving a new roommate, a staff member should give the resident as much notice and information about the new person as possible, while maintaining confidentiality regarding medical information. The facility should support a resident whose roommate has passed away by providing a little time to adjust (a couple days if possible) before moving another person into the room, depending on the resident's level of connection to the previous roommate. The facility should provide necessary social services for a resident who is grieving over the death of a roommate. If the survey team identifies potential compliance issues related to social services, refer to §483.15(g)(1), Social Services, Tag F250.

F248

§483.15(f) Activities

§483.15(f)(1) The facility must provide for an ongoing program of activities designed to meet, in accordance with the comprehensive assessment, the interests and the physical, mental, and psychosocial well-being of each resident.

INTENT §483.15(f)(1) Activities

The intent of this requirement is that:

- The facility identifies each resident's interests and needs; and

- The facility involves the resident in an ongoing program of activities that is designed to appeal to his or her interests and to enhance the resident's highest practicable level of physical, mental, and psychosocial well-being.

DEFINITIONS

Definitions are provided to clarify key terms used in this guidance.

- "Activities" refer to any endeavor, other than routine ADLs, in which a resident participates that is intended to enhance her/his sense of well-being and to promote or enhance physical, cognitive, and emotional health. These include, but are not limited to, activities that promote self-esteem, pleasure, comfort, education, creativity, success, and independence.

   NOTE: ADL-related activities, such as manicures/pedicures, hair styling, and makeovers, may be considered part of the activities program.

- "One-to-One Programming" refers to programming provided to residents who will not, or cannot, effectively plan their own activity pursuits, or residents needing specialized or extended programs to enhance their overall daily routine and activity pursuit needs.

- "Person Appropriate" refers to the idea that each resident has a personal identity and history that involves more than just their medical illnesses or functional impairments. Activities should be relevant to the specific needs, interests, culture, background, etc. of the individual for whom they are developed.

- "Program of Activities" includes a combination of large and small group, one-to-one, and self-directed activities; and a system that supports the development, implementation, and evaluation of the activities provided to the residents in the facility.[1]

OVERVIEW

In long term care, an ongoing program of activities refers to the provision of activities in accordance with and based upon an individual resident's comprehensive assessment. The Institute of Medicine (IOM)'s 1986 report, "Improving the Quality of Care in Nursing Homes," became the basis for the "Nursing Home Reform" part of OBRA '87 and the current OBRA long term care regulations. The IOM Report identified the need for residents in nursing homes to receive care and/or services to maximize their highest practicable quality of life. However, defining "quality of life" has been difficult, as it is subjective for each person. Thus, it is important for the facility to conduct an individualized assessment of each resident to provide additional opportunities to help enhance a resident's self-esteem and dignity.

[This page intentionally left blank]

Research findings and the observations of positive resident outcomes confirm that activities are an integral component of residents' lives. Residents have indicated that daily life and involvement should be meaningful. Activities are meaningful when they reflect a person's interests and lifestyle, are enjoyable to the person, help the person to feel useful, and provide a sense of belonging.[2]

Residents' Views on Activities

Activities are relevant and valuable to residents' quality of life. In a large-scale study commissioned by CMS, 160 residents in 40 nursing homes were interviewed about what quality of life meant to them. The study found that residents "overwhelmingly assigned priority to dignity, although they labeled this concern in many ways." The researchers determined that the two main components of dignity, in the words of these residents, were "independence" and "positive self-image." Residents listed, under the categories of independence and positive self-image, the elements of "choice of activities" and "activities that amount to something," such as those that produce or teach something; activities using skills from residents' former work; religious activities; and activities that contribute to the nursing home.

The report stated that, "Residents not only discussed particular activities that gave them a sense of purpose but also indicated that a lack of appropriate activities contributes to having no sense of purpose." "Residents rarely mentioned participating in activities as a way to just 'keep busy' or just to socialize. The relevance of the activities to the residents' lives must be considered."

According to the study, residents wanted a variety of activities, including those that are not childish, require thinking (such as word games), are gender-specific, produce something useful, relate to previous work of residents, allow for socializing with visitors and participating in community events, and are physically active. The study found that the above concepts were relevant to both interviewable and non-interviewable residents. Researchers observed that non-interviewable residents appeared "happier" and "less agitated" in homes with many planned activities for them.

Non-traditional Approaches to Activities

Surveyors need to be aware that some facilities may take a non-traditional approach to activities. In neighborhoods/households, all staff may be trained as nurse aides and are responsible to provide activities, and activities may resemble those of a private home.[3] Residents, staff, and families may interact in ways that reflect daily life, instead of in formal activities programs. Residents may be more involved in the ongoing activities in their living area, such as care-planned approaches including chores, preparing foods, meeting with other residents to choose spontaneous activities, and leading an activity. It has been reported that, "some culture changed homes might not have a traditional activities calendar, and instead focus on community life to include activities. Instead of an "activities director," some homes have a Community Life Coordinator, a Community Developer, or other title for the individual directing the activities program.[4]

For more information on activities in homes changing to a resident-directed culture, the following websites are available as resources:
www.pioneernetwork.net; www.culturechangenow.com; www.qualitypartnersri.org (click on nursing homes); and www.edenalt.com.

ASSESSMENT

The information gathered through the assessment process should be used to develop the activities component of the comprehensive care plan. The ongoing program of activities should match the skills, abilities, needs, and preferences of each resident with the demands of the activity and the characteristics of the physical, social and cultural environments.[5]

In order to develop individualized care planning goals and approaches, the facility should obtain sufficient, detailed information (even if the Activities RAP is not triggered) to determine what activities the resident prefers and what adaptations, if any, are needed.[6] The facility may use, but need not duplicate, information from other sources, such as the RAI, including the RAPs, assessments by other disciplines, observation, and resident and family interviews. Other sources of relevant information include the resident's lifelong interests, spirituality, life roles, goals, strengths, needs and activity pursuit patterns and preferences.[7] This assessment should be completed by or under the supervision of a qualified professional (see F249 for definition of qualified professional).

NOTE: Some residents may be independently capable of pursuing their own activities without intervention from the facility. This information should be noted in the assessment and identified in the plan of care.

CARE PLANNING

Care planning involves identification of the resident's interests, preferences, and abilities; and any issues, concerns, problems, or needs affecting the resident's involvement/engagement in activities.[8] In addition to the activities component of the comprehensive care plan, information may also be found in a separate activity plan, on a CNA flow sheet, in a progress note, etc.

Activity goals related to the comprehensive care plan should be based on measurable objectives and focused on desired outcomes (e.g., engagement in an activity that matches the resident's ability, maintaining attention to the activity for a specified period of time, expressing satisfaction with the activity verbally or non-verbally), not merely on attendance at a certain number of activities per week.

NOTE: For residents with no discernable response, service provision is still expected and may include one-to-one activities such as talking to the resident, reading to the resident about prior interests, or applying lotion while stroking the resident's hands or feet.

Activities can occur at any time, are not limited to formal activities being provided only by activities staff, and can include activities provided by other facility staff, volunteers, visitors, residents, and family members. All relevant departments should collaborate to develop and implement an individualized activities program for each resident.

Some medications, such as diuretics, or conditions such as pain, incontinence, etc. may affect the resident's participation in activities. Therefore, additional steps may be needed to facilitate the resident's participation in activities, such as:

- If not contraindicated, timing the administration of medications, to the extent possible, to avoid interfering with the resident's ability to participate or to remain at a scheduled activity; or

- If not contraindicated, modifying the administration time of pain medication to allow the medication to take effect prior to an activity the resident enjoys.

The care plan should also identify the discipline(s) that will carry out the approaches. For example:

- Notifying residents of preferred activities;

- Transporting residents who need assistance to and from activities (including indoor, outdoor, and outings);

- Providing needed functional assistance (such as toileting and eating assistance); and

- Providing needed supplies or adaptations, such as obtaining and returning audio books, setting up adaptive equipment, etc.

Concepts the facility should have considered in the development of the activities component of the resident's comprehensive care plan include the following, as applicable to the resident:

- A continuation of life roles, consistent with resident preferences and functional capacity (e.g., to continue work or hobbies such as cooking, table setting, repairing small appliances)[9];

- Encouraging and supporting the development of new interests, hobbies, and skills (e.g., training on using the Internet); and

- Connecting with the community, such as places of worship, veterans' groups, volunteer groups, support groups, wellness groups, athletic or educational connections (via outings or invitations to outside groups to visit the facility).

The facility may need to consider accommodations in schedules, supplies and timing in order to optimize a resident's ability to participate in an activity of choice. Examples of accommodations may include, but are not limited to:

- Altering a therapy or a bath/shower schedule to make it possible for a resident to attend a desired activity that occurs at the same time as the therapy session or bath;

- Assisting residents, as needed, to get to and participate in desired activities (e.g., dressing, toileting, transportation);

- Providing supplies (e.g., books/magazines, music, craft projects, cards, sorting materials) for activities, and assistance when needed, for residents' use (e.g., during weekends, nights, holidays, evenings, or when the activities staff are unavailable); and

- Providing a late breakfast to allow a resident to continue a lifelong pattern of attending religious services before eating.

INTERVENTIONS

The concept of individualized intervention has evolved over the years. Many activity professionals have abandoned generic interventions such as "reality orientation" and large-group activities that include residents with different levels of strengths and needs. In their place, individualized interventions have been developed based upon the assessment of the resident's history, preferences, strengths, and needs. These interventions have changed from the idea of "age-appropriate" activities to promoting "person-appropriate" activities. For example, one person may care for a doll or stroke a stuffed animal, another person may be inclined to reminisce about dolls or stuffed animals they once had, while someone else may enjoy petting a dog but will not be interested in inanimate objects. The surveyor observing these interventions should determine if the facility selected them in response to the resident's history and preferences. Many activities can be adapted in various ways to accommodate the resident's change in functioning due to physical or cognitive limitations.

Some Possible Adaptations that May be Made by the Facility [10, 11]

When evaluating the provision of activities, it is important for the surveyor to identify whether the resident has conditions and/or issues for which staff should have provided adaptations. Examples of adaptations for specific conditions include, but are not limited to the following:

- For the resident with visual impairments: higher levels of lighting without glare; magnifying glasses, light-filtering lenses, telescopic glasses; use of "clock method" to describe where items are located; description of sizes, shapes, colors; large print items including playing cards, newsprint, books; audio books;

- For the resident with hearing impairments: small group activities; placement of resident near speaker/activity leader; use of amplifiers or headphones; decreased background noise; written instructions; use of gestures or sign language to enhance verbal communication; adapted TV (closed captioning, magnified screen, earphones);

- For the resident who has physical limitations, the use of adaptive equipment, proper seating and positioning, placement of supplies and materials [12] (based on clinical assessment and referral as appropriate) to enhance:

  o Visual interaction and to compensate for loss of visual field (hemianopsia);

  o Upper extremity function and range of motion (reach);

  o Hand dexterity (e.g., adapted size of items such as larger handles for cooking and woodworking equipment, built-up paintbrush handles, large needles for crocheting);

  o The ability to manipulate an item based upon the item's weight, such as lighter weight for residents with muscle weakness [13];

- For the resident who has the use of only one hand: holders for kitchen items, magazines/books, playing cards; items (e.g., art work, bingo card, nail file) taped to the table; c-clamp or suction vise to hold wood for sanding;

- For the resident with cognitive impairment: task segmentation and simplification; programs using retained long-term memory, rather than short-term memory; length of activities based on attention span; settings that recreate past experiences or increase/decrease stimulation; smaller groups without interruption; one-to-one activities;

  NOTE: The length, duration, and content of specific one-to-one activities are determined by the specific needs of the individual resident, such as several short interventions (rather than a few longer activities) if someone has extremely low tolerance, or if there are behavioral issues.

  Examples of one-to-one activities may include any of the following:

  o Sensory stimulation or cognitive therapy (e.g., touch/visual/auditory stimulation, reminiscence, or validation therapy) such as special stimulus rooms or equipment; alerting/upbeat music and using alerting aromas or providing fabrics or other materials of varying textures;

  o Social engagement (e.g., directed conversation, initiating a resident to resident conversation, pleasure walk or coffee visit);

  o Spiritual support, nurturing (e.g., daily devotion, Bible reading, or prayer with or for resident per religious requests/desires);

  o Creative, task-oriented activities (e.g., music or pet activities/therapy, letter writing, word puzzles); or

  o Support of self-directed activity (e.g., delivering of library books, craft material to rooms, setting up talking book service).

- For the resident with a language barrier: translation tools; translators; or publications and/or audio/video materials in the resident's language;

- For residents who are terminally ill: life review; quality time with chosen relatives, friends, staff, and/or other residents; spiritual support; touch; massage; music; and/or reading to the resident; [8]

  NOTE: Some residents may prefer to spend their time alone and introspectively. Their refusal of activities does not necessarily constitute noncompliance.

- For the resident with pain: spiritual support, relaxation programs, music, massage, aromatherapy, pet therapy/pet visits, and/or touch;

- For the resident who prefers to stay in her/his own room or is unable to leave her/his room: in-room visits by staff/other residents/volunteers with similar interests/hobbies; touch and sensory activities such as massage or aromatherapy; access to art/craft materials, cards, games, reading materials; access to technology of interest (computer, DVD, hand held video games, preferred radio programs/stations, audio books); and/or visits from spiritual counselors; [14]

- For the resident with varying sleep patterns, activities are available during awake time. Some facilities use a variety of options when activities staff are not available for a particular resident: nursing staff reads a newspaper with resident; dietary staff makes finger foods available; CNA works puzzle with the resident; maintenance staff take the resident on night rounds; and/or early morning delivery of coffee/juice to residents;

- For the resident who has recently moved-in: welcoming activities and/or orientation activities;

- For the short-stay resident: "a la carte activities" are available, such as books, magazines, cards, word puzzles, newspapers, CDs, movies, and handheld games; interesting/contemporary group activities are offered, such as dominoes, bridge, Pinochle, poker, video games, movies, and travelogues; and/or individual activities designed to match the goals of therapy, such as jigsaw puzzles to enhance fine motor skills;

- For the younger resident: individual and group music offerings that fit the resident's taste and era; magazines, books and movies that fit the resident's taste and era; computer and Internet access; and/or contemporary group activities, such as video games, and the opportunity to play musical instruments, card and board games, and sports; and

- For residents from diverse ethnic or cultural backgrounds: special events that include meals, decorations, celebrations, or music; visits from spiritual leaders and other individuals of the same ethnic background; printed materials (newspapers, magazines) about the resident's culture; and/or opportunities for the resident and family to share information about their culture with other residents, families, and staff.

Activity Approaches for Residents with Behavioral Symptoms [15, 7]

When the surveyor is evaluating the activities provided to a resident who has behavioral symptoms, they may observe that many behaviors take place at about the same time every day (e.g., before lunch or mid-afternoon). The facility may have identified a resident's pattern of behavior symptoms and may offer activity interventions, whenever possible, prior to the behavior occurring. Once a behavior escalates, activities may be less effective or may even cause further stress to the resident (some behaviors may be appropriate reactions to feelings of discomfort, pain, or embarrassment, such as aggressive behaviors exhibited by some residents with dementia during bathing[16]). Examples of activities-related interventions that a facility may provide to try to minimize distressed behavior may include, but are not limited to the following:

For the resident who is constantly walking:

- Providing a space and environmental cues that encourages physical exercise, decreases exit behavior and reduces extraneous stimulation (such as seating areas spaced along a walking path or garden; a setting in which the resident may manipulate objects; or a room with a calming atmosphere, for example, using music, light, and rocking chairs);

- Providing aroma(s)/aromatherapy that is/are pleasing and calming to the resident; and

- Validating the resident's feelings and words; engaging the resident in conversation about who or what they are seeking; and using one-to-one activities, such as reading to the resident or looking at familiar pictures and photo albums.

For the resident who engages in name-calling, hitting, kicking, yelling, biting, sexual behavior, or compulsive behavior:

- Providing a calm, non-rushed environment, with structured, familiar activities such as folding, sorting, and matching; using one-to-one activities or small group activities that comfort the resident, such as their preferred music, walking quietly with the staff, a family member, or a friend; eating a favorite snack; looking at familiar pictures;

- Engaging in exercise and movement activities; and

- Exchanging self-stimulatory activity for a more socially-appropriate activity that uses the hands, if in a public space.

For the resident who disrupts group activities with behaviors such as talking loudly and being demanding, or the resident who has catastrophic reactions such as uncontrolled crying or anger, or the resident who is sensitive to too much stimulation:

- Offering activities in which the resident can succeed, that are broken into simple steps, that involve small groups or are one-to-one activities such as using the computer, that are short and repetitive, and that are stopped if the resident becomes overwhelmed (reducing excessive noise such as from the television);

- Involving in familiar occupation-related activities. (A resident, if they desire, can do paid or volunteer work and the type of work would be included in the resident's plan of care, such as working outside the facility, sorting supplies, delivering resident mail, passing juice and snacks, refer to F169, Work);

- Involving in physical activities such as walking, exercise or dancing, games or projects requiring strategy, planning, and concentration, such as model building, and creative programs such as music, art, dance or physically resistive activities, such as kneading clay, hammering, scrubbing, sanding, using a punching bag, using stretch bands, or lifting weights; and

- Slow exercises (e.g., slow tapping, clapping or drumming); rocking or swinging motions (including a rocking chair).

For the resident who goes through others' belongings:

- Using normalizing activities such as stacking canned food onto shelves, folding laundry; offering sorting activities (e.g., sorting socks, ties or buttons); involving in organizing tasks (e.g., putting activity supplies away); providing rummage areas in plain sight, such as a dresser; and

- Using non-entry cues, such as "Do not disturb" signs or removable sashes, at the doors of other residents' rooms; providing locks to secure other resident's belongings (if requested).

For the resident who has withdrawn from previous activity interests/customary routines and isolates self in room/bed most of the day:

- Providing activities just before or after meal time and where the meal is being served (out of the room);

- Providing in-room volunteer visits, music or videos of choice;

- Encouraging volunteer-type work that begins in the room and needs to be completed outside of the room, or a small group activity in the resident's room, if the resident agrees; working on failure-free activities, such as simple structured crafts or other activity with a friend; having the resident assist another person;

- Inviting to special events with a trusted peer or family/friend;

- Engaging in activities that give the resident a sense of value (e.g., intergenerational activities that emphasize the resident's oral history knowledge);

- Inviting resident to participate on facility committees;

- Inviting the resident outdoors; and

- Involving in gross motor exercises (e.g., aerobics, light weight training) to increase energy and uplift mood.

For the resident who excessively seeks attention from staff and/or peers: Including in social programs, small group activities, service projects, with opportunities for leadership.

For the resident who lacks awareness of personal safety, such as putting foreign objects in her/his mouth or who is self-destructive and tries to harm self by cutting or hitting self, head banging, or causing other injuries to self:

- Observing closely during activities, taking precautions with materials (e.g., avoiding sharp objects and small items that can be put into the mouth);

- Involving in smaller groups or one-to-one activities that use the hands (e.g., folding towels, putting together PVC tubing);

- Focusing attention on activities that are emotionally soothing, such as listening to music or talking about personal strengths and skills, followed by participation in related activities; and

- Focusing attention on physical activities, such as exercise.

For the resident who has delusional and hallucinatory behavior that is stressful to her/him:

- Focusing the resident on activities that decrease stress and increase awareness of actual surroundings, such as familiar activities and physical activities; offering verbal reassurance, especially in terms of keeping the resident safe; and acknowledging that the resident's experience is real to her/him.

The outcome for the resident, the decrease or elimination of the behavior, either validates the activity intervention or suggests the need for a new approach.

[**Editor's Note:** See page 388 for endnotes pertaining to this section.]

INVESTIGATIVE PROTOCOL

ACTIVITIES

Objective

To determine if the facility has provided an ongoing program of activities designed to accommodate the individual resident's interests and help enhance her/his physical, mental and psychosocial well-being, according to her/his comprehensive resident assessment.

Use

Use this procedure for each sampled resident to determine through interview, observation and record review whether the facility is in compliance with the regulation.

Procedures

Briefly review the comprehensive assessment and interdisciplinary care plan to guide observations to be made.

1. Observations

Observe during various shifts in order to determine if staff are consistently implementing those portions of the comprehensive plan of care related to activities. Determine if staff take into account the resident's food preferences and restrictions for activities that involve food, and provide ADL assistance and adaptive equipment as needed during activities programs. For a resident with personal assistive devices such as glasses or hearing aides, determine if these devices are in place, glasses are clean, and assistive devices are functional.

For a resident whose care plan includes group activities, observe if staff inform the resident of the activities program schedule and provide timely transportation, if needed, for the resident to attend in-facility activities and help the resident access transportation to out-of-facility and community activities.

Determine whether the facility provides activities that are compatible with the resident's known interests, needs, abilities and preferences. If the resident is in group activity programs, note if the resident is making attempts to leave, or is expressing displeasure with, or sleeping through, an activity program. If so, determine if staff attempted to identify the reason the resident is attempting to leave, and if they addressed the resident's needs. Determine whether the group activity has been adapted for the resident as needed and whether it is "person appropriate."

NOTE: If you observe an activity that you believe would be age inappropriate for most residents, investigate further to determine the reason the resident and staff selected this activity. The National Alzheimer's Association has changed from endorsing the idea of "age-appropriate" activities to promoting "person-appropriate" activities. In general, surveyors should not expect to see the facility providing dolls or stuffed animals for most residents, but some residents are attached to these items and should be able to continue having them available if they prefer.

Regarding group activities in common areas, determine if the activities are occurring in rooms that have sufficient space, light, ventilation, equipment and supplies. Sufficient space includes enough space for residents to participate in the activity and space for a resident to enter and leave the room without having to move several other residents. Determine if the room is sufficiently free of extraneous noise, such as environmental noises from mechanical equipment and staff interruptions.

For a resident who is involved in individual activities in her/his room, observe if staff have provided needed assistance, equipment and supplies. Observe if the room has sufficient light and space for the resident to complete the activity.

2. Interviews

Resident/Representative Interview. Interview the resident, family or resident representative as appropriate to identify their involvement in care plan development, defining the approaches and goals that reflect the resident's preferences and choices. Determine:

- What assistance, if any, the facility should be providing to facilitate participation in activities of choice and whether or not the assistance is being provided;

- Whether the resident is participating in chosen activities on a regular basis, and if not, why not;

- Whether the resident is notified of activities opportunities and is offered transportation assistance as needed to the activity location within the facility or access to transportation, where available and feasible, to outside activities;

- Whether the facility tried, to the extent possible, to accommodate the resident's choices regarding her/his schedule, so that service provision (for example, bathing and therapy services) does not routinely conflict with desired activities;

- Whether planned activity programs usually occur as scheduled (instead of being cancelled repeatedly); and

- Whether the resident desires activities that the facility does not provide.

If the resident has expressed any concerns, determine if the resident has discussed these with staff and, if so, what was the staff's response.

Activity Staff Interview

Interview activities staff as necessary to determine:

- The resident's program of activities and related goals;

- What assistance/adaptations they provide in group activities according to the resident's care plan;

- How regularly the resident participates; if not participating, what is the reason(s);

- How they assure the resident is informed of, and transported to, group activities of choice;

- How special dietary needs and restrictions are handled during activities involving food;

- What assistance they provide if the resident participates in any individual (non-group) activities; and

- How they assure the resident has sufficient supplies, lighting, and space for individual activities.

CNA Interview

Interview CNAs as necessary to determine what assistance, if needed, the CNA provides to help the resident participate in desired group and individual activities, specifically:

- Their role in ensuring the resident is out of bed, dressed, and ready to participate in chosen group activities, and in providing transportation if needed;

- Their role in providing any needed ADL assistance to the resident while she/he is participating in group activities;

- Their role in helping the resident to participate in individual activities (if the resident's plan includes these), for example, setup of equipment/supplies, positioning assistance, providing enough lighting and space; and

- How activities are provided for the resident at times when activities staff are not available to provide care planned activities.

Social Services Staff Interview

Interview the social services staff member as necessary to determine how they help facilitate resident participation in desired activities; specifically, how the social services staff member:

- Addresses the resident's psychosocial needs that impact on the resident's ability to participate in desired activities;

- Obtains equipment and/or supplies that the resident needs in order to participate in desired activities (for example, obtaining audio books, helping the resident replace inadequate glasses or a hearing aid); and

- Helps the resident access his/her funds in order to participate in desired activities that require money, such as attending concerts, plays, or restaurant dining events.

Nurse Interview

Interview a nurse who supervises CNAs who work with the resident to determine how nursing staff:

- Assist the resident in participating in activities of choice by:

  o Coordinating schedules for ADLs, medications, and therapies, to the extent possible, to maximize the resident's ability to participate;

  o Making nursing staff available to assist with activities in and out of the facility;

- If the resident is refusing to participate in activities, how they try to identify and address the reasons; and

- Coordinate the resident's activities participation when activities staff are not available to provide care planned activities.

3. Record Review

Assessment

Review the RAI, activity documentation/notes, social history, discharge information from a previous setting, and other interdisciplinary documentation that may contain information regarding the resident's activity interests, preferences and needed adaptations.

Compare information obtained by observation of the resident and interviews with staff and the resident/responsible party (as possible), to the information in the resident's record, to help determine if the assessment accurately and comprehensively reflects the resident's status. Determine whether staff have identified:

- Longstanding interests and customary routine, and how the resident's current physical, mental, and psychosocial health status affects her/his choice of activities and her/his ability to participate;

- Specific information about how the resident prefers to participate in activities of interest (for example, if music is an interest, what kinds of music; does the resident play an instrument; does the resident have access to music to which she/he likes to listen; and can the resident participate independently, such as inserting a CD into a player);

- Any significant changes in activity patterns before or after admission;

- The resident's current needs for special adaptations in order to participate in desired activities (e.g., auditory enhancement or equipment to help compensate for physical difficulties such as use of only one hand);

- The resident's needs, if any, for time-limited participation, such as a short attention span or an illness that permits only limited time out of bed;

- The resident's desired daily routine and availability for activities; and

- The resident's choices for group, one-to-one, and self-directed activities.

Comprehensive Care Planning

Review the comprehensive care plan to determine if that portion of the plan related to activities is based upon the goals, interests, and preferences of the resident and reflects the comprehensive assessment. Determine if the resident's care plan:

- Includes participation of the resident (if able) or the resident's representative;

- Considers a continuation of life roles, consistent with resident preferences and functional capacity;

- Encourages and supports the development of new interests, hobbies, and skills;

- Identifies activities in the community, if appropriate;

- Includes needed adaptations that address resident conditions and issues affecting activities participation; and

- Identifies how the facility will provide activities to help the resident reach the goal(s) and who is responsible for implementation (e.g., activity staff, CNAs, dietary staff).

If care plan concerns are noted, interview staff responsible for care planning regarding the rationale for the current plan of care.

Care Plan Revision

Determine if the staff have evaluated the effectiveness of the care plan related to activities and made revisions, if necessary, based upon the following:

- Changes in the resident's abilities, interests, or health;

- A determination that some aspects of the current care plan were unsuccessful (e.g., goals were not being met);

- The resident refuses, resists, or complains about some chosen activities;

- Changes in time of year have made some activities no longer possible (e.g., gardening outside in winter) and other activities have become available; and

- New activity offerings have been added to the facility's available activity choices.

For the resident who refused some or all activities, determine if the facility worked with the resident (or representative, as appropriate) to identify and address underlying reasons and offer alternatives.

DETERMINATION OF COMPLIANCE (Task 6, Appendix P)

Synopsis of Regulation (F248)

This requirement stipulates that the facility's program of activities should accommodate the interests and well-being of each resident. In order to fulfill this requirement, it is necessary for the facility to gain awareness of each resident's activity preferences as well as any current limitations that require adaptation in order to accommodate these preferences.

Criteria for Compliance

The facility is in compliance with this requirement if they:

- Recognized and assessed for preferences, choices, specific conditions, causes and/or problems, needs and behaviors;

- Defined and implemented activities in accordance with resident needs and goals;

- Monitored and evaluated the resident's response; and

- Revised the approaches as appropriate.

If not, cite at F248.

Noncompliance for Tag F248

After completing the Investigative Protocol, analyze the information gained in order to determine whether noncompliance with the regulation exists. Activities (F248) is an outcome-oriented requirement in that compliance is determined separately for each resident sampled. The survey team's review of the facility's activities program is conducted through a review of the individualization of activities to meet each resident's needs and preferences. For each sampled resident for whom activities participation was reviewed, the facility is in compliance if they have provided activities that are individualized to that resident's needs and preferences, and they have provided necessary adaptations to facilitate the resident's participation. Non compliance with F248 may look like, but is not limited to the following:

- The facility does not have an activity program and does not offer any activities to the resident;

- A resident with special needs does not receive adaptations needed to participate in individualized activities;

- Planned activities were not conducted or designed to meet the resident's care plan;

Potential Tags for Additional Investigation

During the investigation of the provision of care and services related to activities, the surveyor may have identified concerns with related outcome, process and/or structure requirements. The surveyor is cautioned to investigate these related requirements before determining whether noncompliance may be present. Some examples of requirements that should be considered include the following (not all inclusive):

- 42 CFR 483.10(e), F164, Privacy and Confidentiality

  o Determine if the facility has accommodated the resident's need for privacy for visiting with family, friends, and others, as desired by the resident.

- 42 CFR 483.10(j)(1) and (2), F172, Access and Visitation Rights

  o Determine if the facility has accommodated the resident's family and/or other visitors (as approved by the resident) to be present with the resident as much as desired, even round-the-clock.

- 42 CFR 483.15(b), F242, Self-Determination and Participation

  o Determine if the facility has provided the resident with choices about aspects of her/his life in the facility that are significant to the resident.

- 42 CFR 483.15(e)(1), F246, Accommodation of Needs

  o Determine if the facility has provided reasonable accommodation to the resident's physical environment (room, bathroom, furniture, etc.) to accommodate the resident's individual needs in relation to the pursuit of individual activities, if any.

- 42 CFR 483.15(f)(2), F249, Qualifications of the Activities Director

  o Determine if a qualified activities director is directing the activities program.

- 42 CFR 483.15(g)(1), F250, Social Services

  o Determine if the facility is providing medically-related social services related to assisting with obtaining supplies/equipment for individual activities (if any), and assisting in meeting the resident's psychosocial needs related to activity choices.

- 42 CFR 483.20(b)(1), F272, Comprehensive Assessment

  o Determine if the facility assessed the resident's activity needs, preferences, and interests specifically enough so that an individualized care plan could be developed.

- 42 CFR 483.20(k)(1), F279, Comprehensive Care Plan

  o Determine if the facility developed specific and individualized activities goals and approaches as part of the comprehensive care plan, unless the resident is independent in providing for her/his activities without facility intervention.

- 42 CFR 483.20(k)(2), F280, Care Plan Revision

  o Determine whether the facility revised the plan of care as needed with input of the resident (or representative, as appropriate).

- 42 CFR 483.30(a), F353, Sufficient Staff

  o Determine if the facility had qualified staff in sufficient numbers to assure the resident was provided activities based upon the comprehensive assessment and care plan.

- 42 CFR 483.70(g), F464, Dining and Activities Rooms

  o Determine if the facility has provided sufficient space to accommodate the activities and the needs of participating residents and that space is well lighted, ventilated, and adequately furnished.

- 42 CFR 483.75(g), F499, Staff Qualifications

  o Determine if the facility has employed sufficient qualified professional staff to assess residents and to develop and implement the activities approaches of their comprehensive care plans.

V. DEFICIENCY CATEGORIZATION (Part V*, Appendix P) *[**Editor's Note:** The part number cited is incorrect. The correct part number is IV.]

Deficiencies at F248 are most likely to have psychosocial outcomes. The survey team should compare their findings to the various levels of severity on the Psychosocial Outcome Severity Guide at Appendix P, Part V*. *[**Editor's Note:** The part number cited is incorrect. The correct part number is IV.]

F249

§483.15(f)(2) The activities program must be directed by a qualified professional who—

  (i) Is a qualified therapeutic recreation specialist or an activities professional who--

    (A) Is licensed or registered, if applicable, by the State in which practicing; and

    (B) Is eligible for certification as a therapeutic recreation specialist or as an activities professional by a recognized accrediting body on or after October 1, 1990; or

  (ii) Has 2 years of experience in a social or recreational program within the last 5 years, 1 of which was full-time in a patient activities program in a health care setting; or

  (iii) Is a qualified occupational therapist or occupational therapy assistant; or

  (iv) Has completed a training course approved by the State.

INTENT (F249) §483.15(f)(2) Activities Director

The intent of this regulation is to ensure that the activities program is directed by a qualified professional.

DEFINITIONS

"Recognized accrediting body" refers to those organizations that certify, register, or license therapeutic recreation specialists, activity professionals, or occupational therapists.

ACTIVITIES DIRECTOR RESPONSIBILITIES

An activity director is responsible for directing the development, implementation, supervision and ongoing evaluation of the activities program. This includes the completion and/or directing/delegating the completion of the activities component of the comprehensive assessment; and contributing to and/or directing/delegating the contribution to the comprehensive care plan goals and approaches that are individualized to match the skills, abilities, and interests/preferences of each resident.

Directing the activity program includes scheduling of activities, both individual and groups, implementing and/or delegating the implementation of the programs, monitoring the response and/or reviewing/evaluating the response to the programs to determine if the activities meet the assessed needs of the resident, and making revisions as necessary.

NOTE: Review the qualifications of the activities director if there are concerns with the facility's compliance with the activities requirement at §483.15(f)(1), F248, or if there are concerns with the direction of the activity programs.

A person is a qualified professional under this regulatory tag if they meet any one of the qualifications listed under 483.15(f)(2).

DETERMINATION OF COMPLIANCE (Task 6, Appendix P)

Synopsis of Regulation (F249)

This requirement stipulates that the facility's program of activities be directed by a qualified professional.

Criteria for Compliance

The facility is in compliance with this requirement if they:

- Have employed a qualified professional to provide direction in the development and implementation of activities in accordance with resident needs and goals, and the director:

    o   Has completed or delegated the completion of the activities component of the comprehensive assessment;

    o   Contributed or directed the contribution to the comprehensive care plan of activity goals and approaches that are individualized to match the skills, abilities, and interests/preferences of each resident;

    o   Has monitored and evaluated the resident's response to activities and revised the approaches as appropriate; and

    o   Has developed, implemented, supervised and evaluated the activities program.

If not, cite at F249.

Noncompliance for F249

Tag F249 is a tag that is absolute, which means the facility must have a qualified activities professional to direct the provision of activities to the residents. Thus, it is cited if the facility is non-compliant with the regulation, whether or not there have been any negative outcomes to residents.

Noncompliance for F249 may include (but is not limited to) one or more of the following, including:

- Lack of a qualified activity director; or

- Lack of providing direction for the provision of an activity program;

V. DEFICIENCY CATEGORIZATION (Part V^{*}, Appendix P) *[**Editor's Note:** The part number cited is incorrect. The correct part number is IV.]

Once the team has completed its investigation, reviewed the regulatory requirements, and determined that noncompliance exists, the team must determine the severity of each deficiency, based on the resultant effect or potential for harm to the resident. The key elements for severity determination for F249 are as follows:

1. Presence of harm/negative outcome(s) or potential for negative outcomes due to a lack of an activities director or failure of the director to oversee, implement and/or provide activities programming.

- Lack of the activity director's involvement in coordinating/directing activities; or

- Lack of a qualified activity director.

2. Degree of harm (actual or potential) related to the noncompliance.

   Identify how the facility practices caused, resulted in, allowed or contributed to the actual or potential for harm:

   - If harm has occurred, determine level of harm; and

   - If harm has not yet occurred, determine the potential for discomfort to occur to the resident.

3. The immediacy of correction required.

   Determine whether the noncompliance requires immediate correction in order to prevent serious injury, harm, impairment, or death to one or more residents.

Severity Level 4 Considerations: Immediate Jeopardy to Resident Health or Safety

Immediate jeopardy is not likely to be issued as it is unlikely that noncompliance with F249 could place a resident or residents into a situation with potential to sustain serious harm, injury or death.

Severity Level 3 Considerations: Actual Harm that is not Immediate Jeopardy

Level 3 indicates noncompliance that results in actual harm, and may include, but is not limited to the resident's inability to maintain and/or reach his/her highest practicable well-being. In order to cite actual harm at this tag, the surveyor must be able to identify a relationship between noncompliance cited at Tag F248 (Activities) and failure of the provision and/or direction of the activity program by the activity director. For Severity Level 3, both of the following must be present:

1. Findings of noncompliance at Severity Level 3 at Tag F248; and

2. There is no activity director; or the facility failed to assure the activity director was responsible for directing the activity program in the assessment, development, implementation and/or revision of an individualized activity program for an individual resident; and/or the activity director failed to assure that the facility's activity program was implemented.

NOTE: If Severity Level 3 (actual harm that is not immediate jeopardy) has been ruled out based upon the evidence, then evaluate as to whether Level 2 (no actual harm with the potential for more than minimal harm) exists.

Severity Level 2 Considerations: No Actual Harm with Potential for more than Minimal Harm that is not Immediate Jeopardy

Level 2 indicates noncompliance that results in a resident outcome of no more than minimal discomfort and/or has the potential to compromise the resident's ability to maintain or reach his or her highest practicable level of well being. The potential exists for greater harm to occur if interventions are not provided. In order to cite Level 2 at Tag F249, the surveyor must be able to identify a relationship between noncompliance cited at Level 2 at Tag F248 (Activities) and failure of the provision and/or direction of activity program by the activity director. For Severity Level 2 at Tag F249, both of the following must be present:

1. Findings of noncompliance at Severity Level 2 at Tag F248; and

2. There is no activity director; or the facility failed to involve the activity director in the assessment, development, implementation and/or revision of an individualized activity program for an individual resident; and/or the activity director failed to assure that the facility's activity program was implemented.

Severity Level 1 Considerations: No Actual Harm with Potential for Minimal Harm In order to cite Level 1, no actual harm with potential for minimal harm at this tag, the surveyor must be able to identify that:

There is no activity director and/or the activity director is not qualified, however:

- Tag F248 was not cited;

- The activity systems associated with the responsibilities of the activity director are in place;

- There has been a relatively short duration of time without an activity director; and

- The facility is actively seeking a qualified activity director.

§483.15(g) Social Services

F250

§483.15(g)(1) The facility must provide medically-related social services to attain or maintain the highest practicable physical, mental, and psychosocial well-being of each resident.

Intent §483.15(g)

To assure that sufficient and appropriate social service are provided to meet the resident's needs.

Interpretive Guidelines §483.15(g)(1)

Regardless of size, all facilities are required to provide for the medically related social services needs of each resident. This requirement specifies that facilities aggressively identify the need for medically-related social services, and pursue the provision of these services. It is not required that a qualified social worker necessarily provide all of these services. Rather, it is the responsibility of the facility to identify the medically-related social service needs of the resident and assure that the needs are met by the appropriate disciplines.

"Medically-related social services" means services provided by the facility's staff to assist residents in maintaining or improving their ability to manage their everyday physical, mental, and psychosocial needs. These services might include, for example:

- Making arrangements for obtaining needed adaptive equipment, clothing, and personal items;

- Maintaining contact with facility* (with resident's permission) to report on changes in health, current goals, discharge planning, and encouragement to participate in care planning; *[**Editor's Note**: The word "family" should be substituted for the word "facility."]

- Assisting staff to inform residents and those they designate about the resident's health status and health care choices and their ramifications;

- Making referrals and obtaining services from outside entities (e.g., talking books, absentee ballots, community wheelchair transportation);

- Assisting residents with financial and legal matters (e.g., applying for pensions, referrals to lawyers, referrals to funeral homes for preplanning arrangements);

- Discharge planning services (e.g., helping to place a resident on a waiting list for community congregate living, arranging intake for home care services for residents returning home, assisting with transfer arrangements to other facilities);

- Providing or arranging provision of needed counseling services;

- Through the assessment and care planning process, identifying and seeking ways to support residents' individual needs;

- Promoting actions by staff that maintain or enhance each resident's dignity in full recognition of each resident's individuality;

- Assisting residents to determine how they would like to make decisions about their health care, and whether or not they would like anyone else to be involved in those decisions;

- Finding options that most meet the physical and emotional needs of each resident;

- Providing alternatives to drug therapy or restraints by understanding and communicating to staff why residents act as they do, what they are attempting to communicate, and what needs the staff must meet;

- Meeting the needs of residents who are grieving; and

- Finding options which most meet their physical and emotional needs

Factors with a potentially negative effect on physical, mental, and psychosocial well being include an unmet need for:

- Dental /denture care;

- Podiatric care;

- Eye Care;

- Hearing services

- Equipment for mobility or assistive eating devices; and

- Need for home-like environment, control, dignity, privacy

Where needed services are not covered by the Medicaid State plan, nursing facilities are still required to attempt to obtain these services. For example, if a resident requires transportation services that are not covered under a Medicaid state plan, the facility is required to arrange these services. This could be achieved, for example, through obtaining volunteer assistance.

Types of conditions to which the facility should respond with social services by staff or referral include:

- Lack of an effective family/support system;

- Behavioral symptoms;

- If a resident with dementia strikes out at another resident, the facility should evaluate the resident's behavior. For example, a resident may be re-enacting an activity he or she used to perform at the same time everyday. If that resident senses that another is in the way of his re-enactment, the resident may strike out at the resident impeding his or her progress. The facility is responsible for the safety of any potential resident victims while it assesses the circumstances of the residents behavior);

- Presence of a chronic disabling medical or psychological condition (e.g., multiple sclerosis, chronic obstructive pulmonary disease, Alzheimer's disease, schizophrenia);

- Depression

- Chronic or acute pain;

- Difficulty with personal interaction and socialization skills;

- Presence of legal or financial problems

SOM, Appendix PP, Guidance to Surveyors

- Abuse of alcohol or other drugs;

- Inability to cope with loss of function;

- Need for emotional support;

- Changes in family relationships, living arrangements, and/or resident's condition or functioning; and

- A physical or chemical restraint.

- For residents with or who develop mental disorders as defined by the "Diagnostic and Statistical Manual for Mental Disorders (DSM-IV)," see §483.45, F406.

Probes §483.15(g)(1)

For residents selected for a comprehensive or focused review as appropriate:

- How do facility staff implement social services interventions to assist the resident in meeting treatment goals?

- How do staff responsible for social work monitor the resident's progress in improving physical, mental and psychosocial functioning? Has goal attainment been evaluated and the care plan changed accordingly?

- How does the care plan link goals to psychosocial functioning/well-being?

- Have the staff responsible for social work established and maintained relationships with the resident's family or legal representative?

- [NFs] What attempts does the facility make to access services for Medicaid recipients when those services are not covered by a Medicaid State Plan?

Look for evidence that social services interventions successfully address residents' needs and link social supports, physical care, and physical environment with residents' needs and individuality.

For sampled residents, review MDS, section H.

F251

§483.15(g)(2) and (3)

(2) A facility with more than 120 beds must employ a qualified social worker on a full-time basis.

(3) Qualifications of a social worker. A qualified social worker is an individual with-

(i) A bachelor's degree in social work or a bachelor's degree in a human services field including but not limited to sociology, special education, rehabilitation counseling, and psychology; and

(ii) One year of supervised social work experience in a health care setting working directly with individuals

Procedures §483.15(g)(2) and (3)

If there are problems with the provision of social services in a facility with over 120 beds, determine if a qualified social worker is employed on a full time basis. See also F250.

F252

(Rev. 48; Issued: 06-12-09; Effective/Implementation Date: 06-12-09)

§483.15(h) Environment

The facility must provide--

§483.15(h)(1) A safe, clean, comfortable and homelike environment, allowing the resident to use his or her personal belongings to the extent possible;

Interpretive Guidelines §483.15(h)(1)

For purposes of this requirement, "environment" refers to any environment in the facility that is frequented by residents, including (but not limited to) the residents' rooms, bathrooms, hallways, dining areas, lobby, outdoor patios, therapy areas and activity areas. A determination of "homelike" should include the resident's opinion of the living environment.

A "homelike environment" is one that de-emphasizes the institutional character of the setting, to the extent possible, and allows the resident to use those personal belongings that support a homelike environment. A personalized, homelike environment recognizes the individuality and autonomy of the resident, provides an opportunity for self-expression, and encourages links with the past and family members. The intent of the word "homelike" in this regulation is that the nursing home should provide an environment as close to that of the environment of a private home as possible. This concept of creating a home setting includes the elimination of institutional odors, and practices to the extent possible. Some good practices that serve to decrease the institutional character of the environment include the elimination of:

- Overhead paging and piped-in music throughout the building;

- Meal service in the dining room using trays (some residents may wish to eat certain meals in their rooms on trays);

- Institutional signage labeling work rooms/closets in areas visible to residents and the public;

- Medication carts (some innovative facilities store medications in locked areas in resident rooms);

- The widespread and long-term use of audible (to the resident) chair and bed alarms, instead of their limited use for selected residents for diagnostic purposes or according to their care planned needs. These devices can startle the resident and constrain the resident from normal repositioning movements, which can be problematic. For more information about the detriments of alarms in terms of their effects on residents and alternatives to the widespread use of alarms, see the 2007 CMS satellite broadcast training, "From Institutionalized to Individualized Care," Part 1, available through the National Technical Information Service and other sources such as the Pioneer Network;

- Mass purchased furniture, drapes and bedspreads that all look alike throughout the building (some innovators invite the placement of some residents' furniture in common areas); and

- Large, centrally located nursing/care team stations.

Many facilities cannot immediately make these types of changes, but it should be a goal for all facilities that have not yet made these types of changes to work toward them. A nursing facility is not considered non-compliant if it still has some of these institutional features, but the facility is expected to do all it can within fiscal constraints to provide an environment that enhances quality of life for residents, in accordance with resident preferences.

A "homelike" or homey environment is not achieved simply through enhancements to the physical environment. It concerns striving for person-centered care that emphasizes individualization, relationships and a psychosocial environment that welcomes each resident and makes her/him comfortable.

In a facility in which most residents come for a short-term stay, the "good practices" listed in this section are just as important as in a facility with a majority of long term care residents. A resident in the facility for a short-term stay would not typically move her/his bedroom furniture into the room, but may desire to bring a television, chair or other personal belongings to have while staying in the facility.

Although the regulatory language at this tag refers to "safe," "clean," "comfortable," and "homelike," for consistency, the following specific F-tags should be used for certain issues of safety and cleanliness:

- For issues of safety of the environment, presence of hazards and hazardous practices, use §483.25(h), Accidents, Tag F323;

- For issues of fire danger, use §483.70(a) Life Safety from Fire, Tag F454;

- For issues of cleanliness and maintenance of common living areas frequented by residents, use §483.15(h)(2), Housekeeping and Maintenance, Tag F254;

- For issues of cleanliness of areas of the facility used by staff only (e.g., break room, medication room, laundry, kitchen, etc.) or the public only (e.g., parking lot), use §483.70(h), Tag F465 Other Environmental Conditions; and

- Although this Tag can be used for issues of general comfortableness of the environment such as furniture, there are more specific Tags to use for the following issues:

  o For issues of uncomfortable lighting, use §483.15(h)(5), Tag F256 Adequate and Comfortable Lighting;

  o For issues of uncomfortable temperature, use §483.15(h)(6), Tag F257 Comfortable and Safe Temperature Levels; and

  o For issues of uncomfortable noise levels, use §483.15(h)(7), Tag F258 Comfortable Sound Levels.

Procedures §483.15(h)(1)

During interviews, ask residents and families whether they think the facility is striving to be as homelike as possible, and whether they have been invited to bring in desired personal property items (within space constraints). Observe bedrooms of sampled residents for personalization. By observing the residents' surroundings, what can the survey team learn about their everyday life and interests? Their life prior to residing in the facility? Observe for family photographs, books and magazines, bedspreads, knickknacks, mementos, and furniture that belong to the residents. For residents who have no relatives or friends, and have few assets, determine the extent to which the facility has assisted these residents to make their rooms homelike, if they so desire. If potential issues are discovered, ask responsible staff about their efforts to provide a homelike environment and to invite residents to bring in personal belongings.

NOTE: Many residents who are residing in the facility for a short-term stay may not wish to personalize their rooms nor bring in many belongings. If they express no issues regarding homelike environment or personal property during interviews, there is no need to conduct further investigations for those residents.

F253

§483.15(h)(2)

§483.15(h)(2) Housekeeping and maintenance services necessary to maintain a sanitary, orderly, and comfortable interior;

[This page intentionally left blank]

Intent §483.15(h)(2)

The intent of this requirement is to focus on the facility's responsibility to provide effective housekeeping and maintenance services.

Interpretive Guidelines §483.15(h)(2)

"Sanitary" includes, but is not limited to, preventing the spread of disease-causing organisms by keeping resident care equipment clean and properly stored. Resident care equipment includes toothbrushes, dentures, denture cups, glasses and water pitchers, emesis basins, hair brushes and combs, bed pans, urinals, feeding tubes, leg bags and catheter bags, pads and positioning devices.

For kitchen sanitation, see §483.70(h), Other Environmental Conditions.

For facility-wide sanitary practices affecting the quality of care, see §483.65, Infection Control.

"Orderly" is defined as an uncluttered physical environment that is neat and well-kept.

Procedures §483.15(h)(2)

Balance the resident's need for a homelike environment and the requirements of having a "sanitary" environment in a congregate living situation. For example, a resident may prefer a cluttered room, but does this clutter result in unsanitary or unsafe conditions?

Probes §483.15(h)(2)

Is resident care equipment sanitary?

Is the area orderly?

Is the area uncluttered and in good repair?

Can residents and staff function unimpeded?

F254

§483.15(h)(3)

§483.15(h)(3) Clean bed and bath linens that are in good condition;

Probes §483.15(h)(3)

Are bed linens clean and in good condition? Are there clean towels and wash cloths in good condition available for the resident?

F256

(Rev. 48; Issued: 06-12-09; Effective/Implementation Date: 06-12-09)

§483.15(h)(5) Environment

The facility must provide-

§483.15(h)(5) Adequate and comfortable lighting levels in all areas;

Interpretive Guidelines §483.15(h)(5)

"Adequate lighting" means levels of illumination suitable to tasks the resident chooses to perform or the facility staff must perform.

"Comfortable lighting" means lighting that minimizes glare and provides maximum resident control, where feasible, over the intensity, location, and direction of illumination so that visually impaired residents can maintain or enhance independent functioning.

As a person ages, their eyes usually change so that they require more light to see what they are doing and where they are going. An adequate lighting design has these features:

- Sufficient lighting with minimum glare in areas frequented by residents;

- Even light levels in common areas and hallways, avoiding patches of low light caused by too much space between light fixtures, within limits of building design constraints;

- Use of daylight as much as possible;

- Elimination of high levels of glare produced by shiny flooring and from unshielded window openings (no-shine floor waxes and light filtering curtains help to alleviate these sources of glare);

- Extra lighting, such as table and floor lamps to provide sufficient light to assist residents with tasks such as reading;

- Lighting for residents who need to find their way from bed to bathroom at night (e.g., red colored night lights preserve night vision); and

- Dimming switches in resident rooms (where possible and when desired by the resident) so that staff can tend to a resident at night with limited disturbances to them or a roommate. If dimming is not feasible, another option may be for staff to use flashlights/pen lights when they provide night care.

Some facilities may not be able to make some of these changes due to voltage or wiring issues. For more information about adequate lighting design for long term care facilities, a facility may consult the lighting guidance available from the Illuminating Engineering Society of North America, which provides authoritative minimum lighting guidance.

The following are additional visual enhancements a facility should consider making as fiscal constraints permit in order to make it easier for residents with impaired vision to see and use their environment:

- Use of contrasting color between flooring and baseboard to enable residents with impaired vision to determine the horizontal plane of the floor;

- Use of contrast painting of bathroom walls and/or contrasting colored toilet seats so that residents with impaired vision can distinguish the toilet fixture from the wall; and

- Use of dishware that contrasts with the table or tablecloth color to aid residents with impaired vision to see their food.

Procedures §483.15(h)(5)

Ask residents who receive resident interviews if they have sufficient lighting in all the areas they frequent in the facility that meets their needs, including (but not limited to):

- Available task lighting if this is desired;

- Elimination of excessive glare from windows and flooring;

- Wayfinding nighttime lighting for those residents who need it to find the bathroom); and

- Lights that can be dimmed, if desired, to eliminate being awakened by staff who are tending to their roommate.

Observe sampled residents throughout the survey and note if they are having difficulty reading or doing tasks due to insufficient lighting, or if they are wearing sunglasses or visors indoors due to glare, if they have difficulty seeing food on their plate, experiencing squinting or shading their eyes from glare or other signs that lighting does not meet their needs.

If these are observed, question the resident (if they are able to converse) as to how the lighting situation assists or hinders their pursuit of activities and independence. Discuss with staff these issues, their efforts to alleviate the problems, and any electrical issues in the building's design that prevent making some of these changes.

F257

§483.15(h)(6)

§483.15(h)(6) Comfortable and safe temperature levels. Facilities initially certified after October 1, 1990 must maintain a temperature range of 71 - 81° F; and

Procedures §483.15(h)(6)

"Comfortable and safe temperature levels" means that the ambient temperature should be in a relatively narrow range that minimizes residents' susceptibility to loss of body heat and risk of hypothermia or susceptibility to respiratory ailments and colds. Although there are no explicit temperatures standards for facilities certified on or before October 1, 1990, these facilities still must maintain safe and comfortable temperature levels.

For facilities certified after October 1, 1990, temperatures may exceed the upper range of 81° F for facilities in geographic areas of the country (primarily at the northernmost latitudes) where that temperature is exceeded only during rare, brief unseasonably hot weather. This interpretation would apply in cases where it does not adversely affect resident health and safety, and would enable facilities in areas of the country with relatively cold climates to avoid the expense of installing air conditioning equipment that would only be needed infrequently. Conversely, the temperatures may fall below 71° F for facilities in areas of the country where that temperature is exceeded only during brief episodes of unseasonably cold weather (minimum temperature must still be maintained at a sufficient level to minimize risk of hypothermia and susceptibility to loss of body heat, respiratory ailments and colds.)

[This page intentionally left blank]

Measure the air temperature above floor level in resident rooms, dining areas, and common areas. If the temperature is out of the 71-81 degree range, then ask staff what actions they take when residents complain of heat or cold, e.g., provide extra fluids during heat waves and extra blankets and sweaters in cold.

F258

§483.15(h)(7)

§483.15(h)(7) For the maintenance of comfortable sound levels.

Interpretive Guidelines §483.15(h)(7)

"Comfortable" sound levels do not interfere with resident's hearing and enhance privacy when privacy is desired, and encourage interaction when social participation is desired. Of particular concern to comfortable sound levels is the resident's control over unwanted noise.

Procedures §483.15(h)(7)

Determine if the sound levels are comfortable to residents. Do residents and staff have to raise their voices to communicate over background sounds? Are sound levels suitable for the activities occurring in that space during observation?

Consider whether residents have difficulty hearing or making themselves heard because of background sounds (e.g., overuse or excessive volume of intercom, shouting, loud TV, cleaning equipment). Consider if it is difficult for residents to concentrate because of distractions or background noises such as traffic, music, equipment, or staff behavior. Consider the comfort of sound levels based on the needs of the residents participating in a particular activity, e.g., the sound levels may have to be turned up for hard of hearing individuals watching TV or listening to the radio. Consider the effect of noise on the comfort of residents with dementia.

During resident reviews, ask residents if during evenings and at nighttime, sounds are at comfortable levels? (If yes) Have you told staff about it and how have they responded?

[This page intentionally left blank]

F271 – F287

§483.20 — Resident Assessment

[**Editor's Note:** §483.20 was moved by CMS in Transmittal 5, dated November 19, 2004. See Tag F272.]

F271

§483.20(a) Admission Orders

At the time each resident is admitted, the facility must have physician orders for the resident's immediate care.

Intent §483.20(a)

To ensure the resident receives necessary care and services.

Interpretive Guidelines §483.20(a)

"Physician orders for immediate care" are those written orders facility staff need to provide essential care to the resident, consistent with the resident's mental and physical status upon admission. These orders should, at a minimum, include dietary, drugs (if necessary) and routine care to maintain or improve the resident's functional abilities until staff can conduct a comprehensive assessment and develop an interdisciplinary care plan.

F272

§483.20 Resident Assessment

The facility must conduct initially and periodically a comprehensive, accurate, standardized reproducible assessment of each resident's functional capacity.

Intent §483.20

To provide the facility with ongoing assessment information necessary to develop a care plan, to provide the appropriate care and services for each resident, and to modify the care plan and care/services based on the resident's status. The facility is expected to use resident observation and communication as the primary source of information when completing the RAI. In addition to direct observation and communication with the resident, the facility should use a variety of other sources, including communication with licensed and non-licensed staff members on all shifts and may include discussions with the resident's physician, family members, or outside consultants and review of the resident's record.

§483.20(b) Comprehensive Assessments

§483.20(b)(1) Resident Assessment Instrument. A facility must make a comprehensive assessment of a resident's needs, using the RAI specified by the State. The assessment must include at least the following:

- (i) Indentification and demographic information.
- (ii) Customary routine.
- (iii) Cognitive patterns.
- (iv) Communication.
- (v) Vision.
- (vi) Mood and behavior patterns.
- (vii) Psychological well-being.
- (viii) Physical functioning and structural problems.
- (ix) Continence.

    (x)   **Disease diagnosis and health conditions.**
    (xi)   **Dental and nutritional status.**
    (xii)   **Skin Conditions.**
    (xiii)   **Activity pursuit.**
    (xiv)   **Medications.**
    (xv)   **Special treatments and procedures.**
    (xvi)   **Discharge potential.**
    (xvii) **Documentation of summary information regarding the additional assessment performed through the resident assessment protocols.**
    (xviii) **Documentation of participation in assessment.**

§483.20(b) Intent

To ensure that the RAI is used in conducting comprehensive assessments as part of an ongoing process through which the facility identifies the resident's functional capacity and health status.

§483.20(b) Guidelines

The information required in §483.20(b)(i-xvi) is incorporated into the MDS, which forms the core of each State's approved RAI. Additional assessment information is also gathered using triggered RAPs.

Each facility must use its State-specified RAI (which includes both the MDS and utilization guidelines which include the RAPs) to assess newly admitted residents, conduct an annual reassessment and assess those residents who experience a significant change in status. The facility is responsible for addressing all needs and strengths of residents regardless of whether the issue is included in the MDS or RAPs. The scope of the RAI does not limit the facility's responsibility to assess and address all care needed by the resident. Furthermore:

    (i)   **Identification and demographic information**

        "Identification and demographic information" corresponds to MDS v 2.0 sections AA, BB and A, and refers to information that uniquely identifies each resident and the facility in which he/she resides, date of entry into the facility and residential history.

    (ii)   **Customary routine**

        "Customary routine" corresponds to MDS v 2.0 section AC, and refers to information regarding the resident's usual community lifestyle and daily routine in the year prior to the date of entry to the nursing home.

    (iii)   **Cognitive patterns**

        "Cognitive patterns" (iii) corresponds to MDS v. 2.0 section B. "Cognitive patterns" is defined as the resident's ability to problem solve, decide, remember, and be aware of and respond to safety hazards.

    (iv)   **Communication**

        "Communication" (iv) corresponds to MDS v. 2.0 section C, and refers to the resident's ability to hear, understand others, make him or herself understood (with assistive devices if they are used).

    (v)   **Vision**

        "Vision" (v) corresponds to MDS v. 2.0 section D, and I.1.jj, kk, ll and mm, and refers to the resident's visual acuity, limitations and difficulties, and appliances used to enhance vision.

(vi) Mood and behavior patterns

"Mood and behavior patterns" (vi) corresponds to MDS v. 2.0 section E, and refers to the resident's patterns of mood and behavioral symptoms.

(vii) Psychosocial well-being

"Psychosocial well-being" (vii) corresponds to MDS v. 2.0 sections E1o and p, and F and refers to the resident's positive or negative feelings about him or herself or his/her social relationships.

(viii) Physical functioning and structural problems

"Physical functioning and structural problems" (viii) corresponds to MDS v. 2.0 section G, and refers to the resident's physical functional status, ability to perform activities of daily living, and the resident's need for staff assistance and assistive devices or equipment to maintain or improve functional abilities.

(ix) Continence

"Continence" (ix) corresponds to MDS v. 2.0, section H, and refers to the resident's patterns of bladder and bowel continence (control), pattern of elimination, and appliances used.

(x) Disease diagnosis and health conditions

"Disease diagnoses and health conditions" (x) corresponds to MDS v. 2.0, sections AB.9 and 10, I.1 and 2, and J.

(xi) Dental and nutritional status

"Dental and nutritional status" (xi) corresponds to MDS v. 2.0, sections K1 and L.

"Dental condition status" refers to the condition of the teeth, gums, and other structures of the oral cavity that may affect a resident's nutritional status, communication abilities, or quality of life. The assessment should include the need for, and use of, dentures or other dental appliances.

"Nutritional status" corresponds to MDS v. 2.0, section K2-6.

Nutritional status refers to weight, height, hematologic and biochemical assessments, clinical observations of nutrition, nutritional intake, resident's eating habits and preferences, dietary restrictions, supplements, and use of appliances.

(xii) Skin conditions

"Skin conditions" (xii) corresponds to MDS v. 2.0 sections M, G1a, G6a, H1a, H1b, and P4c, and refers to the resident's development, or risk of development of a pressure sore.

(xiii) Activity pursuit

"Activity pursuit" (xiii) corresponds to MDS v. 2.0 sections N and AC.

"Activity pursuit" refers to the resident's ability and desire to take part in activities which maintain or improve, physical, mental, and psychosocial well-being. Activity pursuits refer to any activity outside of activities of daily living (ADLs) which a person pursues in order to obtain a sense of well-being. Also, includes activities which provide benefits in self-esteem, pleasure, comfort, health education, creativity, success, and financial or emotional independence. The assessment should consider the resident's normal everyday routines and lifetime preferences.

(xiv) Medications

"Medications" (xiv) corresponds to MDS v. 2.0, section O, and section U, if completed.

"Medications" refers to all prescription and over-the-counter medications taken by the resident, including dosage, frequency of administration, and recognition of significant side effects that would be most likely to occur in the resident. This information need not appear in the assessment. However, it must be in the resident's clinical record and included in the care plan.

(xv) Special treatments and procedures

"Special treatments and procedures" (xv) corresponds to MDS v. 2.0 sections K5, M5, and P1, and section T, if completed.

"Special treatments and procedures" refers to treatments and procedures that are not part of basic services provided. For example, treatment for pressure sores, naso-gastric feedings, specialized rehabilitation services, respiratory care, or devices and restraints.

(xvi) Discharge potential

"Discharge potential" (xvi) corresponds to MDS v. 2.0 section Q.

"Discharge potential" refers to the facility's expectation of discharging the resident from the facility within The next 3 months.

(xvii) Documentation of summary information regarding the additional assessment performed through the resident assessment protocols

"Documentation of summary information (xvii) regarding the additional assessment performed through the resident assessment protocols (RAPs)" corresponds to MDS v. 2.0 section V, and refers to documentation concerning which RAPs have been triggered, documentation of assessment information in support of clinical decision making relevant to the RAP, documentation regarding where, in the clinical record, information related to the RAP can be found, and for each triggered RAP, whether the identified problem was included in the care plan.

(xviii) Documentation of participation in assessment

"Documentation of participation in the assessment" corresponds to MDS v. 2.0 section R, and refers to documentation of who participated in the assessment process. The assessment process must include direct observation and communication with the resident, as well as communication with licensed and nonlicensed direct care staff members on all shifts.

F273

§483.20(b)(2)

§483.20(b)(2) When required, a facility must conduct a comprehensive assessment of a resident as follows:

(i) Within 14 calendar days after admission, excluding readmissions in which there is no significant change in the resident's physical or mental condition. (For purposes of this section, "readmission" means a return to the facility following a temporary absence for hospitalization for therapeutic leave.)

Intent §483.20(b)(2)

To assess residents in a timely manner.

F274

§483.20(b)(2)(ii)

(ii) Within 14 days after the facility determines, or should have determined, that there has been a significant change in the resident's physical or mental condition. (For purpose of this section, a "significant change" means a major decline or improvement in the resident's status that will not normally resolve itself without further intervention by staff or by implementing standard disease-related clinical interventions, that has an impact on more than one area of the resident's health status, and requires interdisciplinary review or revision of the care plan, or both.)

§483.20(b)(2)(ii) Guidelines

The following are the criteria for significant changes:

A significant change reassessment is generally indicated if decline or improvement is consistently noted in 2 or more areas of decline or 2 or more areas of improvement:

Decline:

- Any decline in activities of daily living (ADL) physical functioning where a resident is newly coded as 3, 4 or 8 Extensive Assistance, Total Dependency, activity did not occur (note that even if coding in both columns A and B of an ADL category changes, this is considered 1 ADL change);

- Increase in the number of areas where Behavioral Symptoms are coded as "not easily altered" (e.g., an increase in the use of code 1's for E4B);

- Resident's decision-making changes from 0 or 1, to 2 or 3;

- Resident's incontinence pattern changes from 0 or 1 to 2, 3 or 4, or placement of an indwelling catheter;

- Emergence of sad or anxious mood as a problem that is not easily altered;

- Emergence of an unplanned weight loss problem (5% change in 30 days or 10% change in 180 days);

- Begin to use trunk restraint or a chair that prevents rising for a resident when it was not used before;

- Emergence of a condition/disease in which a resident is judged to be unstable;

- Emergence of a pressure ulcer at Stage II or higher, when no ulcers were previously present at Stage II or higher; or

- Overall deterioration of resident's condition; resident receives more support (e.g., in ADLs or decision making).

Improvement:

- Any improvement in ADL physical functioning where a resident is newly coded as 0, 1, or 2 when previously scored as a 3, 4, or 8;

- Decrease in the number of areas where Behavioral Symptoms or Sad or Anxious Mood are coded as "not easily altered";

- Resident's decision making changes from 2 or 3, to 0 or 1;

- Resident's incontinence pattern changes from 2, 3, or 4 to 0 or 1; or

- Overall improvement of resident's condition; resident receives fewer supports.

- If the resident experiences a significant change in status, the next annual assessment is not due until 366 days after the significant change reassessment has been completed.

F275

§483.20(b)(2)(iii)

(iii) Not less than once every 12 months.

Interpretive Guidelines §483.20(b)(2)(iii)

The annual resident assessment must be completed within 366 days after final completion of the most recent comprehensive resident assessment.

Probes §483.20(b)(2)

- Has each resident in the sample been comprehensively assessed using the State-specified RAI within the regulatory timeframes (i.e., within 14 days after admission, on significant change in status, and at least annually)?

- Has the facility identified, in a timely manner, those residents who have experienced a change?

- Has the facility reassessed residents using the State-specific RAI who had a significant change in status within 14 days after determining the change was significant.

- Has the facility gathered supplemental assessment information based on triggered RAPs prior to establishing the care plan?

- Does information in the RAI correspond with information obtained during observations of and interviews with the resident, facility staff and resident's family?

F276

§483.20(c) Quarterly Review Assessment

A facility must assess a resident using the quarterly review instrument specified by the State and approved by CMS not less frequently than once every 3 months.

Intent §483.20(c)

To assure that the resident's assessment is updated on at least a quarterly basis.

Interpretive Guidelines §483.20(c)

At least each quarter, the facility shall review each resident with respect to those MDS items specified under the State's quarterly review requirement. At a minimum, this would include all items contained in CMS' standard quarterly review form. A Quarterly review assessment must be completed within 92 days of the date at MDS Item R2b of the most recent, clinical assessment (AA8a=1,2,3,4,5 or 10). If the resident has experienced a significant change in status, the next quarterly review is due no later than 3 months after the significant change reassessment.

Probes §483.20(c)

Is the facility assessing and acting, no less than once every 3 months, on the results of resident's functional and cognitive status examinations?

Is the quarterly review of the resident's condition consistent with information in the progress notes, the plan of care and your resident observations and interviews?

F286

(Rev. 41; Issued: 04-10-09; Effective/Implementation Dates: 04-10-09)

§483.20(d) Use

A facility must maintain all resident assessments completed within the previous 15 months in the resident's active record.

Intent §483.20(d)

Facilities are required to maintain 15 months of assessment data in the resident's active clinical record.

Interpretive Guidelines §483.20(d)

The requirement to maintain 15 months of data in the resident's active clinical record applies regardless of form of storage to all MDS forms, RAP Summary forms, Quarterly Assessment forms, Face Sheet Information and Discharge and Reentry Tracking Forms and MDS Correction Request Forms (including signed attestation). MDS assessments must be kept in the resident's active clinical record for 15 months following the final completion date, tracking forms for discharge and reentry must be kept for 15 months following the date of the event, Correction Request Forms must be kept for 15 months following the final completion date of the MDS Correction Request form.

The information must be kept in a centralized location, accessible to all professional staff members (including consultants) who need to review the information in order to provide care to the resident.

After the 15-month period, Resident Assessment Instrument (RAI) information may be thinned from the clinical record and stored in the medical records department, provided that it is easily retrievable if requested by clinical staff, the State agency, or CMS.

[**Editor's Note:** Part of §483.20(d) was moved by CMS in Transmittal 5, dated November 19, 2004. See Tag F279.]

[**Editor's Note:** §483.20(e) was moved by CMS in Transmittal 5, dated November 19, 2004. See Tag F285.]

F287

§483.20(f) Automated Data Processing Requirement

§483.20(f)(1) Encoding Data. Within 7 days after a facility completes a resident's assessment, a facility must encode the following information for each resident in the facility:

(i)   Admission assessment.

(ii)   Annual assessment updates.

    (iii)   **Significant change in status assessments.**

    (iv)   **Quarterly review assessments.**

    (v)   **A subset of items upon a resident's transfer, reentry, discharge, and death.**

    (vi)   **Background (face-sheet) information, if there is no admission assessment.**

§483.20(f)(2) Transmitting data. Within 7 days after a facility completes a resident's assessment, a facility must be capable of transmitting to the State information for each resident contained in the MDS in a format that conforms to standard record layouts and data dictionaries, and that passes standardized edits defined by CMS and the State.

§483.20(f)(3) Monthly transmittal requirements. A facility must electronically transmit, at least monthly, encoded, accurate, complete MDS data to the State for all assessments conducted during the previous month, including the following:

    (i)   **Admission assessment.**

    (ii)   **Annual assessment.**

    (iii)   **Significant change in status assessment.**

    (iv)   **Significant correction of prior full assessment.**

    (v)   **Significant correction of prior quarterly assessment.**

    (vi)   **Quarterly review.**

    (vii)   **A subset of items upon a resident's transfer, reentry, discharge, and death.**

    (viii)   **Background (face-sheet) information, for an initial transmission of MDS data on a resident that does not have an admission assessment.**

§483.20(f)(4) Data format. The facility must transmit data in the format specified by CMS or, for a State which has an alternate RAI approved by CMS, in the format specified by the State and approved by CMS.

Intent §483.20(f)(1-4)

The intent is to enable a facility to better monitor a resident's decline and progress over time. Computer-aided data analysis facilitates a more efficient, comprehensive and sophisticated review of health data. The primary purpose of maintaining the assessment data is so a facility can monitor resident progress over time. The information should be readily available at all times.

Interpretive Guidelines §483.20(f)(1-4)

"Encoding" means entering MDS information into a computer.

"Transmitting data" refers to electronically sending encoded MDS information, from the facility to the State database, using a modem and communications software.

"Capable of transmitting" means that the facility has encoded and edited according to CMS specifications, the record accurately reflects the resident's overall clinical status as of the assessment reference date, and the record is ready for transmission.

"Passing standard edits" means that the encoded responses to MDS items are consistent and within range, in accordance with CMS specified standards. In general, inconsistent responses are either not plausible or ignore a skip pattern on the MDS. An example of inconsistency would be if one or more MDS items on a list were checked as present, and the "None of the Above" response was also checked for the same list. Out of range responses are invalid responses, such as using a response code of 2 for an MDS item for which the valid responses are zero or 1.

"Monthly Transmittal" means electronically transmitting to the State, an MDS record that passes CMS' standard edits, within 31 days of the final completion date of the record.

"Accurate" means that the encoded MDS data matches the MDS form in the clinical record. Also refer to guidance regarding accuracy at §483.20(g), and the information accurately reflects the resident's status as of the Assessment Reference Date at MDS Item A3a.

"Complete" means that all items required according to the record type, and in accordance with CMS' record specifications and State required edits are in effect at the time the record is completed.

In accordance with the final rule, facilities will be responsible to edit the encoded MDS data to ensure that it meets the standard edit specifications.

We encourage facilities to use software that has a programmed capability to automatically edit MDS records according to CMS' edit specifications.

For §483.20(f)(1)(v), the subset of items required upon a resident's transfer, discharge, and death are contained in the Discharge Tracking form and the items required for reentry are contained in the Reentry Tracking form. Refer to Appendix R for further information about the Discharge Tracking and Reentry Tracking forms.

All nursing homes must computerize MDS information. The facility must edit MDS information using standard CMS-specified edits, revise the information to conform to the edits and to be accurate, and be capable of transmitting that data to the State system within 7 days of:

- Completing a comprehensive assessment (the date at MDS item VB4);
- Completing an assessment that is not comprehensive (the date at MDS item R2b);
- A discharge event (the date at MDS item R4);
- A reentry event (the date at MDS item A4a); or
- Completing a correction request form (the date at MDS item AT6).

Submission must be according to State and Federal time frames. Therefore the facility must:

- Encode the MDS and RAP Summary (where applicable) in machine readable format;
- Edit the MDS and RAP Summary (where applicable) according to edits specified by CMS. Within the 7 day time period specified above for editing, the facility must revise any information on the encoded MDS and RAP Summary (if applicable) that does not pass CMS-specified edits, revise any otherwise inaccurate information, and make the information ready for submission. The MDS Vendor software used at the facility should have an automated editing process that alerts the user to entries in an MDS record that do not conform with the CMS-specified edits and that prompts the facility to complete revisions within the 7-day editing and revision period. After editing and revision, MDS information and RAP summary information (if applicable) must always accurately reflect the resident's overall clinical status as of the original Assessment Reference date for an assessment or the original event date for a discharge or reentry;

- Print the edited and revised MDS and RAP summary form (where applicable). Discharge or Reentry Tracking form or Correction Request form, and place it in the resident's record. The hard copy of the MDS record must match the record that the facility transmits to the State, and it must accurately reflect the resident's status as of the Assessment Reference date or event date. If a hard copy exists prior to data entry, the facility must correct the hard copy to reflect the changes associated with the editing and revision process.

Electronically submit MDS information to the State MDS database within 31 days of:

- The date the Care Planning Decision process was complete (the date at MDS Item VB4) for comprehensive assessments;

- The date the RN Coordinator certified that the MDS was complete (the date at MDS Item R2b) for assessments that are not comprehensive;

- The date of death or discharge (the date at MDS Item R4) for Discharge Tracking forms;

- The date of reentry (the date at MDS Item A4a) for Reentry Tracking forms; and

- The date of completion of a correction request (the date at MDS Item AT6)

For a discussion of the process that a facility should follow in the event an error is discovered in an MDS record after editing and revision but before it is transmitted to the State, refer to "Correction Policy for MDS Records" in the State Operations Manual, Appendix R, Part IV.

The facility must maintain RAI assessments and Discharge and Reentry Tracking forms, as well as correction information, including Correction Request forms as a part of the resident's clinical record. Whether or not the facility's system is entirely electronic, a hard copy of completed MDS forms, including the signature of the facility staff attesting to the accuracy and completion of the corrected record, must be maintained in the resident's clinical record.

A facility must complete and submit to the State a subset of items when the resident is discharged from the facility (discharge tracking form), or readmitted to the facility (reentry tracking form.

[**Editor's Note**: §483.20(f)(5) was moved by CMS in Transmittal 5, dated November 19, 2004. See Tag F516.]

F278

§483.20(g) Accuracy of Assessment

The assessment must accurately reflect the resident's status.

Intent §483.20(g)

To assure that each resident receives an accurate assessment by staff that are qualified to assess relevant care areas and knowledgeable about the resident's status, needs, strengths, and areas of decline.

Interpretive Guidelines §483.20(g)

"The accuracy of the assessment" means that the appropriate, qualified health professional correctly documents the resident's medical, functional, and psychosocial problems and identifies resident strengths to maintain or improve medical status, functional abilities, and psychosocial status. The initial comprehensive assessment provides baseline data for ongoing assessment of resident progress.

§483.20(h) Coordination

A registered nurse must conduct or coordinate each assessment with the appropriate participation of health professionals.

Intent §483.20(h)

The registered nurse will conduct and/or coordinate the assessment, as appropriate. Whether conducted or coordinated by the registered nurse, he or she is responsible for certifying that the assessment has been completed.

Interpretive Guidelines §483.20(h)

According to the Utilization Guidelines for each State's RAI, the physical, mental and psychosocial condition of the resident determines the appropriate level of involvement of physicians, nurses, rehabilitation therapists, activities professionals, medical social workers, dietitians, and other professionals, such as developmental disabilities specialists, in assessing the resident, and in correcting resident assessments. Involvement of other disciplines is dependent upon resident status and needs.

Probes §483.20(g)(h)

Have appropriate health professionals assessed the resident? For example, has the resident's nutritional status been assessed by someone who is knowledgeable in nutrition and capable of correctly assessing a resident?

If the resident's medical status, functional abilities, or psychosocial status declined and the decline was not clinically unavoidable, were the appropriate health professionals involved in assessing the resident?

Based on your total review of the resident, is each portion of the assessment accurate?

Are the appropriate certifications in place, including the RN Coordinator's certification of completion of an assessment or Correction Request form, and the certification of individual assessors of the accuracy and completion of the portion(s) of the assessment, tracking form or face sheet they completed or corrected. On an assessment or correction request, the RN Assessment Coordinator is responsible for certifying overall completion once all individual assessors have completed and signed their portion(s) of the MDS forms. When MDS forms are completed directly on the facility's computer, (e.g., no paper form has been manually completed), the RN Coordinator signs and dates the computer generated hard copy after reviewing it for completeness, including the signatures of all individual assessors. Backdating a completion date is not acceptable.

§483.20(i) Certification

(1)   **A registered nurse must sign and certify that the assessment is completed.**

(2)   **Each individual who completes a portion of the assessment must sign and certify the accuracy of that portion of the assessment.**

Interpretive Guidelines §483.20(i)

Whether the MDS forms are manually completed, or computer generated following data entry, each individual assessor is responsible for certifying the accuracy of responses on the forms relative to the resident's condition and discharge or reentry status. Manually completed forms are signed and dated by each individual assessor the day they complete their portion(s) of the MDS record. When MDS forms are completed directly on the facility's computer (e.g., no paper form has been manually completed), then each individual assessor signs and dates a computer generated hard copy, after they review it for accuracy of the portion(s) they completed. Backdating completion dates is not acceptable.

§483.20(j) Penalty for Falsification

(1)   **Under Medicare and Medicaid, an individual who willfully and knowingly--**

    (i)   **Certifies a material and false statement in a resident assessment is subject to a civil money penalty of not more than $1,000 for each assessment; or**

(ii) Causes another individual to certify a material and false statement in a resident assessment is subject to a civil money penalty or not more than $5,000 for each assessment.

(2) Clinical disagreement does not constitute a material and false statement.

Interpretive Guidelines §483.20(j)

MDS information serves as the clinical basis for care planning and delivery. With the introduction of additional uses of MDS information such as for payment rate setting and quality monitoring, MDS information as it is reported impacts a nursing home's payment rate and standing in terms of the quality monitoring process. A pattern within a nursing home of clinical documentation or of MDS assessment or reporting practices that result in higher RUG scores, untriggering RAP(s), or unflagging QI(s), where the information does not accurately reflect the resident's status, may be indicative of payment fraud or avoidance of the quality monitoring process. Such practices may include but are not limited to a pattern or high prevalence of the following:

- Submitting MDS Assessments (including any reason(s) for assessment, routine or non-routine), Discharge or Reentry Tracking forms, where the information does not accurately reflect the resident's status as of the Assessment Reference date, or the Discharge or Reentry date, as applicable;

- Submitting correction(s) to information in the State MDS database where the corrected information does not accurately reflect the resident's status as of the original Assessment Reference date, or the original Discharge or Reentry date, as applicable, or where the record it claims to correct does not appear to have been in error;

- Submitting Significant Correction Assessments where the assessment it claims to correct does not appear to have been in error;

- Submitting Significant Change in Status Assessments where the criteria for significant change in the resident's status do not appear to be met;

- Delaying or withholding MDS Assessments (including any reason(s) for assessment, routine or non-routine), Discharge or Reentry Tracking information, or correction(s) to information in the State MDS database.

When such patterns or practices are noticed, they should be reported by the State Agency to the proper authority.

F279

§483.20(d) (A facility must...) use the results of the assessment to develop, review and revise the resident's comprehensive plan of care.

§483.20(k) Comprehensive Care Plans

(1) The facility must develop a comprehensive care plan for each resident that includes measurable objectives and timetables to meet a resident's medical, nursing, and mental and psychosocial needs that are identified in the comprehensive assessment. The care plan must describe the following:

(i) The services that are to be furnished to attain or maintain the resident's highest practicable physical, mental, and psychosocial well-being as required under §483.25; and

(ii) Any services that would otherwise be required under §483.25 but are not provided due to the resident's exercise of rights under §483.10, including the right to refuse treatment under §483.10(b)(4).

Interpretive Guidelines §483.20(k)

An interdisciplinary team, in conjunction with the resident, resident's family, surrogate, or representative, as appropriate, should develop quantifiable objectives for the highest level of functioning the resident may be expected to attain, based on the comprehensive assessment. The interdisciplinary team should show evidence in the RAP summary or clinical record of the following:

- The resident's status in triggered RAP areas;

- The facility's rationale for deciding whether to proceed with care planning; and

- Evidence that the facility considered the development of care planning interventions for all RAPs triggered by the MDS.

The care plan must reflect intermediate steps for each outcome objective if identification of those steps will enhance the resident's ability to meet his/her objectives. Facility staff will use these objectives to monitor resident progress. Facilities may, for some residents, need to prioritize their care plan interventions. This should be noted in the clinical record or on the plan or care.

The requirements reflect the facility's responsibilities to provide necessary care and services to attain or maintain the highest practicable physical, mental and psychosocial well-being, in accordance with the comprehensive assessment and plan of care. However, in some cases, a resident may wish to refuse certain services or treatments that professional staff believe may be indicated to assist the resident in reaching his or her highest practicable level of well-being. Desires of the resident should be documented in the clinical record (see guidelines at §483.10(b)(4) for additional guidance concerning refusal of treatment).

Probes §483.20(k)(1)

Does the care plan address the needs, strengths and preferences identified in the comprehensive resident assessment?

Is the care plan oriented toward preventing avoidable declines in functioning or functional levels? How does the care plan attempt to manage risk factors? Does the care plan build on resident strengths?

Does the care plan reflect standards of current professional practice?

Do treatment objectives have measurable outcomes?

Corroborate information regarding the resident's goals and wishes for treatment in the plan of care by interviewing residents, especially those identified as refusing treatment.

Determine whether the facility has provided adequate information to the resident so that the resident was able to make an informed choice regarding treatment.

If the resident has refused treatment, does the care plan reflect the facility's efforts to find alternative means to address the problem?

For implementation of care plan, see §483.20(k)(3).

F280

§483.10(d)(3) – The resident has the right to -- unless adjudged incompetent or otherwise found to be incapacitated under the laws of the State, participate in planning care and treatment or changes in care and treatment.

Interpretive Guidelines §483.10(d)(3)

"**Participates in planning care and treatment**" means that the resident is afforded the opportunity to select from alternative treatments. This applies both to initial decisions about care and treatment and to decisions about changes in care and treatment. The resident's right to participate in care planning and to refuse treatment are covered in §§483.20(d)(2)* and 483.10(b)(4). *[**Editor's Note**: The reference cited should be §483.20(k)(2).]

A resident whose ability to make decisions about care and treatment is impaired, or a resident who has been formally declared incompetent by a court, should, to the extent practicable, be kept informed and be consulted on personal preferences.

Whenever there appears to be a conflict between a resident's right and the resident's health or safety, determine if the facility attempted to accommodate both the exercise of the resident's rights and the resident's health, including exploration of care alternatives through a thorough care planning process in which the resident may participate.

Procedures §483.10(d)(3)

Look for evidence that the resident was afforded the right to participate in care planning or was consulted about care and treatment changes (e.g., ask residents or their representatives during interviews).

§483.20(k)(2)

§483.20(k)(2) A comprehensive care plan must be--

(i)   **Developed within 7 days after the completion of the comprehensive assessment;**

(ii)   **Prepared by an interdisciplinary team, that includes the attending physician, a registered nurse with responsibility for the resident, and other appropriate staff in disciplines as determined by the resident's needs, and, to the extent practicable, the participation of the resident, the resident's family or the resident's legal representative; and**

(iii) **Periodically reviewed and revised by a team of qualified persons after each assessment.**

Interpretive Guidelines §483.20(k)(2)

As used in this requirement, "Interdisciplinary" means that professional disciplines, as appropriate, will work together to provide the greatest benefit to the resident. It does not mean that every goal must have an interdisciplinary approach. The mechanics of how the interdisciplinary team meets its responsibilities in developing an interdisciplinary care plan (e.g., a face-to-face meeting, teleconference, written communication) is at the discretion of the facility.

The physician must participate as part of the interdisciplinary team, and may arrange with the facility for alternative methods, other than attendance at care planning conferences, of providing his/her input, such as one-on-one discussions and conference calls.

The resident's right to participate in choosing treatment options, decisions in care planning and the right to refuse treatment are addressed at §483.20(k)(2)(ii) and 483.10(b)(4), respectively, and include the right to accept or refuse treatment. The facility has a responsibility to assist residents to participate, e.g., helping residents, and families, legal surrogates or representatives understand the assessment and care planning process; when feasible, holding care planning meetings at the time of day when a resident is functioning best; planning enough time for information exchange and decision making; encouraging a resident's advocate to attend (e.g. family member, friend) if desired by a resident.

The resident has the right to refuse specific treatments and to select among treatment options before the care plan is instituted. (See §483.20(k)(2)(ii) and 483.10(b)(4).) The facility should encourage residents, legal surrogates and representatives to participate in care planning, including attending care planning conferences if they so desire.

While Federal regulations affirm the resident's right to participate in care planning and to refuse treatment, the regulations do not create the right for a resident, legal surrogate or representative to demand that the facility use specific medical intervention or treatment that the facility deems inappropriate. Statutory requirements hold the facility ultimately accountable for the resident's care and safety, including clinical decisions.

Probes §483.20(k)(2)

1. Was interdisciplinary expertise utilized to develop a plan to improve the resident's functional abilities?

   a. For example, did an occupational therapist design needed adaptive equipment or a speech therapist provide techniques to improve swallowing ability?

   b. Do the dietitian and speech therapist determine, for example, the optimum textures and consistency for the resident's food that provide both a nutritionally adequate diet and effectively use oropharyngeal capabilities of the resident?

   c. Is there evidence of physician involvement in development of the care plan (e.g., presence at care plan meetings, conversations with team members concerning the care plan, conference calls)?

2. In what ways do staff involve residents and families, surrogates, and/or representatives in care planning?

3. Do staff make an effort to schedule care plan meetings at the best time of the day for residents and their families?

4. Ask the ombudsman if he/she has been involved in a care planning meeting as a resident advocate. If yes, ask how the process worked.

5. Do facility staff attempt to make the process understandable to the resident/family?

6. Ask residents whether they have brought questions or concerns about their care to the attention of facility's staff. If so, what happened as a result?

Interpretive Guidelines §483.20(k)(2)(iii)

See §483.75(g)(2)(iii)* for "Qualified Person," *[**Editor's Note**: The reference cited should be §483.75(g)(2).]

Probes §483.20(k)(2)(iii)

Is the care plan evaluated and revised as the resident's status changes?

F281

§483.20(k)(3)

(3) The services provided or arranged by the facility must--

(i) Meet professional standards of quality and;

Intent §483.20(k)(3)(i)

The intent of this regulation is to assure that services being provided meet professional standards of quality (in accordance with the definition provided below) and are provided by appropriate qualified persons (e.g., licensed, certified).

Interpretive Guidelines §483.20(k)(3)(i)

"Professional standards of quality" means services that are provided according to accepted standards of clinical practice. Standards may apply to care provided by a particular clinical discipline or in a specific clinical situation or setting. Standards regarding quality care practices may be published by a professional organization, licensing board, accreditation body or other regulatory agency. Recommended practices to achieve desired resident outcomes may also be found in clinical literature. Possible reference sources for standards of practice include:

- Current manuals or textbooks on nursing, social work, physical therapy, etc.

- Standards published by professional organizations such as the American Dietetic Association, American Medical Association, American Medical Directors Association, American Nurses Association, National Association of Activity Professionals, National Association of Social Work, etc.

- Clinical practice guidelines published by the Agency of Health Care Policy and Research.

- Current professional journal articles.

If a negative resident outcome is determined to be related to the facility's failure to meet professional standards, and the team determines a deficiency has occurred, it should be cited under the appropriate quality of care or other relevant requirement.

Probes §483.20(k)(3)

Question only those practices which have a negative outcome or have a potential negative outcome. Ask the facility to produce references upon which the practice is based.

- Do nurses notify physicians, as appropriate, and show evidence of discussions of acute medical problems?

- Are residents with acute conditions who require intensive monitoring and hospital-level treatments that the facility is unable to provide, promptly hospitalized?

- Are there errors in the techniques of medication administration? (Cite actual medication errors at §483.25(m).)

- Is there evidence of assessment and care planning sufficient to meet the needs of newly admitted residents, prior to completion of the first comprehensive assessment and comprehensive care plan?

- Are physicians' orders carried out, unless otherwise indicated by an advanced directive?

F282

§483.20(k)(3)(ii) Be provided by qualified persons in accordance with each resident's written plan of care.

Interpretive Guidelines §483.20(k)(3)(ii)

If you find problems with quality of care, quality of life, or resident rights, are these problems attributable to the qualifications of the facility staff, or lack of, inadequate or incorrect implementation of the care plan?

Probes §483.20(k)(3)(ii)

- Can direct care-giving staff describe the care, services, and expected outcomes of the care they provide; have a general knowledge of the care and services being provided by other therapists; have an understanding of the expected outcomes of this care, and understand the relationship of these expected outcomes to the care they provide?

F283

§483.20(l) Discharge Summary

When the facility anticipates discharge a resident must have a discharge summary that includes:

(1) A recapitulation of the resident's stay;

(2) A final summary of the resident's status to include items in paragraph (b)(2)* of this section, at the time of the discharge that is available for release to authorized persons and agencies, with the consent of the resident or legal representative; and *[Editor's Note: The reference cited should be (b)(1).]

Intent §483.20(l)

To ensure appropriate discharge planning and communication of necessary information to the continuing care provider.

Interpretive Guidelines §483.20(l)

"Anticipates" means that the discharge was not an emergency discharge (e.g., hospitalization for an acute condition) or due to the resident's death.

"Adjust to his or her living environment" means that the post-discharge plan, as appropriate, should describe the resident's and family's preferences for care, how the resident and family will access these services, and how care should be coordinated if continuing treatment involves multiple caregivers. It should identify specific resident needs after discharge such as personal care, sterile dressings, and physical therapy, as well as describe resident/caregiver education needs and ability to meet care needs after discharge.

F284

§483.20(l)(3) A post-discharge plan of care that is developed with the participation of the resident and his or her family, which will assist the resident to adjust to his or her new living environment.

Interpretive Guidelines §483.20(l)(3)

A post-discharge plan of care for an anticipated discharge applies to a resident whom the facility discharges to a private residence, to another NF or SNF, or to another type of residential facility such as a board and care home or an intermediate care facility for individuals with mental retardation. Resident protection concerning transfer and discharge are found at §483.12. A "post-discharge plan of care" means the discharge planning process which includes: assessing continuing care needs and developing a plan designed to ensure the individual's needs will be met after discharge from the facility into the community.

Probes §483.20(l)

- Does the discharge summary have information pertinent to continuing care for the resident?

- Is there evidence of discharge planning in the records of discharged residents who had an anticipated discharge or those residents to be discharged shortly (e.g., in the next 7-14 days)?

- Do discharge plans address necessary post-discharge care?

- Has the facility aided the resident and his/her family in locating and coordinating post-discharge services?

- What types of pre-discharge preparation and education has the facility provided the resident and his/her family?

F285

§483.20(e) Coordination

A facility must coordinate assessments with the pre-admission screening and resident review program under Medicaid in part 483, subpart C to the maximum extent practicable to avoid duplicative testing and effort.

Interpretive Guidelines §483.20(e)

With respect to the responsibilities under the Pre-Admission Screening and Resident Review (PASRR) program, the State is responsible for conducting the screens, preparing the PASRR report, and providing or arranging the specialized services that are needed as a result of conducting the screens. The State is required to provide a copy of the PASRR report to the facility. This report must list the specialized services that the individual requires and that are the responsibility of the State to provide. All other needed services are the responsibility of the facility to provide.

§483.20(m) Preadmission Screening for Mentally Ill Individuals and Individuals With Mental Retardation.

§483.20(m)(1) A nursing facility must not admit, on or after January 1, 1989, any new residents with:

(i) Mental illness as defined in paragraph (m)(2)(i) of this section, unless the State mental health authority has determined, based on an independent physical and mental evaluation performed by a person or entity other than the State mental health authority, prior to admission;

(A) That, because of the physical and mental condition of the individual, the individual requires the level of services provided by a nursing facility; and
(B) If the individual requires such level of services, whether the individual requires specialized services for mental retardation.

(ii) Mental retardation, as defined in paragraph (m)(2)(ii) of this section, unless the State mental retardation or developmental disability authority has determined prior to admission--

(A) That, because of the physical and mental condition of the individual, the individual requires the level of services provided by a nursing facility; and
(B) If the individual requires such level of services, whether the individual requires specialized services for mental retardation.

§483.20(m)(2) Definitions. For purposes of this section:

(i) An individual is considered to have "mental illness" if the individual has a serious mental illness defined at 483.102(b)(1).

(ii) An individual is considered to be "mentally retarded" if the individual is mentally retarded as defined in 483.102(b)(3) or is a person with a related condition as described in 42 CFR 1010[*]. *[Editor's Note: Amended by *Federal Register*, Volume 71, Number 133, dated Wednesday, July 12, 2006. The changes are reflected in the above text.]

Intent §483.20(m)

To ensure that individuals with mental illness and mental retardation receive the care and services they need in the most appropriate setting.

"Specialized services" are those services the State is required to provide or arrange for that raise the intensity of services to the level needed by the resident. That is, specialized services are an "add-on" to NF services--they are of a higher intensity and frequency than specialized rehabilitation services, which are provided by the NF.

The statute mandates preadmission screening for all individuals with mental illness (MI) or mental retardation (MR) who apply to NFs, regardless of the applicant's source of payment, except as provided below. (See §1919(b)(3)(F).) Residents readmitted and individuals who initially apply to a nursing facility directly following a discharge from an acute care stay are exempt if:

- They are certified by a physician prior to admission to require a nursing facility stay of less than 30 days; and

- They require care at the nursing facility for the same condition for which they were hospitalized.

The State is responsible for providing specialized services to residents with MI/MR residing in Medicaid-certified facilities. The facility is required to provide all other care and services appropriate to the resident's condition. Therefore, if a facility has residents with MI/MR, do not survey for specialized services, but survey for all other requirements, including resident rights, quality of life, and quality of care.

If the resident's PAS report indicates that he or she needs specialized services but the resident is not receiving them, notify the Medicaid agency. NF services ordinarily are not of the intensity to meet the needs of residents with MI or MR.

Probes §483.20(m)

If sampled residents have MI or MR, did the State Mental Health or Mental Retardation Authority determine:

- Whether the residents needed the services of a NF?

- Whether the residents need specialized services for their MR or MI?

[This page intentionally left blank]

F309 – F334

§483.25 — Quality of Care

F309

(Rev. 41; Issued: 04-10-09; Effective/Implementation Dates: 04-10-09)

§483.25 Quality of Care

Each resident must receive and the facility must provide the necessary care and services to attain or maintain the highest practicable physical, mental, and psychosocial well-being, in accordance with the comprehensive assessment and plan of care.

Intent: §483.25

The facility must ensure that the resident obtains optimal improvement or does not deteriorate within the limits of a resident's right to refuse treatment, and within the limits of recognized pathology and the normal aging process.

NOTE: Use guidance at F309 for review of quality of care not specifically covered by 42 CFR 483.25 (a)-(m). Tag F309 includes, but is not limited to, care such as end-of-life, diabetes, renal disease, fractures, congestive heart failure, non-pressure-related skin ulcers, pain, or fecal impaction.

Definitions: §483.25

"Highest practicable physical, mental, and psychosocial well-being" is defined as the highest possible level of functioning and well-being, limited by the individual's recognized pathology and normal aging process. Highest practicable is determined through the comprehensive resident assessment and by recognizing and competently and thoroughly addressing the physical, mental or psychosocial needs of the individual.

Interpretive Guidelines §483.25

In any instance in which there has been a lack of improvement or a decline, the survey team must determine if the occurrence was unavoidable or avoidable. A determination of unavoidable decline or failure to reach highest practicable well-being may be made only if all of the following are present:

- An accurate and complete assessment (see §483.20);

- A care plan that is implemented consistently and based on information from the assessment; and

- Evaluation of the results of the interventions and revising the interventions as necessary.

Determine if the facility is providing the necessary care and services based on the findings of the comprehensive assessment and plan of care. If services and care are being provided, determine if the facility is evaluating the resident's outcome and changing the interventions if needed. This should be done in accordance with the resident's customary daily routine.

Procedures §483.25

Assess a facility's compliance with these requirements by determining if the services noted in the plan of care are: based on a comprehensive and accurate functional assessment of the resident's strengths, weaknesses, risk factors for deterioration and potential for improvement; continually and aggressively implemented; and updated by the facility staff. In looking at assessments, use both the MDS and RAPs information, any other pertinent assessments, and resulting care plans.

If the resident has been in the facility for less than 14 days (before completion of all the RAI is required), determine if the facility is conducting ongoing assessment and care planning, and, if appropriate care and services are being provided.

General Investigative Protocol for F309, Quality of Care

Use:

Use this General Investigative Protocol to investigate Quality of Care concerns that are not otherwise covered in the remaining tags at §483.25, Quality of Care or for which specific investigative protocols have not been established. For investigating concerns regarding management of pain, use the pain management investigative protocol below. Surveyors should consider any quality of care issue that is not covered in a specific Quality of Care tag to be covered under this tag, F309.

Procedure:

Briefly review the assessment, care plan and orders to identify whether the facility has recognized and addressed the concerns or resident care needs being investigated. Also use this review to identify facility interventions and to guide observations to be made. Corroborate observations by interview and record review.

Observations:

Observe whether staff consistently implement the care plan over time and across various shifts. During observations of the interventions, note and/or follow up on deviations from the care plan, deviations from current standards of practice, and potential negative outcomes.

Resident/Representative Interview

Interview the resident or representative to the degree possible to determine the resident's or representative's:

- Awareness of the current condition(s) or history of the condition(s) or diagnosis/diagnoses;

- Involvement in the development of the care plan, goals, and if interventions reflect choices and preferences; and

- How effective the interventions have been and if not effective, whether alternate approaches have been tried by the facility.

Nursing Staff Interview

Interview nursing staff on various shifts to determine:

- Their knowledge of the specific interventions for the resident, including facility-specific guidelines/protocols;

- Whether nursing assistants know how, what, when, and to whom to report changes in condition; and

- How the charge nurse monitors for the implementation of the care plan, and changes in condition.

Assessment

Review information such as orders, medication administration records, multi-disciplinary progress notes, the RAI/MDS, and any specific assessments that may have been completed. Determine if the information accurately and comprehensively reflects the resident's condition. In considering the appropriateness of a facility's response to the presence or progression of a condition/diagnosis, take into account the time needed to determine the effectiveness of treatment, and the facility's efforts, where possible, to remove, modify, or stabilize the risk factors and underlying causal factors.

NOTE: Although Federal requirements dictate the completion of RAI assessments according to certain time frames, standards of good clinical practice dictate that the assessment process is more fluid and should be ongoing. (**Federal Register** Vol. 62, No. 246, 12/23/97, page 67193)

Care Planning

Determine whether the facility developed a care plan that was consistent with the resident's specific conditions, risks, needs, behaviors, preferences and with current standards of practice and included measurable objectives and timetables with specific interventions. If the care plan refers to a specific facility treatment protocol that contains details of the treatment regimen, the care plan should refer to that protocol and should clarify any major deviations from or revisions to the protocol for this resident. The treatment protocol must be available to the caregivers and staff should be familiar with the protocol requirements.

NOTE: A specific care plan intervention is not needed if other components of the care plan address related risks adequately. For example, the risk of nutritional compromise for a resident with diabetes mellitus might be addressed in that part of the care plan that deals with nutritional management.

Care Plan Revision

Determine whether staff have monitored the resident's condition and effectiveness of the care plan interventions and revised the care plan with input by the resident and/or the representative, to the extent possible, (or justified the continuation of the existing plan) based upon the following:

- Achieving the desired outcome;

- Resident failure or inability to comply with or participate in a program to attain or maintain the highest practicable level of well-being; and/or

- Change in resident condition, ability to make decisions, cognition, medications, behavioral symptoms or visual problems.

Interview with Health Care Practitioners and Professionals

If the care provided has not been consistent with the care plan or the interventions defined or care provided appear not to be consistent with recognized standards of practice, interview one or more health care practitioners and professionals as necessary (e.g., physician, charge nurse, director of nursing, therapist) who, by virtue of training and knowledge of the resident, should be able to provide information about the causes, treatment and evaluation of the resident's condition or problem. If there is a medical question, contact the physician if he/she is the most appropriate person to interview. If the attending physician is unavailable, interview the medical director, as appropriate. Depending on the issue, ask about:

- How it was determined that chosen interventions were appropriate;

- Risks identified for which there were no interventions;

- Changes in condition that may justify additional or different interventions; or

- How staff validated the effectiveness of current interventions.

DETERMINATION OF COMPLIANCE WITH F309 (Task 6, Appendix P)
THAT IS NOT RELATED TO PAIN OR PAIN MANAGEMENT

Synopsis of Regulation (Tag F309)

The resident must receive and the facility must provide the necessary care and services to attain or maintain his/her highest practicable level of physical, mental, and psychosocial well-being, in accordance with the comprehensive assessment and plan of care.

Criteria for Compliance:

Compliance with F309, Quality of Care - The facility is in compliance with this requirement if staff:

- Recognized and assessed factors placing the resident at risk for specific conditions, causes, and/or problems;

- Defined and implemented interventions in accordance with resident needs, goals, and recognized standards of practice;

- Monitored and evaluated the resident's response to preventive efforts and treatment; and

- Revised the approaches as appropriate.

Concerns with Independent but Associated Structure, Process, and/or Outcome Requirements.

During the investigation, the surveyor may have identified concerns with related structure, process, and/or outcome requirements. If an additional concern has been identified, the surveyor must investigate the identified concern. Do not cite any related or associated requirements before first conducting an investigation to determine compliance or non-compliance with the related or associated requirement. Some examples include, but are not limited to, the following:

- **42 CFR 483.10(b)(11), F157, Notification of Changes**

  Determine whether staff notified the resident and consulted the physician regarding significant changes in the resident's condition or a need to alter treatment significantly or notified the representative of a significant condition change.

- **42 CFR 483.(20)(b), F272, Comprehensive Assessments**

  Determine whether the facility assessed the resident's condition, including existing status, and resident-specific risk factors (including potential causative factors) in relation to the identified concern under review.

- **42 CFR 483.20(k), F279, Comprehensive Care Plan**

  Determine whether the facility established a care plan with timetables and resident specific goals and interventions to address the care needs and treatment related to the clinical diagnosis and/or the identified concern.

- **42 CFR 483.20(k)(2)(iii), 483.10(d)(3), F280, Care Plan Revision**

  Determine whether the staff reviewed and revised the care plan as indicated based upon the resident's response to the care plan interventions, and obtained input from the resident or representative to the extent possible.

- **42 CFR 483.20(k)(3)(i), F281, Services Provided Meets Professional Standards of Quality**

  Determine whether the facility, beginning from the time of admission, provided care and services related to the identified concern that meet professional standards of quality.

- **42 CFR 483.20(k)(3)(ii), F282,Care Provided by Qualified Persons in Accordance with Plan of Care**

Determine whether care was provided by qualified staff and whether staff implemented the care plan correctly and adequately.

- **42 CFR 483.30(a), F353, Sufficient Staff**

Determine whether the facility had qualified nursing staff in sufficient numbers to assure the resident was provided necessary care and services 24 hours a day, based upon the comprehensive assessment and care plan.

- **42 CFR 483.40(a)(1)&(2), F385, Physician Supervision**

Determine whether the physician has assessed and developed a relevant treatment regimen and responded appropriately to the notice of changes in condition.

- **42 CFR 483.75(f), F498, Proficiency of Nurse Aides**

Determine whether nurse aides demonstrate competency in the delivery of care and services related to the concern being investigated.

- **42 CFR 483.75(i)(2), F501, Medical Director**

Determine whether the medical director:

- Assisted the facility in the development and implementation of policies and procedures and that these are based on current standards of practice; and

- Interacts with the physician supervising the care of the resident if requested by the facility to intervene on behalf of the residents.

- **42 CFR 483.75(l), F514, Clinical Records**

Determine whether the clinical records:

- Accurately and completely document the resident's status, the care and services provided in accordance with current professional standards and practices; and

- Provide a basis for determining and managing the resident's progress including response to treatment, change in condition, and changes in treatment.

DEFICIENCY CATEGORIZATION (Part IV, Appendix P)

Once the survey team has completed its investigation, analyzed the data, reviewed the regulatory requirements, and determined that noncompliance exists, the team must determine the severity of each deficiency, based on the harm or potential for harm to the resident. The key elements for severity determination for F309 Quality of Care requirements are as follows:

1. Presence of harm/negative outcome(s) or potential for negative outcomes because of lack of appropriate treatment and care, such as decline in function or failure to achieve the highest possible level of well-being.

2. Degree of harm (actual or potential) related to the non-compliance. Identify how the facility practices caused, resulted in, allowed or contributed to the actual or potential for harm:

    - If harm has occurred, determine if the harm is at the level of serious injury, impairment, death, compromise, or discomfort to the resident(s); and

- • If harm has not yet occurred, determine the potential for serious injury, impairment, death, compromise, or discomfort to occur to the resident(s).

3. The immediacy of correction required. Determine whether the noncompliance requires immediate correction in order to prevent serious injury, harm, impairment, or death to one or more residents.

The survey team must evaluate the harm or potential for harm for F309 based upon the four levels of severity. First, the team must rule out whether Severity Level 4, Immediate Jeopardy to a resident's health or safety, exists by evaluating the deficient practice in relation to immediacy, culpability, and severity. Follow the guidance in Appendix Q, Determining Immediate Jeopardy. If specific guidance and examples have not been established elsewhere for the concern having been reviewed, follow the general guidance in Appendix P regarding Guidance on Severity and Scope Levels and Psychosocial Outcome Severity Guide.

Interpretive Guidelines for Selected Specific Quality of Care Issues at §483.25.

The following sections describe some specific issues or care needs that are not otherwise covered in the remaining tags of §483.25, Quality of Care. These are only some of the issues that may arise with a resident's quality of care. Surveyors should consider any quality of care issue that is not covered in a specific Quality of Care tag to be covered under this tag, F309.

Review of a Resident with Non Pressure-Related Skin Ulcer/Wound.

Residents may develop various types of skin ulceration. At the time of the assessment and diagnosis of a skin ulcer/wound, the clinician is expected to document the clinical basis (e.g., underlying condition contributing to the ulceration, ulcer edges and wound bed, location, shape, condition of surrounding tissues) which permit differentiating the ulcer type, especially if the ulcer has characteristics consistent with a pressure ulcer, but is determined not to be one. This section differentiates some of the different types of skin ulcers/wounds.

NOTE: Guidance regarding pressure ulcers is found at 42 CFR 483.25 (c), F314 Pressure Sore. Use F309 for issues of quality of care regarding non-pressure related ulcers.

An arterial ulcer is ulceration that occurs as the result of arterial occlusive disease when non-pressure related disruption or blockage of the arterial blood flow to an area causes tissue necrosis. Inadequate blood supply to the extremity may initially present as intermittent claudication. Arterial/Ischemic ulcers may be present in individuals with moderate to severe peripheral vascular disease, generalized arteriosclerosis, inflammatory or autoimmune disorders (such as arteritis), or significant vascular disease elsewhere (e.g., stroke or heart attack). The arterial ulcer is characteristically painful, usually occurs in the distal portion of the lower extremity and may be over the ankle or bony areas of the foot (e.g., top of the foot or toe, outside edge of the foot). The wound bed is frequently dry and pale with minimal or no exudate. The affected foot may exhibit: diminished or absent pedal pulse, coolness to touch, decreased pain when hanging down (dependent) or increased pain when elevated, blanching upon elevation, delayed capillary fill time, hair loss on top of the foot and toes, toenail thickening.

A venous ulcer (previously known as a stasis ulcer) is an open lesion of the skin and subcutaneous tissue of the lower leg, often occurring in the lower leg around the medial ankle. Venous ulcers are reported to be the most common vascular ulceration and may be difficult to heal, may occur off and on for several years, and may occur after relatively minor trauma. The ulcer may have a moist, granulating wound bed, may be superficial, and may have minimal to copious serous drainage unless the wound is infected. The resident may experience pain that may increase when the foot is in a dependent position, such as when a resident is seated with her or his feet on the floor.

Recent literature implicates venous hypertension as a causative factor. Venous hypertension may be caused by one (or a combination of) factor(s) including: loss of (or compromised) valve function in the vein, partial or complete obstruction of the vein (e.g., deep vein thrombosis, obesity, malignancy), and/or failure of the calf muscle to pump the blood (e.g., paralysis, decreased activity). Venous insufficiency may result in edema and induration, dilated superficial veins, dry scaly crusts, dark pigmented skin in the lower third of the leg, or dermatitis. The pigmentation may appear as darkening skin, tan or purple areas in light skinned residents and dark purple, black or dark brown in dark skinned residents. Cellulitis may be present if the tissue is infected.

A diabetic neuropathic ulcer requires that the resident be diagnosed with diabetes mellitus and have peripheral neuropathy. The diabetic ulcer characteristically occurs on the foot, e.g., at mid-foot, at the ball of the foot over the metatarsal heads, or on the top of toes with Charcot deformity.

Review of a Resident Receiving Hospice Services.

When a facility resident has also elected the Medicare hospice benefit, the hospice and the nursing home must communicate, establish, and agree upon a coordinated plan of care for both providers which reflects the hospice philosophy, and is based on an assessment of the individual's needs and unique living situation in the facility. The plan of care must include directives for managing pain and other uncomfortable symptoms and be revised and updated as necessary to reflect the individual's current status. This coordinated plan of care must identify the care and services which the SNF/NF and hospice will provide in order to be responsive to the unique needs of the patient/resident and his/her expressed desire for hospice care.

The SNF/NF and the hospice are responsible for performing each of their respective functions that have been agreed upon and included in the plan of care. The hospice retains overall professional management responsibility for directing the implementation of the plan of care related to the terminal illness and related conditions.

For a resident receiving hospice benefit care, evaluate if:

- The plan of care reflects the participation of the hospice, the facility, and the resident or representative to the extent possible;

- The plan of care includes directives for managing pain and other uncomfortable symptoms and is revised and updated as necessary to reflect the resident's current status;

- Medications and medical supplies are provided by the hospice as needed for the palliation and management of the terminal illness and related conditions;

- The hospice and the facility communicate with each other when any changes are indicated to the plan of care;

- The hospice and the facility are aware of the other's responsibilities in implementing the plan of care;

- The facility's services are consistent with the plan of care developed in coordination with the hospice, (the hospice patient residing in a SNF/NF should not experience any lack of SNF/NF services or personal care because of his/her status as a hospice patient); and

- The SNF/NF offers the same services to its residents who have elected the hospice benefit as it furnishes to its residents who have not elected the hospice benefit. The resident has the right to refuse services in conjunction with the provisions of 42 CFR 483.10(b)(4), Tag F155.

NOTE: If a resident is receiving services from a Medicare certified hospice and the hospice was advised of concerns by the facility and failed to address and/or resolve issues related to coordination of care or implementation of appropriate services, refer the concerns as a complaint to the State Agency responsible for oversight of this hospice, identifying the specific resident(s) involved and the concerns identified.

Review of a Resident Receiving Dialysis Services.

When dialysis is provided in the facility by an outside entity, or the resident leaves the facility to obtain dialysis, the nursing home should have an agreement or arrangement with the entity. This agreement/arrangement should include all aspects of how the resident's care is to be managed, including:

- Medical and non-medical emergencies;

- Development and implementation of the resident's care plan;

- Interchange of information useful/necessary for the care of the resident; and

- Responsibility for waste handling, sterilization, and disinfection of equipment.

If there is a sampled resident who is receiving dialysis care, evaluate the following, in addition to the standard Resident Review protocol:

- Review to assure that medications are administered before and after dialysis as ordered by the physician. This should account for the optimal timing to maximize effectiveness and avoid adverse effects of the medications;

- Whether staff know how to manage emergencies and complications, including equipment failure and alarm systems (if any), bleeding/hemorrhaging, and infection/bacteremia/septic shock;

- Whether facility staff are aware of the care of shunts/fistulas, infection control, waste handling, nature and management of end stage renal disease (including nutritional needs, emotional and social well-being, and aspects to monitor); and

- Whether the treatment for this (these) resident(s), affects the quality of life, rights or quality of care for other residents, e.g., restricting access to their own space, risk of infections.

NOTE: If a resident is receiving services from a dialysis provider, and the survey team has concerns about the quality of care and services provided to the resident by that provider, refer the concerns as a complaint to the State Agency responsible for oversight of the dialysis provider, identifying the specific resident(s) involved and the concerns identified.

Review of a Resident Who has Pain Symptoms, is being Treated for Pain, or Who has the Potential for Pain Symptoms Related to Conditions or Treatments.

Recognition and Management of Pain - In order to help a resident attain or maintain his or her highest practicable level of well-being and to prevent or manage pain, the facility, to the extent possible:

- Recognizes when the resident is experiencing pain and identifies circumstances when pain can be anticipated;

- Evaluates the existing pain and the cause(s), and

- Manages or prevents pain, consistent with the comprehensive assessment and plan of care, current clinical standards of practice, and the resident's goals and preferences.

Definitions Related to Recognition and Management of Pain

- **"Addiction"** is a primary, chronic, neurobiological disease, with genetic, psychosocial, and environmental factors influencing its development and manifestations. It is characterized by an overwhelming craving for medication or behaviors that include one or more of the following: impaired control over drug use, compulsive use, continued use despite harm, and craving.[1]

- **"Adjuvant Analgesics"** describes any medication with a primary indication other than pain management but with analgesic properties in some painful conditions.[2]

- **"Adverse Consequence"** is an unpleasant symptom or event that is due to or associated with a medication, such as impairment or decline in a resident's mental or physical condition or functional or psychosocial status. It may include various types of adverse drug reactions and interactions (e.g., medication-medication, medication-food, and medication-disease).

  NOTE: Adverse drug reaction (ADR) is a form of adverse consequences. It may be either a secondary effect of a medication that is usually undesirable and different from the therapeutic effect of the medication or any response to a medication that is noxious and unintended and occurs in doses for prophylaxis, diagnosis, or treatment. The term "side effect" is often used interchangeably with ADR; however, side effects are but one of five ADR categories, the others being hypersensitivity, idiosyncratic response, toxic reactions, and adverse medication interactions. A side effect is an expected, well-known reaction that occurs with a predictable frequency and may or may not constitute an adverse consequence.

- **"Complementary and Alternative Medicine"** (CAM) is a group of diverse medical and health care systems, practices, and products that are not presently considered to be a part of conventional medicine.[3]

- **"Non-pharmacological interventions"** refers to approaches to care that do not involve medications, generally directed towards stabilizing or improving a resident's mental, physical or psychosocial well-being.

- **"Pain"** is an unpleasant sensory and emotional experience that can be acute, recurrent or persistent.[4] Following are descriptions of several different types of pain:

  - <u>"Acute Pain"</u> is generally pain of abrupt onset and limited duration, often associated with an adverse chemical, thermal or mechanical stimulus such as surgery, trauma and acute illness;

  - <u>"Breakthrough Pain"</u> refers to an episodic increase in (flare-up) pain in someone whose pain is generally being managed by his/her current medication regimen;

  - <u>"Incident Pain"</u> refers to pain that is typically predictable and is related to a precipitating event such as movement (e.g., walking, transferring, or dressing) or certain actions (e.g., disimpaction or wound care); and

  - <u>"Persistent Pain"</u> or "Chronic Pain" refers to a pain state that continues for a prolonged period of time or recurs more than intermittently for months or years.

- **"Physical Dependence"** is a physiologic state of neuroadaptation that is characterized by a withdrawal syndrome if a medication or drug is stopped or decreased abruptly, or if an antagonist is administered.

- **"Standards of Practice"** refers to approaches to care, procedures, techniques, treatments, etc., that are based on research and/or expert consensus and that are contained in current manuals, textbooks, or publications, or that are accepted, adopted or promulgated by recognized professional organizations or national accrediting bodies.

- **"Tolerance"** is a physiologic state resulting from regular use of a drug in which an increased dosage is needed to produce the same effect or a reduced effect is observed with a constant dose.[5]

Overview of Pain Recognition and Management

Effective pain recognition and management requires an ongoing facility-wide commitment to resident comfort, to identifying and addressing barriers to managing pain, and to addressing any misconceptions that residents, families, and staff may have about managing pain. Nursing home residents are at high risk for having pain that may affect function, impair mobility, impair mood, or disturb sleep, and diminish quality of life.[6] The onset of acute pain may indicate a new injury or a potentially life-threatening condition or illness. It is important, therefore, that a resident's reports of pain, or nonverbal signs suggesting pain, be evaluated.

The resident's needs and goals as well as the etiology, type, and severity of pain are relevant to developing a plan for pain management. It should be noted that while analgesics can reduce pain and enhance the quality of life, they do not necessarily address the underlying cause of pain. It is important to consider treating the underlying cause, where possible. Addressing underlying causes may permit pain management with fewer analgesics, lower doses, or medications with a lower risk of serious adverse consequences.

Certain factors may affect the recognition, assessment, and management of pain. For example, residents, staff, or practitioners may misunderstand the indications for, and benefits and risks of, opioids and other analgesics; or they may mistakenly believe that older individuals have a higher tolerance for pain than younger individuals, or that pain is an inevitable part of aging, a sign of weakness, or a way just to get attention. Other challenges to successfully evaluating and managing pain may include communication difficulties due to illness or language and cultural barriers, stoicism about pain, and cognitive impairment.[7,8,9]

It is a challenge to assess and manage pain in individuals who have cognitive impairment or communications difficulties.[10,11] Some individuals with advanced cognitive impairment can accurately report pain and/or respond to questions regarding pain.[12,13] One study noted that 83 percent of nursing home residents could respond to questions about pain intensity.[14]

Those who cannot report pain may present with nonspecific signs such as grimacing, increases in confusion or restlessness or other distressed behavior. Effective pain management may decrease distressed behaviors that are related to pain.[15] However, these nonspecific signs and symptoms may reflect other clinically significant conditions (e.g., delirium, depression, or medication-related adverse consequences) instead of, or in addition to, pain. To distinguish these various causes of similar signs and symptoms, and in order to manage pain effectively, it is important to evaluate (e.g., touch, look at, move) the resident in detail, to confirm that the signs and symptoms are due to pain.

Resources Related to Pain Management

Examples of clinical resources available for guidance regarding the assessment and management of pain include:

- American Geriatrics Society Clinical Practice Guideline at: http://www.americangeriatrics.org/education/cp_index.shtml;

- American Medical Directors Association (AMDA) Clinical Practice Guideline "Pain Management in the Long-Term Care Setting" (2003) at: www.amda.com/tools/guidelines.cfm;

- American Academy of Hospice and Palliative Medicine at www.aahpm.org;

- American Academy of Pain Medicine at http://www.painmed.org;

- American Pain Society at www.ampainsoc.org;

- Brown University's Pain and Physical Symptoms Toolkit at http://www.chcr.brown.edu/pcoc/physical.htm;

- Hospice and Palliative Nurses Association at http://www.hpna.org;

- John A Hartford Institute for Geriatric Nursing "Try This" series at http://www.hartfordign.org/Resources/Try_This_Series;

- National Initiative on Pain Control at www.painedu.org;

- Partners Against Pain® at http://www.partnersagainstpain.com;

- Quality Improvement Organizations at www.medqic.org; and

- Resource Center for Pain Medicine and Palliative Care at Beth Israel Medical Center (2000) at http://www.stoppain.org/education_research/index.html.

NOTE   References to non-U.S. Department of Health and Human Services (HHS) sources or sites on the Internet are provided as a service and do not constitute or imply endorsement of these organizations or their programs by CMS or HHS. CMS is not responsible for the content of pages found at these sites. URL addresses were current as of the date of this publication.

Care Process for Pain Management

Processes for the prevention and management of pain include:

- Assessing the potential for pain, recognizing the onset or presence of pain, and assessing the pain;

- Addressing/treating the underlying causes of the pain, to the extent possible;

- Developing and implementing interventions/approaches to pain management, depending on factors such as whether the pain is episodic, continuous, or both;

- Identifying and using specific strategies for different levels or sources of pain or pain-related symptoms, including:

  - Identifying interventions to address the pain based on the resident-specific assessment, a pertinent clinical rationale, and the resident's goals;

    - Trying to prevent or minimize anticipated pain;[16]

    - Considering non-pharmacological and CAM interventions;

  - Using pain medications judiciously to balance the resident's desired level of pain relief with the avoidance of unacceptable adverse consequences;

- Monitoring appropriately for effectiveness and/or adverse consequences (e.g., constipation, sedation) including defining how and when to monitor the resident's symptoms and degree of pain relief; and

- Modifying the approaches, as necessary.

Pain Recognition

Because pain can significantly affect a person's well-being, it is important that the facility recognize and address pain promptly. The facility's evaluation of the resident at admission and during ongoing assessments helps identify the resident who is experiencing pain or for whom pain may be anticipated during specific procedures, care, or treatment. In addition, it is important that a resident be monitored for the presence of pain and be evaluated when there is a change in condition and whenever new pain or an exacerbation of pain is suspected. As with many symptoms, pain in a resident with moderate to severe cognitive impairment may be more difficult to recognize and assess.[17,18,19]

Expressions of pain may be verbal or nonverbal. A resident may avoid the use of the term "pain." Other words used to report or describe pain may differ by culture, language and/or region of the country. Examples of descriptions may include heaviness or pressure, stabbing, throbbing, hurting, aching, gnawing, cramping, burning, numbness, tingling, shooting or radiating, spasms, soreness, tenderness, discomfort, pins and needles, feeling "rough," tearing or ripping. Verbal descriptions of pain can help a practitioner identify the source, nature, and other characteristics of the pain. Nonverbal indicators which may represent pain need to be viewed in the entire clinical context with consideration given to pain as well as other clinically pertinent explanations. Examples of possible indicators of pain include, but are not limited to the following:

- Negative verbalizations and vocalizations (e.g., groaning, crying/whimpering, or screaming);
- Facial expressions (e.g., grimacing, frowning, fright, or clenching of the jaw);
- Changes in gait (e.g., limping), skin color, vital signs (e.g., increased heart rate, respirations and/or blood pressure), perspiration;
- Behavior such as resisting care, distressed pacing, irritability, depressed mood, or decreased participation in usual physical and/or social activities;
- Loss of function or inability to perform Activities of Daily Living (ADLs), rubbing a specific location of the body, or guarding a limb or other body parts;
- Difficulty eating or loss of appetite; and
- Difficulty sleeping (insomnia).

In addition to the pain item sections of the Minimum Data Set (MDS), many sections such as sleep cycle, change in mood, decline in function, instability of condition, weight loss, and skin conditions can be potential indicators of pain. Any of these findings may indicate the need for additional and more thorough evaluation.

Many residents have more than one active medical condition and may experience pain from several different causes simultaneously. Many medical conditions may be painful such as pressure ulcers, diabetes with neuropathic pain, immobility, amputation, post- CVA, venous and arterial ulcers, multiple sclerosis, oral health conditions, and infections. In addition, common procedures, such as moving a resident or performing physical or occupational therapies or changing a wound dressing may be painful. Understanding the underlying causes of pain is an important step in determining optimal approaches to prevent, minimize, or manage pain.

Observations at rest and during movement, particularly during activities that may increase pain (such as dressing changes, exercises, turning and positioning, bathing, rising from a chair, walking) can help to identify whether the resident is having pain. Observations during eating or during the provision of oral hygiene may also indicate dental, mouth and/or facial pain.

Recognizing the presence of pain and identifying those situations where pain may be anticipated involves the participation of health care professionals and direct care and ancillary staff who have contact with the resident. Information may be obtained by talking with the resident, directly examining the resident, and observing the resident's behavior.[20] Staffing consistency and the nursing staff's level of familiarity with the residents was reported in one study to have a significant effect on the staff member's ability to identify and differentiate pain-related behavior from other behavior of cognitively impaired residents.[21]

Nursing assistants may be the first to notice a resident's symptoms; therefore, it is important that they are able to recognize a change in the resident and the resident's functioning and to report the changes to a nurse for follow-up. Family members or friends may also recognize and report when the resident experiences pain and may provide information about the resident's pain symptoms, pain history and previously attempted interventions. Other staff, e.g., dietary, activities, therapy, housekeeping, who have direct contact with the resident may also report changes in resident behavior or resident complaints of pain.

Assessment

Observing the resident during care, activities, and treatments helps not only to detect whether pain is present, but also to potentially identify its location and the limitations it places on the resident. The facility must complete the Resident Assessment Instrument (RAI) (See 42 CFR 483.20 F272). According to the CMS Revised Long-Term Care Facility Resident Assessment Instrument User's Manual, Version 2.0, Manual Chapter 1.14 CMS Clarification Regarding Documentation Requirements, "Completion of the MDS does not remove the facility's responsibility to document a more detailed assessment of particular issues of relevance for the resident....Clinical documentation that contributes to identification and communication of residents' problems, needs and strengths, that monitors their condition on an on-going basis, and that records treatment and response to treatment is a matter of good clinical practice and is an expectation of trained and licensed health care professionals." An assessment or an evaluation of pain based on clinical standards of practice may necessitate gathering the following information, as applicable to the resident:

- History of pain and its treatment (including non-pharmacological and pharmacological treatment);
- Characteristics of pain, such as:

    - Intensity of pain (e.g., as measured on a standardized pain scale);
    - Descriptors of pain (e.g., burning, stabbing, tingling, aching);
    - Pattern of pain (e.g., constant or intermittent);
    - Location and radiation of pain;
    - Frequency, timing and duration of pain;

- Impact of pain on quality of life (e.g., sleeping, functioning, appetite, and mood);
- Factors such as activities, care, or treatment that precipitate or exacerbate pain;
- Strategies and factors that reduce pain;
- Additional symptoms associated with pain (e.g., nausea, anxiety);
- Physical examination (may include the pain site, the nervous system, mobility and function, and physical, psychological and cognitive status);
- Current medical conditions and medications; or
- The resident's goals for pain management and his or her satisfaction with the current level of pain control.

Management of Pain

Based on the evaluation, the facility, in collaboration with the attending physician/prescriber, other health care professionals, and the resident and/or his/her representative, develops, implements, monitors and revises as necessary interventions to prevent or manage each individual resident's pain, beginning at admission. These interventions may be integrated into components of the comprehensive care plan, addressing conditions or situations that may be associated with pain, or may be included as a specific pain management need or goal.

The interdisciplinary team and the resident collaborate to arrive at pertinent, realistic and measurable goals for treatment, such as reducing pain sufficiently to allow the resident to ambulate comfortably to the dining room for each meal or to participate in 30 minutes of physical therapy. Depending on the situation and the resident's wishes, the target may be to reduce the pain level, but not necessarily to become pain-free. To the extent possible, the interdisciplinary team educates the resident and/or representative about the need to report pain when it occurs and about the various approaches to pain management and the need to monitor the effectiveness of the interventions used.

The basis for effective interventions includes several considerations, such as the resident's needs and goals; the source(s), type and severity of pain (recognizing that the resident may experience pain from one or more sources either simultaneously or at different times) and awareness of the available treatment options. Often, sequential trials of various treatment options are needed to develop the most effective approach.

It is important for pain management approaches to follow pertinent clinical standards of practice and to identify who is to be involved in managing the pain and implementing the care or supplying the services (e.g., facility staff, such as RN, LPN, CNA; attending physician or other practitioner; certified hospice; or other contractors such as therapists). Pertinent current standards of practice may provide recommended approaches to pain management even when the cause cannot be or has not been determined.

If a resident or the resident's representative elects the Medicare hospice benefit for end-of-life care, the facility remains the resident's primary care giver and the SNF/NF requirements for participation in Medicare or Medicaid still apply for that resident. According to the Medicare Hospice Conditions of Participation at 42 CFR 418.112(b).

Standard: Professional Management, "The hospice must assume responsibility for professional management of the resident's hospice services provided, in accordance with the hospice plan of care and the hospice conditions of participation, and make nay arrangements necessary for hospice-related inpatient care in a participating Medicare/Medicaid facility according to §418.100 and §418.112(b)." The care of the resident, including pain management, must be appropriately coordinated among all providers.

In order to provide effective pain management, it is important that staff be educated and guided regarding the proper evaluation and management of pain as reflected in or consistent with the protocols, policies, and procedures employed by the facility.

Non-pharmacological interventions

Non-pharmacologic interventions may help manage pain effectively when used either independently or in conjunction with pharmacologic agents.[22] Examples of non-pharmacologic approaches may include, but are not limited to:

- Altering the environment for comfort (such as adjusting room temperature, tightening and smoothing linens, using pressure redistributing mattress and positioning, comfortable seating, and assistive devices);

- Physical modalities, such as ice packs or cold compresses (to reduce swelling and lessen sensation), mild heat (to decrease joint stiffness and increase blood flow to an area), neutral body alignment and repositioning, baths, transcutaneous electrical nerve stimulation (TENS), massage, acupuncture/acupressure, chiropractic, or rehabilitation therapy;

- Exercises to address stiffness and prevent contractures; and

- Cognitive/Behavioral interventions (e.g., relaxation techniques, reminiscing, diversions, activities, music therapy, coping techniques and education about pain).

The list of Complementary and Alternative Medicine (CAM) options is evolving, as those therapies that are proven safe and effective are used more widely.

NOTE: Information on CAM may be found on the following sites:

- National Center for Complementary and Alternative Medicine at www.nccam.nih.gov; and

- Food and Drug Administration (FDA) at www.fda.gov.

Because CAM can include herbal supplements, some of which potentially can interact with prescribed medications, it is important that any such agents are recorded in the resident's chart for evaluation by the physician and consultant pharmacist.

Pharmacological interventions

The interdisciplinary team (nurses, practitioner, pharmacists, etc.) is responsible for developing a pain management regimen that is specific to each resident who has pain or who has the potential for pain, such as during a treatment. The regimen considers factors such as the causes, location, and severity of the pain, the potential benefits, risks and adverse consequences of medications; and the resident's desired level of relief and tolerance for adverse consequences. The resident may accept partial pain relief in order to experience fewer significant adverse consequences (e.g., desire to stay alert instead of experiencing drowsiness/confusion). The interdisciplinary team works with the resident to identify the most effective and acceptable route for the administration of analgesics, such as orally, topically, by injection, by infusion pump, and/or transdermally.

It is important to follow a systematic approach for selecting medications and doses to treat pain. Developing an effective pain management regimen may require repeated attempts to identify the right interventions. General guidelines for choosing appropriate categories of medications in various situations are widely available. [23,24]

Factors influencing the selection and doses of medications include the resident's medical condition, current medication regimen, nature, severity, and cause of the pain and the course of the illness. Analgesics may help manage pain; however, they often do not address the underlying cause of pain. Examples of different approaches may include, but are not limited to: administering lower doses of medication initially and titrating the dose slowly upward, administering medications "around the clock" rather than "on demand" (PRN); or combining longer acting medications with PRN medications for breakthrough pain. Recurrent use of or repeated requests for PRN medications may indicate the need to reevaluate the situation, including the current medication regimen. Some clinical conditions or situations may require using several analgesics and/or adjuvant medications (e.g., antidepressants or anticonvulsants) together. Documentation helps to clarify the rationale for a treatment regimen and to acknowledge associated risks.

Opioids or other potent analgesics have been used for residents who are actively dying, those with complex pain syndromes, and those with more severe acute or chronic pain that has not responded to non-opioid analgesics or other measures. Opioids should be selected and dosed in accordance with current standards of practice and manufacturers' guidelines in order to optimize their effectiveness and minimize their adverse consequences. Adverse consequences may be especially problematic when the resident is receiving other medications with significant effects on the cardiovascular and central nervous systems. Therefore, careful titration of dosages based on monitoring/evaluating the effectiveness of the medication and the occurrence of adverse consequences is necessary. The clinical record should reflect the ongoing communication between the prescriber and the staff is necessary for the optimal and judicious use of pain medications.

Other interventions have been used for some residents with more advanced, complex, or poorly controlled pain. Examples include, but are not limited to: radiation therapy, neurostimulation, spinal delivery of analgesics (implanted catheters and pump systems), and neurolytic procedures (chemical or surgical) [25] that are administered under the close supervision of expert practitioners.

Monitoring, Reassessment, and Care Plan Revision

Monitoring the resident over time helps identify the extent to which pain is controlled, relative to the individual's goals and the availability of effective treatment. The ongoing evaluation of the status (presence, increase or reduction) of a resident's pain is vital, including the status of underlying causes, the response to interventions to prevent or manage pain, and the possible presence of adverse consequences of treatment. Adverse consequences related to analgesics can often be anticipated and to some extent prevented or reduced. For example, opioids routinely cause constipation, which may be minimized by an appropriate bowel regimen.

Identifying target signs and symptoms (including verbal reports and non-verbal indicators from the resident) and using standardized assessment tools can help the interdisciplinary team evaluate the resident's pain and responses to interventions and determine whether the care plan should be revised, for example:

- If pain has not been adequately controlled, it may be necessary to reconsider the current approaches and revise or supplement them as indicated; or

- If pain has resolved or there is no longer an indication or need for pain medication, the facility works with the practitioner to discontinue or taper (as needed to prevent withdrawal symptoms) analgesics.

[Editor's Note: See page 394 for endnotes pertaining to this section.]

Investigative Protocol for Pain Management

Quality of Care Related to the Recognition and Management of Pain

Objective

The objective of this protocol is to determine whether the facility has provided and the resident has received care and services to address and manage the resident's pain in order to support his or her highest practicable level of physical, mental, and psychosocial well-being, in accordance with the comprehensive assessment and plan of care.

Use

Use this protocol for a resident who has pain symptoms or who has the potential for pain symptoms related to conditions or treatments. This includes a resident:

- Who states he/she has pain or discomfort;
- Who displays possible indicators of pain that cannot be readily attributed to another cause;
- Who has a disease or condition or who receives treatments that cause or can reasonably be anticipated to cause pain;
- Whose assessment indicates that he/she experiences pain;
- Who receives or has orders for treatment for pain; and/or
- Who has elected a hospice benefit for pain management.

Procedures

Briefly review the care plan and orders to identify any current pain management interventions and to focus observations. Corroborate observations by interview and record review.

NOTE: Determine who is involved in the pain management process (for example, the staff and practitioner, and/or another entity such as a licensed/certified hospice).

1. Observation

Observe the resident during various activities, shifts, and interactions with staff. Use the observations to determine:

- If the resident exhibits signs or symptoms of pain, verbalizes the presence of pain, or requests interventions for pain, or whether the pain appears to affect the resident's function or ability to participate in routine care or activities;
- If there is evidence of pain, whether staff have assessed the situation, identified, and implemented interventions to try to prevent or address the pain and have evaluated the status of the resident's pain after interventions;
- If care and services are being provided that reasonably could be anticipated to cause pain, whether staff have identified and addressed these issues, to the extent possible;
- Staff response, if there is a report from the resident, family, or staff that the resident is experiencing pain;
- If there are pain management interventions for the resident, whether the staff implements them. Follow up on:
  - Deviations from the care plan;
  - Whether pain management interventions have a documented rationale and if it is consistent with current standards of practice; and
  - Potential adverse consequence(s) associated with treatment for pain (e.g., medications); and
- How staff responded, if the interventions implemented did not reduce the pain consistent with the goals for pain management.

2. Resident/Representative Interviews

Interview the resident, or representative to the degree possible in order to determine the resident's/representative's involvement in the development of the care plan, defining the approaches and goals, and if interventions reflect choices and preferences, and how they are involved in developing and revising pain management strategies; revisions to the care plan, if the interventions do not work. If the resident is presently or periodically experiencing pain, determine:

- Characteristics of the pain, including the intensity, type (e.g., burning, stabbing, tingling, aching), pattern of pain (e.g., constant or intermittent), location and radiation of pain and frequency, timing and duration of pain;

- Factors that may precipitate or alleviate the pain;

- How the resident typically has expressed pain and responded to various interventions in the past;

- Who the resident and/or representative has told about the pain/discomfort, and how the staff responded;

- What treatment options (e.g., pharmacological and/or non-pharmacological) were discussed;

- How effective the interventions have been; and

- If interventions have been refused, whether there was a discussion of the potential impact on the resident, and whether alternatives or other approaches were offered.

3. Nurse Aide(s) Interview. Interview staff who provide direct care on various shifts to determine:

- If they are aware of a resident's pain complaints or of signs and symptoms that could indicate the presence of pain;

- To whom they report the resident's complaints and signs, or symptoms; and

- If they are aware of, and implement, interventions for pain/discomfort management for the resident consistent with the resident's plan of care, (for example, allowing a period of time for a pain medication to take effect before bathing and/or dressing).

4. Record review

Assessment. Review information such as orders, medication administration records, multidisciplinary progress notes, The RAI/MDS, and any specific assessments regarding pain that may have been completed. Determine if the information accurately and comprehensively reflects the resident's condition, such as:

- Identifies the pain indicators and the characteristics, causes, and contributing factors related to pain;

- Identifies a history of pain and related interventions, including the effectiveness and any adverse consequences of such interventions;

- Identifies the impact of pain on the resident's function and quality of life; and

- Identifies the resident's response to interventions including efficacy and adverse consequences, and any modification of interventions as indicated.

NOTE Although Federal requirements dictate the completion of RAI assessments according to certain time frames, standards of good clinical practice dictate that the assessment process is more fluid and should be ongoing. (**Federal Register,** Vol. 62, No. 246, 12/23/97, Page 67193)

Care Plan. Review the care plan. Determine if pain management interventions include as appropriate:

- Measurable pain management goals, reflecting resident needs and preferences;

- Pertinent non-pharmacological and/or pharmacological interventions;

- Time frames and approaches for monitoring the status of the resident's pain, including the effectiveness of the interventions; and

- Identification of clinically significant medication-related adverse consequences such as falling, constipation, anorexia, or drowsiness, and a plan to try to minimize those adverse consequences.

If the care plan refers to a specific facility pain management protocol, determine whether interventions are consistent with that protocol. If a resident's care plan deviates from the protocol, determine through staff interview or record review the reason for the deviation.

If the resident has elected a hospice benefit, all providers must coordinate their care of the resident. This care includes aspects of pain management, such as choice of palliative interventions, responsibility for assessing pain and providing interventions, and responsibility for monitoring symptoms and adverse consequences of interventions and for modifying interventions as needed.

NOTE   If a resident is receiving services from a Medicare certified hospice and the hospice was advised of concerns by the facility and failed to address and/or resolve issues related to coordination of care or implementation of appropriate services, file a complaint with the State Agency responsible for oversight of this hospice, identifying the specific resident(s) involved and the concerns identified.

Care Plan Revisions

Determine whether the pain has been reassessed and the care plan has been revised as necessary (with input from the resident or representative, to the extent possible). For example, if the current interventions are not effective, if the pain has resolved, or the resident has experienced a change of condition or status.

5.   **Interviews with health care practitioners and professionals:**

Nurse Interview. Interview a nurse who is knowledgeable about the needs and care of the resident to determine:

- How and when staff try to identify whether a resident is experiencing pain and/or circumstances in which pain can be anticipated;
- How the resident is assessed for pain;
- How the interventions for pain management have been developed and the basis for selecting them;
- If the resident receives pain medication (including PRN and adjuvant medications), how, when, and by whom the results of medications are evaluated (including the dose, frequency of PRN use, schedule of routine medications, and effectiveness);
- How staff monitor for the emergence or presence of adverse consequences of interventions;
- What is done if pain persists or recurs despite treatment, and the basis for decisions to maintain or modify approaches;
- How staff communicate with the prescriber/practitioner about the resident's pain status, current measures to manage pain, and the possible need to modify the current pain management interventions; and
- For a resident who is receiving care under a hospice benefit, how the hospice and the facility coordinate their approaches and communicate about the resident's needs and monitor the outcomes (both effectiveness and adverse consequences).

Interviews with Other Health Care Professionals. If the interventions or care provided do not appear to be consistent with current standards of practice and/or the resident's pain appears to persist or recur, interview one or more health care professionals as necessary (e.g., attending physician, medical director, consultant pharmacist, director of nursing or hospice nurse) who, by virtue of training and knowledge of the resident, should be able to provide information about the evaluation and management of the resident's pain/symptoms. Depending on the issue, ask about:

- How chosen interventions were determined to be appropriate;
- How they guide and oversee the selection of pain management interventions;
- The rationale for not intervening, if pain was identified and no intervention was selected and implemented;

- Changes in pain characteristics that may warrant review or revision of interventions; or

- When and with whom the professional discussed the effectiveness, ineffectiveness and possible adverse consequences of pain management interventions.

If during the course of this review, the surveyor needs to contact the attending physician regarding questions related to the treatment regimen, it is recommended that the facility's staff have the opportunity to provide the necessary information about the resident and the concerns to the physician for his/her review prior to responding to the surveyor's inquiries. If the attending physician is unavailable, interview the medical director as appropriate.

DETERMINATION OF COMPLIANCE WITH F309 FOR PAIN MANAGEMENT (Task 6, Appendix P)

Synopsis of Regulation (Tag F309)

The resident must receive and the facility must provide the necessary care and services to attain or maintain his/her highest practicable level of physical, mental, and psychosocial well-being, in accordance with the comprehensive assessment and plan of care.

Criteria for Compliance with F309 for a Resident with Pain or the Potential for Pain

For a resident with pain or the potential for pain (such as pain related to treatments), the facility is in compliance with F309 Quality of Care as it relates to the recognition and management of pain, if each resident has received and the facility has provided the necessary care and services to attain or maintain the highest practicable physical, mental, and psychosocial well-being, in accordance with the comprehensive assessment and plan of care i.e., the facility:

- Recognized and evaluated the resident who experienced pain to determine (to the extent possible) causes and characteristics of the pain, as well as factors influencing the pain;

- Developed and implemented interventions for pain management for a resident experiencing pain, consistent with the resident's goals, risks, and current standards of practice; or has provided a clinically pertinent rationale why they did not do so;

- Recognized and provided measures to minimize or prevent pain for situations where pain could be anticipated;

- Monitored the effects of interventions and modified the approaches as indicated; and

- Communicated with the health care practitioner when a resident was having pain that was not adequately managed or was having a suspected or confirmed adverse consequence related to the treatment.

If not, cite at F309.

Noncompliance with F309 for a Resident with Pain or the Potential for Pain

After completing the Investigative Protocol, analyze the data in order to determine whether or not noncompliance with the regulation exists. Noncompliance for F309, with regard to pain management, may include, for example, failure to:

- Recognize and evaluate the resident who is experiencing pain in enough detail to permit pertinent individualized pain management;

- Provide interventions for pain management in situations where pain can be anticipated;

- Develop interventions for a resident who is experiencing pain (either specific to an overall pain management goal or as part of another aspect of the care plan);

- Implement interventions to address pain to the greatest extent possible consistent with the resident's goals and current standards of practice and have not provided a clinically pertinent rationale why this was not done;

- Monitor the effectiveness of intervention to manage pain; or

- Coordinate pain management as needed with an involved hospice to meet the resident's needs.

Concerns with Independent but Associated Structure, Process, and/or Outcome Requirements for a Resident with Pain or the Potential for Pain

During the investigation of care and services provided regarding pain management, the surveyor may have identified concerns with related structure, process, and/or outcome requirements. If an additional concern has been identified, the surveyor must investigate the identified concern. Do not cite any related or associated requirements before first conducting an investigation to determine compliance or non-compliance with the related or associated requirement. Some examples include, but are not limited to, the following:

- **42 CFR 483.10(b)(4) F155, The Right to Refuse Treatment**

  If a resident has refused treatment or services, determine whether the facility has assessed the reason for this resident's refusal, clarified and educated the resident as to the consequences of refusal, offered alternative treatments, and continued to provide all other services.

- **42 CFR 483.10(b)(11), F157, Notification of Changes**

  Determine if staff notified:

  - The physician when pain persisted or recurred despite treatment or when they suspected or identified adverse consequences related to treatments for pain; and

  - The resident's representative (if known) of significant changes in the resident's condition in relation to pain management and/or the plan of care for pain.

- **42 CFR 483.15(b), F242, Self-determination and Participation.**

  Determine if the facility has provided the resident with relevant choices about aspects of pain management.

- **42 CFR 483.15(e)(1), F246, Accommodation of Needs**

  Determine whether the facility has adapted the resident's physical environment (room, bathroom, furniture) to reasonably accommodate the resident's individual needs, related to pain management.

- **42 CFR 483.20, F272, Comprehensive Assessments**

  Determine if the facility comprehensively assessed the resident's physical, mental, and psychosocial needs to identify characteristics and determine underlying causes (to the extent possible) of the resident's pain and the impact of the pain upon the resident's function, mood, and cognition.

- **42 CFR 483.20(g) F278, Accuracy of Assessments**

  Determine whether the assessment accurately reflects the resident's status.

- **42 CFR 483.20(k), F279, Comprehensive Care Plans**

  Determine if the facility's comprehensive care plan for the resident included measurable objectives, time frames, and specific interventions/services to meet the resident's pain management needs, consistent with the resident's specific conditions, risks, needs, goals, and preferences and current standards of practice.

- **42 CFR 483.20(k)(2)(iii), 483.10(d)(3), F280, Comprehensive Care Plan Revision**

  Determine if the care plan was periodically reviewed and revised by a team of qualified persons with input from the resident or representative to try to reduce pain or discomfort.

- **42 CFR 483.20(k)(3)(i), F281, Services provided meet professional standards of quality**

  Determine if care was provided in accordance with accepted professional standards of quality for pain management.

- **42 CFR 483.20(k)(3)(ii), F282, Care provided by qualified persons in accordance with the plan of care**

  Determine whether care is being provided by qualified staff, and/or whether the care plan is adequately and/or correctly implemented.

- **42 CFR 483.25(l), F329, Unnecessary Drugs**

  Determine whether medications ordered to treat pain are being monitored for effectiveness and for adverse consequences, including whether any symptoms could be related to the medications.

- **42 CFR 483.40(a), F385, Physician Supervision**

  Determine if pain management is being supervised by a physician, including participation in the comprehensive assessment process, development of a treatment regimen consistent with current standards of practice, monitoring, and response to notification of change in the resident's medical status related to pain.

- **42 CFR 483.60, F425, Pharmacy Services**

  Determine if the medications required to manage a resident's pain were available and administered as indicated and ordered at admission and throughout the stay.

- **42 CFR 483.75(i)(2), F501, Medical Director**

  Determine whether the medical director helped the facility develop and implement policies and procedures related to preventing, identifying and managing pain, consistent with current standards of practice; and whether the medical director interacted with the physician supervising the care of the resident if requested by the facility to intervene on behalf of a resident with pain or one who may have been experiencing adverse consequences related to interventions to treat pain.

- **42 CRF 483.75(l) F514, Clinical Records**

  Determine whether the clinical record:

  - Accurately and completely documents the resident's status, the care and services provided, (e.g., to prevent to the extent possible, or manage the resident's pain) in accordance with current professional standards and practices and the resident's goals; and

  - Provide a basis for determining and managing the resident's progress including response to treatment, change in condition, and changes in treatment.

DEFICIENCY CATEGORIZATION (Part IV, Appendix P) for a Resident with Pain or Potential for Pain

Once the survey team has completed its investigation, analyzed the data, reviewed the regulatory requirements, and determined that noncompliance exists, the team must determine the severity of each deficiency, based on the harm or potential for harm to the resident. The key elements for severity determination for F309 Quality of Care regarding pain assessment and management are as follows:

1. Presence of harm/negative outcome(s) or potential for negative outcomes because of lack of appropriate treatment and care. Actual or potential harm/negative outcome for F309 related to pain assessment and management may include, but is not limited to:

- Persisting or recurring pain and discomfort related to failure to recognize, assess, or implement interventions for pain; and

- Decline in function resulting from failure to assess a resident after facility clinical staff became aware of new onset of moderate to severe pain.

2. Degree of harm (actual or potential) related to the non-compliance. Identify how the facility practices caused, resulted in, allowed or contributed to the actual or potential for harm:

- If harm has occurred, determine if the harm is at the level of serious injury, impairment, death, compromise, or discomfort; and

- If harm has not yet occurred, determine the potential for serious injury, impairment, death, compromise, or discomfort to occur to the resident.

3. The immediacy of correction required. Determine whether the noncompliance requires immediate correction in order to prevent serious injury, harm, impairment, or death to one or more residents.

The survey team must evaluate the harm or potential for harm based upon the following levels of severity for Tag F309 when related to recognition, assessment and management of pain. First, the team must rule out whether Severity Level 4, Immediate Jeopardy to a resident's health or safety, exists by evaluating the deficient practice in relation to immediacy, culpability, and severity, (Follow the guidance in Appendix Q, Determining Immediate Jeopardy).

Severity Level 4 Considerations: Immediate Jeopardy to Resident Health or Safety for a resident with pain or potential for pain.

Immediate Jeopardy is a situation in which the facility's non-compliance with one or more requirements of participation:

- Has allowed, caused, or resulted in (or is likely to allow, cause, or result in) serious injury, harm, impairment, or death to a resident; and

- Requires immediate correction, as the facility either created the situation or allowed the situation to continue by failing to implement preventative or corrective measures.

NOTE: The death or transfer of a resident who was harmed or injured as a result of facility noncompliance does not remove a finding of immediate jeopardy. The facility is required to implement specific actions to correct the noncompliance, which allowed or caused the immediate jeopardy.

Level 4 indicates noncompliance that results, or has the potential to result, in expressions (verbal and/or non-verbal) of severe, unrelenting, excruciating, and unrelieved pain; pain has become all-consuming and overwhelms the resident.

Examples may include, but are not limited to:

- Resident experienced continuous, unrelenting, excruciating pain or incapacitating distress because the facility has failed to recognize or address the situation, or failed to develop, implement, monitor, or modify a pain management plan to try to meet the resident's needs; or

- Resident experienced recurring, episodic excruciating pain or incapacitating distress related to specific situations where pain could be anticipated (e.g., because pain has already been identified during dressing changes or therapies) and the facility failed to attempt pain management strategies to try to minimize the pain.

NOTE: If immediate jeopardy has been ruled out based upon the evidence, then evaluate whether actual harm that is not immediate jeopardy exists at Severity Level 3.

Severity Level 3 Considerations: Actual Harm that is not Immediate Jeopardy for a resident with pain or potential for pain.

Level 3 indicates non-compliance that resulted in actual harm, and may include, but is not limited to, clinical compromise, decline, or the resident's inability to maintain and/or reach his/her highest practicable well-being.

Level 3 indicates noncompliance that results in expressions (verbal and non-verbal) of pain that has compromised the resident's functioning such as diminished level of participation in social interactions and/or ADLs, intermittent crying and moaning, weight loss and/or diminished appetite. Pain has become a central focus of the resident's attention, but it is not all-consuming or overwhelming (as in Severity Level 4).

Examples may include, but are not limited to:

- The resident experienced pain that compromised his/her function (physical and/or psychosocial) and/or ability to reach his/her highest practicable well-being as a result of the facility's failure to recognize or address the situation, or failure to develop, implement, monitor, or modify a pain management plan to try to meet the resident's needs. For example, the pain was intense enough that the resident experienced recurrent insomnia, anorexia with resultant weight loss, reduced ability to move and perform ADLs, a decline in mood, or reduced social engagement and participation in activities; or

- The resident experienced significant episodic pain (that was not all-consuming or overwhelming but was greater than minimal discomfort to the resident) related to care/treatment, as a result of the facility's failure to develop, implement, monitor, or modify pain management interventions. Some examples include lack of pain management interventions prior to dressing changes, wound care, exercise or physical therapy.

NOTE: If Severity Level 3 (actual harm that is not immediate jeopardy) has been ruled out based upon the evidence, then evaluate as to whether Level 2 (no actual harm with the potential for more than minimal harm) exists.

Severity Level 2 Considerations: No Actual Harm with potential for more than minimal harm that is Not Immediate Jeopardy for a resident with pain or potential for pain.

Severity Level 2 indicates noncompliance that resulted in a resident outcome of no more than minimal discomfort and/or has the potential to compromise the resident's ability to maintain or reach his or her highest practicable level of well-being. The potential exists for greater harm to occur if interventions are not provided.

Level 2 indicates noncompliance that results in feelings and/or complaints of discomfort or moderate pain. The resident may be irritable and/or express discomfort.

Examples may include, but are not limited to:

- The resident experienced daily or less than daily discomfort with no compromise in physical, mental, or psychosocial functioning as a result of the facility's failure to adequately recognize or address the situation, or failure to develop, implement, monitor, or modify a pain management plan to try to meet the resident's needs; or

- The resident experienced minimal episodic pain or discomfort (that was not significant pain) related to care/treatment, as a result of the facility's failure to develop, implement, monitor, or modify a pain management plan.

Severity Level 1: No actual harm with potential for no more than minimal harm for a resident with pain or potential for pain.

The failure of the facility to provide appropriate care and services for pain management places the resident at risk for more than minimal harm. Therefore, Severity Level 1 does not apply for this regulatory requirement.

---

§483.25(a) Activities of Daily Living

Based on the comprehensive assessment of a resident, the facility must ensure that

Intent §483.25(a)

The intent of this regulation is that the facility must ensure that a resident's abilities in ADLs do not deteriorate unless the deterioration was unavoidable.

F310

§483.25(a)(1) A resident's abilities in activities of daily living do not diminish unless circumstances of the individual's clinical condition demonstrate that diminution was unavoidable. This includes the resident's ability to --

(i) Bathe, dress, and groom;

(ii) Transfer and ambulate;

(iii) Toilet;

(iv) Eat; and

(v) Use speech, language, or other functional communication systems.

Interpretive Guidelines §483.25(a)

The mere presence of a clinical diagnosis, in itself, justify a decline in a resident's ability to perform ADLs. Conditions which may demonstrate unavoidable diminution in ADLs include:

- The natural progression of the resident's disease;

- Deterioration of the resident's physical condition associated with the onset of a physical or mental disability while receiving care to restore or maintain functional abilities; and

- The resident's or his/her surrogate's or representative's refusal of care and treatment to restore or maintain functional abilities after aggressive efforts by the facility to counsel and/or offer alternatives to the resident, surrogate, or representative. Refusal of such care and treatment should be documented in the clinical record. Determine which interventions were identified on the care plan and/or could be in place to minimize or decrease complications. Note also that depression is a potential cause of excess disability and, where appropriate, therapeutic interventions should be initiated.

Appropriate treatment and services includes all care provided to residents by employees, contractors, or volunteers of the facility to maximize the individual's functional abilities. This includes pain relief and control, especially when it is causing a decline or a decrease in the quality of life of the resident.

If the survey team identifies a pattern of deterioration in ADLs, i.e., a number of residents have deteriorated in more than one ADL or a number of residents have deteriorated in only one ADL (one in bathing, one in eating, one in toileting) and it is determined there is deficient practice, cite at F310.

For evaluating a resident's ADLs and determining whether a resident's abilities have declined, improved or stayed the same within the last twelve months, use the following definitions as specified in the State's RAI:

1. **Independent** - No help or staff oversight; or staff help/oversight provided only 1 or 2 times during prior 7 days.

2. **Supervision** - Oversight encouragement or cuing provided 3 or more times during the last 7 days, or supervision plus physical assistance provided only 1 or 2 times during the last 7 days.

3. **Limited Assistance** - Resident highly involved in activity, received physical help in guided maneuvering of limbs, and/or other non-weight bearing assistance 3 or more times; or more help provided only 1 or 2 times over 7-day period.

4. **Extensive Assistance** - While resident performed part of activity, over prior 7-day period, help of following type(s) was provided 3 or more times;

   a. Weight-bearing support; or

   b. Full staff performance during part (but not all) of week.

5. **Total Dependence** - Full staff performance of activity over entire 7-day period.

§483.25(a)(1)(i) Bathing, Dressing, Grooming

Interpretive Guidelines §483.25(a)(1)(i)

This corresponds to MDS section E; version 2.0, section G, when specified for use by the State.

"Bathing" means how resident takes full-body bath, sponge bath, and transfers in/out of tub/shower. Exclude washing of back and hair.

"Dressing" means how resident puts on, fastens, and takes off all items of clothing, including donning/removing prosthesis.

"Grooming" means how resident maintains personal hygiene, including preparatory activities, combing hair, brushing teeth, shaving, applying make-up, washing/drying face, hands and perineum. Exclude baths and showers.

BATHING, DRESSING, GROOMING

Procedures §483.25(a)(1)(i)

For each sampled resident selected for the comprehensive review or the focused review, as appropriate, determine:

1. Whether the resident's ability to bathe, dress and/or groom has changed since admission, or over the past 12 months;

2. Whether the resident's ability to bathe, dress and groom has improved, declined or stayed the same;

3. Whether any deterioration or lack of improvement was avoidable or unavoidable by:

4. Identifying if resident triggers RAPs for ADL functional/rehabilitation potential.

   a. What risk factors for decline of bathing, dressing, and/or grooming abilities did the facility identify?

   b. What care did the resident receive to address unique needs to maintain his/her bathing, dressing, and/or grooming abilities (e.g., resident needs a button hook to button his shirt; staff teaches the resident how to use it; staff provides resident with dementia with cues that allow him/her to dress him or herself)?

   c. Were individual objectives of the plan of care periodically evaluated, and if the objectives were not met, were alternative approaches developed to encourage maintenance of bathing, dressing, and/or grooming abilities (e.g., resident now unable to button dress, even with encouragement; will ask family if we may use velcro in place of buttons so resident can continue to dress herself)?

Probes §483.25(a)(1)(i)

If the resident's abilities in bathing, dressing, and grooming have been maintained, what evidence is there that the resident could have improved if appropriate treatment and services were provided:

- Identify relevant sections of the MDS and consider whether assessment triggers the RAPs and the RAPs were followed.

- Are there physical and psychosocial deficits that could affect improvement in functional abilities?

- Was the care plan driven by resident strengths identified in the comprehensive assessment?

- Was the care plan consistently implemented?

- What changes were made in treatment if the resident failed to progress or when initial rehabilitation goals were achieved, but additional progress might have been possible?

TRANSFER AND AMBULATION

§483.25(a)(1)(ii)

Interpretive Guidelines §483.25(a)(1)(ii)

This corresponds to MDS section E; MDS 2.0 section G when specified for use by the State.

"Transfer" means how resident moves between surfaces - to/from: bed, chair, wheelchair, standing position. (Exclude to/from bath/toilet.)

"Ambulation" means how resident moves between locations in his/her room and adjacent corridor on same floor. If in wheelchair, self-sufficiency once in chair.

Procedures §483.25(a)(1)(ii)

Determine for each resident selected for a comprehensive review, or a focused review as appropriate, whether the resident's ability to transfer and ambulate has declined, improved or stayed the same and whether any deterioration or decline in function was avoidable or unavoidable.

Probes §483.25(a)(1)(ii)

If the resident's transferring and ambulating abilities have declined, what evidence is there that the decline was unavoidable:

- What risk factors for decline of transferring or ambulating abilities did the facility identify (e.g., necrotic area of foot ulcer becoming larger, postural hypotension)?

- What care did the resident receive to address risk factors and unique needs to maintain transferring or ambulating abilities (e.g., a transfer board is provided to maintain ability to transfer from bed to wheelchair and staff teaches the resident how to use it)?

- What evidence is there that sufficient staff time and assistance are provided to maintain transferring and ambulating abilities?

- Has resident been involved in activities that enhance mobility skills?

- Were individual objectives of the plan of care periodically evaluated, and if goals were not met, were alternative approaches developed to encourage maintenance of transferring and ambulation abilities (e.g., resident remains unsteady when using a cane, returns to walker, with staff encouraging the walker's consistent use)?

- Identify if resident triggers RAPs for ADL functional/rehabilitation potential, psychosocial well-being, or mood state and the RAPs are followed.

If the resident's abilities in transferring and ambulating have been maintained, is there evidence that the resident could have improved if appropriate treatment and services were provided?

- Are there physical and psychosocial deficits that could affect improvement in functional abilities?

- Was the care plan driven by resident strengths identified in the comprehensive assessment?

- Was the care plan consistently implemented? What changes were made in treatment if the resident failed to progress or when initial rehabilitation goals were achieved, but additional progress seemed possible?

TOILETING

§483.25(a)(1)(iii) `

Interpretive Guidelines §483.25(a)(1)(iii)

This corresponds to MDS sections E; MDS 2.0 sections G and H when specified for use by the State.

"Toilet use" means how the resident uses the toilet room (or commode, bedpan, urinal); transfers on/off the toilet, cleanses self, changes pad, manages ostomy or catheter, adjusts clothes.

Procedures §483.25(a)(1)(iii)

Determine for each resident selected for a comprehensive review, or focused review as appropriate, whether the resident's ability to use the toilet has improved, declined or stayed the same and whether any deterioration or decline in improvement was avoidable or unavoidable.

Probes §483.25(a)(1)(iii)

If the resident's toilet use abilities have declined, what evidence is there that the decline was unavoidable.

- What risk factors for the decline of toilet use abilities did the facility identify (e.g., severe arthritis in hands makes use of toilet paper difficult)?

- What care did resident receive to address risk factors and unique needs to maintain toilet use abilities (e.g., assistive devices to maintain ability to use the toilet such as using a removable elevated toilet seat or wall grab bar to facilitate rising from seated position to standing position)?

- Is there sufficient staff time and assistance provided to maintain toilet use abilities (e.g., allowing residents enough time to use the toilet independently or with limited assistance)?

- Were individual objectives of the plan of care periodically evaluated, and if objectives were not met, were alternative approaches developed to encourage maintaining toilet use abilities (e.g., if resident has not increased sitting stability, seek occupational therapy consult to determine the need for therapy to increase sitting balance, ability to transfer safely and manipulate clothing during the toileting process. For residents with dementia, remind periodically to use the toilet)?

- Identify if resident triggers RAPs for urinary incontinence, and ADL functional/rehabilitation potential and the RAPs were used to assess causal factors for decline or potential for decline or lack of improvement.

If the resident's toilet use abilities have been maintained, what evidence is there that the resident could have improved if appropriate treatment and services were provided?

- Are there physical and psychosocial deficits that could affect improvement in functional abilities?

- Was the care plan driven by resident strengths identified in the comprehensive assessment?

- Was the care plan consistently implemented? What changes were made to treatment if the resident failed to progress or when initial rehabilitation goals were achieved, but additional progress seemed possible?

- Identify if resident triggers RAPs for mood state and psychosocial well-being.

EATING

§483.25(a)(1)(iv)

Interpretive Guidelines §483.25(a)(1)(iv)

This corresponds to MDS sections E, L1 and MI; MDS 2.0, sections G and K when specified for use by the State.

"Eating" means how resident ingests and drinks (regardless of self-feeding skill).

Procedures §483.25(a)(1)(iv)

Determine for each resident selected for a comprehensive review, or focused review, as appropriate, whether the resident's ability to eat or eating skills has improved, declined, or stayed the same and whether any deterioration or lack of improvement was avoidable or unavoidable.

If the resident's eating abilities have declined, is there any evidence that the decline was unavoidable?

1. What risk factors for decline of eating skills did the facility identify?

   a. A decrease in the ability to chew and swallow food;

   b. Deficit in neurological and muscular status necessary for moving food onto a utensil and into the mouth;

   c. Oral health status affecting eating ability;

   d. Depression or confused mental state.

2. What care did the resident receive to address risk factors and unique needs to maintain eating abilities?

   a. Assistive devices to improve resident's grasp or coordination;

   b. Seating arrangements to improve sociability;

   c. Seating in a calm, quiet setting for residents with dementia.

3. Is there sufficient staff time and assistance provided to maintain eating abilities (e.g., allowing residents enough time to eat independently or with limited assistance)?

4. Identify if resident triggers RAPs for ADL functional/rehabilitation potential, feeding tubes, and dehydration/fluid maintenance, and the RAPs were used to assess causal reasons for decline, potential for decline or lack of improvement.

5. Were individual objectives of the plan of care periodically evaluated, and if the objectives were not met, were alternative approaches developed to encourage maintaining eating abilities?

Probes §483.25(a)(1)(iv)

If the resident's eating abilities have been maintained, what evidence is there that the resident could have improved if appropriate treatment and services were provided:

- Are there physical and psychosocial deficits that could affect improvement in functional abilities?

- Was the care plan driven by resident strengths identified in the comprehensive assessment?

- Was the care plan consistently implemented? What changes are made to treatment if the resident failed to progress or when initial rehabilitation goals were achieved, but additional progress seemed possible?

Interpretive Guidelines §483.25(a)(1)(v)

This corresponds to MDS, section C; MDS 2.0 sections B and C when specified for use by the State.

"Speech, language or other functional communication systems" is defined as the ability to effectively communicate requests, needs, opinions, and urgent problems; to express emotion, to listen to others and to participate in social conversation whether in speech, writing, gesture or a combination of these (e.g., a communication board or electronic augmentative communication device).

USE OF SPEECH, LANGUAGE, OR OTHER FUNCTIONAL COMMUNCATION SYSTEMS

§483.25(a)(1)(v)

Procedures §483.25(a)(1)(v)

Determine for each resident selected for a comprehensive review, or focused review, as appropriate, if resident's ability to communicate has declined, improved or stayed the same and whether any deterioration or lack of improvement was avoidable or unavoidable.

Identify if resident triggers RAPs for communication, psychosocial well-being, mood state, and visual function, and if the RAPs were used to assess causal factors for decline, potential for decline or lack of improvement.

Probes §483.25(a)(1)(v)

If the resident's communication abilities have diminished, is there any evidence that the decline was unavoidable:

- What risk factors for decline of communication abilities did the facility identify and how did they address them (e.g., dysarthria, poor fitting dentures, few visitors, poor relationships with staff, Alzheimer's disease)?

- Has the resident received audiologic and vision evaluation? If not, did the resident refuse such services? (See also §483.10(b)(4).)

- What unique resident needs and risk factors did the facility identify (e.g., does the resident have specific difficulties in transmitting messages, comprehending messages, and/or using a variety of communication skills such as questions and commands; does the resident receive evaluation and training in the use of assistive devices to increase and/or maintain writing skills)?

- What care does the resident receive to improve communication abilities (e.g.,nurse aides communicate in writing with deaf residents or residents with severe hearing problems; practice exercises with residents receiving speech-language pathology services; increase number of resident's communication opportunities; non-verbal means of communication; review of the effect of medications on communication ability)?

- Is there sufficient staff time and assistance provided to maintain communication abilities?

- Were individual objectives of the plan of care periodically evaluated, and if the objectives were not met, were alternative approaches developed to encourage maintenance of communication abilities (e.g., if drill-oriented therapy is frustrating the resident, a less didactic approach should be attempted)?

Probes §483.25(a)(1)(v)

If the resident's speech, language, and other communication abilities have been maintained, what evidence is there that the resident could have improved if appropriate treatment and services were provided:

- Are there physical and psychosocial deficits that could affect improvement in functional abilities?

- Was the care plan driven by resident strengths identified in the comprehensive assessment?

- Was the care plan consistently implemented?

- What changes were made to treatment if the resident failed to progress or when initial rehabilitation goals were achieved, but additional progress seemed possible?

F311

§483.25(a)(2)

(2) A resident is given the appropriate treatment and services to maintain or improve his or her abilities specified in paragraph (a)(1) of this section; and

Intent §483.25(a)(2)

The intent of this regulation is to stress that the facility is responsible for providing maintenance and restorative programs that will not only maintain, but improve, as indicated by the resident's comprehensive assessment to achieve and maintain the highest practicable outcome.

Procedures §483.25(a)(2)

Use the survey procedures and probes at §483.25(a)(1)(i) through (v) to assist in making this determination.

F312

§483.25(a)(3)

(3) A resident who is unable to carry out activities of daily living receives the necessary services to maintain good nutrition, grooming, and personal and oral hygiene.

Intent §483.25(a)(3)

The intent of this regulation is that the resident receives the care and services needed because he/she is unable to do their own ADL care independently.

Interpretive Guidelines §483.25(a)(3)

This corresponds to MDS section L; MDS 2.0 section K when specified by the State.

"Unable to carry out ADLs" means those residents who need extensive or total assistance with maintenance of nutrition, grooming and personal and oral hygiene, receive this assistance from the facility.

Methods for maintenance of good nutrition may include hand feeding of foods served on dishes; tube feedings provided through naso-gastric, gastrostomy, or other external tubes; or total parenteral nutrition provided through a central intravenous line.

"Grooming" - See §483.25(a)(1)(i) for definition.

"Personal hygiene" - Those activities described in dressing and bathing as defined in §483.25(a)(1)(i).

"Oral hygiene" means maintaining the mouth in a clean and intact condition and treating oral pathology such as ulcers of the mucosa. Services to maintain oral hygiene may include brushing the teeth, cleaning dentures, cleaning the mouth and tongue either by assisting the resident with a mouth wash or by manual cleaning with a gauze sponge; and application of medication as prescribed.

Procedures §483.25(a)(3)

For residents selected for a comprehensive review, or focused review, as appropriate, who are unable to carry out these ADLs without extensive assistance, determine if poor nutritional status, poor grooming, or lack of effective personal and oral hygiene exist. To what extent are these negative outcomes attributable to the lack of receiving necessary services?

Identify if residents trigger RAPs for nutritional status, ADL functional/rehabilitation potential, behavior problems, and dental care. Consider whether the RAPs were used to assess causal factors for decline, potential for decline, or lack of improvement. Determine if the facility proceeded properly with care planning and delivery of care for these residents.

F313

§483.25(b) Vision and Hearing

To ensure that residents receive proper treatment and assistive devices to maintain vision and hearing abilities, the facility must, if necessary, assist the resident --

1. In making appointments, and

2. By arranging for transportation to and from the office of a practitioner specializing in the treatment of vision or hearing impairment or the office of a professional specializing in the provision of vision or hearing assistive devices.

Intent §483.25(b)

The intent of this regulation is to require a facility to assist residents in gaining access to vision and hearing services by making appointments and arranging for transportation, and assistance with the use of any devices needed to maintain vision and hearing.

Interpretive Guidelines §483.25(b)

This corresponds to MDS, sections C and O; MDS 2.0 sections C, D, and P when specified for use by the State.

Assistive devices to maintain vision include glasses, contact lenses, and magnifying glasses. Assistive devices to maintain hearing include hearing aids.

This requirement does not mean that the facility must provide refractions, glasses, contact lenses, conduct comprehensive audiological evaluations (although screening is a part of the required assessment in §483.20(b)) or provide hearing aids.

The facility's responsibility is to assist residents and their families in locating and utilizing any available resources (e.g., Medicare or Medicaid program payment, local health organizations offering items and services which are available free to the community) for the provision of the services the resident needs. This includes making appointments and arranging transportation to obtain needed services.

Probes §483.25(b)

- Identify if resident triggers RAPs for visual function, and communication. Consider whether the RAPs were used to assess causal factors for decline, potential for decline or lack of improvement.

- If the resident needs, and/or requests and does not have vision and/or hearing assistive devices, what has the facility done to assist the resident in making appointments and obtaining transportation to obtain these services?

- If the resident has assistive devices but is not using them, why not (e.g., are repairs or batteries needed)?

F314

§483.25(c) Pressure Sores

Based on the Comprehensive Assessment of a resident, the facility must ensure that-

(1) A resident who enters the facility without pressure sores does not develop pressure sores unless the individual's clinical condition demonstrates that they were unavoidable; and

(2) A resident having pressure sores receives necessary treatment and services to promote healing, prevent infection and prevent new sores from developing.

Intent: (F314) 42 CFR 483.25(c)

The intent of this requirement is that the resident does not develop pressure ulcers unless clinically unavoidable and that the facility provides care and services to:

- Promote the prevention of pressure ulcer development;

- Promote the healing of pressure ulcers that are present (including prevention of infection to the extent possible); and

- Prevent development of additional pressure ulcers.

NOTE: Although the regulatory language refers to pressure sores, the nomenclature widely accepted presently refers to pressure ulcers, and the guidance provided in this document will refer to pressure ulcers.

DEFINITIONS

Definitions are provided to clarify clinical terms related to pressure ulcers and their evaluation and treatment.

- "Pressure Ulcer"- A pressure ulcer is any lesion caused by unrelieved pressure that results in damage to the underlying tissue(s).[1] Although friction and shear are not primary causes of pressure ulcers, friction and shear are important contributing factors to the development of pressure ulcers.

- "Avoidable/Unavoidable" Pressure Ulcers

  o   "Avoidable" means that the resident developed a pressure ulcer and that the facility did not do one or more of the following: evaluate the resident's clinical condition and pressure ulcer risk factors; define and implement interventions that are consistent with resident needs, resident goals, and recognized standards of practice; monitor and evaluate the impact of the interventions; or revise the interventions as appropriate.

o   "Unavoidable" means that the resident developed a pressure ulcer even though the facility had evaluated the resident's clinical condition and pressure ulcer risk factors; defined and implemented interventions that are consistent with resident needs, goals, and recognized standards of practice; monitored and evaluated the impact of the interventions; and revised the approaches as appropriate.

- "Cleansing/Irrigation"

o   "Cleansing" refers to the use of an appropriate device and solution to clean the surface of the wound bed and to remove the looser foreign debris or contaminants in order to decrease microbial growth.[2]

o   "Irrigation" refers to a type of mechanical debridement, which uses an appropriate solution delivered under pressure to the wound bed to vigorously attempt to remove debris from the wound bed.[3]

- "Colonized/Infected" Wound [4, 5]

o   "Colonized" refers to the presence of bacteria on the surface or in the tissue of a wound without the signs and symptoms of an infection.

o   "Infected" refers to the presence of micro-organisms in sufficient quantity to overwhelm the defenses of viable tissues and produce the signs and symptoms of infection.

- "Debridement"- Debridement is the removal of devitalized/necrotic tissue and foreign matter from a wound to improve or facilitate the healing process.[6, 7, 8] Various debridement methods include:

o   "Autolytic debridement" refers to the use of moisture retentive dressings to cover a wound and allow devitalized tissue to self-digest by the action of enzymes present in the wound fluids.

o   "Enzymatic (chemical) debridement" refers to the topical application of substances e.g., enzymes to break down devitalized tissue.

o   "Mechanical debridement" refers to the removal of foreign material and devitalized or contaminated tissue from a wound by physical rather than by chemical or autolytic means.

o   "Sharp or surgical debridement" refers to removal of foreign material or devitalized tissue by a surgical instrument.

o   "Maggot debridement therapy (MDT)" or medicinal maggots refers to a type of sterile intentional biological larval or biosurgical debridement that uses disinfected (sterile) maggots to clean wounds by dissolving the dead and infected tissue and by killing bacteria.[9]

- "Eschar/Slough"

o   "Eschar" is described as thick, leathery, frequently black or brown in color, necrotic (dead) or devitalized tissue that has lost its usual physical properties and biological activity. Eschar may be loose or firmly adhered to the wound.

o   "Slough" is necrotic/avascular tissue in the process of separating from the viable portions of the body and is usually light colored, soft, moist, and stringy (at times).

- "Exudate"

o   "Exudate" is any fluid that has been forced out of the tissues or its capillaries because of inflammation or injury. It may contain serum, cellular debris, bacteria and leukocytes.

o "Purulent exudate/drainage/discharge" is any product of inflammation that contains pus (e.g., leukocytes, bacteria, and liquefied necrotic debris).

o "Serous drainage or exudate" is watery, clear, or slightly yellow/tan/pink fluid that has separated from the blood and presents as drainage.

- "Friction/Shearing"

o "Friction" is the mechanical force exerted on skin that is dragged across any surface.

o "Shearing" is the interaction of both gravity and friction against the surface of the skin. Friction is always present when shear force is present.[10] Shear occurs when layers of skin rub against each other or when the skin remains stationary and the underlying tissue moves and stretches and angulates or tears the underlying capillaries and blood vessels causing tissue damage.

- "Granulation Tissue"

o "Granulation tissue" is the pink-red moist tissue that fills an open wound, when it starts to heal. It contains new blood vessels, collagen, fibroblasts, and inflammatory cells.

- "Tunnel/Sinus Tract/Undermining"-Tunnel and sinus tract are often used interchangeably.

o "Tunneling" is a passageway of tissue destruction under the skin surface that has an opening at the skin level from the edge of the wound.

o A "sinus tract" is a cavity or channel underlying a wound that involves an area larger than the visible surface of the wound.

o "Undermining" is the destruction of tissue or ulceration extending under the skin edges (margins) so that the pressure ulcer is larger at its base than at the skin surface. Undermining often develops from shearing forces and is differentiated from tunneling by the larger extent of the wound edge involved in undermining and the absence of a channel or tract extending from the pressure ulcer under the adjacent intact skin.

OVERVIEW

A pressure ulcer can occur wherever pressure has impaired circulation to the tissue. Critical steps in pressure ulcer prevention and healing include: identifying the individual resident at risk for developing pressure ulcers, identifying and evaluating the risk factors and changes in the resident's condition, identifying and evaluating factors that can be removed or modified, implementing individualized interventions to attempt to stabilize, reduce or remove underlying risk factors, monitoring the impact of the interventions, and modifying the interventions as appropriate. It is important to recognize and evaluate each resident's risk factors and to identify and evaluate all areas at risk of constant pressure.

A complete assessment is essential to an effective pressure ulcer prevention and treatment program. A comprehensive individual evaluation helps the facility to:

- Identify the resident at risk of developing pressure ulcers, the level and nature of risk(s); and

- Identify the presence of pressure ulcers.

This information allows the facility to develop and implement a comprehensive care plan that reflects each resident's identified needs.

The care process should include efforts to stabilize, reduce or remove underlying risk factors; to monitor the impact of the interventions; and to modify the interventions as appropriate.

The facility should have a system/procedure to assure: assessments are timely and appropriate; interventions are implemented, monitored, and revised as appropriate; and changes in condition are recognized, evaluated, reported to the practitioner, and addressed. The quality assessment and assurance committee may help the facility evaluate existing strategies to reduce the development and progression of pressure ulcers, monitor the incidence and prevalence of pressure ulcers within the facility, and ensure that facility policies and procedures are consistent with current standards of practice.

Research into appropriate practices for the prevention, management and treatment of pressure ulcers, continues to evolve. As such, there are many recognized clinical resources regarding the prevention and management of pressure ulcers (including wound care, and complications such as infections and pain). Some of these resources include:

- The Clinical Practice Guidelines from the Agency for Healthcare Research and Quality (AHRQ) www.ahrq.gov (Guideline No. 15: *Treatment of Pressure Ulcers and Guideline* No.3: *Pressure Ulcers in Adults: Prediction and Prevention*)(AHRQ was previously known as the Agency for Health Care Policy and Research [AHCPR]);

- The National Pressure Ulcer Advisory Panel (NPUAP) www.npuap.org;

- The American Medical Directors Association (AMDA) www.amda.com (*Clinical Practice Guidelines: Pressure Ulcers*, 1996 and *Pressure Ulcer Therapy Companion*, 1999);

- The Quality Improvement Organizations, Medicare Quality Improvement Community Initiatives site at www.medqic.org;

- The Wound, Ostomy, and Continence Nurses Society (WOCN) www.wocn.org; and

- The American Geriatrics Society guideline *"The Management of Persistent Pain in Older Persons"*, www.healthinaging.org.

NOTE: References to non-CMS sources or sites on the Internet are provided as a service and do not constitute or imply endorsement of these organizations or their programs by CMS or the U.S. Department of Health and Human Services. CMS is not responsible for the content of pages found at these sites. URL addresses were current as of the date of this publication.

PREVENTION OF PRESSURE ULCERS

The citation at 42 CFR 483.25 (c) requires that a resident who is admitted without a pressure ulcer doesn't develop a pressure ulcer unless clinically unavoidable, and that a resident who has an ulcer receives care and services to promote healing and to prevent additional ulcers.

The first step in prevention is the identification of the resident at risk of developing pressure ulcers. This is followed by implementation of appropriate individualized interventions and monitoring for the effectiveness of the interventions.

ASSESSMENT

An admission evaluation helps identify the resident at risk of developing a pressure ulcer, and the resident with existing pressure ulcer(s) or areas of skin that are at risk for breakdown. Because a resident at risk can develop a pressure ulcer within 2 to 6 hours of the onset of pressure,[11] the at-risk resident needs to be identified and have interventions implemented promptly to attempt to prevent pressure ulcers. The admission evaluation helps define those initial care approaches.

In addition, the admission evaluation may identify pre-existing signs (such as a purple or very dark area that is surrounded by profound redness, edema, or induration)[12] suggesting that deep tissue damage has already occurred and additional deep tissue loss may occur. This deep tissue damage could lead to the appearance of an unavoidable Stage III or IV pressure ulcer or progression of a Stage I pressure ulcer to an ulcer with eschar or exudate within days after admission. Some situations, which may have contributed to this tissue damage, include pressure resulting from immobility during hospitalization or surgical procedures, during prolonged ambulance transport, or while waiting to be discovered or assisted after a debilitating event, such as a fall or a cerebral vascular accident.

Some evidence suggests that because it may be harder to identify erythema in an older adult with darkly pigmented skin, older individuals with darkly pigmented skin may be more at risk for developing pressure ulcers.[13, 14, 15, 16] It may be necessary, therefore, in a darker skinned individual to focus more on other evidence of pressure ulcer development, such as bogginess, induration, coolness, or increased warmth as well as signs of skin discoloration.

Multiple factors, including pressure intensity, pressure duration, and tissue tolerance, significantly affect the potential for the development and healing of pressure ulcers. An individual may also have various intrinsic risks due to aging, for example: decreased subcutaneous tissue and lean muscle mass, decreased skin elasticity, and impaired circulation or innervation.

The comprehensive assessment, which includes the Resident Assessment Instrument (RAI), evaluates the resident's intrinsic risks, the resident's skin condition, other factors (including causal factors) which place the resident at risk for developing pressure ulcers and/or experiencing delayed healing, and the nature of the pressure to which the resident may be subjected. The assessment should identify which risk factors can be removed or modified.

The assessment also helps identify the resident who has multi-system organ failure or an end-of-life condition or who is refusing care and treatment. If the resident is refusing care, an evaluation of the basis for the refusal, and the identification and evaluation of potential alternatives is indicated.

This comprehensive assessment should address those factors that have been identified as having an impact on the development, treatment and/or healing of pressure ulcers, including, at a minimum: risk factors, pressure points, under-nutrition and hydration deficits, and moisture and the impact of moisture on skin. Each of these factors is discussed in additional detail in the following sections.

Risk Factors

Many studies and professional documents identify risk factors that increase a resident's susceptibility to develop or to not heal pressure ulcers.[17, 18, 19] Examples of these risk factors include, but are not limited to:

- Impaired/decreased mobility and decreased functional ability;

- Co-morbid conditions, such as end stage renal disease, thyroid disease or diabetes mellitus;

- Drugs such as steroids that may affect wound healing;

- Impaired diffuse or localized blood flow, for example, generalized atherosclerosis or lower extremity arterial insufficiency;

- Resident refusal of some aspects of care and treatment;

- Cognitive impairment;

- Exposure of skin to urinary and fecal incontinence;

- Under nutrition, malnutrition, and hydration deficits; and

- A healed ulcer. The history of a healed pressure ulcer and its stage [if known] is important, since areas of healed Stage III or IV pressure ulcers are more likely to have recurrent breakdown.

Some residents have many risk factors for developing pressure ulcers, such as diabetic neuropathy, frailty, cognitive impairment, and under nutrition. Not all factors are fully modifiable and some potentially modifiable factors (e.g., under-nutrition) may not be corrected immediately, despite prompt intervention, while other factors such as pressure may be modified promptly. It may be necessary to stabilize, when possible, the underlying causes (e.g., control blood sugars or ensure adequate food and fluid intake).

Although the requirements do not mandate any specific assessment tool, other than the RAI, validated instruments are available to assess risk for developing pressure ulcers. Research has shown that a significant number of pressure ulcers develop within the first four weeks after admission to a long term care facility.[20] Therefore, many clinicians recommend using a standardized pressure ulcer risk assessment tool to assess a resident's pressure ulcer risks upon admission, weekly for the first four weeks after admission for each resident at risk, then quarterly, or whenever there is a change in cognition or functional ability.[21, 22] A resident's risk may increase due to an acute illness or condition change (e.g., upper respiratory infection, pneumonia, or exacerbation of underlying congestive heart failure) and may require additional evaluation.

Regardless of any resident's total risk score, the clinicians responsible for the resident's care should review each risk factor and potential cause(s) individually[23] to: a) Identify those that increase the potential for the resident to develop pressure ulcers; b) Decide whether and to what extent the factor(s) can be modified, stabilized, removed, etc., and c) Determine whether targeted management protocols need to be implemented. In other words, an overall risk score indicating the resident is not at high risk of developing pressure ulcers does not mean that existing risk factors or causes should be considered less important or addressed less vigorously than those factors or causes in the resident whose overall score indicates he or she is at a higher risk of developing a pressure ulcer.

Pressure Points and Tissue Tolerance

Assessment of a resident's skin condition helps define prevention strategies. The skin assessment should include an evaluation of the skin integrity and tissue tolerance (ability of the skin and its supporting structures to endure the effects of pressure without adverse effects) after pressure to that area has been reduced or redistributed.

Tissue closest to the bone may be the first tissue to undergo necrosis. Pressure ulcers are usually located over a bony prominence, such as the sacrum, heel, the greater trochanter, ischial tuberosity, fibular head, scapula, and ankle (malleolus).

An at-risk resident who sits too long on a static surface may be more prone to get ischial ulceration. Slouching in a chair may predispose an at-risk resident to pressure ulcers of the spine, scapula, or elbow (elbow ulceration is often related to arm rests or lap boards). Friction and shearing are also important factors in tissue ischemia, necrosis and pressure ulcer formation.

Pressure ulcers may develop at other sites where pressure has impaired the circulation to the tissue, such as pressure from positioning or use of medical devices. For example, pressure ulcers may develop from pressure on an ear lobe related to positioning of the head; pressure or friction on areas (e.g., nares, urinary meatus, extremities) caused by tubes, casts, orthoses, braces, cervical collars, or other medical devices; pressure on the labia or scrotum related to positioning (e.g., against a pommel type cushion); pressure on the foot related to ill-fitting shoes causing blistering; or pressure on legs, arms and fingers due to contractures or deformity resulting from rheumatoid arthritis, etc.

While pressure ulcers on the sacrum remain the most common location, pressure ulcers on the heel are occurring more frequently,[24] are difficult to assess and heal, and require early identification of skin compromise over the heel.

It is, therefore, important for clinical staff to regularly conduct thorough skin assessments on each resident who is at risk for developing pressure ulcers.

Under-Nutrition and Hydration Deficits

Adequate nutrition and hydration are essential for overall functioning. Nutrition provides vital energy and building blocks for all of the body's structures and processes. Any organ or body system may require additional energy or structural materials for repair or function. The skin is the body's largest organ system. It may affect, and be affected by, other body processes and organs. Skin condition reflects overall body function; skin breakdown may be the most visible evidence of a general catabolic state.

Weight reflects a balance between intake and utilization of energy. Significant unintended weight loss may indicate under-nutrition or worsening health status. Weight stability (in the absence of fluid excess or loss) is a useful indicator of overall caloric balance. Severely impaired organs (heart, lungs, kidneys, liver, etc.) may be unable to use nutrients effectively. A resident with a pressure ulcer who continues to lose weight either needs additional caloric intake or correction (where possible) of conditions that are creating a hypermetabolic state. Continuing weight loss and failure of a pressure ulcer to heal despite reasonable efforts to improve caloric and nutrient intake may indicate the resident is in multi-system failure or an end-stage or end-of-life condition warranting an additional assessment of the resident's overall condition.

Before instituting a nutritional care plan, it helps to summarize resident specific evidence, including: severity of nutritional compromise, rate of weight loss or appetite decline, probable causes, the individual's prognosis and projected clinical course, and the resident's wishes and goals. Because there are no wound-specific nutritional measures, the interdisciplinary team should develop nutritional goals for the whole person. Unless contraindicated, nutritional goals for a resident with nutritional compromise who has a pressure ulcer or is at risk of developing pressure ulcers should include protein intake of approximately 1.2-1.5 gm/kg body weight daily (higher end of the range for those with larger, more extensive, or multiple wounds). A simple multivitamin is appropriate, but unless the resident has a specific vitamin or mineral deficiency, supplementation with additional vitamins or minerals may not be indicated.

NOTE: Although some laboratory tests may help clinicians evaluate nutritional issues in a resident with pressure ulcers, no laboratory test is specific or sensitive enough to warrant serial/repeated testing. Serum albumin, pre-albumin and cholesterol may be useful to help establish overall prognosis; however, they may not correlate well with clinical observation of nutritional status.[25, 26] At his or her discretion, a practitioner may order test(s) that provide useful additional information or help with management of treatable conditions.

Water is essential to maintain adequate body functions. As a major component of blood, water dissolves vitamins, minerals, glucose, amino acids, etc.; transports nutrients into cells; removes waste from the cells; and helps maintain circulating blood volume as well as fluid and electrolyte balance. It is critical that each resident at risk for hydration deficit or imbalance, including the resident with a pressure ulcer or at risk of developing an ulcer, be identified and that hydration needs be addressed.

(The surveyor should refer to the Guidance at 42 CFR 483.25 (i), F325, Nutrition, and 483.25(j), F327 Hydration for investigation of potential non-compliance with the nutrition and hydration requirements. A low albumin level combined with the facility's lack of supplementation, for example, is not sufficient to cite a pressure ulcer deficiency.)

Moisture and Its Impact

Both urine and feces contain substances that may irritate the epidermis and may make the skin more susceptible to breakdown. Some studies have found that fecal incontinence may pose a greater threat to skin integrity,[27] most likely due to bile acids and enzymes in the feces. Irritation or maceration resulting from prolonged exposure to urine and feces may hasten skin breakdown, and moisture may make skin more susceptible to damage from friction and shear during repositioning.

It may be difficult to differentiate dermatitis related to incontinence from partial thickness skin loss (pressure ulcer). This differentiation should be based on the clinical evidence and review of presenting risk factors. A Stage I pressure ulcer usually presents as a localized area of erythema or skin discoloration, while perineal dermatitis may appear as a more diffuse area of erythema or discoloration where the urine or stool has come into contact with the skin. The dermatitis may occur in the area where the incontinence brief or underpad has been used. Also, the dermatitis/rash more typically presents as intense erythema, scaling, itching, papules, weeping and eruptions.[28]

INTERVENTIONS

The comprehensive assessment should provide the basis for defining approaches to address residents at risk of developing or already having a pressure ulcer. A determination that a resident is at high risk to develop a pressure ulcer has significant implications for preventive and treatment strategies, but does not by itself indicate that development of a pressure ulcer was unavoidable. Effective prevention and treatment are based upon consistently providing routine and individualized interventions.

In the context of the resident's choices, clinical condition, and physician input, the resident's plan of care should establish relevant goals and approaches to stabilize or improve co-morbidities, such as attempts to minimize clinically significant blood sugar fluctuations and other interventions aimed at limiting the effects of risk factors associated with pressure ulcers. Alternatively, facility staff and practitioners should document clinically valid reasons why such interventions were not appropriate or feasible. Repeated hospitalizations or emergency room visits within a 6-month period may indicate overall decline or instability.

Resident Choice

In order for a resident to exercise his or her right appropriately to make informed choices about care and treatment or to refuse treatment, the facility and the resident (or the resident's legal representative) must discuss the resident's condition, treatment options, expected outcomes, and consequences of refusing treatment. The facility is expected to address the resident's concerns and offer relevant alternatives, if the resident has refused specific treatments. (See Resident Rights at 42 CFR 483.10(b)(3) and (4), F154 and F155.)

Advance Directive

A resident at the end of life, in terminal stages of an illness or having multiple system failures may have written directions for his or her treatment goals (or a decision has been made by the resident's surrogate or representative, in accordance with state law).

If a resident has a valid Advance Directive, the facility's care must reflect a resident's wishes as expressed in the Directive, in accordance with state law. However, the presence of an Advance Directive does not absolve the facility from giving supportive and other pertinent care that is not prohibited by the Advance Directive. If the facility has implemented individualized approaches for end-of-life care in accordance with the resident's wishes, and has implemented appropriate efforts to try to stabilize the resident's condition (or indicated why the condition cannot or should not be stabilized) and to provide care to prevent or treat the pressure ulcer (including pertinent, routine, lesser aggressive approaches, such as, cleaning, turning, repositioning), then the development, continuation, or progression of a pressure ulcer may be consistent with regulatory requirements.

NOTE: The presence of a "Do Not Resuscitate" (DNR) order is not sufficient to indicate the resident is declining other appropriate treatment and services. It only indicates that the resident should not be resuscitated if respirations and/or cardiac function cease.

Based upon the assessment and the resident's clinical condition, choices and identified needs, basic or routine care should include interventions to: a) Redistribute pressure (such as repositioning, protecting heels, etc); b) Minimize exposure to moisture and keep skin clean, especially of fecal contamination; c) Provide appropriate, pressure-redistributing, support surfaces; d) Provide non-irritating surfaces; and e) Maintain or improve nutrition and hydration status, where feasible. Adverse drug reactions related to the resident's drug regimen may worsen risk factors for development of pressure ulcers or for non-healing pressure ulcers (for example, by causing lethargy or anorexia or creating/increasing confusion) and should be identified and addressed. These interventions should be incorporated into the plan of care and revised as the condition of the resident indicates.

Repositioning

Repositioning is a common, effective intervention for an individual with a pressure ulcer or who is at risk of developing one.[29, 30] Assessment of a resident's skin integrity after pressure has been reduced or redistributed should guide the development and implementation of repositioning plans. Such plans should be addressed in the comprehensive plan of care consistent with the resident's need and goals. Repositioning is critical for a resident who is immobile or dependent upon staff for repositioning. The care plan for a resident at risk of friction or shearing during repositioning may require the use of lifting devices for repositioning. Positioning the resident on an existing pressure ulcer should be avoided since it puts additional pressure on tissue that is already compromised and may impede healing.

Surveyors should consider the following repositioning issues:

- A resident who can change positions independently may need supportive devices to facilitate position changes. The resident also may need instruction about why repositioning is important and how to do it, encouragement to change positions regularly, and monitoring of frequency of repositioning.

- The care plan for a resident who is reclining and is dependent on staff for repositioning should address position changes to maintain the resident's skin integrity. This may include repositioning at least every 2 hours or more frequently depending upon the resident's condition and tolerance of the tissue load (pressure). Depending on the individualized assessment, more frequent repositioning may be warranted for individuals who are at higher risk for pressure ulcer development or who show evidence (e.g., Stage I pressure ulcers) that repositioning at 2-hour intervals is inadequate.

With rare exception (e.g., both sacral and ischial pressure ulcers are present) the resident should not be placed directly on the greater trochanter for more thanmomentary placement. Elevating the head of the bed or the back of a reclining chair to or above a 30 degree angle creates pressure comparable to that exerted while sitting, and requires the same considerations regarding repositioning as those for a dependent resident who is seated.

- Many clinicians recommend a position change "off loading" hourly for dependent residents who are sitting or who are in a bed or a reclining chair with the head of the bed or back of the chair raised 30 degrees or more.[31] Based upon an assessment including evidence of tissue tolerance while sitting (checking for Stage I ulcers as noted above), the resident may not tolerate sitting in a chair in the same position for1 hour at a time and may require a more frequent position change.

- Postural alignment, weight distribution, sitting balance and stability, and pressure redistribution should all be considered when positioning a resident in a chair.[32] A teachable resident should be taught to shift his/her weight approximately every 15 minutes while sitting in a chair.

- Wheelchairs are often used for transporting residents, but they may severely limit repositioning options and increase the risk of pressure ulcer development. Therefore, wheelchairs with sling seats may not be optimal for prolonged sitting during activities or meals, etc. However, available modifications to the seating can provide a more stable surface and provide better pressure reduction.

- There isn't evidence that momentary pressure relief followed by return to the same position (that is a "microshift" of five or 10 degrees or a 10-15 second lift from a seated position) is beneficial. This approach does not allow sufficient capillary refill and tissue perfusion for a resident at risk of developing pressure ulcers. Ongoing monitoring of the resident's skin integrity and tissue tolerance is critical to prevent development or deterioration of pressure ulcers.

Support Surfaces and Pressure Redistribution

Pressure redistribution refers to the function or ability to distribute a load over a surface or contact area. Redistribution results in shifting pressure from one area to another and requires attention to all affected areas. Pressure redistribution has incorporated the concepts of both pressure reduction (reduction of interface pressure, not necessarily below capillary closure pressure) and pressure relief (reduction of interface pressure below capillary closure pressure).

Appropriate support surfaces or devices should be chosen by matching a device's potential therapeutic benefit with the resident's specific situation; for example, multiple ulcers, limited turning surfaces, ability to maintain position. The effectiveness of pressure redistribution devices (e.g., 4-inch convoluted foam pads, gels, air fluidized mattresses, and low loss air mattresses) is based on their potential to address the individual resident's risk, the resident's response to the product, and the characteristics and condition of the product. For example, an overinflated overlay product, or one that "bottoms out" (completely compressing the overlay, when, for example, the caregiver can feel less than one inch between the resident and support material) is unlikely to effectively reduce the pressure risk. These products are more likely to reduce pressure effectively if they are used in accord with the manufacturer's instructions. The effectiveness of each product used needs to be evaluated on an ongoing basis. Surveyors should consider the following pressure redistribution issues:

- Static pressure redistribution devices (e.g., solid foam, convoluted foam, gel mattress) may be indicated when a resident is at risk for pressure ulcer development or delayed healing. A specialized pressure redistribution cushion or surface, for example, might be used to extend the time a resident is sitting in a chair; however, the cushion does not eliminate the necessity for periodic repositioning.

- Dynamic pressure reduction surfaces may be helpful when: 1) The resident cannot assume a variety of positions without bearing weight on a pressure ulcer, 2) The resident completely compresses a static device that has retained its original integrity, or 3) The pressure ulcer is not healing as expected, and it is determined that pressure may be contributing to the delay in healing.

- Because the heels and elbows have relatively little surface area, it is difficult to redistribute pressure on these two surfaces. Therefore, it is important to pay particular attention to reducing the pressure on these areas for the resident at risk in accord with resident's overall goals and condition. Pillows used to support the entire lower leg may effectively raise the heel from contact with the bed, but use of the pillows needs to take into account the resident's other conditions. The use of donut-type cushions is not recommended by the clinicians.

- A resident with severe flexion contractures also may require special attention to effectively reduce pressure on bony prominences or prevent breakdown from skin-to-skin contact.

Some products serve mainly to provide comfort and reduce friction and shearing forces, e.g., sheepskin, heel and elbow protectors. Although these products are not effective at redistributing pressure, they (in addition to pillows, foam wedges, or other measures) may be employed to prevent bony prominences from rubbing together.

MONITORING

At least daily, staff should remain alert to potential changes in the skin condition and should evaluate and document identified changes. For example, a resident's complaint about pain or burning at a site where there has been pressure or a nursing assistant's observation during the resident's bath that there is a change in skin condition should be reported so that the resident may be evaluated further.

After completing a thorough evaluation, the interdisciplinary team should develop a relevant care plan to including prevention and management interventions with measurable goals. Many clinicians recommend evaluating skin condition (e.g., skin color, moisture, temperature, integrity, and turgor) at least weekly, or more often if indicated, such as when the resident is using a medical device that may cause pressure.

The resident should be monitored for condition changes that might increase the risk for breakdown and the defined interventions should be implemented and monitored for effectiveness.

ASSESSMENT AND TREATMENT OF PRESSURE ULCER(S)

It is important that each existing pressure ulcer be identified, whether present on admission or developed after admission, and that factors that influenced its development, the potential for development of additional ulcers or for the deterioration of the pressure ulcer(s) be recognized, assessed and addressed (see discussion under Prevention regarding overall assessment and interventions). Any new pressure ulcer suggests a need to reevaluate the adequacy of the plan for preventing pressure ulcers.

When assessing the ulcer itself, it is important to:

- Differentiate the type of ulcer (pressure-related versus non-pressure-related) because interventions may vary depending on the specific type of ulcer;

- Determine the ulcer's stage;

- Describe and monitor the ulcer's characteristics;

- Monitor the progress toward healing and for potential complications;

- Determine if infection is present;

- Assess, treat and monitor pain, if present; and

- Monitor dressings and treatments.

TYPES OF ULCERS

Three of the more common types of ulcers are pressure, vascular insufficiency/ischemia (venous stasis and arterial ischemic ulcers) and neuropathic. See Guidance to Surveyors at 42 CFR 483.25 (F309) for definition and description of ulcer types other than pressure ulcers.

At the time of the assessment, clinicians (physicians, advance practice nurses, physician assistants, and certified wound care specialists, etc.) should document the clinical basis (for example, type of skin injury/ulcer, location, shape, ulcer edges and wound bed, condition of surrounding tissues) for any determination that an ulcer is not pressure-related, especially if the injury/ulcer has characteristics consistent with a pressure ulcer, but is determined not to be one.

ULCER CHARACTERISTICS

It is important that the facility have a system in place to assure that the protocols for daily monitoring and for periodic documentation of measurements, terminology, frequency of assessment, and documentation are implemented consistently throughout the facility.

When a pressure ulcer is present, daily monitoring, (with accompanying documentation, when a complication or change is identified), should include:

- An evaluation of the ulcer, if no dressing is present;

- An evaluation of the status of the dressing, if present (whether it is intact and whether drainage, if present, is or is not leaking);

- The status of the area surrounding the ulcer (that can be observed without removing the dressing);

- The presence of possible complications, such as signs of increasing area of ulceration or soft tissue infection (for example: increased redness or swelling around the wound or increased drainage from the wound); and

- Whether pain, if present, is being adequately controlled.

The amount of observation possible will depend upon the type of dressing that is used, since some dressings are meant to remain in place for several days, according to manufacturers' guidelines.

With each dressing change or at least weekly (and more often when indicated by wound complications or changes in wound characteristics), an evaluation of the pressure ulcer wound should be documented. At a minimum, documentation should include the date observed and:

- Location and staging;

- Size (perpendicular measurements of the greatest extent of length and width of the ulceration), depth; and the presence, location and extent of any undermining or tunneling/sinus tract;

- Exudate, if present: type (such as purulent/serous), color, odor and approximate amount;

- Pain, if present: nature and frequency (e.g., whether episodic or continuous);

- Wound bed: Color and type of tissue/character including evidence of healing (e.g., granulation tissue), or necrosis (slough or eschar); and

- Description of wound edges and surrounding tissue (e.g., rolled edges, redness, hardness/induration, maceration) as appropriate.

Photographs may be used to support this documentation, if the facility has developed a protocol consistent with accepted standards[33] (e.g., frequency, consistent distance from the wound, type of equipment used, means to assure digital images are accurate and not modified, inclusion of the resident identification/ulcer location/dates/etc. within the photographic image, and parameters for comparison).

STAGES OF PRESSURE ULCERS

The staging system is one method of summarizing certain characteristics of pressure ulcers, including the extent of tissue damage. This is the system used within the RAI.

Stage I pressure ulcers may be difficult to identify because they are not readily visible and they present with greater variability. Advanced technology (not commonly available in nursing homes) has shown that a Stage I pressure ulcer may have minimal to substantial tissue damage in layers beneath the skin's surface, even when there is no visible surface penetration. The Stage I indicators identified below will generally persist or be evident after the pressure on the area has been removed for 30-45 minutes.

The definitions for the stages of pressure ulcers identified below, are from the NPUAP and used with permission.[34]

- **"Stage I"** - An observable, pressure-related alteration of intact skin, whose indicators as compared to an adjacent or opposite area on the body may include changes in one or more of the following parameters:

  o Skin temperature (warmth or coolness);

  o Tissue consistency (firm or boggy);

  o Sensation (pain, itching); and/or

  o A defined area of persistent redness in lightly pigmented skin, whereas in darker skin tones, the ulcer may appear with persistent red, blue, or purple hues.

- **"Stage II"** - Partial thickness skin loss involving epidermis, dermis, or both. The ulcer is superficial and presents clinically as an abrasion, blister, or shallow crater.

- **"Stage III"** - Full thickness skin loss involving damage to, or necrosis of, subcutaneous tissue that may extend down to, but not through, underlying fascia. The ulcer presents clinically as a deep crater with or without undermining of adjacent tissue.

- **"Stage IV"** - Full thickness skin loss with extensive destruction, tissue necrosis, or damage to muscle, bone, or supporting structures (e.g., tendon, joint capsule). Undermining and sinus tracts also may be associated with Stage IV pressure ulcers.

NOTE: If eschar and necrotic tissue are covering and preventing adequate staging of a pressure ulcer, the RAI User's Manual Version 2 instructs the assessor to code the pressure ulcer as a Stage IV. These instructions must be followed for MDS coding purposes until they are revised. Although the AHCPR and NPUAP system for staging pressure ulcers indicates that the presence of eschar precludes accurate staging of the ulcer, the facility must use the RAI directions in order to code the MDS, but not necessarily to render treatment.

THE HEALING PRESSURE ULCER

Ongoing evaluation and research have indicated that pressure ulcers do not heal in a reverse sequence, that is, the body does not replace the types and layers of tissue (e.g., muscle, fat and dermis) that were lost during the pressure ulcer development.

There are different types of clinical documentation to describe the progression of the healing pressure ulcer(s). The regulation at 42 CFR 483.20(b)(1), F272, requires that facilities use the Resident Assessment Instrument (RAI), which includes direction to describe the healing of the pressure ulcer(s)for coding purposes for the MDS: The RAI User's Manual Version 2.0, instructs staff to identify the stages of pressure ulcer(s) by describing depth in reverse order from deepest to lesser stages to describe the healing or improvement of a pressure ulcer (e.g., a Stage IV becomes a Stage III and so forth. This has been referred to as "reverse staging" or "back staging").

Some clinicians utilize validated instruments to describe the healing of a pressure ulcer. Although such instruments are appropriate for making treatment decisions, they may not be utilized for coding the MDS. Until the MDS is revised, the present coding system (reverse staging) must be used for completion of the RAI.

Clinicians may use the National Pressure Ulcer Advisory Panel - Pressure Ulcer Scale for Healing (NPUAP-PUSH) tool. The NPUAP always refers to a healed pressure ulcer as a healed ulcer at the deepest stage of its development (e.g., a healed Stage IV or a healing Stage IV). The NPUAP cautions that the tool does not represent a comprehensive pressure ulcer assessment, and other factors may need to be considered when selecting pressure ulcer treatment options.

Since surveyors may encounter clinician's notes in which the NPUAP-PUSH tool is used as part of the facility's documentation protocol, the following description of the tool is provided. The NPUAP-PUSH tool documents pressure ulcer healing consistent with the healing process, describes a healing pressure ulcer in terms of three ulcer characteristics, and assigns a numeric value to the characteristics: length (cm) x width (cm), exudate amount, and type of tissue (closed with epithelium; new pink, shiny epithelial tissue; clean, pink or beefy red, shiny, moist granulation tissue; slough tissue; or necrotic, eschar tissue).

The 1994 AHCPR Guidelines and current literature[35] indicate that a clean pressure ulcer with adequate blood supply and innervation should show evidence of stabilization or some healing within 2-4 weeks. Evidence accumulating since 1962 indicates that management of wound exudate coupled with a clean, moist wound environment allows a chronic wound (e.g., pressure ulcer) to lay down healthy granulating tissue more efficiently.[36, 37]

If a pressure ulcer fails to show some evidence of progress toward healing within 2-4 weeks, the pressure ulcer (including potential complications) and the resident's overall clinical condition should be reassessed. Re-evaluation of the treatment plan including determining whether to continue or modify the current interventions is also indicated. Results may vary depending on the resident's condition and interventions/treatments used. The complexity of the resident's condition may limit responsiveness to treatment or tolerance for certain treatment modalities. The clinicians, if deciding to retain the current regimen, should document the rationale for continuing the present treatment (for example, why some, or all, of the plan's interventions remain relevant despite little or no apparent healing).

Pressure ulcers may progress or may be associated with complications such as infection of the soft tissues around the wound (cellulitis), infection of the bone (osteomyelitis), infection of a joint (septic arthritis), abscess, spread of bacteria into the bloodstream (bacteremia/septicemia), chronic infection, or development of a sinus tract. Sometimes these complications may occur despite apparent improvement in the pressure ulcer itself. The physician's involvement is integral whenever significant changes in the nature of the wound or overall resident condition are identified.

INFECTIONS RELATED TO PRESSURE ULCERS

Current literature reports that all Stage II, III, and IV pressure ulcers are colonized with bacteria but may not be infected. Identification, diagnosis and treatment of infection, when present, are critical to healing a pressure ulcer.[38] The infection occurs when the bacteria have invaded the tissue surrounding or within the pressure ulcer.

As with any infection, classic signs and symptoms of infection may include purulent exudate, peri-wound warmth, swelling, induration or erythema (erythema may not be readily determined in individuals with dark skin pigmentation), increasing pain or tenderness around the site or delayed wound healing. These classic signs may not be as evident in someone with a granulating, chronic wound or an immuno-compromised or aged resident. Some infections may present primarily with pain or delayed healing without other typical clinical signs of infection.[39] Clinicians have developed some tools, which may facilitate identifying and assessing an infection[40, 41] and documenting progress toward healing.

Wounds may be classified as infected if the signs and symptoms of infection are present and/or a wound culture (obtained in accord with accepted standards, such as sterile tissue aspirate, a "quantitative surface swab" using the Levine technique or semi-quantitative swab) contains 100,000 (105) or greater micro-organisms per gram of tissue. A superficial swab may show the presence of bacteria, but is not a reliable method to identify infection.

Findings such as an elevated white blood cell count, bacteremia, sepsis, or fever may signal an infection related to a pressure ulcer area or a co-existing infection from a different source.

PAIN

The assessment and treatment of a resident's pain are integral components of pressure ulcer prevention and management. "The goal of pain management in the pressure ulcer patient is to eliminate the cause of pain, to provide analgesia, or both."[42] Pain that interferes with movement and/or affects mood may contribute to immobility and contribute to the potential for developing a pressure ulcer or for delayed healing or non-healing of an already existing ulcer.

It may be difficult to assess the degree of pain in a resident who is cognitively impaired. Some strategies and tools exist to help determine the presence and characteristics of pain (e.g., nature, intensity and frequency).[43, 44] Recent research suggests that a resident with a Stage IV pressure ulcer can feel as much pain as those with a Stage I or II ulcer.[45] The relationship of pain to the pressure ulcer healing process is not yet clear. Pain is an individual perception and response and an individual's report of pain is a generally valid indicator of pain. One resident may experience pain of varying intensity and frequency (e.g., continually or periodically) or episodically in association with treatments (e.g., debridement, dressing changes) or movement or infection, while another resident may not have or report pain.

DRESSINGS AND TREATMENTS

Research has found that chronic wounds such as pressure ulcers heal differently from acute wounds, primarily because of differing biochemical and cellular characteristics. Current clinical practice indicates that Stage III and Stage IV ulcers should be covered. Determination of the need for a dressing for a Stage I or Stage II ulcer is based upon the individual practitioner's clinical judgment and facility protocols based upon current clinical standards of practice. No particular dressing promotes healing of all pressure ulcers within an ulcer classification.[46]

For those pressure ulcers with significant exudate, management of the exudate is critical for healing. A balance is needed to assure that the wound is moist enough to support healing but not too moist to interfere with healing.[47] Since excess wound exudate generally impairs wound healing, selecting an appropriate absorptive dressing is an important part of managing chronic wound exudate.

Product selection should be based upon the relevance of the specific product to the identified pressure ulcer(s) characteristics, the treatment goals, and the manufacturer's recommendations for use. Current literature does not indicate significant advantages of any single specific product over another, but does confirm that not all products are appropriate for all pressure ulcers. Wound characteristics should be assessed throughout the healing process to assure that the treatments and dressings being used are appropriate to the nature of the wound.

Present literature suggests that pressure ulcer dressing protocols may use clean technique rather than sterile, but that appropriate sterile technique may be needed for those wounds that recently have been surgically debrided or repaired.[48]

Debridement of non-viable tissue is frequently performed to reduce the amount of wound debris or non-viable tissue and to reduce the risk of sepsis. A variety of debridement methods (e.g., mechanical, sharp or surgical, enzymatic, autolytic, MDT) are available. Removal of necrotic tissue should enhance wound healing. Ongoing monitoring (and timely intervention in case of change in the character of the wound) is critical for areas with eschar and those areas that have been debrided.[49] Many clinicians believe that stable, dry, adherent and intact eschar on the foot/heel should not be debrided, unless signs and symptoms of local infection or instability are detected.[50]

Some facilities may use "wet to dry gauze dressings" or irrigation with chemical solutions to remove slough. The use of wet-to-dry dressings or irrigations may be appropriate in limited circumstances, but repeated use may damage healthy granulation tissue in healing ulcers and may lead to excessive bleeding and increased resident pain.

A facility should be able to show that its treatment protocols are based upon current standards of practice and are in accord with the facility's policies and procedures as developed with the medical director's review and approval.

[**Editor's Note:** See page 388 for endnotes pertaining to this section.]

INVESTIGATIVE PROTOCOL

PRESSURE ULCER

Objectives

- To determine if the identified pressure ulcer(s) is avoidable or unavoidable; and

- To determine the adequacy of the facility's interventions and efforts to prevent and treat pressure ulcers.

Use

Use this protocol for a sampled resident having--or at risk of developing-- a pressure ulcer.

If the resident has an ulcer, determine if it was identified as non-pressure related, e.g., vascular insufficiency or a neuropathic ulcer. If record review, staff and/or physician interview, and observation (unless the dressing protocol precludes observing the wound) support the conclusion that the ulcer is not pressure related, do not proceed with this protocol unless the resident is at risk for developing, or also has, pressure ulcers. Evaluate care and services regarding non-pressure related ulcers at F309, Quality of Care.

Procedures

Briefly review the assessment, care plan and orders to identify facility interventions and to guide observations to be made. For a newly admitted resident either at risk or with a pressure ulcer, the staff is expected to assess and provide appropriate care from the day of admission. Corroborate observations by interview and record review.

1. Observation

Observe whether staff consistently implements the care plan over time and across various shifts. During observations of the interventions, note and/or follow up on deviations from the care plan as well as potential negative outcomes, including but not limited to the following:

- Erythema or color changes on areas such as the sacrum, buttocks, trochanters, posterior thigh, popliteal area, or heels when moved off an area:

  o If erythema or color change are noted, return approximately ½ - ¾ hours later to determine if the changes or other Stage I characteristics persist;

  o If the changes persist and exhibit tenderness, hardness, or alteration in temperature from surrounding skin, ask staff how they determine repositioning schedules and how they evaluate and address a potential Stage I pressure ulcer;

- Previously unidentified open areas;

- Whether the positioning avoids pressure on an existing pressure ulcer(s);

- Measures taken to prevent or reduce the potential for shearing or friction during transfers, elevation, and repositioning; and

- Whether pressure-redistributing devices for the bed and/or chair, such as gel-type surfaces or overlays are in place, working, and used according to the manufacturer's recommendations.

Observation of Existing Ulcer/Wound Care

If a dressing change is scheduled during the survey, observe the wound care to determine if the record reflects the current status of the ulcer(s) and note:

- Characteristics of the wound and surrounding tissues such as presence of granulation tissue, the Stage, presence of exudates, necrotic tissue such as eschar or slough, or evidence of erythema or swelling around the wound;

- The form or type of debridement, if used;

- Whether treatment and infection control practices reflect current standards of practice; and

- Based on location, steps taken to cleanse and protect the wound from likely contamination by urine or fecal incontinence.

If unable to observe the dressing change due to the dressing protocol, observe the area surrounding the ulcer(s). For ulcers with dressings that are not scheduled to be changed, the surveyor may request that the dressing be removed to observe the wound and surrounding area if other information suggests a possible treatment or assessment problem.

If the resident expresses (or appears to be in) pain related to the ulcer or treatment, determine if the facility:

- Assessed for pain related to the ulcer, addressed and monitored interventions for effectiveness; and/or

- Assessed and took preemptive measures for pain related to dressing changes or other treatments, such as debridement/irrigations, and monitored for effectiveness.

2. **Resident/Staff Interviews**

Interview the resident, family or responsible party to the degree possible to identify:

- Involvement in care plan, choices, goals, and if interventions reflect preferences;

- Awareness of approaches, such as pressure redistribution devices or equipment, turning/repositioning, weight shifting to prevent or address pressure ulcer(s);

- Presence of pain, if any, and how it is managed;

- If treatment(s) was refused, whether counseling on alternatives, consequences, and/or other interventions was offered; and

- Awareness of current or history of an ulcer(s). For the resident who has or has had a pressure ulcer, identify, as possible, whether acute illness, weight loss or other condition changes occurred prior to developing the ulcer.

Interview staff on various shifts to determine:

- Knowledge of prevention and treatment, including facility-specific guidelines/protocols and specific interventions for the resident;

- If nursing assistants know what, when, and to whom to report changes in skin condition; and

- Who monitors for the implementation of the care plan, changes in the skin, the development of pressure ulcers, and the frequency of review and evaluation of an ulcer.

3. Record Review

Assessment

Review the RAI and other documents such as physician orders, progress notes, nurses' notes, pharmacy or dietary notes regarding the assessment of the resident's overall condition, risk factors and presence of a pressure ulcer(s) to determine if the facility identified the resident at risk and evaluated the factors placing the resident at risk:

- For a resident who was admitted with an ulcer or who developed one within 1 to 2 days, review the admission documentation regarding the wound site and characteristics at the time of admission, the possibility of underlying tissue damage because of immobility or illness prior to admission, skin condition on or within a day of admission, history of impaired nutrition; and history of previous pressure ulcers; and

- For a resident who subsequently developed or has an existing pressure ulcer, review documentation regarding the wound site, characteristics, progress and complications including reassessment if there were no signs of progression towards healing within 2 to 4 weeks.

In considering the appropriateness of a facility's response to the presence, progression, or deterioration of a pressure ulcer, take into account the resident's condition, complications, time needed to determine the effectiveness of a treatment, and the facility's efforts, where possible, to remove, modify, or stabilize the risk factors and underlying causal factors.

Care Plan

For the resident at risk for developing or who has a pressure ulcer, determine if the facility developed an individualized care plan that addresses prevention, care and treatment of any existing pressure ulcers, including specific interventions, measurable objectives and approximate time frames.

If the facility's care of a specific resident refers to a treatment protocol that contains details of the treatment regimen, the care plan should refer to that protocol. The care plan should clarify any major deviations from, or revisions to, that protocol in a specific resident.

A specific care plan intervention for risk of pressure ulcers is not needed if other components of the care plan address related risks adequately. For example, the risk of skin breakdown posed by fecal/urinary incontinence might be addressed in that part of the care plan that deals with incontinence management.

If the resident refuses or resists staff interventions to reduce risk or treat existing pressure ulcers, determine if the care plan reflects efforts to seek alternatives to address the needs identified in the assessment.

Revision of the Care Plan

Determine if the staff have been monitoring the resident's response to interventions for prevention and/or treatment and have evaluated and revised the care plan based on the resident's response, outcomes, and needs. Review the record and interview staff for information and/or evidence that:

- Continuing the current approaches meets the resident's needs, if the resident has experienced recurring pressure ulcers or lack of progression toward healing and staff did not revise the care plan; and

- The care plan was revised to modify the prevention strategies and to address the presence and treatment of a newly developed pressure ulcer, for the resident who acquired a new ulcer.

4. Interviews with Health Care Practitioners and Professionals

If the interventions defined or care provided appear not to be consistent with recognized standards of practice, interview one or more health care practitioners and professionals as necessary (e.g., physician, charge nurse, director of nursing) who, by virtue of training and knowledge of the resident, should be able to provide information about the causes, treatment and evaluation of the resident's condition or problem. Depending on the issue, ask about:

- How it was determined that chosen interventions were appropriate;

- Risks identified for which there were no interventions;

- Changes in condition that may justify additional or different interventions; or

- How they validated the effectiveness of current interventions.

If the attending physician is unavailable, interview the medical director, as appropriate.

DETERMINATION OF COMPLIANCE (Task 6, Appendix P)

Synopsis of Regulation (F314)

The pressure ulcer requirement has two aspects. The first aspect requires the facility to prevent the development of pressure ulcer(s) in a resident who is admitted without pressure ulcer(s), unless the development is clinically unavoidable. The second aspect requires the facility to provide necessary treatment and services to promote healing, prevent infection and prevent new ulcers from developing. A facility may have non-compliance in either or both aspects of this requirement.

Criteria for Compliance

- Compliance with 42 CFR 483.25(c)(1), F314, Pressure Sore

  o For a resident who developed a pressure ulcer after admission, the facility is in compliance with this requirement, if staff have:

    - Recognized and assessed factors placing the resident at risk for developing a pressure ulcer, including specific conditions, causes and/or problems, needs and behaviors;

    - Defined and implemented interventions for pressure ulcer prevention in accordance with resident needs, goals and recognized standards of practice;

    - Monitored and evaluated the resident's response to preventive efforts; and

    - Revised the approaches as appropriate.

      If not, the development of the pressure ulcer is avoidable, cite at F314.

- Compliance with 42 CFR 483.25(c)(2), F314, Pressure Sore

  o For a resident who was admitted with a pressure ulcer, who has a pressure ulcer that is not healing, or who is at risk of developing subsequent pressure ulcers, the facility is in compliance with this requirement if they:

    - Recognized and assessed factors placing the resident at risk of developing a new pressure ulcer or experiencing non-healing or delayed healing of a current pressure ulcer, including specific conditions, causes and/or problems, needs and behaviors;

    - Defined and implemented interventions for pressure ulcer prevention and treatment in accordance with resident needs, goals and recognized standards of practice;

    - Addressed the potential for infection;

    - Monitored and evaluated the resident's response to preventive efforts and treatment interventions; and

- Revised the approaches as appropriate.

  If not, cite at F314.

Non-compliance for F314

After completing the Investigative Protocol, analyze the data in order to determine whether or not noncompliance with the regulation exists. Non-compliance for F314 may include (but is not limited to) one or more of the following, including failure to:

- Accurately or consistently assess a resident's skin integrity on admission and as indicated thereafter;

- Identify a resident at risk of developing a pressure ulcer(s);

- Identify and address risk factors for developing a pressure ulcer, or explain adequately why they could not or should not do so;

- Implement preventive interventions in accord with the resident's need and current standards of practice;

- Provide clinical justification for the unavoidable development or non-healing/ delayed healing or deterioration of a pressure ulcer;

- Provide appropriate interventions, care and treatment to an existing pressure ulcer to minimize infections and to promote healing;

- Implement interventions for existing wounds;

- Notify the physician of the resident's condition or changes in the resident's wound(s);

- Adequately implement pertinent infection management practices in relation to wound care; and

- Identify or know how to apply relevant policies and procedures for pressure ulcer prevention and treatment.

Potential Tags for Additional Investigation

During the investigation of F314, the surveyor may have determined that concerns may also be present with related outcome, process and/or structure requirements. The surveyor is cautioned to investigate these related requirements before determining whether non-compliance may be present. Some examples of related requirements that should be considered include the following:

- 42 CFR 483.10(b)(11)(i)(B)&(C), F157, Notification of Changes

  o Determine if staff notified the physician of significant changes in the resident's condition or failure of the treatment plan to prevent or heal pressure ulcers; or the resident's representative (if known) of significant changes in the resident's condition in relation to the development of a pressure ulcer or a change in the progression of healing of an existing pressure ulcer.

- 42 CFR 483.20(b)(1), F272, Comprehensive Assessments

  o Determine if the facility comprehensively assessed the resident's skin condition, including existing pressure ulcers, and resident-specific risk factors (including potential causative factors) for the development of a pressure ulcer or non-healing of the ulcer.

- 42 CFR 483.20(k)(1), F279, Comprehensive Care Plans

    o   Determine if the facility developed a care plan that was consistent with the resident's specific conditions, risks, needs, behaviors, and preferences and current standards of practice and included measurable objectives and timetables, specific interventions/services to prevent the development of pressure ulcers and/or to treat existing pressures ulcers.

- 42 CFR 483.20(k)(2)(iii), F280, Comprehensive Care Plan Revision

    o   Determine if the care plan was periodically reviewed and revised as necessary to prevent the development of pressure ulcers and to promote the healing of existing pressure ulcers.

- 42 CFR 483.20(k)(3)(i), F281, Services Provided Meet Professional Standards

    o   Determine if pressure ulcer care was provided in accordance with accepted professional standards.

- 42 CFR 483.25, F309, Quality of Care

    o   Determine if staff identified and implemented appropriate measures for the management of pain as indicated as related to pressure ulcers and pressure ulcer treatment.

- 42 CFR 482.30(a), F353, Sufficient Staff

    o   Determine if the facility had qualified staff in sufficient numbers to assure the resident was provided necessary care and services, based upon the comprehensive assessment and care plan, to prevent or treat pressure ulcers.

- 42 CFR 483.40(a)(1), F385, Physician Supervision

    o   Determine if the physician has assessed and developed a treatment regimen relevant to preventing or healing a pressure ulcer and responded appropriately to the notice of changes in condition.

- 42 CFR 483.75(i)(2), F501, Medical Director

    o   Determine whether the medical director assisted the facility in the development and implementation of policies and procedures for pressure ulcer prevention and treatment, and that these are based on current standards of practice; and whether the medical director interacts with the physician supervising the care of the resident if requested by the facility to intervene on behalf of the resident with a pressure ulcer(s).

V. DEFICIENCY CATEGORIZATION (*Part V, Appendix P) *[Editor's Note: The part number cited is incorrect. The correct part number is IV.]

Once the team has completed its investigation, analyzed the data, reviewed the regulatory requirement, and identified the deficient practices that demonstrate that the facility failed to provide care and treatment to prevent or treat pressure ulcers and that non-compliance exists, the team must determine the severity of the deficient practice(s) and the resultant harm or potential for harm to the resident. The key elements for severity determination for F314 are as follows:

1. **Presence of harm/negative outcome(s) or potential for negative outcomes because of lack of appropriate treatment and care.** Actual or potential harm/negative outcome for F314 may include but is not limited to:

- Potential for development of, occurrence or recurrence of (an) avoidable pressure ulcer(s);

- Complications such as sepsis or pain related to the presence of avoidable pressure ulcer(s); and/or

- Pressure ulcers that fail to improve as anticipated or develop complications such as sepsis or pain because of the lack of appropriate treatment and care.

2. Degree of harm (actual or potential) related to the non-compliance.

Identify how the facility practices caused, resulted in, allowed or contributed to the actual or potential for harm:

- If harm has occurred, determine if the harm is at the level of serious injury, impairment, death, compromise or discomfort; and

- If harm has not yet occurred, determine how likely is the potential for serious injury, impairment, death, compromise or discomfort to occur to the resident.

3. The immediacy of correction required.

Determine whether the non-compliance requires immediate correction in order to prevent serious injury, harm, impairment, or death to one or more residents.

The survey team must evaluate the harm or potential for harm based upon the following levels of severity for tag F314. First, the team must rule out whether Severity Level 4, Immediate Jeopardy to a resident's health or safety exists by evaluating the deficient practice in relation to immediacy, culpability and severity. (Follow the guidance in Appendix Q.)

Severity Level 4 Considerations: Immediate Jeopardy to Resident Health or Safety

Immediate Jeopardy is a situation in which the facility's non-compliance:

- With one or more requirements of participation has caused/resulted in, or is likely to cause, serious injury, harm, impairment or death to a resident; and

- Requires immediate correction as the facility either created the situation or allowed the situation to continue by failing to implement preventative or corrective measures.

Examples of possible avoidable negative outcomes may include:

- Development of avoidable Stage IV pressure ulcer(s): As a result of the facility's non-compliance, permanent tissue damage (whether or not healing occurs) has compromised the resident, increasing the potential for serious complications including osteomyelititis and sepsis.

- Admitted with a Stage IV pressure ulcer(s) that has shown no signs of healing or shows signs of deterioration: As a result of the facility's non-compliance, a Stage IV pressure ulcer has shown signs of deterioration or a failure to progress towards healing with an increased potential for serious complications including osteomyelitis and sepsis.

- Stage III or IV pressure ulcers with associated soft tissue or systemic infection: As a result of the facility's failure to assess or treat a resident with an infectious complication of a pressure ulcer. (See discussion in guidelines and definitions that distinguishes colonization from infection.)

- Extensive failure in multiple areas of pressure ulcer care: As a result of the facility's extensive noncompliance in multiple areas of pressure ulcer care, the resident developed recurrent and/or multiple, avoidable Stage III or Stage IV pressure ulcer(s).

NOTE: If immediate jeopardy has been ruled out based upon the evidence, then evaluate whether actual harm that is not immediate jeopardy exists at Severity Level 3.

Severity Level 3 Considerations: Actual Harm that is not Immediate Jeopardy

Level 3 indicates noncompliance that results in actual harm, and can include but may not be limited to clinical compromise, decline, or the resident's ability to maintain and/or reach his/her highest practicable well-being.

Examples of avoidable negative outcomes may include but are not limited to:

- **The development of avoidable Stage III pressure ulcer(s):** As a result of the facility's non-compliance, Stage III pressure ulcers occurred, which are open wounds in which damage has occurred into the subcutaneous level and may be painful.

- **The development of recurrent or multiple avoidable Stage II pressure ulcer(s):** As a result of the facility's non-compliance, the resident developed multiple and/or recurrent avoidable Stage II ulcers.

- **Failure to implement the comprehensive care plan for a resident who has a pressure ulcer:** As a result of a facility's failure to implement a portion of an existing plan related to pressure ulcer care, such as failure to provide for pressure redistribution, or inappropriate treatment/dressing changes, a wound increased in size or failed to progress towards healing as anticipated, or the resident experienced untreated pain.

NOTE: If Severity Level 3 (actual harm that is not immediate jeopardy) has been ruled out based upon the evidence, then evaluate as to whether Level 2 (no actual harm with the potential for more than minimal harm) exists.

Severity Level 2 Considerations: No Actual Harm with Potential for More Than Minimal Harm that is Not Immediate Jeopardy

Level 2 indicates noncompliance that results in a resident outcome of no more than minimal discomfort and/or has the potential to compromise the resident's ability to maintain or reach his or her highest practicable level of well being. The potential exists for greater harm to occur if interventions are not provided.

Examples of avoidable negative outcomes may include but are not limited to:

- **The development of a single avoidable Stage II pressure ulcer that is receiving appropriate treatment:** As a result of the facility's non-compliance, a resident developed an avoidable Stage II pressure ulcer.

- **The development of an avoidable Stage I pressure ulcer:** As a result of the facility's non-compliance, a resident developed an avoidable Stage I pressure ulcer.

- **Failure to implement an element of the care plan for a resident who has a pressure ulcer however, there has been no evidence of decline or failure to heal.**

- **Failure to recognize or address the potential for developing a pressure ulcer:** As a result of the facility's non-compliance, staff failed to identify the risks, develop a plan of care and/or consistently implement a plan that has been developed to prevent pressure ulcers.

Severity Level 1: No Actual Harm with Potential for Minimal Harm

The failure of the facility to provide appropriate care and services to prevent pressure ulcers or heal existing pressure ulcers is more than minimal harm. Therefore, Severity Level 1 doesn't apply for this regulatory requirement.

F315

§483.25(d) Urinary Incontinence

Based on the resident's comprehensive assessment, the facility must ensure that—

§483.25(d)(1) A resident who enters the facility without an indwelling catheter is not catheterized unless the resident's clinical condition demonstrates that catheterization was necessary; and

§483.25(d)(2) A resident who is incontinent of bladder receives appropriate treatment and services to prevent urinary tract infections and to restore as much normal bladder function as possible.

INTENT: (F315) 42 CFR 483.25 (d)(1) and (2) Urinary Incontinence and Catheters

The intent of this requirement is to ensure that:

- Each resident who is incontinent of urine is identified, assessed and provided appropriate treatment and services to achieve or maintain as much normal urinary function as possible;

- An indwelling catheter is not used unless there is valid medical justification;

- An indwelling catheter for which continuing use is not medically justified is discontinued as soon as clinically warranted;

- Services are provided to restore or improve normal bladder function to the extent possible, after the removal of the catheter; and

- A resident, with or without a catheter, receives the appropriate care and services to prevent infections to the extent possible.

DEFINITIONS

Definitions are provided to clarify clinical terms related to evaluation and treatment of urinary incontinence and catheter use.

- "Bacteremia" is the presence of bacteria in the bloodstream.

- "Bacteriuria" is defined as the presence of bacteria in the urine.

- "Urinary Incontinence" is the involuntary loss or leakage of urine. There are several types of urinary incontinence, and the individual resident may experience more than one type at a time. Some of the more common types include:

  o "Functional Incontinence" refers to loss of urine that occurs in residents whose urinary tract function is sufficiently intact that they should be able to maintain continence, but who cannot remain continent because of external factors (e.g., inability to utilize the toilet facilities in time);

  o "Mixed Incontinence" is the combination of stress incontinence and urge incontinence;

  o "Overflow Incontinence" is associated with leakage of small amounts of urine when the bladder has reached its maximum capacity and has become distended;

  o "Stress Incontinence" (outlet incompetence) is associated with impaired urethral closure (malfunction of the urethral sphincter) which allows small amounts of urine leakage when intra-abdominal pressure on the bladder is increased by sneezing, coughing, laughing, lifting, standing from a sitting position, climbing stairs, etc.;

  o "Transient Incontinence" refers to temporary episodes of urinary incontinence that are reversible once the cause(s) of the episode(s) is (are) identified and treated; and

  o "Urge Incontinence" (overactive bladder) is associated with detrusor muscle overactivity (excessive contraction of the smooth muscle in the wall of the urinary bladder resulting in a sudden, strong urge (also known as urgency) to expel moderate to large amounts of urine before the bladder is full).

- "Urinary Retention" is the inability to completely empty the urinary bladder by micturition.

- "Urinary Tract Infection" (UTI) is a clinically detectable condition associated with invasion by disease causing microorganisms of some part of the urinary tract, including the urethra (urethritis), bladder (cystitis), ureters (ureteritis), and/or kidney (pyelonephritis). An infection of the urethra or bladder is classified as a lower tract UTI and infection involving the ureter or kidney is classified as an upper tract UTI.

- "Urosepsis" refers to the systemic inflammatory response to infection (sepsis) that appears to originate from a urinary tract source. It may present with symptoms such as fever, hypotension, reduced urine output, or acute change in mental status.

OVERVIEW

Urinary incontinence is not normal. Although aging affects the urinary tract and increases the potential for urinary incontinence, urinary incontinence is not a normal part of aging. In the younger person, urinary incontinence may result from a single cause. In the older individual, urinary incontinence generally involves psychological, physiological, pharmacological and/or pathological factors or co-morbid conditions (e.g., later stages of dementia, diabetes, prostatectomy, medical conditions involving dysfunction of the central nervous system, urinary tract infections, etc.). Because urinary incontinence is a symptom of a condition and may be reversible, it is important to understand the causes and to address incontinence to the extent possible. If the underlying condition is not reversible, it is important to treat or manage the incontinence to try to reduce complications.

Many older adults are incontinent of urine prior to admission to a nursing home. Urinary incontinence and related loss of independence are prominent reasons for a nursing home admission. Articles[1] and data currently available, including CMS data (e.g., MDS Active Resident Information Report (Item H1b) at www.cms.hhs.gov/states/mdsreports), indicate that more than 50% of the nursing home population experience some degree of urinary incontinence. Whether the resident is incontinent of urine on admission or develops incontinence after admission, the steps of assessment, monitoring, reviewing, and revising approaches to care (as needed) are essential to managing urinary incontinence and to restoring as much normal bladder function as possible.

Various conditions or situations may aggravate the severity of urinary incontinence in nursing home residents. In addition, urinary incontinence may be associated with changes in skin integrity, skin irritation or breakdown, urinary tract infections, falls and fractures, sleep disturbances, and psychosocial complications including social withdrawal, embarrassment, loss of dignity, feelings of isolation, and interference with participation in activities.

Various factors common to elderly individuals may increase the risk of infection including: underlying diseases (e.g., diabetes mellitus), medications that affect immune responses to infection (e.g., steroids and chemotherapy, history of multiple antibiotic usage), conditions that cause incontinence, and indwelling urinary catheters.

The urinary tract is a common source of bacteremia in nursing home residents. Urinary tract infection (UTI) is one of the most common infections occurring in nursing homes and is often related to an indwelling urinary catheter. Without a valid clinical rationale for an indwelling catheter, its use is not an acceptable approach to manage urinary incontinence. Although UTIs can result from the resident's own flora, they may also be the result of microorganisms transmitted by staff when handling the urinary catheter drainage system and/or providing incontinence care. Hand washing remains one of the most effective infection control tools available.

Resources

It is important for the facility to have in place systems/procedures to assure: assessments are timely and appropriate; interventions are defined, implemented, monitored, and revised as appropriate in accordance with current standards of practice; and changes in condition are recognized, evaluated, reported to the practitioner, and addressed. The medical director and the quality assessment and assurance committee may help the facility evaluate existing strategies for identifying and managing incontinence, catheter use, and UTIs, and ensure that facility policies and procedures are consistent with current standards of practice.

Research into appropriate practices to prevent, manage, and treat urinary incontinence, urinary catheterization, and UTI continues to evolve. Many recognized clinical resources on the prevention and management of urinary incontinence, infection, and urinary catheterization exist. Some of these resources include:

- The American Medical Directors Association (AMDA) at www.amda.com (Clinical Practice Guidelines: Clinical Practice Guidelines, 1996);

- The Quality Improvement Organizations, Medicare Quality Improvement Community Initiatives at www.medqic.org;

- The CMS Sharing Innovations in Quality website at www.cms.hhs.gov/medicaid/survey-cert/siqhome.asp;

- Association for Professionals in Infection Control and Epidemiology (APIC) at www.apic.org;

- Centers for Disease Control at www.cdc.gov;

- The Annals of Long Term Care publications at www.mmhc.com;

- American Foundation for Urologic Disease, Inc. at www.afud.org; and

- The American Geriatrics Society at www.americangeriatrics.org.

NOTE: References to non-CMS sources or sites on the internet are provided as a service and do not constitute or imply endorsement of these organizations or their programs by CMS or the U. S. Department of Health and Human Services. CMS is not responsible for the content of pages found at these sites. URL addresses were current as of the date of this publication.

Resident Choice

In the course of developing and implementing care plan interventions for treatment and services related to achieving the highest practicable level of urinary continence, preventing and treating urinary tract infections, and avoiding the use of indwelling catheters without medical justification, it is important to involve the resident and/or her or his surrogate in care decisions and to consider whether the resident has an advance directive in place.

In order for a resident to exercise his or her right appropriately to make informed choices about care and treatment or to refuse treatment, the facility and the resident (or the resident's legal representative) must discuss the resident's condition, treatment options, expected outcomes, and consequences of refusing treatment. The facility should address the resident's concerns and offer relevant alternatives, if the resident has refused specific treatments. (See Resident Rights 483.10(b)(3) and (4) (F154 and F155).)

Advance Directive. A resident who is at the end of life or in terminal stages of an illness or who has multiple organ system failures may have written directions for his or her treatment goals (or a decision has been made by the resident's surrogate or representative, in accordance with State law).

Although a facility's care must reflect a resident's wishes as expressed in the Directive, in accordance with State law, the presence of an Advance Directive does not absolve the facility from giving supportive and other pertinent care that is not prohibited by the Advance Directive. The presence of a "Do Not Resuscitate" (DNR) order does not indicate that the resident is declining appropriate treatment and services. It only indicates that the resident should not be resuscitated if respirations and/or cardiac function cease.

If the facility has implemented individualized approaches for end-of-life care in accordance with the resident's wishes, and has implemented appropriate efforts to try to stabilize the resident's condition (or indicated why the condition cannot or should not be stabilized), and has provided care based on the assessed needs of the resident, then the development, continuation, or progression of urinary incontinence; the insertion and prolonged use of an indwelling urinary catheter; the development of infection or skin-related complications from urine or an indwelling catheter may be consistent with regulatory requirements.

URINARY INCONTINENCE

42 CFR 483.25 (d)(2) Urinary Incontinence requires that a resident who is incontinent of bladder receives appropriate treatment and services to prevent urinary tract infections and to restore as much normal bladder function as possible.

Urinary incontinence generally involves a number of transitory or chronic progressive factors that affect the bladder and/or the urethral sphincter. Any condition, medication, or factor that affects lower urinary tract function, bladder capacity, urination, or the ability to toilet can predispose residents to urinary incontinence and may contribute to incomplete bladder emptying.

The first steps toward assuring that a resident receives appropriate treatment and services to restore as much bladder function as possible or to treat and manage the incontinence are to identify the resident already experiencing some level of incontinence or at risk of developing urinary incontinence and to complete an accurate, thorough assessment of factors that may predispose the resident to having urinary incontinence. This is followed by implementing appropriate, individualized interventions that address the incontinence, including the resident's capabilities and underlying factors that can be removed, modified, or stabilized, and by monitoring the effectiveness of the interventions and modifying them, as appropriate. The practitioner, may at his or her option, refer residents to various practitioners who specialize in diagnosing and treating conditions that affect urinary function.

Assessment

Factors contributing to urinary incontinence sometimes may be resolved after a careful examination and review of history. In addition, for a resident who is incontinent of urine, determining the type of urinary incontinence can allow staff to provide more individualized programming or interventions to enhance the resident's quality of life and functional status. A resident should be evaluated at admission and whenever there is a change in cognition, physical ability, or urinary tract function. This evaluation is to include identification of individuals with reversible and irreversible (e.g., bladder tumors and spinal cord disease) causes of incontinence. If the resident has urinary incontinence that has already been investigated, documented, and determined to be irreversible or not significantly improvable, additional studies may be of limited value, unless there has been advancement in available treatments.

Documentation of assessment information may be found throughout the medical record, such as in an admission assessment, hospital records, history and physical, and the Resident Assessment Instrument (RAI). The location of RAI assessment information is identified on the Resident Assessment Protocol (RAP) summary form. It is important that staff, when completing the comprehensive assessment, consider the following:

- Prior history of urinary incontinence, including onset, duration and characteristics, precipitants of urinary incontinence, associated symptoms (e.g., dysuria, polyuria, hesitancy) and previous treatment and/or management, including the response to the interventions and the occurrence of persistent or recurrent UTI;

- Voiding patterns (such as frequency, volume, nighttime or daytime, quality of stream) and, for those already experiencing urinary incontinence, voiding patterns over several days;

- Medication review, particularly those that might affect continence, such as medications with anticholinergic properties (may cause urinary retention and possible overflow incontinence), sedative/hypnotics (may cause sedation leading to functional incontinence), diuretics (may cause urgency, frequency, overflow incontinence), narcotics, alpha-adrenergic agonists (may cause urinary retention in men) or antagonists (may cause stress incontinence in women) calcium channel blockers (may cause urinary retention);[2]

- Patterns of fluid intake, such as amounts, time of day, alterations and potential complications, such as decreased or increased urine output;

- Use of urinary tract stimulants or irritants (e.g., frequent caffeine intake);[3]

- Pelvic and rectal examination to identify physical features that may directly affect urinary incontinence, such as prolapsed uterus or bladder, prostate enlargement, significant constipation or fecal impaction, use of a urinary catheter, atrophic vaginitis, distended bladder, or bladder spasms;

- Functional and cognitive capabilities that could enhance urinary continence and limitations that could adversely affect continence, such as impaired cognitive function or dementia, impaired immobility, decreased manual dexterity, the need for task segmentation, decreased upper and lower extremity muscle strength, decreased vision, pain with movement;

- Type and frequency of physical assistance necessary to assist the resident to access the toilet, commode, urinal, etc. and the types of prompting needed to encourage urination;

- Pertinent diagnoses such as congestive heart failure, stroke, diabetes mellitus, obesity, and neurological disorders (e.g., Multiple Sclerosis, Parkinson's Disease or tumors that could affect the urinary tract or its function);

- Identification of and/or potential of developing complications such as skin irritation or breakdown;

- Tests or studies indicated to identify the type(s) of urinary incontinence (e.g., post-void residual(s) for residents who have, or are at risk of, urinary retention, results of any urine culture if the resident has clinically significant systemic or urinary symptoms), or evaluations assessing the resident's readiness for bladder rehabilitation programs; and

- Environmental factors and assistive devices that may restrict or facilitate a resident's ability to access the toilet (e.g., grab bars, raised or low toilet seats, inadequate lighting, distance to toilet or bedside commodes, availability of urinals, use of bed rails or restraints, or fear of falling).

Types of Urinary Incontinence

Identifying the nature of the incontinence is a key aspect of the assessment and helps identify the appropriate program/interventions to address incontinence.

- Urge Incontinence is characterized by abrupt urgency, frequency, and nocturia (part of the overactive bladder diagnosis). It may be age-related or have neurological causes (e.g., stroke, diabetes mellitus, Parkinson's Disease, multiple sclerosis) or other causes such as bladder infection, urethral irritation, etc. The resident can feel the need to void, but is unable to inhibit voiding long enough to reach and sit on the commode. It is the most common cause of urinary incontinence in elderly persons.

- Stress Incontinence is the loss of a small amount of urine with physical activity such as coughing, sneezing, laughing, walking stairs or lifting. Urine leakage results from an increase in intra-abdominal pressure on a bladder that is not over distended and is not the result of detrusor contractions. It is the second most common type of urinary incontinence in older women.

- Mixed Incontinence is the combination of urge incontinence and stress incontinence. Many elderly persons (especially women) will experience symptoms of both urge and stress called mixed incontinence.

- Overflow Incontinence occurs when the bladder is distended from urine retention. Symptoms of overflow incontinence may include: weak stream, hesitancy, or intermittency; dysuria; nocturia; frequency; incomplete voiding; frequent or constant dribbling. Urine retention may result from outlet obstruction (e.g., benign prostatic hypertrophy (BPH), prostate cancer, and urethral stricture), hypotonic bladder (detrusor under activity) or both. Hypotonic bladder may be caused by outlet obstruction, impaired or absent contractility of the bladder (neurogenic bladder) or other causes. Neurogenic bladder may also result from neurological conditions such as diabetes mellitus, spinal cord injury, or pelvic nerve damage from surgery or radiation therapy. In overflow incontinence, post void residual (PVR) volume (the amount of urine remaining in the bladder within 5 to 10 minutes following urination) exceeds 200 milliliters (ml). Normal PVR is usually 50 ml. or less. A PVR of 150 to 200 may suggest a need for retesting to determine if this finding is clinically significant. Overflow incontinence may mimic urge or stress incontinence but is less common than either of those.

- Functional Incontinence refers to incontinence that is secondary to factors other than inherently abnormal urinary tract function. It may be related to physical weakness or poor mobility/dexterity (e.g., due to poor eyesight, arthritis, deconditioning, stroke, contracture), cognitive problems (e.g., confusion, dementia, unwillingness to toilet), various medications (e.g., anti-cholinergics, diuretics) or environmental impediments (e.g., excessive distance of the resident from the toilet facilities, poor lighting, low chairs that are difficult to get out of, physical restraints and toilets that are difficult to access). Refer to 42 CFR 483.15(e)(1) for issues regarding unmet environmental needs (e.g., handicap toilet, lighting, assistive devices).

  NOTE: Treating the physiological causes of incontinence, without attending to functional components that may have an impact on the resident's continence, may fail to solve the incontinence problem.

- Transient Incontinence refers to temporary or occasional incontinence that may be related to a variety of causes, for example: delirium, infection, atrophic urethritis or vaginitis, some pharmaceuticals (such as sedatives/hypnotics, diuretics, anticholinergic agents), increased urine production, restricted mobility or fecal impaction. The incontinence is transient because it is related to a potentially improvable or reversible cause.

Interventions

It is important that the facility follow the care process (accurate assessment, care planning, consistent implementation and monitoring of the care plan with evaluation of the effectiveness of the interventions, and revision, as appropriate). Recording and evaluating specific information (such as frequency and times of incontinence and toileting and response to specific interventions) is important for determining progress, changes, or decline.

A number of factors may contribute to the decline or lack of improvement in urinary continence, for example: underlying medical conditions, an inaccurate assessment of the resident's type of incontinence (or lack of knowledge about the resident's voiding patterns) may contribute to inappropriate interventions or unnecessary use of an indwelling catheter. Facility practices that may promote achieving the highest practicable level of functioning, may prevent or minimize a decline or lack of improvement in degree of continence include providing treatment and services to address factors that are potentially modifiable, such as:

- Managing pain and/or providing adaptive equipment to improve function for residents suffering from arthritis, contractures, neurological impairments, etc;

- Removing or improving environmental impediments that affect the resident's level of continence (e.g., improved lighting, use of a bedside commode or reducing the distance to the toilet);

- Treating underlying conditions that have a potentially negative impact on the degree of continence (e.g., delirium causing urinary incontinence related to acute confusion);

- Possibly adjusting medications affecting continence (e.g., medication cessation, dose reduction, selection of an alternate medication, change in time of administration); and

- Implementing a fluid and/or bowel management program to meet the assessed needs.

Options for managing urinary incontinence in nursing home residents include primarily behavioral programs and medication therapy. Other measures and supportive devices used in the management of urinary incontinence and/or urinary retention may include intermittent catheterization; pelvic organ support devices (pessaries); the use of incontinence products, garments and an external collection system for men and women; and environmental accommodation and/or modification.

Behavioral Programs

Interventions involving the use of behavioral programs are among the least invasive approaches to address urinary incontinence and have no known adverse complications. Behavior programs involve efforts to modify the resident's behavior and/or environment. Critical aspects of a successful behavioral program include education of the caregiver and the resident, availability of the staff and the consistent implementation of the interventions.

NOTE: It is important for the comprehensive assessment to identify the essential skills the resident must possess to be successful with specific interventions being attempted. These skills include the resident's ability to: comprehend and follow through on education and instructions; identify urinary urge sensation; learn to inhibit or control the urge to void until reaching a toilet; contract the pelvic floor muscle (Kegel exercises) to lessen urgency and/or urinary leakage; and/or respond to prompts to void.[4] Voiding records help detect urinary patterns or intervals between incontinence episodes and facilitate planning care to avoid or reduce the frequency of episodes.

Programs that require the resident's cooperation and motivation in order for learning and practice to occur include the following:

- "Bladder Rehabilitation/Bladder Retraining" is a behavioral technique that requires the resident to resist or inhibit the sensation of urgency (the strong desire to urinate), to postpone or delay voiding, and to urinate according to a timetable rather than to the urge to void. Depending upon the resident's successful ability to control the urge to void, the intervals between voiding may be increased progressively. Bladder training generally consists of education, scheduled voiding with systematic delay of voiding, and positive reinforcement. This program is difficult to implement in cognitively impaired residents and may not be successful in frail, elderly, or dependent residents. The resident who may be appropriate for a bladder rehabilitation (retraining) program is usually fairly independent in activities of daily living, has occasional incontinence, is aware of the need to urinate (void), may wear incontinence products for episodic urine leakage, and has a goal to maintain his/her highest level of continence and decrease urine leakage. Successful bladder retraining usually takes at least several weeks. Residents who are assessed with urge or mixed incontinence and are cognitively intact may be candidates for bladder retraining; and

- "Pelvic Floor Muscle Rehabilitation," also called Kegel and pelvic floor muscle exercise, is performed to strengthen the voluntary periuretheral and perivaginal muscles that contribute to the closing force of the urethra and the support of the pelvic organs. These exercises are helpful in dealing with urge and stress incontinence. Pelvic floor muscle exercises (PFME) strengthen the muscular components of urethral supports and are the cornerstone of noninvasive treatment of stress urinary incontinence. PFME requires residents who are able and willing to participate and the implementation of careful instructions and monitoring provided by the facility. Poor resident adherence to the exercises may occur even with close monitoring.

Programs that are dependent on staff involvement and assistance, as opposed to resident function, include the following:

- "Prompted Voiding" is a behavioral technique appropriate for use with dependent or more cognitively impaired residents. Prompted voiding techniques have been shown to reduce urinary incontinence episodes up to 40% for elderly incontinent nursing home residents, regardless of their type of urinary incontinence or cognitive deficit—provided that they at least are able to say their name or reliably point to one of two objects.[5] Prompted voiding has three components: regular monitoring with encouragement to report continence status; prompting to toilet on a scheduled basis; and praise and positive feedback when the resident is continent and attempts to toilet. These methods require training, motivation and continued effort by the resident and caregivers to ensure continued success. Prompted voiding focuses on teaching the resident, who is incontinent, to recognize bladder fullness or the need to void, to ask for help, or to respond when prompted to toilet.

  Residents who are assessed with urge or mixed incontinence and are cognitively impaired may be candidates for prompted voiding. As the resident's cognition changes, the facility should consider other factors, such as mobility, when deciding to conduct a voiding trial to determine feasibility of an ongoing toileting program; and

- "Habit Training/Scheduled Voiding" is a behavioral technique that calls for scheduled toileting at regular intervals on a planned basis to match the resident's voiding habits. Unlike bladder retraining, there is no systematic effort to encourage the resident to delay voiding and resist urges. Habit training includes timed voiding with the interval based on the resident's usual voiding schedule or pattern. Scheduled voiding is timed voiding, usually every three to four hours while awake. Residents who cannot self-toilet may be candidates for habit training or scheduled voiding programs.

Intermittent Catheterization

Sterile insertion and removal of a catheter through the urethra every 3-6 hours for bladder drainage may be appropriate for the management of acute or chronic urinary retention. See additional discussion below in "Catheterization."

Medication Therapy

Medications are often used to treat specific types of incontinence, including stress incontinence and those categories associated with an overactive bladder, which may involve symptoms including urge incontinence, urinary urgency, frequency and nocturia. The current literature identifies classifications and names of medications used for various types of incontinence. When using medications, potentially problematic anticholinergic and other side effects must be recognized. The use of medication therapy to treat urinary incontinence may not be appropriate for some residents because of potential adverse interactions with their other medications or other co-morbid conditions. Therefore, it is important to weigh the risks and benefits before prescribing medications for continence management and to monitor for both effectiveness and side effects. As with all approaches attempting to improve control or management of incontinence, the education and discussion with the resident (or the resident's surrogate) regarding the benefits and risks of pharmacologic therapies is important.

Pessary

A pessary is an intra-vaginal device used to treat pelvic muscle relaxation or prolapse of pelvic organs. Women whose urine retention or urinary incontinence is exacerbated by bladder or uterine prolapse may benefit from placement of a pessary. Female residents may be admitted to the nursing home with a pessary device. The assessment should note whether the resident has a pessary in place or has had a history of successful pessary use. If a pessary is to be used, it is important to develop a plan of care for ongoing management and for the prevention of and monitoring for complications.

Absorbent Products, Toileting Devices, and External Collection Devices

Absorbent incontinence products include perineal pads or panty liners for slight leakage, undergarments and protective underwear for moderate to heavy leakage, guards and drip collection pouches for men, and products (called adult briefs) for moderate or heavy loss. Absorbent products can be a useful, rational way to manage incontinence; however, every absorbent product has a saturation point. Factors contributing to the selection of the type of product to be used should include the severity of incontinence, gender, fit, and ease of use.

Advantages of using absorbent products to manage urinary incontinence include the ability to contain urine (some may wick the urine away from the skin), provide protection for clothing, and preserve the resident's dignity and comfort.

NOTE: Although many residents have used absorbent products prior to admission to the nursing home and the use of absorbent products may be appropriate, absorbent products should not be used as the primary long term approach to continence management until the resident has been appropriately evaluated and other alternative approaches have been considered.

The potential disadvantages of absorbent products are the impact on the resident's dignity, cost, the association with skin breakdown and irritation, and the amount of time needed to check and change them.[6]

It is important that residents using various toileting devices, absorbent products, external collection devices, etc., be checked (and changed as needed) on a schedule based upon the resident's voiding pattern, accepted standards of practice, and the manufacturer's recommendations.

Skin-Related Complications

Skin problems associated with incontinence and moisture can range from irritation to increased risk of skin breakdown. Moisture may make the skin more susceptible to damage from friction and shear during repositioning.

One form of early skin breakdown is maceration or the softening of tissue by soaking. Macerated skin has a white appearance and a very soft, sometimes "soggy" texture.

The persistent exposure of perineal skin to urine and/or feces can irritate the epidermis and can cause severe dermatitis or skin erosion. Skin erosion is the loss of some or all of the epidermis (comparable to a deep chemical peel) leaving a slightly depressed area of skin.

One key to preventing skin breakdown is to keep the perineal skin clean and dry. Research has shown that a soap and water regimen alone may be less effective in preventing skin breakdown compared with moisture barriers and no-rinse incontinence cleansers.[7] Because frequent washing with soap and water can dry the skin, the use of a perineal rinse may be indicated. Moisturizers help preserve the moisture in the skin by either sealing in existing moisture or adding moisture to the skin. Moisturizers include creams, lotions or pastes. However, moisturizers should be used sparingly—if at all—on already macerated or excessively moist skin.

CATHETERIZATION

42 CFR 483.25 (d)(1) Urinary Incontinence requires that a resident who enters the facility without an indwelling catheter is not catheterized unless the resident's clinical condition demonstrates that catheterization was necessary. Some residents are admitted to the facility with indwelling catheters that were placed elsewhere (e.g., during a recent acute hospitalization). The facility is responsible for the assessment of the resident at risk for urinary catheterization and/or the ongoing assessment for the resident who currently has a catheter. This is followed by implementation of appropriate individualized interventions and monitoring for the effectiveness of the interventions.

Assessment

A resident may be admitted to the facility with or without an indwelling urinary catheter (urethral or suprapubic) and may be continent or incontinent of urine. Regardless of the admission status, a comprehensive assessment should address those factors that predispose the resident to the development of urinary incontinence and the use of an indwelling urinary catheter.

An admission evaluation of the resident's medical history and a physical examination helps identify the resident at risk for requiring the use of an indwelling urinary catheter. This evaluation is to include detection of reversible causes of incontinence and identification of individuals with incontinence caused by conditions that may not be reversible, such as bladder tumors and spinal cord diseases. (See the assessment factors discussed under incontinence.) The assessment of continence/incontinence is based upon an interdisciplinary review. The comprehensive assessment should include underlying factors supporting the medical justification for the initiation and continuing need for catheter use, determination of which factors can be modified or reversed (or rationale for why those factors should not be modified), and the development of a plan for removal. The clinician's decision to use an indwelling catheter in the elderly should be based on valid clinical indicators.

For the resident with an indwelling catheter, the facility's documented assessment and staff knowledge of the resident should include information to support the use of an indwelling catheter. Because of the risk of substantial complications with the use of indwelling urinary catheters, they should be reserved primarily for short-term decompression of acute urinary retention. The assessment should include consideration of the risks and benefits of an indwelling (suprapubic or urethral) catheter; the potential for removal of the catheter; and consideration of complications resulting from the use of an indwelling catheter, such as symptoms of blockage of the catheter with associated bypassing of urine, expulsion of the catheter, pain, discomfort and bleeding.

Intermittent Catheterization

Intermittent catheterization can often manage overflow incontinence effectively. Residents who have new onset incontinence from a transient, hypotonic/atonic bladder (usually seen following indwelling catheterization in the hospital) may benefit from intermittent bladder catheterization until the bladder tone returns (e.g., up to approximately 7 days). A voiding trial and post void residual can help identify when bladder tone has returned.

Indwelling Catheter Use

The facility's documented assessment and staff approach to the resident should be based on evidence to support the use of an indwelling catheter. Appropriate indications for continuing use of an indwelling catheter beyond 14 days may include:[8]

- Urinary retention that cannot be treated or corrected medically or surgically, for which alternative therapy is not feasible, and which is characterized by:

  o Documented post void residual (PVR) volumes in a range over 200 milliliters (ml);
  o Inability to manage the retention/incontinence with intermittent catheterization; and
  o Persistent overflow incontinence, symptomatic infections, and/or renal dysfunction.

- Contamination of Stage III or IV pressure with urine which has impeded healing, despite appropriate personal care for the incontinence; and

- Terminal illness or severe impairment, which makes positioning or clothing changes uncomfortable, or which is associated with intractable pain.

Catheter-Related Complications

An indwelling catheter may be associated with significant complications, including bacteremia, febrile episodes, bladder stones, fistula formation, erosion of the urethra, epididymitis, chronic renal inflammation and pyelonephritis. In addition, indwelling catheters are prone to blockage. Risk factors for catheter blockage include alkaline urine, poor urine flow, proteinuria, and preexisting bladder stones. In the absence of evidence indicating blockage, catheters need not be changed routinely as long as monitoring is adequate. Based on the resident's individualized assessment, the catheter may need to be changed more or less often than every 30 days.

Some residents with indwelling catheters experience persistent leakage around the catheter. Examples of factors that may contribute to leakage include irritation by a large balloon or by catheter materials, excessive catheter diameter, fecal impaction, and improper catheter positioning. Because leakage around the catheter is frequently caused by bladder spasm, leakage should generally not be treated by using increasingly larger catheter sizes, unless medically justified. Current standards indicate that catheterization should be accomplished with the narrowest, softest tube that will serve the purpose of draining the bladder. Additional care practices related to catheterization include:

- Educating the resident or responsible party on the risks and benefits of catheter use;

- Recognizing and assessing for complications and their causes, and maintaining a record of any catheter-related problems;

- Attempts to remove the catheter as soon as possible when no indications exist for its continuing use;

- Monitoring for excessive post void residual, after removing a catheter that was inserted for obstruction or overflow incontinence;

- Keeping the catheter anchored to prevent excessive tension on the catheter, which can lead to urethral tears or dislodging the catheter; and

- Securing the catheter to facilitate flow of urine.

Research has shown that catheterization is an important, potentially modifiable, risk factor for UTI. By the 30th day of catheterization, bacteriuria is nearly universal.[9] The potential for complications can be reduced by:

- Identifying specific clinical indications for the use of an indwelling catheter;

- Assessing whether other treatments and services would appropriately address those conditions; and

- Assessing whether residents are at risk for other possible complications resulting from the continuing use of the catheter, such as obstruction resulting from catheter encrustation, urethral erosion, bladder spasms, hematuria, and leakage around the catheter.

URINARY TRACT INFECTIONS

Catheter-Related Bacteriuria and UTIs/Urosepsis

Most individuals with indwelling catheters for more than 7 days have bacteriuria. Bacteriuria alone in a catheterized individual should not be treated with antibiotics.

A long term indwelling catheter (>2 to 4 weeks) increases the chances of having a symptomatic UTI and urosepsis. The incidence of bacteremia is 40 times greater in individuals with a long term indwelling catheter than in those without one. For suspected UTIs in a catheterized individual, the literature recommends removing the current catheter and inserting a new one and obtaining a urine sample via the newly inserted catheter.[10]

Clinical Evidence That May Suggest UTI

Clinically, an acute deterioration in stable chronic symptoms may indicate an acute infection. Multiple co-existing findings such as fever with hematuria are more likely to be from a urinary source.

No one lab test alone proves that a UTI is present. For example, a positive urine culture will show bacteriuria but that alone is not enough to diagnose a symptomatic UTI. However, several test results in combination with clinical findings can help to identify UTIs such as the presence of pyuria (more than minimal white cells in the urine) on microscopic urinalysis, or a positive urine dipstick test for leukocyte esterase (indicating significant pyuria) or for nitrites (indicating the presence of Enterobacteriaceae). A negative leukocyte esterase or the absence of pyuria strongly suggests that a UTI is not present. A positive leukocyte esterase test alone does not prove that the individual has a UTI.[11]

In someone with nonspecific symptoms such as a change in function or mental status, bacteriuria alone does not necessarily warrant antibiotic treatment. Additional evidence that could confirm a UTI may include hematuria, fever (which could include a variation from the individual's normal or usual temperature range), or evidence of pyuria (either by microscopic examination or by dipstick test). In the absence of fever, hematuria, pyuria, or local urinary tract symptoms, other potential causes of nonspecific general symptoms, such as fluid and electrolyte imbalance or adverse drug reactions, should be considered instead of, or in addition to, a UTI. Although sepsis, including urosepsis, can cause dizziness or falling, there is not clear evidence linking bacteriuria or a localized UTI to an increased fall risk.[12]

Indications to Treat a UTI

Because many residents have chronic bacteriuria, the research-based literature suggests treating only symptomatic UTIs. Symptomatic UTIs are based on the following criteria:[13]

- Residents without a catheter should have at least three of the following signs and symptoms:

  o Fever (increase in temperature of >2 degrees F (1.1 degrees C) or rectal temperature >99.5 degrees F (37.5 degrees C) or single measurement of temperature >100 degrees F (37.8 degrees C));[14]

o New or increased burning pain on urination, frequency or urgency;

o New flank or suprapubic pain or tenderness;

o Change in character of urine (e.g., new bloody urine, foul smell, or amount of sediment) or as reported by the laboratory (new pyuria or microscopic hematuria); and/or

o Worsening of mental or functional status (e.g., confusion, decreased appetite, unexplained falls, incontinence of recent onset, lethargy, decreased activity).[15]

- Residents with a catheter should have at least two of the following signs and symptoms:

o Fever or chills;

o New flank pain or suprapubic pain or tenderness;

o Change in character of urine (e.g., new bloody urine, foul smell, or amount of sediment) or as reported by the laboratory (new pyuria or microscopic hematuria); and/or

o Worsening of mental or functional status. Local findings such as obstruction, leakage, or mucosal trauma (hematuria) may also be present.[16]

Follow-Up of UTIs

The goal of treating a UTI is to alleviate systemic or local symptoms, not to eradicate all bacteria. Therefore, a post-treatment urine culture is not routinely necessary but may be useful in select situations. Continued bacteriuria without residual symptoms does not warrant repeat or continued antibiotic therapy. Recurrent UTIs (2 or more in 6 months) in a noncatheterized individual may warrant additional evaluation (such as a determination of an abnormal post void residual (PVR) urine volume or a referral to a urologist) to rule out structural abnormalities such as enlarged prostate, prolapsed bladder, periurethral abscess, strictures, bladder calculi, polyps and tumors.

Recurrent symptomatic UTIs in a catheterized or noncatheterized individual should lead the facility to check whether perineal hygiene is performed consistently to remove fecal soiling in accordance with accepted practices. Recurrent UTIs in a catheterized individual should lead the facility to look for possible impairment of free urine flow through the catheter, to re-evaluate the techniques being used for perineal hygiene and catheter care, and to reconsider the relative risks and benefits of continuing the use of an indwelling catheter.

Because the major factors (other than an indwelling catheter) that predispose individuals to bacteriuria, including physiological aging changes and chronic comorbid illnesses, cannot be modified readily, the facility should demonstrate that they:

- Employ standard infection control practices in managing catheters and associated drainage system;

- Strive to keep the resident and catheter clean of feces to minimize bacterial migration into the urethra and bladder (e.g., cleaning fecal material away from, rather than towards, the urinary meatus);

- Take measures to maintain free urine flow through any indwelling catheter; and

- Assess for fluid needs and implement a fluid management program (using alternative approaches as needed) based on those assessed needs.

[**Editor's Note:** See page 391 for endnotes pertaining to this section.]

INVESTIGATIVE PROTOCOL

URINARY INCONTINENCE AND CATHETERS

Objectives

- To determine whether the initial insertion or continued use of an indwelling catheter is based upon clinical indication for use of a urinary catheter;

- To determine the adequacy of interventions to prevent, improve and/or manage urinary incontinence; and

- To determine whether appropriate treatment and services have been provided to prevent and/or treat UTIs.

Use

Use this protocol for a sampled resident with an indwelling urinary catheter or for a resident with urinary incontinence.

Procedures

Briefly review the assessment, care plan and orders to identify facility interventions and to guide observations to be made. Staff are expected to assess and provide appropriate care from the day of admission, for residents with urinary incontinence or a condition that may contribute to incontinence or the presence of an indwelling urinary catheter (including newly admitted residents). Corroborate observations by interview and record review.

NOTE: Criteria established in this protocol provide general guidelines and best practices which should be considered when making a determination of compliance, and is not an exhaustive list of mandatory elements.

1. Observation

Observe whether staff consistently implemented care plan interventions across various shifts. During observations of the interventions, note and/or follow up on deviations from the care plan or from current standards of practice, as well as potential negative outcomes.

Observe whether staff make appropriate resident accommodations consistent with the assessment, such as placing the call bell within reach and responding to the call bell, in relation to meeting toileting needs; maintaining a clear pathway and ready access to toilet facilities; providing (where indicated) elevated toilet seats, grab bars, adequate lighting, and assistance needed to use devices such as urinals, bedpans and commodes.

Observe whether assistance has been provided to try to prevent incontinence episodes, such as whether prompting, transfer, and/or stand-by assist to ambulate were provided as required for toileting.

For a resident who is on a program to restore continence or is on a prompted void or scheduled toileting program, note:

- The frequency of breakthrough or transient incontinence;

- How staff respond to the incontinence episodes; and

- Whether care is provided in accord with standards of practice (including infection control practices) and with respect for the resident's dignity.

For a resident who has been determined by clinical assessment to be unable to participate in a program to restore continence or in a scheduled toileting program and who requires care due to incontinence of urine, observe:

- Whether the resident is on a scheduled check and change program; and

- Whether staff check and change in a timely fashion.

For a resident who has experienced an incontinent episode, observe:

- The condition of the pads/sheets/clothing (a delay in providing continence care may be indicated by brown rings/circles, saturated linens/clothing, odors, etc.);

- The resident's physical condition (such as skin integrity, maceration, erythema, erosion);

- The resident's psychosocial outcomes (such as embarrassment or expressions of humiliation, resignation, about being incontinent);

- Whether staff implemented appropriate hygiene measures (e.g., cleansing, rinsing, drying and applying protective moisture barriers or barrier films as indicated) to try to prevent skin breakdown from prolonged exposure of the skin to urine; and

- Whether the staff response to incontinence episodes and the provision of care are consistent with standards of practice (including infection control practices) and with respect for the resident's dignity.

For a resident with an indwelling catheter, observe the delivery of care to evaluate:

- Whether staff use appropriate infection control practices regarding hand washing, catheter care, tubing, and the collection bag;

- Whether staff recognize and assess potential evidence of symptomatic UTI or other related changes in urine condition (such as onset of bloody urine, cloudiness, or oliguria, if present);

- How staff manage and assess urinary leakage from the point of catheter insertion to the bag, if present;

- If the resident has catheter-related pain, how staff assess and manage the pain; and

- What interventions (such as anchoring the catheter, avoiding excessive tugging on the catheter during transfer and care delivery) are being used to prevent inadvertent catheter removal or tissue injury from dislodging the catheter.

For a resident experiencing incontinence and who has an indwelling or intermittent catheter, observe whether the resident is provided and encouraged to take enough fluids to meet the resident's hydration needs, as reflected in various measures of hydration status (approximately 30ml/kg/day or as indicated based on the resident's clinical condition). For issues regarding hydration, see Guidance at 42 CFR 483.25(j), F327.

2. Interviews

Interview the resident, family or responsible party to the degree possible to identify:

- Their involvement in care plan development including defining the approaches and goals, and whether interventions reflect preferences and choices;

- Their awareness of the existing continence program and how to use devices or equipment;

- If timely assistance is provided as needed for toileting needs, hydration and personal hygiene and if continence care and/or catheter care is provided according to the care plan;

- If the resident comprehends and applies information and instructions to help improve or maintain continence (where cognition permits);

- Presence of urinary tract-related pain, including causes and management;

- If interventions were refused, whether consequences and/or other alternative approaches were presented and discussed; and

- Awareness of any current UTI, history of UTIs, or perineal skin problems.

If the resident has a skin problem that may be related to incontinence, or staff are not following the resident's care plan and continence/catheter care program, interview the nursing assistants to determine if they:

- Are aware of, and understand, the interventions specific to this resident (such as the bladder or bowel restorative/management programs);

- Have been trained and know how to handle catheters, tubing and drainage bags and other devices used during the provision of care; and

- Know what, when, and to whom to report changes in status regarding bowel and bladder function, hydration status, urine characteristics, and complaints of urinary-related symptoms.

3. Record Review

Assessment and Evaluation. Review the RAI, the history and physical, and other information such as physician orders, progress notes, nurses' notes, pharmacist reports, lab reports and any flow sheets or forms the facility uses to document the resident's voiding history, including the assessment of the resident's overall condition, risk factors and information about the resident's continence status, rationale for using a catheter, environmental factors related to continence programs, and the resident's responses to catheter/continence services. Request staff assistance, if the information is not readily available.

Determine if the facility assessment is consistent with or corroborated by documentation within the record and comprehensively reflects the status of the resident for:

- Patterns of incontinent episodes, daily voiding patterns or prior routines;

- Fluid intake and hydration status;

- Risks or conditions that may affect urinary continence;

- Use of medications that may affect continence and impaired continence that could reflect adverse drug reactions;

- Type of incontinence (stress, urge, overflow, mixed, functional, or transient incontinence) and contributing factors;

- Environmental factors that might facilitate or impede the ability to maintain bladder continence, such as access to the toilet, call bell, type of clothing and/or continence products, ambulation devices (walkers, canes), use of restraints, side rails;

- Type and frequency of physical assistance necessary to facilitate toileting;

- Clinical rationale for use of an indwelling catheter;

- Alternatives to extended use of an indwelling catheter (if possible); and

- Evaluation of factors possibly contributing to chronically recurring or persistent UTIs.

Care Plan. If the care plan refers to a specific facility treatment protocol that contains details of the treatment regimen, the protocol must be available to the direct care staff, so that they may be familiar with it and use it. The care plan should clarify any significant deviations from such a protocol for a specific resident. If care plan interventions that address aspects of continence and skin care related to incontinence are integrated within the overall care plan, the interventions do not need to be repeated in a separate continence care plan.

Review the care plan to determine if the plan is based upon the goals, needs and strengths specific to the resident and reflects the comprehensive assessment. Determine if the plan:

- Identifies quantifiable, measurable objectives with time frames to be able to assess whether the objectives have been met;

- Identifies interventions specific enough to guide the provision of services and treatment (e.g., toilet within an hour prior to each meal and within 30 minutes after meals, or check for episodes of incontinence within 30 minutes after each meal or specific times based upon the assessment of voiding patterns);

- Is based upon resident choices and preferences;

- Promotes maintenance of resident dignity;

- Addresses potential psychosocial complications of incontinence or catheterization such as social withdrawal, embarrassment, humiliation, isolation, resignation;

- Includes a component to inform the resident and representative about the risks and benefits of catheter use, on continence management approaches, medications selected, etc.;

- Addresses measures to promote sufficient fluid intake, including alternatives such as food substitutes that have a high liquid content, if there is reduced fluid intake;

- Defines interventions to prevent skin breakdown from prolonged exposure to urine and stool;

- Identifies and addresses the potential impact on continence of medication and urinary tract stimulants or irritants (e.g., caffeine) in foods and beverages;

- Identifies approaches to minimize risk of infection (personal hygiene measures and catheter/tubing/bag care); and

- Defines environmental approaches and devices needed to promote independence in toileting, to maintain continence, and to maximize independent functioning.

For the resident who is not on a scheduled toileting program or a program to restore normal bladder function to the extent possible, determine if the care plan provides specific approaches for a check and change program.

For the resident who is on a scheduled toileting or restorative program (e.g., retraining, habit training, scheduled voiding, prompted voiding, toileting devices), determine whether the care plan:

- Identifies the type of urinary incontinence and bases the program on the resident's voiding/elimination patterns; and

- Has been developed by considering the resident's medical/health condition, cognitive and functional ability to participate in a relevant continence program, and needed assistance.

For the resident with a catheter, determine whether the care plan:

- Defines the catheter, tubing and bag care, including indications, according to facility protocol, for changing the catheter, tubing or bag;

- Provides for assessment and removal of the indwelling catheter when no longer needed; and

- Establishes interventions to minimize catheter-related injury, pain, encrustation, excessive urethral tension, accidental removal, or obstruction of urine outflow.

Care Plan Revision. Determine if the resident's condition and effectiveness of the care plan interventions have been monitored and care plan revisions were made (or justifications for continuing the existing plan) based upon the following:

- The outcome and/or effects of goals and interventions;

- A decline or lack of improvement in continence status;

- Complications associated with catheter usage;

- Resident failure to comply with a continence program and alternative approaches that were offered to try to maintain or improve continence, including counseling regarding the potential consequences of not following the program;

- Change in condition, ability to make decisions, cognition, medications, behavioral symptoms or visual problems;

- Input by the resident and/or the responsible person; and

- An evaluation of the resident's level of participation in, and response to, the continence program.

4. Interviews with Health Care Practitioners and Professionals

If inconsistencies in care or potential negative outcomes have been identified, or care is not in accord with standards of practice, interview the nurse responsible for coordinating or overseeing the resident's care. Determine:

- How the staff monitor implementation of the care plan, changes in continence, skin condition, and the status of UTIs;

- If the resident resists toileting, how staff have been taught to respond;

- Types of interventions that have been attempted to promote continence (i.e., special clothing, devices, types and frequency of assistance, change in toileting schedule, environmental modifications);

- If the resident is not on a restorative program, how it was determined that the resident could not benefit from interventions such as a scheduled toileting program;

- For the resident on a program of toileting, whether the nursing staff can identify the programming applicable to the resident, and:

  o The type of incontinence;

  o The interventions to address that specific type;

  o How it is determined that the schedule and program is effective (i.e., how continence is maintained or if there has been a decline or improvement in continence, how the program is revised to address the changes); and

  o Whether the resident has any physical or cognitive limitations that influence potential improvement of his/her continence;

- For residents with urinary catheters, whether the nursing staff:

  o Can provide appropriate justification for the use of the catheter;
  o Can identify previous attempts made (and the results of the attempts) to remove a catheter; and
  o Can identify a history of UTIs (if present), and interventions to try to prevent recurrence.

If the interventions defined or care provided do not appear to be consistent with recognized standards of practice, interview one or more health care practitioners and professionals as necessary (e.g., physician, charge nurse, director of nursing) who, by virtue of training and knowledge of the resident, should be able to provide information about the causes, treatment and evaluation of the resident's condition or problem. Depending on the issue, ask about:

- How it was determined that the chosen interventions were appropriate;

- Risks identified for which there were no interventions;

- Changes in condition that may justify additional or different interventions; or how they validated the effectiveness of current interventions; and

- How they monitor the approaches to continence programs (e.g., policies/procedures, staffing requirements, how staff identify problems, assess the toileting pattern of the resident, develop and implement continence-related action plans, how staff monitor and evaluate resident's responses, etc.).

If the attending physician is unavailable, interview the medical director, as appropriate.

DETERMINATION OF COMPLIANCE (Task 6, Appendix P)

Synopsis of regulation (F315)

The urinary incontinence requirement has three aspects. The first aspect requires that a resident who does not have an indwelling urinary catheter does not have one inserted unless the resident's clinical condition demonstrates that it was necessary. The second aspect requires the facility to provide appropriate treatment and services to prevent urinary tract infections; and the third is that the facility attempt to assist the resident to restore as much normal bladder function as possible.

Criteria for Compliance

- Compliance with 42 CFR 483.25(d)(1) and (2), F315, Urinary Incontinence

    o   For a resident who was admitted with an indwelling urinary catheter or who had one placed after admission, the facility is in compliance with this requirement, if staff have:

    -   Recognized and assessed factors affecting the resident's urinary function and identified the medical justification for the use of an indwelling urinary catheter;

    -   Defined and implemented pertinent interventions to try to minimize complications from an indwelling urinary catheter, and to remove it if clinically indicated, consistent with resident conditions, goals, and recognized standards of practice;

    -   Monitored and evaluated the resident's response to interventions; and

    -   Revised the approaches as appropriate.

    If not, the use of an indwelling urinary catheter is not medically justified, and/or the ongoing treatment and services for catheter care were not provided consistent with the resident's needs. Cite F315.

    o   For a resident who is incontinent of urine, the facility is in compliance with this requirement if they:

    -   Recognized and assessed factors affecting the risk of symptomatic urinary tract infections and impaired urinary function;

    -   Defined and implemented interventions to address correctable underlying causes of urinary incontinence and to try to minimize the occurrence of symptomatic urinary tract infections in accordance with resident needs, goals, and recognized standards of practice;

    -   Monitored and evaluated the resident's response to preventive efforts and treatment interventions; and

    -   Revised the approaches as appropriate.

    If not, the facility is not in compliance with the requirement to assist the resident to maintain or improve the continence status, and/or prevent the decline of the condition of urinary incontinence for the resident. Cite F315.

    o   For a resident who has or has had a symptomatic urinary tract infection, the facility is in compliance with this requirement if they have:

    -   Recognized and assessed factors affecting the risk of symptomatic urinary tract infections and impaired urinary function;

    -   Defined and implemented interventions to try to minimize the occurrence of symptomatic urinary tract infections and to address correctable underlying causes, in accordance with resident needs, goals, and recognized standards of practice;

    -   Monitored and evaluated the resident's responses to preventive efforts and treatment interventions; and

    -   Revised the approaches as appropriate.

    If not, the development of a symptomatic urinary tract infection, and/or decline of the resident with one, was not consistent with the identified needs of the resident. Cite F315.

Noncompliance for F315

After completing the Investigative Protocol, analyze the data in order to determine whether or not noncompliance with the regulation exists. Noncompliance for F315 may include (but is not limited to) one or more of the following, including failure to:

- Provide care and treatment to prevent incontinence and/or improve urinary continence and restore as much normal bladder function as possible;

- Provide medical justification for the use of a catheter or provide services for a resident with a urinary catheter;

- Assess, prevent (to the extent possible) and treat a symptomatic urinary tract infection (as indicated by the resident's choices, clinical condition and physician treatment plan);

- Accurately or consistently assess a resident's continence status on admission and as indicated thereafter;

- Identify and address risk factors for developing urinary incontinence;

- Implement interventions (such as bladder rehabilitative programs) to try to improve, maintain or prevent decline of urinary incontinence, consistent with the resident's assessed need and current standards of practice;

- Provide clinical justification for developing urinary incontinence or for the failure of existing urinary incontinence to improve;

- Identify and manage symptomatic urinary tract infections, or explain adequately why they could or should not do so;

- Implement approaches to manage an indwelling urinary catheter based upon standards of practice, including infection control procedures;

- Identify and apply relevant policies and procedures to manage urinary incontinence, urinary catheters and/or urinary tract infections;

- Notify the physician of the resident's condition or changes in the resident's continence status or development of symptoms that may represent a symptomatic UTI (in contrast to asymptomatic bacteriuria).

Potential Tags for Additional Investigation

During the investigation of 42 CFR 483.25(d)(1) and (2), the surveyor may have identified concerns related to outcome, process and/or structure requirements. The surveyor should investigate these requirements before determining whether noncompliance may be present. The following are examples of related outcome, process and/or structure requirements that should be considered:

- 42 CFR 483.10(b)(11), F157, Notification of Changes

  o Determine if staff notified the physician of significant changes in the resident's continence, catheter usage, or the development, treatment and/or change in symptomatic UTIs; or notified the resident or resident's representative (where one exists) of significant changes as noted above.

- 42 CFR 483.15(a), F241, Dignity

  o Determine if staff provide continence care and/or catheter care to the resident in a manner that respects his/her dignity, strives to meet needs in a timely manner, monitors and helps the resident who cannot request assistance, and strives to minimize feelings of embarrassment, humiliation and/or isolation related to impaired continence.

- 42 CFR 483.20(b)(1), F272, Comprehensive Assessments

  o Determine if the facility comprehensively assessed the resident's continence status and resident-specific risk factors (including potential causes), and assessed for the use of continence-related devices, including an indwelling catheter.

- 42 CFR 483.20(k), F279, Comprehensive Care Plans

  o Determine if the facility developed a care plan (1) that was consistent with the resident's specific conditions, risks, needs, behaviors, and preferences and with current standards of practice and (2) that includes measurable objectives, approximate timetables, specific interventions and/or services needed to prevent or address incontinence, provide catheter care; and to prevent UTIs to the extent possible.

- 42 CFR 483.20(k)(2)(iii), F280, Comprehensive Care Plan Revision

  o Determine if the care plan was reviewed and revised periodically, as necessary, related to preventing, managing, or improving incontinence, managing an indwelling urinary catheter, possible discontinuation of an indwelling catheter, and attempted prevention and management of UTIs.

- 42 CFR 483.20(k)(3)(i), F281, Services Provided Meet Professional Standards

  o Determine if services and care were provided for urinary incontinence, catheter care and/or symptomatic UTIs in accordance with accepted professional standards.

- 42 CFR 483.25, F309, Quality of Care

  o Determine if staff identified and implemented appropriate measures to address any pain related to the use of an indwelling urinary catheter or skin complications such as maceration, and to provide the necessary care and services in accordance with the comprehensive assessment plan of care.

- 42 CFR 483.25 (a)(3) F312, Quality of Care

  o Determine if staff identified and implemented appropriate measures to provide good personal hygiene for the resident who cannot perform relevant activities of daily living, and who has been assessed as unable to achieve and/or restore normal bladder function.

- 42 CFR 483.40(a), F385, Physician Supervision

  o Determine if the physician has evaluated and addressed, as indicated, medical issues related to preventing or managing urinary incontinence, catheter usage, and symptomatic UTIs.

- 42 CFR 483.65(b)(3), F444[*], Infection Control: Hand Washing [*][Editor's Note: The tag number cited is incorrect. The correct tag number is F441.]

  o Determine if staff wash their hands after providing incontinence care, and before and after providing catheter care.

- 42 CFR 483.75(f), F498, Proficiency of Nurse Aides

  o Determine if nurse aides correctly deliver continence and catheter care, including practices to try to minimize skin breakdown, UTIs, catheter-related injuries, and dislodgement.

- 42 CFR 483.30(a), F353, Sufficient Staff

  o Determine if the facility had qualified staff in sufficient numbers to provide necessary care and services on a 24-hour basis, based upon the comprehensive assessment and care plan, to prevent, manage and/or improve urinary incontinence where possible.

- 42 CFR 483.75(i)(2), F501, Medical Director

  o Determine whether the medical director, in collaboration with the facility and based on current standards of practice, has developed policies and procedures for the prevention and management of urinary incontinence, for catheter care, and for the identification and management of symptomatic urinary tract infections; and whether the medical director interacts, if requested by the facility, with the physician supervising the care of the resident related to the management of urinary incontinence, catheter or infection issues.

V. DEFICIENCY CATEGORIZATION ([*]Part V, Appendix P) *[Editor's Note: The part number cited is incorrect. The correct part number is IV.]

Once the team has completed its investigation, analyzed the data, reviewed the regulatory requirements, and determined that non-compliance exists, the team must determine the severity of each deficiency, based on the resultant effect or potential for harm to the resident.

The key elements for severity determination for F315 are as follows:

1. Presence of harm/negative outcome(s) or potential for negative outcomes because of lack of appropriate treatment and care. Actual or potential harm/negative outcome for F315 may include, but is not limited to:

    *   Development, recurrence, persistence, or increasing frequency of urinary incontinence, which is not the result of underlying clinical conditions;

    *   Complications such as urosepsis or urethral injury related to the presence of an indwelling urinary catheter that is not clinically justified;

    *   Significant changes in psychosocial functioning, such as isolation, withdrawal, or embarrassment, related to the presence of un-assessed or unmanaged urinary incontinence and/or a decline in continence, and/or the use of a urinary catheter without a clinically valid medical justification; and

    *   Complications such as skin breakdown that are related to the failure to manage urinary incontinence;

2. Degree of harm (actual or potential) related to the noncompliance. Identify how the facility practices caused, resulted in, allowed or contributed to the actual or potential for harm:

    *   If harm has occurred, determine if the harm is at the level of serious injury, impairment, death, compromise, or discomfort; and

    *   If harm has not yet occurred, determine the potential for serious injury, impairment, death, or compromise or discomfort to occur to the resident; and

3. The immediacy of correction required. Determine whether the noncompliance requires immediate correction in order to prevent serious injury, harm, impairment, or death to one or more residents.

    The survey team must evaluate the harm or potential for harm based upon the following levels of severity for tag F315. First, the team must rule out whether Severity Level 4, Immediate Jeopardy to a resident's health or safety exists by evaluating the deficient practice in relation to immediacy, culpability, and severity. (Follow the guidance in Appendix Q, Immediate Jeopardy.)

Severity Level 4 Considerations: Immediate Jeopardy to Resident Health or Safety

Immediate Jeopardy is a situation in which the facility's noncompliance with one or more requirements of participation:

*   Has allowed/caused/resulted in, or is likely to allow/cause /result in serious injury, harm, impairment, or death to a resident; and

*   Requires immediate correction, as the facility either created the situation or allowed the situation to continue by failing to implement preventative or corrective measures.

Examples of possible negative outcomes as a result of the facility's deficient practices may include:

*   **Complications resulting from utilization of urinary appliance(s) without medical justification:** As a result of incorrect or unwarranted (i.e., not medically indicated) utilization of a urinary catheter, pessary, etc., the resident experiences injury or trauma (e.g., urethral tear) that requires surgical intervention or repair.

*   **Extensive failure in multiple areas of incontinence care and/or catheter management:** As a result of the facility's noncompliance in multiple areas of continence care or catheter management, the resident developed urosepsis with complications leading to prolonged decline or death.

NOTE: If immediate jeopardy has been ruled out based upon the evidence, then evaluate whether actual harm that is not immediate jeopardy exists at Severity Level 3.

Severity Level 3 Considerations: Actual Harm that is not Immediate Jeopardy

Level 3 indicates noncompliance that results in actual harm, and can include but may not be limited to clinical compromise, decline, or the resident's ability to maintain and/or reach his/her highest practicable well-being.

Examples of avoidable negative outcomes may include, but are not limited to:

- **The development of a symptomatic UTI:** As a result of the facility's noncompliance, the resident developed a symptomatic UTI, without long term complications, associated with the use of an indwelling catheter for which there was no medical justification.

- **The failure to identify, assess and mange urinary retention:** As a result of the facility's noncompliance, the resident had persistent overflow incontinence and/or developed recurrent symptomatic UTIs.

- **The failure to provide appropriate catheter care:** As a result of the facility's noncompliance, the catheter was improperly managed, resulting in catheter-related pain, bleeding, urethral tears or urethral erosion.

- **Medically unjustified use of an indwelling catheter with complications:** As a result of the facility's noncompliance, a resident who was admitted with a urinary catheter had the catheter remain for an extended period of time without a valid medical justification for its continued use, or a urinary catheter was inserted after the resident was in the facility and used for an extended time without medical justification, during which the resident experienced significant complications such as recurrent symptomatic UTIs.

- **Decline or failure to improve continence status:** As a result of the facility's failure to assess and/or re-assess the resident's continence status, utilize sufficient staffing to implement continence programs and provide other related services based on the resident's assessed needs, and/or to evaluate the possible adverse effects of medications on continence status, the resident failed to maintain or improve continence status.

- **Complications due to urinary incontinence:** As a result of the facility's failure to provide care and services to a resident who is incontinent of urine, in accordance with resident need and accepted standards of practice, the resident developed skin maceration and/or erosion or declined to attend or participate in social situations (withdrawal) due to embarrassment or humiliation related to unmanaged urinary incontinence.

NOTE: If Severity Level 3 (actual harm that is not immediate jeopardy) has been ruled out based upon the evidence, then evaluate as to whether Level 2 (no actual harm with the potential for more than minimal harm) exists.

Severity Level 2 Considerations: No Actual Harm with potential for more than minimal harm that is Not Immediate Jeopardy

Level 2 indicates noncompliance that results in a resident outcome of no more than minimal discomfort and/or has the potential to compromise the resident's ability to maintain or reach his or her highest practicable level of well being. The potential exists for greater harm to occur if interventions are not provided.

Examples of potentially avoidable negative outcomes may include, but are not limited to:

- **Medically unjustified use of an indwelling catheter:** As a result of the facility's noncompliance, the resident has the potential for experiencing complications, such as symptomatic UTIs, bladder stones, pain, etc.

- **Complications associated with inadequate care and services for an indwelling catheter:** As a result of the facility's noncompliance, the resident has developed potentially preventable non-life-threatening problems related to the catheter, such as leaking of urine due to blockage of urine outflow, with or without skin maceration and/or dermatitis.

- **Potential for decline or complications:** As a result of the facility's failure to consistently implement a scheduled voiding program defined in accordance with the assessed needs, the resident experiences repeated episodes of incontinence but has not demonstrated a decline or developed complications.

Severity Level 1: No actual harm with potential for minimal harm

The failures of the facility to provide appropriate care and services to improve continence, manage indwelling catheters, and minimize negative outcome places residents at risk for more than minimal harm. Therefore, Severity Level 1 does not apply for this regulatory requirement.

§483.25(e) Range of Motion

Based on the comprehensive assessment of a resident, the facility must ensure that

See Tag F318 for intent, guidelines, procedures, and probes for §483.25(e).

F317

§483.25(e)(1) A resident who enters the facility without a limited range of motion does not experience reduction in range of motion unless the resident's clinical condition demonstrates that a reduction in range of motion is unavoidable; and

SEE INTERPRETIVE GUIDELINES AT TAG F318

F318

§483.25(e)(2) A resident with a limited range of motion receives appropriate treatment and services to increase range of motion and/or to prevent further decrease in range of motion.

Intent §483.25(e)

The intent of this regulation is to ensure that the resident reaches and maintains his or her highest level of range of motion and to prevent avoidable decline of range of motion.

Interpretive Guidelines §483.25(e)

This corresponds to MDS 2.0 sections G and P when specified for use by the State.

"Range of motion (ROM)" is defined as the extent of movement of a joint.

The clinical condition that may demonstrate that a reduction in ROM is unavoidable is: limbs or digits immobilized because of injury or surgical procedures (e.g., surgical adhesions).

Adequate preventive care may include active ROM performed by the resident's passive ROM performed by staff; active-assistive ROM exercise performed by the resident and staff; and application of splints and braces, if necessary.

Examples of clinical conditions that are the primary risk factors for a decreased range of motion are:

- Immobilization (e.g., bedfast);

- Deformities arising out of neurological deficits (e.g., strokes, multiple sclerosis, cerebral palsy, and polio); and

- Pain, spasms, and immobility associated with arthritis or late state Alzheimer's disease.

This clinical condition may demonstrate that a reduction in ROM is unavoidable only if adequate assessment, appropriate care planning, and preventive care was provided, and resulted in limitation in ROM or muscle atrophy.

Procedures §483.25(e)

For each resident selected for a comprehensive review, or focused review, as appropriate, who needs routine preventive care:

- Observe staff providing routine ROM exercises. Are they done according to the care plan?

Probes §483.25(e)

Is there evidence that there has been a decline in sampled residents' ROM or muscle atrophy that was avoidable?

- Was the resident at risk for decline in ROM? If so, why?

- What care did the facility provide, including routine preventive measures that addressed the resident's unique risk factors (e.g., use muscle strengthening exercises in residents with muscle atrophy)?

- Was this care provided consistently?

For all sampled residents who have limited ROM, what is the facility doing to prevent further declines in ROM?

- Are passive ROM exercises provided and active ROM exercises supervised per the plan of care?

- Have care plan objectives identified resident's needs and has resident progress been evaluated?

- Is there evidence that care planning is changed as the resident's condition changes?

- Identify if resident triggers RAPs for ADL functional/rehabilitation potential, visual function, and communication. Consider whether the RAPs used to assess causal factors for decline, potential for decline or lack of improvement.

---

§483.25(f) Mental and Psychosocial Functioning

Based on the comprehensive assessment of a resident, the facility must ensure that--

See **Tag F319** for intent, guidelines, and probes for §483.25(f).

F319

§483.25(f)(1) A resident who displays mental or psychosocial adjustment difficulty, receives appropriate treatment and services to correct the assessed problem; and

Intent §483.25(f)

The intent of this regulation is that the resident receives care and services to assist him or her to reach and maintain the highest level of mental and psychosocial functioning.

Interpretive Guidelines §483.25(f)

This corresponds to MDS 2.0 sections B, F, E, and I when specified for use by the State.

"Mental and psychosocial adjustment difficulties" refer to problems residents have in adapting to changes in life's circumstances. The former focuses on internal thought processes; the latter, on the external manifestations of these thought patterns.

Mental and psychosocial adjustment difficulties are characterized primarily by an overwhelming sense of loss of one's capabilities; of family and friends; of the ability to continue to pursue activities and hobbies; and of one's possessions. This sense of loss is perceived as global and uncontrollable and is supported by thinking patterns that focus on helplessness and hopelessness; that all learning and essentially all meaningful living ceases once one enters a nursing home. A resident with a mental adjustment disorder will have a sad or anxious mood, or a behavioral symptom such as aggression.

The "Diagnostic and Statistical Manual of Mental Disorders, Fourth Edition (DSM/IV)," specifies that adjustment disorders develop within 3 months of a stressor (e.g., moving to another room) and are evidenced by significant functional impairment. Bereavement with the death of a loved one is not associated with adjustment disorders developed within 3 months of a stressor.

Other manifestations of mental and psychosocial adjustment difficulties may, over a period of time, include:

- Impaired verbal communication;

- Social isolation (e.g., loss or failure to have relationships);

- Sleep pattern disturbance (e.g., disruptive change in sleep/rest pattern as related to one's biological and emotional needs);

- Spiritual distress (disturbances in one's belief system);

- Inability to control behavior and potential for violence (aggressive behavior directed at self or others); and

- Stereotyped response to any stressor (i.e., the same characteristic response, regardless of the stimulus).

Appropriate treatment and services for psychosocial adjustment difficulties may include providing residents with opportunities for self-governance; systematic orientation programs; arrangements to keep residents in touch with their communities, cultural heritage, former lifestyle, and religious practices; and maintaining contact with friends and family Appropriate treatment for mental adjustment difficulties may include crisis intervention services; individual, group or family psychotherapy, drug therapy and training in monitoring of drug therapy and other rehabilitative services. (See §483.45(a).)

Clinical conditions that may produce apathy, malaise, and decreased energy levels that can be mistaken for depression associated with mental or psychosocial adjustment difficulty are: (This list is not all inclusive.)

- Metabolic diseases (e.g., abnormalities of serum glucose, potassium, calcium, and blood urea nitrogen, hepatic dysfunction);

- Endocrine diseases (e.g., hypothyroidism, hyperthyroidism, diabetes, hypoparathyroidism, hyperparathyroidism, Cushing's disease, Addison's disease);

- Central nervous system diseases (e.g., tumors and other mass lesions, Parkinson's disease, multiple sclerosis, Alzheimer's disease, vascular disease);

- Miscellaneous diseases (e.g., pernicious anemia, pancreatic disease, malignancy, infections, congestive heart failure);

- Over-medication with anti-hypertensive drugs; and

- Presence of restraints.

Probes §483.25(f)(1)

For sampled residents selected for a comprehensive or focused review, determine, as appropriate, for those residents exhibiting difficulties in mental and psychosocial adjustment:

- Is there a complete accurate assessment of resident's usual and customary routines?

- What evidence is there that the facility makes accommodations for the resident's usual and customary routines?

- What programs/activities has the resident received to improve and maintain maximum mental and psychosocial functioning?

- Has the resident's mental and psychosocial functioning been maintained or improved (e.g., fewer symptoms of distress)? Have treatment plans and objectives been re-evaluated?

- Has the resident received a psychological or psychiatric evaluation to evaluate, diagnose, or treat her/his condition, if necessary?

- Identify if resident triggers RAPs for activities, mood state, psychosocial well-being, and psychotropic drug use. Consider whether the RAPs were used to assess the causal factors for decline, potential for decline or lack of improvement.

- How are mental and psychosocial adjustment difficulties addressed in the care plan?

See §483.45(a), F406 for health rehabilitative services for mental illness and mental retardation.

Psychosocial adjustment difficulty does not display a pattern of decreased social interaction and/or increased withdrawn, angry, or depressive behaviors, unless the resident's clinical condition demonstrates that such a pattern was unavoidable.

F320

§483.25(f)(2)

(2) A resident whose assessment did not reveal a mental or psychosocial adjustment difficulty does not display a pattern of decreased social interaction and/or increased withdrawn, angry, or depressive behaviors, unless the resident's clinical condition demonstrates that such a pattern is unavoidable.

Procedures §483.25(f)(2)

For sampled residents whose assessment did not reveal a mental or psychosocial adjustment difficulty, but who display decreased social interaction or increased withdrawn, angry, or depressed behaviors, determine, as appropriate, was this behavior unavoidable.

Probes §483.25(f)(2)

- Did the facility attempt to evaluate whether this behavior was attributable to organic causes or other risk factors not associated with adjusting to living in the nursing facility?

- What care did the resident receive to maintain his/her mental or psychosocial functioning?

- Were individual objectives of the plan of care periodically evaluated, and if progress was not made in reducing, maintaining, or increasing behaviors that assist the resident to have his/her needs met, were alternative treatment approaches developed to maintain mental or psychosocial functioning?

- Identify if resident triggers RAPs for behavior problem, cognitive loss/dementia, and psychosocial well-being. Consider whether the RAPs were used to assess causal factors for decline, potential for decline or lack of improvement.

- Did the facility use the RAPs for behavior problems, cognitive loss/dementia, and psychosocial well-being to assess why the behaviors or change in mental or psychosocial functioning was occurring?

---

§483.25(g) Naso-Gastric Tubes

Based on the comprehensive assessment of a resident, the facility must ensure that--

See Tag F322 for intent, guidelines, and probes for §483.25(g).

F321

§483.25(g)(1) A resident who has been able to eat enough alone or with assistance is not fed by naso-gastric tube unless the resident's clinical condition demonstrates that use of a naso-gastric tube was unavoidable; and

F322

§483.25(g)(2) A resident who is fed by a naso-gastric or gastrostomy tube receives the appropriate treatment and services to prevent aspiration pneumonia, diarrhea, vomiting, dehydration, metabolic abnormalities, and nasal-pharyngeal ulcers and to restore, if possible, normal eating skills.

Intent §483.25(g)

The intent of this regulation is that a naso-gastric tube feeding is utilized only after adequate assessment, and the resident's clinical condition makes this treatment necessary.

Interpretive Guidelines §483.25(g)

This corresponds to MDS 2.0 sections G, K, P when specified for use by the State.

This requirement is also intended to prevent the use of tube feeding when ordered over the objection of the resident. Decisions about the appropriateness of tube feeding for a resident are developed with the resident or his/her family, surrogate or representative as part of determining the care plan.

Complications in tube feeding are not necessarily the result of improper care, but assessment for the potential for complications and care and treatment are provided to prevent complications in tube feeding by the facility.

Clinical conditions demonstrating that nourishment via an naso-gastric tube is unavoidable include:

- The inability to swallow without choking or aspiration, i.e., in cases of Parkinson's disease, pseudobulbar palsy, or esophageal diverticulum;

- Lack of sufficient alertness for oral nutrition (e.g., resident comatose); and

- Malnutrition not attributable to a single cause or causes that can be isolated and reversed. There is documented evidence that the facility has not been able to maintain or improve the resident's nutritional status through oral intake.

Probes §483.25(g)

For sampled residents who, upon admission to the facility, were not tube fed and now have a feeding tube, was tube feeding unavoidable? To determine if the tube feeding was unavoidable, assess the following:

- Did the facility identify the resident at risk for malnutrition?

- What did the facility do to maintain oral feeding, prior to inserting a feeding tube? Did staff provide enough assistance in eating? Did staff cue resident as needed, assist with the use of assistive devices, or feed the resident, if necessary?

- Is the resident receiving therapy to improve or enhance swallowing skills, as need, is identified in the comprehensive assessment?

- Was an assessment done to determine the cause of decreased oral intake/weight loss or malnutrition?

- If there was a dietitian consultation, were recommendations followed?

- For all sampled residents who are tube fed?

- Is the NG tube properly placed?

- Are staff responsibilities for providing enteral feedings clearly assigned (i.e., who administers the feeding, formula, amount, feeding intervals, flow rate)?

- Do staff monitor feeding complications (e.g., diarrhea, gastric distension, aspiration) and administer corrective actions to allay complications (e.g., changing rate of formula administration)?

- Are there negative consequences of tube use (e.g., agitation, depression, self-extubation, infections, aspiration and restraint use without a medical reason for the restraint)?

- When long term use is anticipated, is G tube placement considered?

Is the potential for complications from feedings minimized by:

- Use of a small bore, flexible naso-gastric tube, unless contraindicated;

- Securely attached the tube to the nose/face;

- Checking for correct tube placement prior to beginning a feeding or administering medications and after episodes of vomiting or suctioning;

- Checking a resident with a newly inserted gastric tube for gastric residual volume every 2-4 hours until the resident has demonstrated an ability to empty his/her stomach;

- Properly elevating the resident's head;

- Providing the type, rate and volume of the feeding as ordered;

- Using universal precautions and clean technique and as per facility/manufacturer's directions when stopping, starting, flushing, and giving medications through the tube;

- Using hang time recommendations by the manufacturer to prevent excessive microbial growth;

- Implement the procedures to ensure cleanliness of supplies, e.g. irrigating syringes changed on a regular bases as per facility policy. It is not necessary to change the irrigating syringe each time it is used;

- Using a pump equipped with a functional alarm (if pump used);

- The facility's criteria for determining that a resident may be able to return to eating by mouth (e.g., a resident whose Parkinson's symptoms have been controlled);

- There are sampled residents who* meet these criteria; *[**Editor's Note**: The word "who" was missing from this bullet.]

- If so, the facility has assisted them in returning to normal eating; and

- Identify if resident triggers RAPs for feeding tubes, nutritional status, and dehydration/fluid maintenance. Consider whether the RAPs were used to assess causal factors for decline, potential for decline and lack of improvement.

F323

(Rev. 27; Issued: 08-17-07; Effective/Implementation: 08-17-07)

§483.25(h) Accidents

The facility must ensure that –

(1) **The resident environment remains as free from accident hazards as is possible; and**

(2) **Each resident receives adequate supervision and assistance devices to prevent accidents.**

Intent: 42 CFR 483.25(h) (1) and (2) Accidents and Supervision

The intent of this requirement is to ensure the facility provides an environment that is free from accident hazards over which the facility has control and provides supervision and assistive devices to each resident to prevent avoidable accidents. This includes:

- Identifying hazard(s) and risk(s);

- Evaluating and analyzing hazard(s) and risk(s);

- Implementing interventions to reduce hazard(s) and risk(s); and

- Monitoring for effectiveness and modifying interventions when necessary.

DEFINITIONS

Definitions are provided to clarify terms related to providing supervision and other interventions to prevent accidents.

- "Accident" refers to any unexpected or unintentional incident, which may result in injury or illness to a resident. This does not include adverse outcomes that are a direct consequence of treatment or care that is provided in accordance with current standards of practice (e.g., drug side effects or reaction).

    o "Avoidable Accident" means that an accident occurred because the facility failed to:

      - Identify environmental hazards and individual resident risk of an accident, including the need for supervision; and/or

      - Evaluate/analyze the hazards and risks; and/or

      - Implement interventions, including adequate supervision, consistent with a resident's needs, goals, plan of care, and current standards of practice in order to reduce the risk of an accident; and/or

      - Monitor the effectiveness of the interventions and modify the interventions as necessary, in accordance with current standards of practice.

    o "Unavoidable Accident" means that an accident occurred despite facility efforts to:

      - Identify environmental hazards and individual resident risk of an accident, including the need for supervision; and

      - Evaluate/analyze the hazards and risks; and

- Implement interventions, including adequate supervision, consistent with the resident's needs, goals, plan of care, and current standards of practice in order to reduce the risk of an accident; and

- Monitor the effectiveness of the interventions and modify the interventions as necessary, in accordance with current standards of practice.

- "Assistance Device" or "Assistive Device" refers to any item (e.g., fixtures such as handrails, grab bars, and devices/equipment such as transfer lifts, canes, and wheelchairs, etc.) that is used by, or in the care of a resident to promote, supplement, or enhance the resident's function and/or safety.

  NOTE: The currently accepted nomenclature refers to "assistive devices." Although the term "assistance devices" is used in the regulation, the Guidance provided in this document will refer to "assistive devices."

- "Environment" refers to the resident environment. (See definition for "resident environment.")

- "Fall" refers to unintentionally coming to rest on the ground, floor, or other lower level, but not as a result of an overwhelming external force (e.g., resident pushes another resident). An episode where a resident lost his/her balance and would have fallen, if not for staff intervention, is considered a fall. A fall without injury is still a fall. Unless there is evidence suggesting otherwise, when a resident is found on the floor, a fall is considered to have occurred.[1]

- "Hazards" refer to elements of the resident environment that have the potential to cause injury or illness.

  o "Hazards over which the facility has control" are those hazards in the resident environment where reasonable efforts by the facility could influence the risk for resulting injury or illness.

  o "Free of accident hazards as is possible" refers to being free of accident hazards over which the facility has control.

- "Resident environment" includes the physical surroundings to which the resident has access (e.g., room, unit, common use areas, and facility grounds, etc.).

- "Risk" refers to any external factor or characteristic of an individual resident that influences the likelihood of an accident.

- "Supervision/Adequate Supervision" refers to an intervention and means of mitigating the risk of an accident. Facilities are obligated to provide adequate supervision to prevent accidents. Adequate supervision is defined by the type and frequency of supervision, based on the individual resident's assessed needs and identified hazards in the resident environment. Adequate supervision may vary from resident to resident and from time to time for the same resident.

OVERVIEW

Numerous and varied accident hazards exist in everyday life. Not all accidents are avoidable. The frailty of some residents increases their vulnerability to hazards in the resident environment and can result in life threatening injuries. It is important that all facility staff understand the facility's responsibility, as well as their own, to ensure the safest environment possible for residents.

The facility is responsible for providing care to residents in a manner that helps promote quality of life. This includes respecting residents' rights to privacy, dignity and self determination, and their right to make choices about significant aspects of their life in the facility.

For various reasons, residents are exposed to some potential for harm. Although hazards should not be ignored, there are varying degrees of potential for harm. It is reasonable to accept some risks as a trade off for the potential benefits, such as maintaining dignity, self-determination, and control over one's daily life. The facility's challenge is to balance protecting the resident's right to make choices and the facility's responsibility to comply with all regulations.

The responsibility to respect a resident's choices is balanced by considering the potential impact of these choices on other individuals and on the facility's obligation to protect the residents from harm. The facility has a responsibility to educate a resident, family, and staff regarding significant risks related to a resident's choices. Incorporating a resident's choices into the plan of care can help the facility balance interventions to reduce the risk of an accident, while honoring the resident's autonomy. Consent by resident or responsible party alone does not relieve the provider of its responsibility to assure the health, safety, and welfare of its residents, including protecting them from avoidable accidents. While Federal regulations affirm the resident's right to participate in care planning and to refuse treatment, the regulations do not create the right for a resident, legal surrogate, or representative to demand the facility use specific medical interventions or treatments that the facility deems inappropriate. The regulations hold the facility ultimately accountable for the resident's care and safety. Verbal consent or signed consent forms do not eliminate a facility's responsibility to protect a resident from an avoidable accident.

An effective way for the facility to avoid accidents is to commit to safety and implement systems that address resident risk and environmental hazards to minimize the likelihood of accidents.[2, 3] A facility with a commitment to safety:

- Acknowledges the high-risk nature of its population and setting;

- Develops a reporting system that does not place blame on the staff member for reporting resident risks and environmental hazards;

- Involves all staff in helping identify solutions to ensure a safe resident environment;

- Directs resources to address safety concerns; and

- Demonstrates a commitment to safety at all levels of the organization.

A SYSTEMS APPROACH

Establishing and utilizing a systematic approach to resident safety helps facilities comply with the regulations at 42 CFR §483.25(h)(1) and (2). Processes in a facility's system approach may include:

- Identification of hazards, including inadequate supervision, and a resident's risks of potentially avoidable accidents in the resident environment;

- Evaluation and analysis of hazards and risks;

- Implementation of interventions, including adequate supervision and assistive devices, to reduce individual risks related to hazards in the environment; and

- Monitoring for effectiveness and modification of interventions when necessary.

A key element of a systematic approach is the consistent application of a process to consistently address identified hazards and/or risks. Risks may pertain to individual residents, groups of residents, or the entire facility. Hazards may include, but are not limited to, aspects of the physical plant, equipment, and devices that are defective or are not used properly (per manufacturer's specifications), are disabled/removed, or are not individually adapted or fitted to the resident's needs. An effective system not only identifies environmental hazards and the resident's risk for an avoidable accident, but also the resident's need for supervision.

Identifying and addressing risks, including the potential for accidents, includes consideration of the environment, the resident's risk factors, and the need for supervision, care, and assistive devices. This will allow the facility to communicate information about observed hazards, identify resident-specific information, develop and implement an individualized plan of care to address each resident's needs and goals, and to monitor the results of the planned interventions. The plan of care should strive to balance the resident's wishes with the potential impact on other residents.

A systematic approach allows the facility to adjust its responses depending on the urgency of the situation and the hazards identified. The system includes a means for communicating the observations of hazards and the recording of resident specific information. Risks identified by the facility can pertain to individual residents or groups of residents. The facility-centered approach addresses risks for groups of residents; whereas, the resident-directed approach addresses risks for the individual residents.

Identification of Hazards and Risks

Identification of hazards and risks is the process through which the facility becomes aware of potential hazards in the resident environment and the risk of a resident having an avoidable accident. All staff (e.g., professional, administrative, maintenance, etc.) are to be involved in observing and identifying potential hazards in the environment, while taking into consideration the unique characteristics and abilities of each resident. The facility should make a reasonable effort to identify the hazards and risk factors for each resident. Various sources provide information about hazards and risks in the resident environment. These sources may include, but are not limited to, quality assurance activities, environmental rounds, MDS/RAPs data, medical history and physical exam, and individual observation. This information is to be documented and communicated across all disciplines.

Evaluation and Analysis

Evaluation and analysis is the process of examining data to identify specific hazards and risks and to develop targeted interventions to reduce the potential for accidents. Interdisciplinary involvement is a critical component of this process. Analysis may include, for example, considering the severity of hazards, the immediacy of risk, and trends such as time of day, location, etc.

Both the facility-centered and resident-directed approaches include evaluating hazard and accident risk data, analyzing potential causes for each hazard and accident risk, and identifying or developing interventions based on the severity of the hazards and immediacy of risk. Evaluations also look at trends such as time of day, location, etc.

Implementation of Interventions

Implementation refers to using specific interventions to try to reduce a resident's risks from hazards in the environment. The process includes: Communicating the interventions to all relevant staff, assigning responsibility, providing training as needed, documenting interventions (e.g., plans of action developed by the Quality Assurance Committee or care plans for the individual resident), and ensuring that the interventions are put into action.

Interventions are based on the results of the evaluation and analysis of information about hazards and risks and are consistent with relevant standards, including evidence-based practice. Development of interim safety measures may be necessary if interventions cannot immediately be implemented fully.

Facility-based interventions may include, but are not limited to, educating staff, repairing the device/equipment, and developing or revising policies and procedures. Resident-directed approaches may include implementing specific interventions as part of the plan of care, supervising staff and residents, etc. Facility records document the implementation of these interventions.

Monitoring and Modification

Monitoring is the process of evaluating the effectiveness of interventions. Modification is the process of adjusting interventions as needed to make them more effective in addressing hazards and risks.

Monitoring and modification processes include:

(1)   Ensuring that interventions are implemented correctly and consistently;

(2)   Evaluating the effectiveness of interventions;

(3)   Modifying or replacing interventions as needed and

(4)   Evaluating the effectiveness of new interventions.

An example of facility-specific modification is additional training of staff when equipment has been upgraded. An example of a resident-specific modification is revising the plan of care to reflect the resident's current condition and risk factors that may have changed since the previous assessment.

SUPERVISION

Supervision is an intervention and a means of mitigating accident risk. Facilities are obligated to provide adequate supervision to prevent accidents. Adequacy of supervision is defined by type and frequency, based on the individual resident's assessed needs, and identified hazards in the resident environment. Adequate supervision may vary from resident to resident and from time to time for the same resident. Tools or items such as personal alarms can help to monitor a resident's activities, but do not eliminate the need for adequate supervision.

The resident environment may contain temporary hazards (e.g., construction, painting, housekeeping activities, etc.) that warrant additional supervision or alternative measures such as barriers to prevent access to affected areas of the resident environment.

Adequate supervision to prevent accidents is enhanced when the facility:

- Accurately assesses a resident and/or the resident environment to determine whether supervision to avoid an accident is necessary; and/or

- Determines that supervision of the resident was necessary and provides supervision based on the individual resident's assessed needs and the risks identified in the environment.

Resident Smoking

Some facilities permit residents to smoke tobacco products. In these facilities, assessment of the resident's capabilities and deficits determines whether or not supervision is required. If the facility identifies that the resident needs supervision for smoking, the facility includes this information in the resident's plan of care, and reviews and revises the plan periodically as needed.

The facility may designate certain areas for resident smoking. The facility must ensure precautions are taken for the resident's individual safety, as well as the safety of others in the facility. Such precautions may include smoking only in designated areas, supervising residents whose assessment and plans of care indicate a need for supervised smoking, and limiting the accessibility of matches and lighters by residents who need supervision when smoking. Smoking by residents when oxygen is in use is prohibited, and any smoking by others near flammable substances is also problematic. Additional measures may include informing all visitors of smoking policies and hazards.

Guidance concerning resident smoking regulations can be found in NFPA 101, the Life Safety Code at 19.7.4, Smoking, including requirements for signage, prohibiting smoking by residents classified as not responsible, and disposal of smoking materials. Refer to the guidance at 42 CFR 483.15(b)(3) [F242] for information about facilities that desire to be smoke-free.

Resident-to-Resident Altercations

NOTE: An incident involving a resident who willfully inflicts injury upon another resident should be reviewed as abuse under the guidance for 42 CFR §483.13(b) at F223. "Willful" means that the individual intended the action itself that he/she knew or should have known could cause physical harm, pain, or mental anguish. Even though a resident may have a cognitive impairment, he/she could still commit a willful act. However, there are instances when a resident's willful intent cannot be determined. In those cases, a resident-to-resident altercation should be reviewed under this tag, F323.

It is important that a facility take reasonable precautions, including providing adequate supervision, when the risk of resident-to-resident altercation is identified, or should have been identified. Certain situations or conditions may increase the potential for such altercations, including, but not limited to:

- A history of aggressive behaviors including striking out, verbal outbursts, or negative interactions with other resident(s); and/or

- Behavior that tends to disrupt or annoy others such as constant verbalization (e.g., crying, yelling, calling out for help), making negative remarks, restlessness, repetitive behaviors, taking items that do not belong to them, going into others' rooms, drawers, or closets, and undressing in inappropriate areas. Although these behaviors may not be aggressive in nature, they may precipitate a negative response from others, resulting in verbal, physical, and/or emotional harm.

The facility is responsible for identifying residents who have a history of disruptive or intrusive interactions, or who exhibit other behaviors that make them more likely to be involved in an altercation. The facility should identify the factors (e.g., illness, environment, etc.) that increase the risks associated with individual residents, including those (e.g., disease, environment) that could trigger an altercation. The care planning team reviews the assessment along with the resident and/or his/her representative, in order to identify interventions to try to prevent altercations.

The interventions listed below include supervision and other actions that could address potential or actual negative interactions:

- Providing safe supervised areas for unrestricted movement;

- Eliminating or reducing underlying causes of distressed behavior such as boredom and pain;

- Monitoring environmental influences such as temperatures, lighting, and noise levels;

- Evaluating staffing assignments to ensure consistent staff who are more familiar with the resident and who thus may be able to identify changes in a resident's condition and behavior;

- Evaluating staffing levels to ensure adequate supervision (if it is adequate, it is meeting the resident's needs); and

- Ongoing staff training and supervision, including how to approach a resident who may be agitated, combative, verbally or physically aggressive, or anxious, and how and when to obtain assistance in managing a resident with behavior symptoms.

RESIDENT RISKS AND ENVIRONMENTAL HAZARDS

This section discusses common, but not all, potential hazards found in the resident environment.

NOTE: The information included in the following sections is based on current standards of practice or "best practice" models as described in the industry literature.

The physical plant, devices, and equipment described in this section may not be hazards by themselves. But they can become hazardous when a vulnerable resident interacts with them. Some temporary hazards in the resident environment can affect most residents who have access to them (e.g., construction, painting, and housekeeping activities). Other situations may be hazardous only for certain individuals (e.g., accessible smoking materials).

In order to be considered hazardous, an element of the resident environment must be accessible to a vulnerable resident. Resident vulnerability is based on risk factors including the individual resident's functional status, medical condition, cognitive abilities, mood, and health treatments (e.g., medications). Resident vulnerability to hazards may change over time. Ongoing assessment helps identify when elements in the environment pose hazards to a particular resident.

Certain sharp items, such as scissors, kitchen utensils, knitting needles, or other items, may be appropriate for many residents but hazardous for others with cognitive impairments. Handrails, assistive devices, and any surface that a resident may come in contact with may cause injury, if the surface is not in good condition and free from sharp edges or other hazards.

Improper actions or omissions by staff can create hazards in the physical plant (e.g., building and grounds), environment, and/or with devices and equipment. Examples of such hazards might include fire doors that have been propped open, disabled locks or latches, nonfunctioning alarms, buckled or badly torn carpets, cords on floors, irregular walking surfaces, improper storage and access to toxic chemicals, exposure to unsafe heating unit surfaces, and unsafe water temperatures. Other potential hazards may include furniture that is not appropriate for a resident (e.g., chairs or beds that are too low or unstable as to present a fall hazard) and lighting that is either inadequate or so intense as to create glare. Devices for resident care, such as pumps, ventilators, and assistive devices, may be hazardous when they are defective, disabled, or improperly used (i.e., used in a manner that is not per manufacturer's recommendations or current standards of practice).

Resident Vulnerabilities

Falls and unsafe wandering/elopement are of particular concern. The following section reviews these issues along with some common potential hazards.

Falls - The MDS defines a fall as unintentionally coming to rest on the ground, floor, or other lower level but not as a result of an overwhelming external force (e.g., resident pushes another resident). An episode where a resident lost his/her balance and would have fallen, if not for staff intervention, is considered a fall. A fall without injury is still a fall. Unless there is evidence suggesting otherwise, when a resident is found on the floor, a fall is considered to have occurred.[1]

Some factors that may result in resident falls include (but are not limited to) environmental hazards, underlying medical conditions, medication side effects, and other factors (e.g., lower extremity weakness, balance disorders, poor grip strength, functional and cognitive impairment, visual deficits, etc.).

Older persons have both a high incidence of falls and a high susceptibility to injury.[4] Falls can have psychological and social consequences, including the loss of self-confidence to try to ambulate. Evaluation of the causal factors leading to a resident fall helps support relevant and consistent interventions to try to prevent future occurrences. Proper actions following a fall include:

- Ascertaining if there were injuries, and providing treatment as necessary;

- Determining what may have caused or contributed to the fall;

- Addressing the factors for the fall; and

- Revising the resident's plan of care and/or facility practices, as needed, to reduce the likelihood of another fall.

NOTE: A fall by a resident does not necessarily indicate a deficient practice because not every fall can be avoided.

Unsafe Wandering or Elopement - Wandering is random or repetitive locomotion. This movement may be goal-directed (e.g., the person appears to be searching for something such as an exit) or may be non-goal-directed or aimless. Non-goal-directed wandering requires a response in a manner that addresses both safety issues and an evaluation to identify root causes to the degree possible. Moving about the facility aimlessly may indicate that the resident is frustrated, anxious, bored, hungry, or depressed. Unsafe wandering and elopement can be associated with falls and related injuries.[5]

Unsafe wandering may occur when the resident at risk enters an area that is physically hazardous or that contains potential safety hazards (e.g., chemicals, tools, and equipment, etc.). Entering into another resident's room may lead to an altercation or contact with hazardous items.[5]

While alarms can help to monitor a resident's activities, staff must be vigilant in order to respond to them in a timely manner. Alarms do not replace necessary supervision.

Elopement occurs when a resident leaves the premises or a safe area without authorization (i.e., an order for discharge or leave of absence) and/or any necessary supervision to do so. A resident who leaves a safe area may be at risk of (or has the potential to experience) heat or cold exposure, dehydration and/or other medical complications, drowning, or being struck by a motor vehicle. Facility policies that clearly define the mechanisms and procedures for monitoring and managing residents at risk for elopement can help to minimize the risk of a resident leaving a safe area without authorization and/or appropriate supervision. In addition, the resident at risk should have interventions in their comprehensive plan of care to address the potential for elopement. Furthermore, a facility's disaster and emergency preparedness plan should include a plan to locate a missing resident.[5]

Physical Plant Hazards

Supervision and/or containment of hazards are needed to protect residents from harm caused by environmental hazards. Examples of such hazards can range from common chemical cleaning materials to those caused by adverse water temperatures or improper use of electrical devices.

Chemicals and Toxins - Various materials in the resident environment can pose a potential hazard to residents. Hazardous materials can be found in the form of solids, liquids, gases, mists, dusts, fumes, and vapors. The routes of exposure for toxic materials may include inhalation, absorption, or ingestion.

For a material to pose a safety hazard to a resident, it must be toxic, caustic, or allergenic; accessible and available in a sufficient amount to cause harm. Toxic materials that may be present in the resident environment are unlikely to pose a hazard unless residents have access or are exposed to them. Some materials that would be considered harmless when used as designed could pose a hazard to a resident who accidentally ingests or makes contact with them.

Examples of materials that may pose a hazard to a resident include (but are not limited to):

- Chemicals used by the facility staff in the course of their duties (e.g., housekeeping chemicals) and chemicals or other materials brought into the resident environment by staff, other residents, or visitors;

- Drugs and therapeutic agents;

- Plants and other "natural" materials found in the resident environment or in the outdoor environment (e.g., poison ivy).

One source of information concerning the hazards of a material that a facility may obtain is its Material Safety Data Sheet (MSDS).[6] The Occupational Safety and Health Administration (OSHA) requires employers to have a MSDS available for all hazardous materials that staff use while performing their duties.[7] MSDSs are available on-line for numerous chemicals and non-toxic materials, and should be reviewed carefully to determine if the material is toxic and poses a hazard. Poison control centers are another source of information for potential hazards, including non-chemical hazards such as plants.

NOTE: Toxicological profiles for a limited number of hazardous materials are accessible on the Agency for Toxic Substances & Disease Registry Web site.[6]

Water Temperature - Water may reach hazardous temperatures in hand sinks, showers, and tubs. Burns related to hot water/liquids may also be due to spills and/or immersion. Many residents in long-term care facilities have conditions that may put them at increased risk for burns caused by scalding. These conditions include: decreased skin thickness, decreased skin sensitivity, peripheral neuropathy, decreased agility (reduced reaction time), decreased cognition or dementia, decreased mobility, and decreased ability to communicate.[8]

The degree of injury depends on factors including the water temperature, the amount of skin exposed, and the duration of exposure. Some States have regulations regarding allowable maximum water temperature. Table 1 illustrates damage to skin in relation to the temperature of the water and the length of time of exposure.[9]

Table 1. Time and Temperature Relationship to Serious Burns

Water Temperature		Time Required for a 3rd Degree Burn to Occur
155°F	68°C	1 sec
148°F	64°C	2 sec
140°F	60°C	5 sec
133°F	56°C	15 sec
127°F	52°C	1 min
124°F	51°C	3 min
120°F	48°C	5 min
100°F	37°C	Safe Temperatures For Bathing (see Note)

NOTE: Burns can occur even at water temperatures below those identified in the table, depending on an individual's condition and the length of exposure.

Based upon the time of the exposure and the temperature of the water, the severity of the harm to the skin is identified by the degree of burn, as follows.[10]

- First-degree burns involve the top layer of skin (e.g., minor sunburn). These may present as red and painful to touch, and the skin will show mild swelling.

- Second-degree burns involve the first two layers of skin. These may present as deep reddening of the skin, pain, blisters, glossy appearance from leaking fluid, and possible loss of some skin.

- Third-degree burns penetrate the entire thickness of the skin and permanently destroy tissue. These present as loss of skin layers, often painless (pain may be caused by patches of first- and second-degree burns surrounding third-degree burns), and dry, leathery skin. Skin may appear charred or have patches that appear white, brown, or black.

Electrical Safety - Any electrical device, whether or not it needs to be plugged into an electric outlet, can become hazardous to the residents through improper use or improper maintenance. Electrical equipment such as electrical cords can become tripping hazards. Halogen lamps or heat lamps can cause burns or fires if not properly installed away from combustibles in the resident environment. The Life Safety Code prohibits the use of portable electrical space heaters in resident areas.

Extension cords should not be used to take the place of adequate wiring in a facility. If extension cords are used, the cords should be properly secured and not be placed overhead, under carpets or rugs, or anywhere that the cord can cause trips, falls, or overheat. Extension cords should be connected to only one device to prevent overloading of the circuit. The cord itself should be of a size and type for the expected electrical load and made of material that will not fray or cut easily. Electrical cords including extension cords should have proper grounding if required and should not have any grounding devices removed or not used if required.

Power strips may not be used as a substitute for adequate electrical outlets in a facility. Power strips may be used for a computer, monitor, and printer. Power strips are not designed to be used with medical devices in patient care areas. Precautions needed if power strips are used include: installing internal ground fault and over-current protection devices; preventing cords from becoming tripping hazards; and using power strips that are adequate for the number and types of devices used. Overload on any circuit can potentially cause overheating and fire. The use of ground fault circuit interruption (GFCIs) may be required in locations near water sources to prevent electrocution of staff or residents.[11]

The proper use of electric blankets and heating pads is essential to avoid thermal injuries. These items should not be tucked in or squeezed. Constriction can cause the internal wires to break. A resident should not go to sleep with an electric blanket or heating pad turned on. Manufacturer's instructions for use should be followed closely. Injuries and deaths have been related to burns and fires related to the use of heating pads. Most deaths are attributable to heating pads that generated fires, but most injuries are burns from prolonged use or inappropriate temperature setting. Prolonged use on one area of the body can cause a severe burn, even when the heating pad is at a low temperature setting.[12]

Lighting - The risk of an accident increases when there is insufficient light or too much light, which often results in glare. Vision among older persons varies widely; therefore, no single level of illumination can ensure safety for all residents. The proper amount of light depends on the resident's visual needs and the task he/she is performing.

An older person typically needs more light to see. However, a resident with cataracts or glaucoma may be overly sensitive to bright light, and excessive lighting could make it more difficult to see clearly and thereby increase his/her fall risk.[13] Creating transitional zones between light and dark spaces helps to improve sight recovery and enable safer mobility. Providing extra visual cues that clearly define needed items or spaces in areas with limited or variable light can help to enable safe performance of tasks (e.g., turning on a light). Providing supplemental light near beds for patients who are mobile may assist in safe mobility at night.[14]

NOTE: Refer to guidance for 42 CFR 483.15(h)(5) [F256] for lighting issues related to Quality of Life.

Assistive Devices/Equipment Hazards

Assistive devices also can help to prevent accidents. Assistive devices and equipment can help residents move with increased independence, transfer with greater comfort, and feel physically more secure. However, there are risks associated with the use of such devices and equipment, and these risks need to be balanced with the benefits gained from their use. Training of staff, residents, family members and volunteers on the proper use of assistive devices/equipment is crucial to prevent accidents. It is also important to communicate clearly the approaches identified in the care plan to all staff, including temporary staff. It is important to train staff regarding resident assessment, safe transfer techniques, and the proper use of mechanical lifts including device weight limitations.

NOTE: The Safe Medical Devices Act of 1990 (SMDA) requires hospitals, nursing homes, and other user facilities to report deaths, serious illnesses, and injuries associated with the use of medical devices to manufacturers and the Food and Drug Administration.

Assistive Devices for Mobility - Mobility devices include all types of assistive devices, such as, but not limited to, canes, standard and rolling walkers, manual or non-powered wheelchairs, and powered wheelchairs. Three primary factors that may be associated with an increased accident risk related to the use of assistive devices include:

1.   Resident Condition. Lower extremity weakness, gait disturbances, decreased range of motion, and poor balance may affect some residents. These conditions combined with cognitive impairment can increase the accident risks of using mobility devices. Unsafe behavior, such as failure to lock wheelchair brakes and trying to stand or transfer from a wheelchair unsafely, can result in falls and related injuries;

2.   Personal Fit and Device Condition. Devices can pose a hazard if not fitted and/or maintained properly.[15] Personal fit, or how well the assistive device meets the individual needs of the resident, may influence the likelihood of an avoidable accident; and

3.   Staff Practices. Mobility devices that a resident cannot readily reach may create a hazardous situation. Unsafe transfer technique used by staff may result in an accident. Inadequate supervision by staff of a resident during the initial trial period of assistive device use or after a change in the resident's functional status can increase the risk of falls and/or injury. Additionally, staff needs to ensure assistive devises properly fit the resident and the resident has received proper training in the use of the assistive device.

Assistive Devices for Transfer - Mechanical assistive devices for transfer include, but are not limited to, portable total body lifts, sit-to-stand devices, and transfer or gait belts. The resident assessment helps to determine the resident's degree of mobility and physical impairment and the proper transfer method; for example, whether one or more caregivers or a mechanical device is needed for a safe transfer. Residents who become frightened during transfer in a mechanical lift may exhibit resistance movements that can result in avoidable accidents. Communicating with the resident and addressing the resident's fear may reduce the risk.

Factors that may influence a resident's risk of accident during transfer include staff availability, resident abilities, and staff training.[16] The resident's ability to communicate and identify physical limitations or to aid in the transfer will help determine the need for an assistive device, such as a mechanical lift.

Devices Associated with Entrapment Risks - Devices can be therapeutic and beneficial; however, devices are not necessarily risk free so it is important to weigh the relative risks and benefits of using certain devices. For example, while physical restraints may be used to treat a resident's medical symptom, the devices may create a risk for entrapment. Physical restraints are defined in the SOM at F221 as any manual method, physical or mechanical device, material, or equipment attached or adjacent to the resident's body that the individual cannot remove easily and that restricts freedom of movement or normal access to one's body.

In 1992, the Food and Drug Administration (FDA) issued a Safety Alert entitled "Potential Hazards with Restraint Devices".[17] Serious injuries, as well as death, have been reported as a result of using physical restraints. Some physical restraints carry a risk of severe injury, strangulation, and asphyxiation. Restrained residents may be injured or die when they try to remove restraints, to ambulate while restrained, or due to an improperly fitted or used device.

Regardless of the purpose for use, bed rails (also referred to as "side rails," "bed side rails," and "safety rails") and other bed accessories (e.g., transfer bar, bed enclosures), while assisting with transfer and positioning, can increase resident safety risk. Bed rails include rails of various sizes (e.g., full length rails, half rails, quarter rails) that may be positioned in various locations on the bed. In 1995, the FDA issued a Safety Alert entitled "Entrapment Hazards with Hospital Bed Side Rails."[18] Residents most at risk for entrapment are those who are frail or elderly or those who have conditions such as agitation, delirium, confusion, pain, uncontrolled body movement, hypoxia, fecal impaction, acute urinary retention, etc. that may cause them to move about the bed or try to exit from the bed. The timeliness of toileting, appropriateness of positioning, and other care-related activities can contribute to the risk of entrapment.[19]

Entrapment may occur when a resident is caught between the mattress and bed rail or in the bed rail itself. Technical issues, such as the proper sizing of mattresses, fit and integrity of bed rails or other design elements (e.g., wide spaces between bars in the bed rails) can also affect the risk of resident entrapment.[19]

The use of a specialty air-filled mattress or a therapeutic air-filled bed may also present an entrapment risk that is different from rail entrapment with a regular mattress. The high compressibility of an air-filled mattress compared to a regular conventional mattress requires appropriate precautions when used for a resident at risk for entrapment. An air-filled mattress compresses on the side to which a person moves, thus raising the center of the mattress and lowering the side. This may make it easier for a resident to slide off the mattress or against the rail. Mattress compression widens the space between the mattress and rail. When a resident is between the mattress and rail, the mattress can re-expand and press the chest, neck, or head against the rail. While using air therapy to prevent and treat pressure ulcers, facilities should also take precautions to reduce the risk of entrapment. Precautions may include following manufacturer equipment alerts and increasing supervision.[20]

NOTE: 42 CFR 483.13(a), F221, applies to the use of physical restraints. 42 CFR 483.25(h)(2), F323 applies to assistive devices that create hazards (e.g., devices that are defective; not used properly or according to manufacturer's specifications; disabled or removed; not provided or do not meet the resident's needs (poor fit or not adapted); and/or used without adequate supervision when required).

[Editor's Note: See page 391 for endnotes pertaining to this section.]

SOM, Appendix PP, Guidance to Surveyors

Investigative Protocol

Accidents and Supervision

Objectives

- To determine if the facility has identified hazard(s) present in the resident environment and the individual resident's risks for an avoidable accident posed by those hazards;

- To determine if a resident accident was avoidable or unavoidable;

- To evaluate whether the facility provides an environment that is as free as possible of hazards over which the facility has control, and minimizes the potential for harm; and

- To determine if the facility provides adequate supervision and assistive devices to prevent avoidable accidents.

Use

Use this protocol:

- For a sampled resident who is at risk for, or who has a history of accidents, falls, or unsafe wandering/elopement, to determine if the facility provided care and services, including assistive devices as necessary, to prevent avoidable accidents and to reduce the resident's risk to the extent possible;

- For a sampled resident who is at risk for accidents or who creates a risk to others, to determine if the facility has provided adequate supervision; and

- For identified hazards/risks, to determine if there are facility practices in place to identify, evaluate and analyze hazards/risks; implement interventions to reduce or eliminate the hazards/risks, to the extent possible; and monitor the effectiveness of the interventions.

Procedures

Observe the general environment and sampled resident environment. For a sampled resident, briefly review the assessment and plan of care to determine whether the facility identified resident risks and implemented interventions as necessary to guide observations during the investigation. For a newly admitted resident at risk for avoidable accidents, determine if the staff assessed and provided appropriate care from the day of admission. Corroborate observations through interview and record review.

1. Observation

The survey team should make observations and investigate potential hazards that may be encountered throughout the survey. The existence of hazards may indicate a more serious problem; for example, that the organization lacks an effective system to identify and correct the problem independently. The previous discussion of specific common hazards guides surveyors to look for items indicating a failure or absence of an organization's systems and processes to enable safety.

During observation of the facility, the survey team may see individual residents who are smoking tobacco products. Whether or not these residents are part of the sample, the issue of facility fires is important enough that the survey team should determine if the situation is hazardous, requiring further investigation.

Observe the environment for the presence of potential/actual hazards including, but not limited to, the following:

- Accessibility of chemicals, toxics or other hazards such as housekeeping chemicals and supplies, medications, sharp utensils/tools, and cigarette lighters/smoking materials;

- Environmental conditions such as unstable or slippery floor surfaces, loose hand rails, excessive water temperatures, electrical hazards, insufficient or excessive light (glare), arrangement of living spaces, obstacles in corridors, unsupervised access into or egress out of the facility, low or loose toilet seats, defective or non-functioning beds, or malfunctioning wheelchair brakes;

- Staff responses to verbal calls for help and alarms such as door, personal, and equipment alarms, and call bells;

- Assistive devices/equipment (e.g., mobility devices, lifts and transfer aids, bed rails, call lights, physical restraints, pumps, belts) that are defective; not used properly or according to manufacturer's specifications; disabled or removed; not provided or do not meet the resident's needs (poor fit or not adapted); and/or used without adequate supervision, in relation to the facility's assessment of the resident; and/or

- Staff response to potential/actual hazard(s) (e.g., cleaning up spilled liquids in a resident area, keeping residents away from the hazard).

For a sampled resident at risk, observe whether staff implement the care plan consistently over time and across various shifts. Observe how staff respond to any identified resident hazards. Observe how staff supervise the resident, such as during transfers and/or meals, and if caregivers have removed or modified observed hazards. During observations of the interventions, follow up on deviations from the plan of care, as well as potential negative outcomes.

For a resident who smokes, the facility's determination regarding the resident's abilities and capabilities would indicate whether supervision is required. If the resident is found to need supervision for smoking, this information is included in the resident's plan of care. Observe sampled resident(s) in the facility's designated smoking area. If the resident's care plan states supervision is required while smoking, confirm that supervision is provided. For others, note any concerns such as difficulty holding or lighting a cigarette or burned areas in clothing that may indicate the need for supervision.

Observe the resident to determine how the resident's risk influences his/her vulnerability to the observed potential hazard(s) and potential for an accident. Evaluate how the resident's risks relate to the observed potential hazards such as:

- The resident's access to the hazard and the ability to react appropriately; and/or

- The adequacy of the supervision provided for the resident who has been assessed to need supervision in relation to the identified potential hazard(s).

2. Interview

Conduct interviews to determine the relationship between the resident's risk and hazards.

Interview the resident, family, and/or responsible party to the degree possible to identify:

- If the resident and/or responsible party reported, or helped identify the resident's risks for an accident and significant hazards in the resident's environment;

- If the resident and/or responsible party was aware of or identified a potential hazard for other residents;

- If the resident and/or responsible party reported a hazard or potential risk to staff; and

- How and when staff responded to a hazard once it was identified.

Interview staff to determine:

- If they were aware of planned interventions to reduce a resident's risk for an avoidable accident;

- If they reported potential resident risks or environmental hazards to the supervisor or others according to facility policy;

- If they acted to correct an immediate hazard, such as spilled liquids; and

- If they are aware of, and follow facility procedures correctly to remove or reduce hazards.

3. Record Review

Assessment and Evaluation: Review the RAI and other documents such as progress notes, physician orders, and nurses' and consultants' notes regarding the assessment of the resident's overall condition and risk factors to determine if the facility identified the resident's risk for avoidable accidents, evaluated and analyzed any risks, implemented interventions to try to prevent accidents and reduce the resident's risks, and monitored and modified interventions as necessary.

Determine if the facility assessment is consistent with or corroborated by documentation within the record and reflects the status of the resident for:

- Behavior such as unsafe wandering, elopement, ingesting nonfood items, altercations with others;

- Hearing, visual, and sensory impairments;

- Impaired physical functioning, balance, or gait problems;

- Diagnoses that could relate to safety awareness and safe practices, such as Alzheimer's and other dementias, arthritis, Parkinson's disease, seizure disorder, osteoporosis, cardiovascular/cerebrovascular diseases, depression/psychosis;

- Symptoms/conditions that could affect safety risk, such as vertigo, postural hypotension, or acute illness;

- Use of physical restraints and/or other devices that might limit movement;

- Medications that could affect function, level of consciousness, gait, balance, visual acuity, or cognitive ability, use such as antidepressants, anticholinergic medications, anti-hypertensives, diuretics, psychotropic medications, or initiation of new medication therapy; and

- History of falls.

Plan of Care: Review the plan of care to determine if the facility developed interventions based on the resident's risks to try to prevent avoidable accidents, and if the plan was modified as needed based on the response, outcomes, and needs of the resident.

If the resident has had an accident, review the record to determine if the accident is:

- The result of an order not being followed; and/or

- A care need not being addressed; and/or

- A plan of care not being implemented.

In addition, determine if the facility (1) investigated the cause of the accident and (2) if indicated, implemented revised interventions to prevent additional avoidable accidents.

Plan of Care Revision: Determine if the facility has monitored a resident's condition and the effectiveness of the plan of care interventions and has made revisions (or has documented justification for continuing the existing plan) based upon the following:

- The outcome and/or effects of goals and interventions;

- Resident failure to comply with the plan of care and interventions;

- Input by the resident and/or the responsible person; and

- Changes in condition such as the ability to make decisions, cognition, functional impairment, or changes in the medication regimen.

4. Review of Facility Practices

The presence or absence of effective facility practices to provide a safe resident environment can influence the likelihood of an accident occurring and subsequent harm to a resident(s). Hazards that have been allowed to exist for a long time, or a facility history of similar problems, could indicate inadequate or ineffective facility practices.

If, during the tour, surveyors identify care delivery, hazards or potential hazards, or a history of resident accidents, the survey team should share the findings with the entire team and determine who will lead the investigation of the facility's systems for identifying, evaluating and preventing avoidable accidents or hazards. Review of facility practices may involve a review of policies and procedures, staffing, staff training, and equipment manufacturer's information, as well as interviews with staff and management. If there is a pattern of accidents involving one or more residents, determine how the facility evaluates its responses to the accidents. Determine if the facility ensured that the resident environment remained as free of accident hazards as possible and if each resident received adequate supervision and assistive devices to try to prevent accidents by:

- Identifying potential hazards and risks (may require various strategies to gather such information);

- Evaluating and analyzing the information gathered to identify the underlying causes of the hazard and/or risk;

- Implementing interventions that addressed the causes and prioritized actions based on severity of the hazard and immediacy of the risk; and

- Monitoring implementation of interventions and determining if modification is needed.

DETERMINATION OF COMPLIANCE (Task 6, Appendix P)

Synopsis of Regulation

The requirements at 42 CFR 483.25(h)(1) and (2) have three aspects. The first aspect requires that a resident's environment remains as free of accident hazards as possible; the second aspect requires that the facility provide adequate supervision; and the third is that the facility provides assistive devices to prevent accidents.

Criteria for Compliance

The facility's responsibility to accommodate individual needs and preferences and abide by the resident's right to choice and self-determination must be balanced against compliance with F323 to protect the resident. Documentation regarding the resident's choices will assist the survey team in making compliance decisions.

NOTE: It is important to remember that not all accidents in a facility, regardless of outcome to a resident, are necessarily due to facility noncompliance. A resident can sustain bodily injury as a result of an accident over which the facility had no control (i.e., an unavoidable accident). The survey team needs to review the situation that led to the injury or potential for injury, as well as the facility practices, and resident's rights, preferences, and choices, to determine if the potential or negative outcome was avoidable or unavoidable.

Compliance with 42 CFR 483.25(h)(1) and (2), F323, Accidents and Supervision

For the resident who has had an accident or was assessed at risk for an avoidable accident, the facility is in compliance with this requirement, if staff have:

- Identified hazards and risk of an avoidable accident based on the facility's assessment of the resident environment and the resident, including the need for supervision and/or assistive devices;

- Evaluated/analyzed the hazards and risks;

- Implemented interventions, including adequate supervision and/or assistive devices, to reduce the risks of an accident that were consistent with a resident's needs, goals, plan of care, and current standards of practice;

- Provided assistive devices consistent with a resident's needs;

- Properly deployed and maintained resident specific equipment (e.g., lifts, canes, wheelchairs, walkers);

- Provided a safe environment, such as by monitoring chemicals, wet floors, cords and other equipment;

- Operated equipment in accordance with manufacturer's recommendations and resident need;

- Provided and maintain a secure environment (e.g., resident room, unit, common use areas, stairs and windows, facility grounds, etc.) to prevent negative outcomes (e.g., prevent falling/tumbling down stairs or jumping from windows or eloping through exit doors) for residents who exhibit unsafe wandering and/or elopement behavior (regardless of whether ambulatory, in wheelchair or using walker); and

- Monitored the effectiveness of the interventions and modified the interventions as necessary, in accordance with current standards of practice.

    If not, cite F323.

Noncompliance for F323

After completing the investigation, determine whether or not compliance with the regulation exists. Noncompliance for F323 may include, but is not limited to, one or more of the following failures to:

- Provide each resident an environment that is as free as possible from hazards over which the facility has control, such as assuring safe storage of toxic chemicals and medications, and safe use of equipment and electrical appliances;

- Provide adequate supervision for a resident who has exhibited unsafe wandering and/or has a risk of and/or a history of elopement;

- Identify and correct hazards such as non-functional alarms or call systems, disabled locks, fire doors that have been propped open, irregular walking surfaces, inadequate lighting or unsafe water temperatures;

- Supervise and monitor a resident who smokes and whose comprehensive assessment and plan of care indicates a need for supervision;

- Provide assistive devices and/or appropriate training for the use of assistive devices, based upon the assessed needs of the resident;

- Monitor for defective or disabled equipment, such as pumps, ventilators or other equipment, or the improper use of assistive devices;

- Assess, develop interventions, and/or revise the plan of care for a resident who has experienced falls, or who is identified as having risk factors for falling; and

- Assess, develop interventions, and/or revise the plan of care for a resident who has exhibited or has a risk for unsafe wandering or elopement.

Potential Tags for Additional Investigation

During the investigation of 42 CFR 483.25(h)(1) and (2), the surveyor may have identified concerns related to outcome, process, and/or structure requirements. The surveyor should investigate these requirements before determining whether noncompliance may be present. The following are examples of related outcome, process, and/or structure requirements that should be considered:

- 42 CFR 483.13(a), F221, Restraints

    o Determine if staff attempted alternative approaches prior to the use of a restraint and if a medical indication for its use is present.

- 42 CFR 483.13(b), F223, Abuse

    o Determine if the resident was free from verbal, sexual, physical, and mental abuse, corporal punishment, and involuntary seclusion.

- 42 CFR 483.20(b)(1), F272, Comprehensive Assessments

    o Determine if the facility comprehensively assessed resident-specific risk factors (including potential causes) and assessed the need for and use of assistive devices.

- 42 CFR 483.20(k)(1), F279, Comprehensive Care Plans

    o Determine if the facility developed a plan of care based on the comprehensive resident assessment consistent with the resident's specific conditions, risks, needs, behaviors, and preferences and with current standards of practice, and that includes measurable objectives and approximate timetables, specific interventions and/or services including necessary supervision and/or any assistive devices needed to prevent accidents to the extent possible.

- 42 CFR 483.20(k)(2), F280, Comprehensive Care Plan Revision

    o Determine if the plan of care was reviewed and revised periodically, as necessary, related to preventing accidents, supervision required, and the use of assistive devices.

- 42 CFR 483.20(k)(3)(i), F281, Services Provided Meet Professional Standards

    o Determine if services and care were provided for the use of assistive devices, supervision, and prevention of accidents in accordance with accepted professional standards.

- 42 CFR 483.30(a), F353, Sufficient Staff

    o Determine if the facility had qualified staff in sufficient numbers to provide necessary care and services, including supervision, based upon the comprehensive assessment and care plan, to prevent accidents, as possible.

- 42 CFR 483.75(o), F520, Quality Assessment and Assurance

    o Determine whether the quality assessment and assurance committee has identified issues, and developed and implemented appropriate plans of action to correct identified quality deficiencies in relation to hazards, accident prevention, and supervision of residents.

V. DEFICIENCY CATEGORIZATION (Part V[*], Appendix P) (Editor's Note: The part cited is incorrect. The correct part is IV.]

Once the survey team has completed its investigation, analyzed the data, reviewed the regulatory requirements, and determined that noncompliance exists, the team must determine the severity of each deficiency, based on the resultant effect or potential for harm to the resident.

The key elements for severity determination for F323 are as follows:

1. Presence of harm/negative outcome(s) or potential for negative outcomes because of presence of environmental hazards, lack of adequate supervision to prevent accidents, or failure to provide assistive devices to prevent accidents. Actual or potential harm/negative outcome for F323 may include, but is not limited to:

   - Injuries sustained from falls and/or unsafe wandering/elopement;

   - Resident-to-resident altercations;

   - Thermal burns from spills/immersion of hot water/liquids;

   - Falls due to environmental hazards;

   - Ingestion of chemical substances; and

   - Burns related to smoking materials.

2. Degree of harm (actual or potential) related to the noncompliance. Identify how the facility noncompliance caused, resulted in, allowed, or contributed to the actual or potential for harm.

   - If harm has occurred, determine if the harm is at the level of serious injury, impairment, death, compromise, or discomfort; and

   - If harm has not yet occurred, determine the potential for serious injury, impairment, death, or compromise or discomfort to occur to the resident.

3. The immediacy of correction required. Determine whether the noncompliance requires immediate correction in order to prevent serious injury, harm, impairment, or death to one or more residents.

The survey team must evaluate the harm or potential for harm based upon the following levels of severity for Tag F323. First, the team must rule out whether Severity Level 4, Immediate Jeopardy to a resident's health or safety, exists by evaluating the deficient practice in relation to immediacy, culpability, and severity. (Follow the guidance in Appendix Q, **Guidelines for Determining Immediate Jeopardy**.)

Severity Level 4 Considerations: Immediate Jeopardy to Resident Health or Safety

Immediate Jeopardy is a situation in which the facility's noncompliance with one or more requirements of participation:

- Has allowed, caused, or resulted in (or is likely to allow, cause, or result in) serious injury, harm, impairment, or death to a resident; and

- Requires immediate correction, as the facility either created the situation or allowed the situation to continue by failing to implement preventive or corrective measures.

NOTE: The death or transfer of a resident, who was harmed or injured as a result of facility noncompliance, does not always remove a finding of Immediate Jeopardy. The facility is required to implement specific actions to correct the noncompliance which allowed or caused the Immediate Jeopardy.

When considering Severity Level 4, the survey team must have already determined noncompliance in the facility practices to provide a safe resident environment. Examples of negative outcomes that occurred or have the potential to occur as a result of the noncompliance might include the following:

- Esophageal damage due to ingestion of corrosive substances;

- Loss of consciousness related to head injuries;

- 3rd degree burn, or a 2nd degree burn covering a large surface area;

- Fracture or other injury that may require surgical intervention and results in significant decline in mental and/or physical functioning;

- Electric shock due to use of unsafe or improperly maintained equipment;

- Entrapment of body parts, such as limbs, head, neck, or chest that cause injury or death as a result of defective or improperly latched side rails or spaces within side rails, between split rails, between rails and the mattress, between side rails and the bed frame, or spaces between side rails and the head or foot board of the bed;

- Entrapment of body parts, such as limbs, head, neck, or chest that causes or has the potential to cause serious injury, harm, impairment or death as a result of any manual method, physical or mechanical device, material, or equipment;

- Fall(s) that resulted in or had the potential to result in serious injury, impairment, harm or death (e.g. fracture or other injury that may require surgical intervention and/or results in significant decline in mental and/or physical functioning), and the facility had no established measure(s) or practice(s), or ineffective measure(s) or practice(s), that would have prevented the fall or limited the resident's injury; or

- Unsafe wandering and/or elopement that resulted in or had the potential to result in serious injury, impairment, harm or death (e.g., resident leaves facility or locked unit unnoticed and sustained or had potential to sustain serious injury, impairment, harm or death), and the facility had no established measure(s) or practice(s), or ineffective measure(s) or practice(s), that would have prevented or limited the resident's exposure to hazards.

NOTE: If Immediate Jeopardy has been ruled out based upon the evidence, then evaluate whether actual harm that is not immediate jeopardy exists at Severity Level 3.

Severity Level 3 Considerations: Actual Harm that is Not Immediate Jeopardy

Severity Level 3 indicates noncompliance that results in actual harm and can include but may not be limited to clinical compromise, decline, or the resident's ability to maintain and/or reach his/her highest practicable well-being.

When considering Severity Level 3, the survey team must have already determined noncompliance in the facility practices to provide a safe resident environment. As a result of the noncompliance, a negative outcome occurred. Some examples of compromise include:

- Short-term disability;

- Pain that interfered with normal activities;

- 2nd degree burn;

- Fracture or other injury that may require surgical intervention and does not result in significant decline in mental and/or physical functioning;

- Medical evaluation was necessary, and treatment beyond first aid (e.g., sutures) was required;

- Fall(s) that resulted in actual harm (e.g., short-term disability; pain that interfered with normal activities; fracture or other injury that may require surgical intervention and does not result in significant decline in mental and/or physical functioning; or medical evaluation was necessary, and treatment beyond first aid (e.g., sutures) was required) and the facility had established measure(s) or practice(s) in place that limited the resident's potential to fall and limited the resident's injury and prevented the harm from rising to a level of immediate jeopardy; or

- Unsafe wandering and/or elopement that resulted in actual harm <u>and</u> the facility had established measure(s) or practice(s) in place that limited the resident's exposure to hazards and prevented the harm from rising to a level of immediate jeopardy.

  NOTE: Unsafe wandering or elopement that resulted in actual harm <u>and</u> the facility had no established measure(s) or practice(s), or ineffective measure(s) or practice(s) that would have prevented or limited the resident's exposure to hazards should be cited at Level 4, Immediate Jeopardy.

NOTE: If Severity Level 3 (actual harm that is not immediate jeopardy) has been ruled out based upon the evidence, evaluate whether Severity Level 2 (no actual harm with the potential for more than minimal harm) exists.

Severity Level 2 Considerations: No Actual Harm with Potential for More Than Minimal Harm that is Not Immediate Jeopardy

Severity Level 2 indicates noncompliance that results in a resident outcome of no more than minimal discomfort and/or has the potential to compromise the resident's ability to maintain or reach his or her highest practicable level of well being. The potential exists for greater harm to occur if interventions are not provided.

When considering Severity Level 2, the survey team must have already determined noncompliance in the facility practices to provide a safe resident environment. As a result of the noncompliance, a negative outcome occurred, or the potential for a negative outcome exists, such as the following:

- Bruising, minor skin abrasions, and rashes;

- Pain that does not impair normal activities;

- 1st degree burn;

- Medical evaluation or consultation may or may not have been necessary, and treatment such as first aid may have been required;

- Fall(s) which resulted in no more than minimal harm (e.g., bruising or minor skin abrasions; pain that does not impair normal activities; or medical evaluation or consultation may or may not have been necessary, and/or treatment such as first aid may have been required) because the facility had additional established measure(s) or practice(s) that limited the resident's potential to fall or limited the injury or potential for injury; or

- Unsafe wandering and/or elopement, which resulted in no more than minimal harm because the facility had additional established measure(s) or practice(s) that limited the resident's exposure to hazards. For example, a resident with Alzheimer's disease left the locked unit and was quickly found unharmed on another unit, and the building was considered a safe environment, as there was no way for the resident to leave the building.

Severity Level 1 Considerations: No Actual Harm with Potential for Minimal Harm

The failure of the facility to provide a safe environment and adequate supervision places residents at risk for more than minimal harm. Therefore, Severity Level 1 does not apply for this regulatory requirement.

F325

(Rev. 36; Issued: 08-01-08; Effective/Implementation Date: 09-01-08)

§483.25(i) Nutrition

Based on a resident's comprehensive assessment, the facility must ensure that a resident--

§483.25(i)(1) Maintains acceptable parameters of nutritional status, such as body weight and protein levels, unless the resident's clinical condition demonstrates that this is not possible; and

§483.25(i)(2) Receives a therapeutic diet when there is a nutritional problem.

INTENT: §483.25(i) Nutritional Status

The intent of this requirement is that the resident maintains, to the extent possible, acceptable parameters of nutritional status and that the facility:

- Provides nutritional care and services to each resident, consistent with the resident's comprehensive assessment;

- Recognizes, evaluates, and addresses the needs of every resident, including but not limited to, the resident at risk or already experiencing impaired nutrition; and

- Provides a therapeutic diet that takes into account the resident's clinical condition, and preferences, when there is a nutritional indication.

DEFINITIONS

Definitions are provided to clarify clinical terms related to nutritional status.

- "Acceptable parameters of nutritional status" refers to factors that reflect that an individual's nutritional status is adequate, relative to his/her overall condition and prognosis.

- "Albumin" is the body's major plasma protein, essential for maintaining osmotic pressure and also serving as a transport protein.

- "Anemia" refers to a condition of low hemoglobin concentration caused by decreased production, increased loss, or destruction of red blood cells.

- "Anorexia" refers to loss of appetite, including loss of interest in seeking and consuming food.

- "Artificial nutrition" refers to nutrition that is provided through routes other than the usual oral route, typically by placing a tube directly into the stomach, the intestine or a vein.

- "Avoidable/Unavoidable " failure to maintain acceptable parameters of nutritional status:

    o "Avoidable" means that the resident did not maintain acceptable parameters of nutritional status and that the facility did not do one or more of the following: evaluate the resident's clinical condition and nutritional risk factors; define and implement interventions that are consistent with resident needs, resident goals and recognized standards of practice; monitor and evaluate the impact of the interventions; or revise the interventions as appropriate.

o "Unavoidable " means that the resident did not maintain acceptable parameters of nutritional status even though the facility had evaluated the resident's clinical condition and nutritional risk factors; defined and implemented interventions that are consistent with resident needs, goals and recognized standards of practice; monitored and evaluated the impact of the interventions; and revised the approaches as appropriate.

- "Clinically significant" refers to effects, results, or consequences that materially affect or are likely to affect an individual's physical, mental, or psychosocial well-being either positively by preventing, stabilizing, or improving a condition or reducing a risk, or negatively by exacerbating, causing, or contributing to a symptom, illness, or decline in status.

- "Current standards of practice " refers to approaches to care, procedures, techniques, treatments, etc., that are based on research or expert consensus and that are contained in current manuals, textbooks, or publications, or that are accepted, adopted or promulgated by recognized professional organizations or national accrediting bodies.

- "Dietary supplements" refers to nutrients (e.g., vitamins, minerals, amino acids, and herbs) that are added to a person's diet when they are missing or not consumed in enough quantity.

- "Insidious weight loss" refers to a gradual, unintended, progressive weight loss over time.

- "Nutritional Supplements" refers to products that are used to complement a resident's dietary needs (e.g., total parenteral products, enteral products, and meal replacement products).

- "Parameters of nutritional status" refers to factors (e.g., weight, food/fluid intake, and pertinent laboratory values) that reflect the resident's nutritional status.

- "Qualified dietitian" refers to one who is qualified based upon either registration by the Commission on Dietetic Registration of the American Dietetic Association or as permitted by State law, on the basis of education, training, or experience in identification of dietary needs, planning, and implementation of dietary programs.

- "Therapeutic diet" refers to a diet ordered by a health care practitioner as part of the treatment for a disease or clinical condition, to eliminate, decrease, or increase certain substances in the diet (e.g., sodium or potassium), or to provide mechanically altered food when indicated.

- "Usual body weight" refers to the resident's usual weight through adult life or a stable weight over time.

OVERVIEW

Nutrients are essential for many critical metabolic processes, the maintenance and repair of cells and organs, and energy to support daily functioning. Therefore, it is important to maintain adequate nutritional status, to the extent possible.

Other key factors in addition to intake can influence weight and nutritional status. For example, the body may not absorb or use nutrients effectively. Low weight may also pertain to: age-related loss of muscle mass, strength, and function (sarcopenia),[1] wasting (cachexia) that occurs as a consequence o f illness and inflammatory processes, or disease causing changes in mental status.[2] Changes in the ability to taste food may accompany later life.[3]

Impaired nutritional status is not an expected part of normal aging. It may be associated with an increased risk of mortality and other negative outcomes such as impairment of anticipated wound healing, decline in function, fluid and electrolyte imbalance/dehydration, and unplanned weight change.[4] The early identification of residents with, or at risk for, impaired nutrition, may allow the interdisciplinary team to develop and implement interventions to stabilize or improve nutritional status before additional complications arise. However, since intake is not the only factor that affects nutritional status, nutrition-related interventions only sometimes improve markers of nutritional status such as body weight and laboratory results.[5] While they can often be stabilized or improved, nutritional deficits and imbalances may take time to improve or they may not be fully correctable in some individuals.

A systematic approach can help staff's efforts to optimize a resident's nutritional status. This process includes identifying and assessing each resident's nutritional status and risk factors, evaluating/analyzing the assessment information, developing and consistently implementing pertinent approaches, and monitoring the effectiveness of interventions and revising them as necessary.

ASSESSMENT

According to the American Dietetic Association, "Nutritional assessment is a systematic process of obtaining, verifying and interpreting data in order to make decisions about the nature and cause of nutrition-related problems."[6,7] The assessment also provides information that helps to define meaningful interventions to address any nutrition-related problems.

The interdisciplinary team clarifies nutritional issues, needs, and goals in the context of the resident's overall condition, by using observation and gathering and considering information relevant to each resident's eating and nutritional status. Pertinent sources of such information may include interview of the resident or resident representative, and review of information (e.g., past history of eating patterns and weight and a summary of any recent hospitalizations) from other sources.

The facility identifies key individuals who should participate in the assessment of nutritional status and related causes and consequences. For example, nursing staff provide details about the resident's nutritional intake. Health care practitioners (e.g., physicians and nurse practitioners) help define the nature of the problem (e.g., whether the resident has anorexia or sarcopenia), identify causes of anorexia and weight loss, tailor interventions to the resident's specific causes and situation, and monitor the continued relevance of those interventions. Qualified dietitians help identify nutritional risk factors and recommend nutritional interventions, based on each resident's medical condition, needs, desires, and goals. Consultant pharmacists can help the staff and practitioners identify medications that affect nutrition by altering taste or causing dry mouth, lethargy, nausea, or confusion.

Although the Resident Assessment Instrument (RAI) is the only assessment tool specifically required, a more in-depth nutritional assessment may be needed to identify the nature and causes of impaired nutrition and nutrition-related risks. Completion of the RAI does not remove the facility's responsibility to document a more detailed resident assessment, where applicable. The in-depth nutritional assessment may utilize existing information from sources, such as the RAI, assessments from other disciplines, observation, and resident and family interviews. The assessment will identify usual body weight, a history of reduced appetite or progressive weight loss or gain prior to admission, medical conditions such as a cerebrovascular accident, and events such as recent surgery, which may have affected a resident's nutritional status and risks. The in-depth nutritional assessment may also include the following information:

General Appearance - General appearance includes a description of the resident's overall appearance (e.g., robust, thin, obese, or cachectic) and other findings (e.g., level of consciousness, responsiveness, affect, oral health and dentition, ability to use the hands and arms, and the condition of hair, nails, and skin) that may affect or reflect nutritional status.

Height - Measuring a resident's height provides information that is relevant (in conjunction with his or her weight) to his/her nutritional status. There are various ways to estimate height if standing height cannot be readily measured.[8] A protocol for determining height helps to ensure that it will be measured as consistently as possible.

Weight - Weight can be a useful indicator of nutritional status, when evaluated within the context of the individual's personal history and overall condition. When weighing a resident, adjustment for amputations or prostheses may be indicated. Significant unintended changes in weight (loss or gain) or insidious weight loss may indicate a nutritional problem.

Current standards of practice recommend weighing the resident on admission or readmission (to establish a baseline weight), weekly for the first 4 weeks after admission and at least monthly thereafter to help identify and document trends such as insidious weight loss. Weighing may also be pertinent if there is a significant change in condition, food intake has declined and persisted (e.g., for more than a week), or there is other evidence of altered nutritional status or fluid and electrolyte imbalance. In some cases, weight monitoring is not indicated (e.g., the individual is terminally ill and requests only comfort care).

Obtaining accurate weights for each resident may be aided by having staff follow a consistent approach to weighing and by using an appropriately calibrated and functioning scale (e.g., wheelchair scale or bed scale). Since weight varies throughout the day, a consistent process and technique (e.g., weighing the resident wearing a similar type of clothing, at approximately the same time of the day, using the same scale, either consistently wearing or not wearing orthotics or prostheses, and verifying scale accuracy) can help make weight comparisons more reliable.

A system to verify weights can help to ensure accuracy. Weights obtained in different settings may differ substantially. For example, the last weight obtained in the hospital may differ markedly from the initial weight upon admission to the facility, and is not to be used in lieu of actually weighing the resident. Approaches to improving the accuracy of weights may include reweighing the resident and recording the current weight, reviewing approaches to obtaining and verifying weight, and modifying those approaches as needed.

Examples of other factors that may impact weight and the significance of apparent weight changes include:

- The resident's usual weight through adult life;

- Current medical conditions;

- Calorie restricted diet;

- Recent changes in dietary intake; and

- Edema.

Food and fluid intake - The nutritional assessment includes an estimate of calorie, nutrient and fluid needs, and whether intake is adequate to meet those needs. It also includes information such as the route (oral, enteral or parenteral) of intake, any special food formulation, meal and snack patterns (including the time of supplement or medication consumption in relation to the meals), dislikes, and preferences (including ethnic foods and form of foods such as finger foods); meal/snack patterns, and preferred portion sizes.

Fluid loss or retention can cause short term weight change. Much of a resident's daily fluid intake comes from meals; therefore, when a resident has decreased appetite, it can result in fluid/electrolyte imbalance. Abrupt weight changes, change in food intake, or altered level of consciousness are some of the clinical manifestations of fluid and electrolyte imbalance. Laboratory tests (e.g., electrolytes, BUN, creatinine and serum osmolality) can help greatly to identify, manage, and monitor fluid and electrolyte status.[9]

Altered Nutrient intake, absorption, and utilization. Poor intake, continuing or unabated hunger, or a change in the resident's usual intake that persists for multiple meals, may indicate an underlying problem or illness. Examples of causes include:

- The inability to consume meals provided (e.g., as a result of the form or consistency of food/fluid, cognitive or functional decline, arthritis-related impaired movement, neuropathic pain, or insufficient assistance);

- Insufficient availability of food and fluid (e.g., inadequate amount of food or fluid or inadequate tube feedings);

- Environmental factors affecting food intake or appetite (e.g., comfort and level of disruption in the dining environment);

- Adverse consequences related to medications; and

- Diseases and conditions such as cancer, diabetes mellitus, advanced or uncontrolled heart or lung disease, infection and fever, liver disease, hyperthyroidism, mood disorders, and repetitive movement disorders (e.g., wandering, pacing, or rocking).

The use of diuretics and other medications may cause weight loss that is not associated with nutritional issues, but can also cause fluid and electrolyte imbalance/dehydration that causes a loss of appetite and weight.

Various gastrointestinal disorders such as pancreatitis, gastritis, motility disorders, small bowel dysfunction, gall bladder disease, and liver dysfunction may affect digestion or absorption of food. Prolonged diarrhea or vomiting may increase nutritional requirements due to nutrient and fluid losses. Constipation or fecal impaction may affect appetite and excretion.

Pressure ulcers and some other wounds and other health impairments may also affect nutritional requirements. A hypermetabolic state results from an increased demand for energy and protein and may increase the risk of weight loss or under-nutrition. Examples of causes include advanced chronic obstructive pulmonary disease (COPD), pneumonia and other infections, cancer, hyperthyroidism, and fever.

Early identification of these factors, regardless of the presence of any associated weight changes, can help the facility choose appropriate interventions to minimize any subsequent complications.[10] Often, several of these factors affecting nutrition coexist.

Chewing abnormalities - Many conditions of the mouth, teeth, and gums can affect the resident's ability to chew foods. For example, oral pain, dry mouth, gingivitis, periodontal disease, ill-fitting dentures, and broken, decayed or missing teeth can impair oral intake.

Swallowing abnormalities - Various direct and indirect causes can affect the resident's ability to swallow. These include but are not limited to stroke, pain, lethargy, confusion, dry mouth, and diseases of the oropharynx and esophagus. Swallowing ability may fluctuate from day to day or over time. In some individuals, aspiration pneumonia can complicate swallowing abnormalities.[10]

NOTE: Swallowing studies are not always required in order to assess eating and swallowing; however, when they are indicated, it is essential to interpret any such tests in the proper context. A clinical evaluation of swallowing may be used to evaluate average daily oral function.[11]

Functional ability - The ability to eat independently may be helped by addressing factors that impair function or by providing appropriate individual assistance, supervision, or assistive devices. Conditions affecting functional ability to eat and drink include impaired upper extremity motor coordination and strength or reduced range of motion (any of which may be hampered by stroke, Parkinson's disease, multiple sclerosis, tardive dyskinesia, or other neuromuscular disorders or by sensory limitations (e.g., blindness)). Cognitive impairment may also affect a resident's ability to use a fork, or to eat, chew, and swallow effectively.

Medications - Medications and nutritional supplements may affect, or be affected by, the intake or utilization of nutrients (e.g., liquid phenytoin taken with tube feedings or grapefruit juice taken with some antihyperlipidemics).[12] Medications from almost every pharmaceutical class can affect nutritional status, directly or indirectly; for example, by causing or exacerbating anorexia, lethargy, confusion, nausea, constipation, impairing taste, or altering gastrointestinal function. Inhaled or ingested medications can affect food intake by causing pharyngitis, dry mouth, esophagitis, or gastritis. To the extent possible, consideration of medication/nutrient interactions and adverse consequences should be individualized.

Goals and prognosis - Goals and prognosis refer to a resident's projected personal and clinical outcomes. These are influenced by the resident's preferences (e.g., willingness to participate in weight management interventions or desire for nutritional support at end-of-life), anticipated course of a resident's overall condition and progression of a disease (e.g., end-stage, terminal, or other irreversible conditions affecting food intake, nutritional status, and weight goals), and by the resident's willingness and capacity to permit additional diagnostic testing, monitoring and treatment.

Laboratory/Diagnostic Evaluation

Laboratory tests are sometimes useful to help identify underlying causes of impaired nutrition or when the clinical assessment alone is not enough to define someone's nutritional status.

Abnormal laboratory values may, but do not necessarily, imply that treatable clinical problems exist or that interventions are needed. Confirmation is generally desirable through additional clinical evaluation and evidence such as food intake, underlying medical condition, etc.[13] For example, serum albumin may help establish prognosis but is only sometimes helpful in identifying impaired nutrition or guiding interventions. Serum albumin may drop significantly during an acute illness for reasons unrelated to nutrition; therefore, albumin may not improve, or may fall further, despite consumption of adequate amounts of calories and protein.

The decision to order laboratory tests, and the interpretation of subsequent results, is best done in light of a resident's overall condition and prognosis.[14] Before ordering laboratory tests it is appropriate for the health care practitioner to determine and indicate whether the tests would potentially change the resident's diagnosis, management, outcome or quality of life or otherwise add to what is already known. Although laboratory tests such as albumin and pre-albumin may help in some cases in deciding to initiate nutritional interventions, there is no evidence that they are useful for the serial follow-up of undernourished individuals.[14]

NOTE: If laboratory tests were done prior to or after admission to the facility and the test results are abnormal, the physician or other licensed health care practitioner, in collaboration with the interdisciplinary team, reviews the information and determines whether to intervene or order additional diagnostic testing.

ANALYSIS

Analysis refers to using the information from multiple sources to include, but not limited to, the Resident Assessment Instrument (RAI), and additional nutritional assessments as indicated to determine a resident's nutritional status and develop an individualized care plan.

Resultant conclusions may include, but are not limited to: a target range for weight based on the individual's overall condition, goals, prognosis, usual body weight, etc; approximate calorie, protein, and other nutrient needs; whether and to what extent weight stabilization or improvement can be anticipated; and whether altered weight or nutritional status could be related to an underlying medical condition (e.g., fluid and electrolyte imbalance, medication-related anorexia, or an infection).

Suggested parameters for evaluating significance of unplanned and undesired weight loss are:

Interval	Significant Loss	Severe Loss
1 month	5%	Greater than 5%
3 months	7.5%	Greater than 7.5%
6 months	10%	Greater than 10%

The following formula determines percentage of weight loss:

$$\% \text{ of body weight loss} = (\text{usual weight} - \text{actual weight}) / (\text{usual weight}) \times 100$$

Based on analysis of relevant information, the facility identifies a clinically pertinent basis for any conclusions that a resident could not attain or maintain acceptable parameters of nutritional status.

Specification of the Nutritional Concern

A clear statement of the nature of the nutritional concern provides the basis for resident-specific interventions. Many residents have multiple coexisting issues. For example:

- Poor food and fluid intake: The resident has poor intake, is not consuming specific food groups, and has increased nutritional needs specific to clinical conditions. The resident also has lost significant weight over a few days while taking medications that may affect appetite.

- Specific clinical conditions: The resident has an infection with fever and is in a hyper-metabolic state associated with an increased demand for energy and protein. The resident also has a neuromuscular disorder affecting the ability to eat or swallow, and has impaired cognition affecting attention and appetite.

CARE PLANNING AND INTERVENTIONS

The management of nutrition in nursing homes involves various medical, psychosocial, ethical, and functional considerations. Based on information generated by the comprehensive assessment and any pertinent additional nutritional assessment, the interdisciplinary team (including a physician or other licensed health care practitioner and the resident or the resident's representative) develops an individualized care plan. The care plan addresses, to the extent possible, identified causes of impaired nutritional status, reflects the resident's goals and choices, and identifies resident-specific interventions and a time frame and parameters for monitoring. The care plan is updated as needed; e.g., as conditions change, goals are met, interventions are determined to be ineffective, or as specific treatable causes of nutrition-related problems (anorexia, impaired chewing, etc.) are identified. If nutritional goals are not achieved, different or additional pertinent approaches are considered and implemented as indicated. Pertinent documentation can help identify the basis (e.g., current resident status, comorbid conditions, prognosis, and resident choices) for nutrition-related goals and interventions.

Resident Choice

A resident or resident representative has the right to make informed choices about accepting or declining care and treatment. The facility can help the resident exercise those rights effectively by discussing with the resident (or the resident's representative) the resident's condition, treatment options (including related risks and benefits, and expected outcomes), personal preferences, and any potential consequences of accepting or refusing treatment. If the resident declines specific interventions, the facility must address the resident's concerns and offer relevant alternatives.

The facility's care reflects a resident's choices, either as offered by the resident directly or via a valid advance directive, or based on a decision made by the resident's surrogate or representative in accordance with state law. The presence of care instructions, such as an advance directive, declining some interventions does not necessarily imply that other support and care was declined or is not pertinent. When preferences are not specified beforehand, decisions related to the possible provision of supplemental or artificial nutrition should be made in conjunction with the resident or resident's representative in accordance with state law, taking into account relevant considerations such as condition, prognosis, and a resident's known values and choices.

NOTE: The presence of a "Do Not Resuscitate" (DNR) order does not by itself indicate that the resident is declining other appropriate treatment and services. It only indicates that the resident has chosen not to be resuscitated if cardiopulmonary functions cease.

Meeting Nutritional Needs

The scope of interventions to meet residents' nutritional needs depends on many factors, including, but not limited to a resident's current food intake, the degree of nutritional impairment or risk, resident choices, the response to initial interventions, and the feasibility of addressing underlying conditions and causes. Basic energy needs can generally be met by providing a diet that includes enough calories to stabilize current body weight. Adjustments may be necessary when factors exist such as those discussed within this document. For example, limits on dairy products may be desirable in individuals with lactose intolerance, and additional amounts of nutrients and calories may be needed for individuals with hypermetabolic states (e.g., fever, hyperthyroidism, acute wounds, or heart or lung disease), to try to keep the body from using lean body mass for energy and wound repair.

Diet Liberalization

Research suggests that a liberalized diet can enhance the quality of life and nutritional status of older adults in long-term care facilities.[15] Thus, it is often beneficial to minimize restrictions, consistent with a resident's condition, prognosis, and choices before using supplementation. It may also be helpful to provide the residents their food preferences, before using supplementation. This pertains to newly developed meal plans as well as to the review of existing diets.

Dietary restrictions, therapeutic (e.g., low fat or sodium restricted) diets, and mechanically altered diets may help in select situations. At other times, they may impair adequate nutrition and lead to further decline in nutritional status, especially in already undernourished or at-risk individuals. When a resident is not eating well or is losing weight, the interdisciplinary team may temporarily abate dietary restrictions and liberalize the diet to improve the resident's food intake to try to stabilize their weight.

Sometimes, a resident or resident's representative decides to decline medically relevant dietary restrictions. In such circumstances, the resident, facility and practitioner collaborate to identify pertinent alternatives.

Weight-Related Interventions

For many residents (including overweight individuals), the resident's usual body weight prior to decline or admission is the most relevant basis for weight-related interventions. Basing interventions on ideal body weight can be misleading, because ideal body weight has not been definitively established for the frail elderly and those with chronic illnesses and disabilities.

The care plan includes nutritional interventions that address underlying risks and causes of weight loss (e.g., the need for eating assistance, reduction of medication side effects, and additional food that the resident will eat) or unplanned weight gain. It is important that the care plan address insidious, abrupt, or sudden decline in intake or insidious weight loss that does not trigger review of the Nutritional Status Resident Assessment Protocol (RAP); for example, by intensifying observation of intake and eating patterns, monitoring for complications related to poor intake, and seeking underlying cause(s).

Many risk factors and some causes of weight loss can be addressed, at least partially, while others may not be modifiable. In some cases, certain interventions may not be indicated or appropriate, based on individual goals and prognosis.

Weight stability, rather than weight gain, may sometimes be the most pertinent short-term or long-term objective for the nutritionally at-risk or compromised resident. After an acute illness or as part of an advanced or end-stage medical condition, the resident's weight and other nutritional parameters may not return to previous levels and may stabilize at a lower level, sometimes indefinitely.

NOTE: There should be a documented clinical basis for any conclusion that nutritional status or significant weight change are unlikely to stabilize or improve (e.g., physician's documentation as to why weight loss is medically unavoidable).

Weight Gain. Unplanned weight gain in a resident may have significant health implications. Rapid or abrupt increases in weight may also indicate significant fluid excess. After assessing the resident for the cause of the weight gain, care plan interventions may include dietary alterations based on the resident's medical condition, choices, and needs. If the resident exercises his/her right to choose and declines dietary restrictions, the facility discusses with the resident the benefits of maintaining a lower weight and the possible consequences of not doing so. A health care practitioner can help inform the resident about the rationale for the recommended plan of care.

Environmental Factors

Appetite is often enhanced by the appealing aroma, flavor, form, and appearance of food. Resident-specific facility practices that may help improve intake include providing a pleasant dining experience (e.g., flexible dining environments, styles and schedules), providing meals that are palatable, attractive and nutritious (e.g., prepare food with seasonings, serve food at proper temperatures, etc.), and making sure that the environment where residents eat (e.g., dining room and/or resident's room) is conducive to dining.

Anorexia

The facility, in consultation with the practitioner, identifies and addresses treatable causes of anorexia. For example, the practitioner may consider adjusting or stopping medications that may have caused the resident to have dyspepsia or become lethargic, constipated, or confused, and reevaluate the resident to determine whether the effects of the medications are the reasons for the anorexia and subsequent weight loss.

Where psychosis or a mood disorder such as depression has been identified as a cause of anorexia or weight change, treatment of the underlying disorder (based on an appropriate diagnostic evaluation) may improve appetite. However, other coexisting conditions or factors instead of, or in addition to, depression, may cause or contribute to anorexia. In addition, the use of antidepressants is not generally considered to be an adequate substitute for appropriately investigating and addressing modifiable risk factors or other underlying causes of anorexia and weight loss.

Wound Healing

Healing of acute (e.g., postoperative) and chronic (e.g., pressure ulcer) wounds requires enough calories and protein so that the body will not use lean body mass (muscle) for energy and wound repair. However, to date, no routinely beneficial wound-specific nutritional measures have been identified.[16]

Care plan interventions for a resident who has a wound or is at risk of developing a wound may include providing enough calories to maintain a stable weight and a daily protein intake of approximately 1.2-1.5 gm protein/Kg body weight. The recommended daily protein intake may be adjusted according to clinical need and standards of clinical practice for situations in which more calories and protein are indicated. Sometimes, it may be most appropriate to try to encourage the resident to eat as many calories and as much protein as tolerated, because he/she does not desire or cannot tolerate more aggressive nutritional interventions.

Additional strategies for wound healing may be considered when indicated. A multivitamin/mineral supplement may be prescribed, however current evidence does not definitively support any specific dietary supplementation (e.g., Vitamin C and Zinc) unless the resident has a specific vitamin or mineral deficiency.

Functional Factors

Based on the comprehensive interdisciplinary assessment, the facility provides the necessary assistance to allow the resident to eat and drink adequately. A resident with functional impairment may need help with eating. Examples of such interventions may include, but are not limited to: ensuring that sensory devices such as eyeglasses, dentures, and hearing aids are in place; providing personal hygiene before and after meals, properly positioning the individual, providing eating assistance where needed, and providing the assistive devices/utensils identified in the assessment. [17]

Chewing and Swallowing

In deciding whether and how to intervene for chewing and swallowing abnormalities, it is essential to take a holistic approach and look beyond the symptoms to the underlying causes. Pertinent interventions may help address the resident's eating, chewing, and swallowing problems and optimize comfort and enjoyment of meals. Examples of such interventions may include providing proper positioning for eating; participation in a restorative eating program; use of assistive devices/utensils; and prompt assistance (e.g., supervision, cueing, hand-over-hand) during every meal/snack where assistance is needed.

Treating medical conditions (e.g., gastroesophageal reflux disease and oral and dental problems) that can impair swallowing or cause coughing may improve a chewing or swallowing problem. Examples of other relevant interventions include adjusting medications that cause dry mouth or coughing, and providing liquids to moisten the mouth of someone with impaired saliva production.

Excessive modification of food and fluid consistency may unnecessarily decrease quality of life and impair nutritional status by affecting appetite and reducing intake.[18] Many factors influence whether a swallowing abnormality eventually results in clinically significant complications such as aspiration pneumonia.[19] Identification of a swallowing abnormality alone does not necessarily warrant dietary restrictions or food texture modifications. No interventions consistently prevent aspiration and no tests consistently predict who will develop aspiration pneumonia.[20] For example, tube feeding may be associated with aspiration, and is not necessarily a desirable alternative to allowing oral intake, even if some swallowing abnormalities are present.[21,22]

Decisions to downgrade or alter the consistency of diets must include the resident (or the resident's representative), consider ethical issues (such as the right to decline treatment), and be based on a careful review of the resident's overall condition, correctable underlying causes of the risk or problem, the benefits and risks of a more liberalized diet, and the resident's preferences to accept risks in favor of a more liberalized food intake.

Medications

When a resident is eating poorly or losing weight, the immediate need to stabilize weight and improve appetite may supersede long-term medical goals for which medications were previously ordered. It may be appropriate to change, stop, or reduce the doses of medications (e.g., antiepileptics, cholinesterase inhibitors, or iron supplements) that are associated either with anorexia or with symptoms such as lethargy or confusion that can cause or exacerbate weight loss.[23] The medical practitioner in collaboration with the staff and the pharmacist reviews and adjusts medications as appropriate. (For additional Guidance related to medications, refer to 42 CFR 483.25(l)(1), F329, Unnecessary Drugs.)

Food Fortification and Supplementation

With any nutrition program, improving intake via wholesome foods is generally preferable to adding nutritional supplements. However, if the resident is not able to eat recommended portions at meal times or to consume between-meal snacks/nourishments, or if he/she prefers the nutritional supplement, supplements may be used to try to increase calorie and nutrient intake. Since some research suggests that caloric intake may increase if nutritional supplements are consumed between meals, and may be less effective when given with meals, the use of nutritional supplements is generally recommended between meals instead of with meals.[24] Taking a nutritional supplement during medication administration may also increase caloric intake without reducing the resident's appetite at mealtime.

Examples of interventions to improve food/fluid intake include:

- Fortification of foods (e.g., adding protein, fat, and/or carbohydrate to foods such as hot cereal, mashed potatoes, casseroles, and desserts);

- Offering smaller, more frequent meals;

- Providing between-meal snacks or nourishments; or

- Increasing the portion sizes of a resident's favorite foods and meals; and providing nutritional supplements.

Maintaining Fluid and Electrolyte Balance

If a resident has poor intake or abnormal laboratory values related to fluid/electrolyte balance, the care plan addresses the potential for hydration deficits.[25] Examples of interventions include adjusting or discontinuing medications that affect fluid balance or appetite; offering a variety of fluids (water, fruit juice, milk, etc.) between meals, and encouraging and assisting residents as appropriate. Serving (except to those with fluid restrictions) additional beverages with meals will also help increase fluid intake. Examples of ways to encourage fluid intake include maintaining filled water pitchers and drinking cups easily accessible to residents (except those with fluid restrictions) and offering alternate fluid sources such as popsicles, gelatin, and ice cream.

Use of Appetite Stimulants

To date, the evidence is limited about benefits from appetite stimulants. While their use may be appropriate in specific circumstances, they are not a substitute for appropriate investigation and management of potentially modifiable risk factors and underlying causes of anorexia and weight loss.[26]

Feeding Tubes

Feeding tubes have potential benefits and complications, depending on an individual's underlying medical conditions and prognosis, and the causes of his or her anorexia or weight loss. Possible feeding tube use, especially for residents with advanced dementia or at the end-of-life, should be considered carefully. The resident's values and choices regarding artificial nutrition should be identified and considered. The health care practitioner should be involved in reviewing whether potentially modifiable causes of anorexia, weight loss, and eating or swallowing abnormalities have been considered and addressed, to the extent possible. For residents with dementia, studies have shown that tube feeding does not extend life, prevent aspiration pneumonia, improve function or limit suffering. [27]

End-of-Life

Resident choices and clinical indications affect decisions about the use of a feeding tube at the end-of-life. A resident at the end of life may have an advance directive addressing his or her treatment goals (or the resident's surrogate or representative, in accordance with State law, may have made a decision).

Decreased appetite and altered hydration are common at the end of life, and do not require interventions other than for comfort. Multiple organ system failure may impair the body's capacity to accept or digest food or to utilize nutrients. Thus, the inability to maintain acceptable parameters of nutritional status for someone who is at the end-of-life or in the terminal stages of an illness may be an expected outcome.

Care and services, including comfort measures, are provided based on the resident's choices and a pertinent nutritional assessment. The facility can help to support intake, to the extent desired and feasible, based on the information from the assessment and on considering the resident's choices.

If individualized approaches for end-of-life care are provided in accordance with the care plan and the resident's choices, then the failure to maintain acceptable parameters of nutritional status may be an expected outcome for residents with terminal conditions.

MONITORING

Monitoring after care plan implementation is necessary for residents with impaired or at-risk nutritional status, as well as for those whose current nutritional status is stable. Monitoring includes a review of the resident-specific factors identified as part of the comprehensive resident assessment and any supplemental nutrition assessment.

Identifying and reporting information about the resident's nutritional status and related issues such as level of consciousness and function are obtainable through various staff observations. For example, nursing assistants may be most familiar with the resident's habits and preferences, symptoms such as pain or discomfort, fluctuating appetite, and nausea or other gastrointestinal symptoms. More intensive and frequent monitoring may be indicated for residents with impaired or at-risk nutritional status than for those who are currently nutritionally stable. Such monitoring may include, but is not limited to, observing for and recognizing emergence of new risk factors (e.g., acute medical illness, pressure ulcers, or fever), evaluating consumption of between-meal snacks and nutritional supplements, and reviewing the continued relevance of any current nutritional interventions (e.g., therapeutic diets, tube feeding orders or nutritional supplements).

Evaluating the care plan to determine if current interventions are being followed and if they are effective in attaining identified nutritional and weight goals allows the facility to make necessary revisions. Subsequent adjustment of interventions will depend on, but are not limited to, progress, underlying causes, overall condition and prognosis. The resident's current nutritional and medical status helps the staff determine the frequency of reweighing the resident. For example, reweighing a resident within a week of initiating or substantially revising nutritional interventions to address anorexia or weight loss assists in monitoring responses to interventions. Monitoring residents who experience unplanned weight loss, including reweighing at least weekly until weight is stable or increasing and then routinely thereafter, helps clarify his/her responses to interventions. However in some residents, subsequent weight monitoring may not be clinically indicated (e.g., palliative care resident).

Nutrition-related goals may need to be modified, depending on factors such as further clarification of underlying causes (e.g., when evidence suggests that unmodifiable factors may prevent improved or stabilized nutritional status) and responses to current interventions. In some cases, the current plan of care may need to be modified and new or additional interventions implemented. The facility explains any decisions to continue current interventions when the resident's nutritional status continues to decline. For example, because the goal of care for someone with a terminal, advanced, or irreversible condition has changed to palliation.

[**Editor's Note:** See page 392 for endnotes pertaining to this section.]

INVESTIGATIVE PROTOCOL

NUTRITIONAL STATUS

Objectives

- To determine if the facility has practices in place to maintain acceptable parameters of nutritional status for each resident based on his/her comprehensive assessment.

- To determine if failure to maintain acceptable parameters of nutritional status for each resident was avoidable or unavoidable (the resident's clinical condition demonstrates that maintaining acceptable parameters is not possible).

- To determine if the resident has received a therapeutic diet when there is a nutritional indication.

Use

Use this protocol for each sampled resident to determine through interview, observation and record review whether the facility is in compliance with the regulation, specifically:

- To determine if residents maintained acceptable parameters of nutritional status, relative to his/her comprehensive assessment;

- For a resident who did not maintain acceptable parameters of nutritional status, to determine if the facility assessed and intervened (e.g., therapeutic diet) to enable the resident to maintain acceptable parameters of nutritional status, unless the resident's clinical condition demonstrated that this was not possible; and

- For a resident who is at nutritional risk, to determine if the facility has identified and addressed risk factors for, and causes of, impaired nutritional status, or demonstrated why they could not or should not do so.

Procedures

Briefly review the RAI, care plan, and any additional relevant nutritional assessment information that may be available to identify facility evaluations, conclusions, and interventions to guide subsequent observations.

NOTE: For the purposes of this investigation, conduct record reviews prior to meal observations to note the resident's therapeutic diet, food texture and level of required assistance with meals.

1. Observation

Observe residents during the initial tour of the facility and throughout the survey process. To facilitate the investigation, gather appropriate information (e.g., dining style, nourishment list, schedules, and policies).

During observations, surveyors may see non-traditional or alternate approaches to dining services such as buffet, restaurant style or family style dining. These alternate dining approaches may include more choices in meal options, preparations, dining areas and meal times. Such alternate dining approaches are acceptable and encouraged.

While conducting the resident dining observations:

- Observe at least two meals during the survey;

- Observe a resident's physical appearance for signs that might indicate altered nutritional status (e.g., cachectic) and note any signs of dental and oral problems;

- Observe the delivery of care (such as assistance and encouragement during dining) to determine if interventions are consistent with the care plan;

- Observe the serving of food as planned with attention to portion sizes, preferences, nutritional supplements, prescribed therapeutic diets and between-meal snacks to determine if the interventions identified in the care plan were implemented;

- Follow up and note differences between the care plan and interventions; and

- Determine if staff responded appropriately to the resident's needs (e.g., for assistance, positioning, and supervision).

2. Interview

Interview the resident, family or resident's representative to identify:

- Whether staff are responsive to the resident's eating abilities and support needs, including the provision of adaptive equipment and personal assistance with meals as indicated;

- Whether the resident's food and dining preferences are addressed to the extent possible, e.g., whether the resident is offered substitutions or choices at meal times as appropriate and in accordance with his/her preferences;

- Whether pertinent nutritional interventions, such as snacks, frequent meals, and calorie-dense foods, are provided; and

- If the resident refused needed therapeutic approaches, whether treatment options, related risks and benefits, expected outcomes and possible consequences were discussed with the resident or resident's representative, and whether pertinent alternatives or other interventions were offered.

Interview interdisciplinary team members on various shifts (e.g., certified nursing assistant, registered dietitian, dietary supervisor/manager, charge nurse, social worker, occupational therapist, attending physician, medical director, etc.) to determine, how:

- Food and fluid intake, and eating ability and weight (and changes to any of these) are monitored and reported;

- Nutrition interventions, such as snacks, frequent meals, and calorie-dense foods are provided to prevent or address impaired nutritional status (e.g., unplanned weight changes);

- Nutrition-related goals in the care plan are established, implemented, and monitored periodically;

- Care plans are modified when indicated to stabilize or improve nutritional status (e.g., reduction in medications, additional assistance with eating, therapeutic diet orders); and

- A health care practitioner is involved in evaluating and addressing underlying causes of nutritional risks and impairment (e.g., review of medications or underlying medical causes).

If the interventions defined, or the care provided, appear to be inconsistent with current standards of practice, interview one or more physicians or other licensed health care practitioners who can provide information about the resident's nutritional risks and needs. Examples include, but are not limited to:

- The rationale for chosen interventions;

- How staff evaluated the effectiveness of current interventions;

- How staff managed the interventions;

- How the interdisciplinary team decided to maintain or change interventions; and

- Rationale for decisions not to intervene to address identified needs.

3. Record Review

Review the resident's medical record to determine how the facility:

- Has evaluated and analyzed nutritional status;

- Has identified residents who are at nutritional risk;

- Has investigated and identified causes of anorexia and impaired nutritional status;

- Has identified and implemented relevant interventions to try to stabilize or improve nutritional status;

- Has identified residents' triggered Resident Assessment Instrument (RAI) for nutritional status;

- Has evaluated the effectiveness of the interventions; and

- Has monitored and modified approaches as indicated.

Documentation

Documentation of findings and conclusions related to nutritional status may be found in various locations in the medical record, including but not limited to interdisciplinary progress notes, nutrition progress notes, the RAP summary, care plan, or resident care conference notes. Review of the documentation will help the surveyor determine how the facility developed approaches to meet each resident's nutritional needs. This information will help the surveyor determine whether a resident's decline or failure to improve his/her nutritional status was avoidable or unavoidable.

Assessment and Monitoring

Review information including the RAI, diet and medication orders, activities of daily living worksheets, and nursing, dietitian, rehabilitation, and social service notes. Determine if the resident's weight and nutritional status were assessed in the context of his/her overall condition and prognosis, if nutritional requirements and risk factors were identified, and if causes of the resident's nutritional risks or impairment were sought.

Determine:

- Whether the facility identified a resident's desirable weight range, and identified weight loss/gain;

- Whether the facility identified the significance of any weight changes, and what interventions were needed;

- Whether there have been significant changes in the resident's overall intake;

- Whether the reasons for the change were identified and if appropriate interventions were implemented;

- Whether the facility has calculated nutritional needs (i.e., calories, protein and fluid requirements) and identified risk factors for malnutrition;

- Whether the facility met those needs and if not, why;

- Whether the resident's weight stabilized or improved as anticipated;

- Whether a need for a therapeutic diet was identified and implemented, consistent with the current standards of practice;

- Whether the facility indicated the basis for dietary restrictions;

- Whether the reasons for dietary changes were identified and appropriate interventions implemented;

- Whether the facility accommodated resident choice, individual food preferences, allergies, food intolerances, and fluid restrictions and if the resident was encouraged to make choices;

- Whether the facility identified and addressed underlying medical and functional causes (e.g., oral cavity lesions, mouth pain, decayed teeth, poorly fitting dentures, refusal to wear dentures, gastroesophageal reflux, or dysphagia) of any chewing or swallowing difficulties to the extent possible;

- Whether the facility identified residents requiring any type of assistance to eat and drink (e.g., assistive devices/utensils, cues, hand-over-hand, and extensive assistance), and provided such assistance;

- Whether the facility has identified residents receiving any medications that are known to cause clinically significant medication/nutrient interactions or that may affect appetite, and determined risk/benefit;

- Whether the facility identified and addressed to the extent possible medical illnesses and psychiatric disorders that may affect overall intake, nutrient utilization, and weight stability;

- Whether the facility reviewed existing abnormal laboratory test results and either implemented interventions, if appropriate, or provided a clinical justification for not intervening (see note in Laboratory/Diagnostic Evaluation);

- Whether the resident's current nutritional status is either at or improving towards goals established by the care team; and

- Whether alternate interventions were identified when nutritional status is not improving or clinical justification is provided as to why current interventions continue to be appropriate.

Care Plan

Review the comprehensive care plan to determine if the plan is based on the comprehensive assessment and additional pertinent nutritional assessment information. Determine if the facility developed measurable objectives, approximate time frames, and specific interventions to try to maintain acceptable parameters of nutritional status, based on the resident's overall goals, choices, preferences, prognosis, conditions, assessed risks, and needs.

If care plan concerns, related to nutritional status are noted, interview staff responsible for care planning about the rationale for the current plan of care. If questions remain after reviewing available information including documentation in the medical record, interview the resident's attending physician or licensed health care practitioner or the facility's medical director (e.g., if the attending physician or licensed health care practitioner is unavailable) concerning the resident's plan of care.

NOTE: Because the physician may not be present in the facility and have immediate access to the resident's medical record when the surveyor has questions, allow the facility the opportunity to first provide any pertinent information to the physician before responding to the interview.

Care Plan Revision

Determine if the staff has evaluated the effectiveness of the care plan related to nutritional status and made revisions if necessary based upon the following:

- Evaluation of nutrition-related outcomes;

- Identification of changes in the resident's condition that require revised goals and care approaches; and

- Involvement of the resident or the resident's representative in reviewing and updating the resident's care plan.

Review of Facility Practices

Related concerns may have been identified that would suggest the need for a review of facility practices. Examples of such activities may include a review of policies, staffing, and staff training, functional responsibilities, and interviews with staff (to include but not limited to management). If there is a pattern of residents who have not maintained acceptable parameters of nutritional status without adequate clinical justification, determine if quality assurance activities were initiated in order to evaluate the facility's approaches to nutrition and weight issues.

Interviews with Health Care Practitioners

If the interventions defined, or the care provided, appear to be inconsistent with recognized standards of practice, interview one or more health care practitioners as necessary (e.g., physician, hospice nurse, dietitian, charge nurse, director of nursing or medical director). Depending on the issue, ask:

- How it was determined that chosen interventions were appropriate;

- Why identified needs had no interventions;

- How changes in condition that may justify additional or different interventions were addressed; and

- How staff evaluated the effectiveness of current interventions.

DETERMINATION OF COMPLIANCE (Appendix P)

Synopsis of Regulation (Tag F325)

This regulation requires that, based on the resident's comprehensive assessment, the facility ensures that each resident maintains acceptable parameters of nutritional status unless the resident's clinical condition demonstrates that this is not possible, and that to the extent possible the resident receives a therapeutic diet when indicated.

Criteria for Compliance

The facility is in compliance with 42 CFR 483.25(i), Tag F325, Nutrition, if staff have:

- Assessed the resident's nutritional status and identified factors that put the resident at risk of not maintaining acceptable parameters of nutritional status;

- Analyzed the assessment information to identify the medical conditions, causes and problems related to the resident's condition and needs;

- Provided a therapeutic diet when indicated;

- Defined and implemented interventions to maintain or improve nutritional status that are consistent with the resident's assessed needs, choices, goals, and recognized standards of practice, or provided clinical justification why they did not do so; and

- Monitored and evaluated the resident's response to the interventions; and revised the approaches as appropriate, or justified the continuation of current approaches.

If not, failure to maintain acceptable parameters of nutritional status is avoidable, cite at Tag F325.

Noncompliance with Tag F325

After completing the investigative protocol, the survey team must analyze the data to determine whether noncompliance with the regulation exists. Noncompliance must be established before determining severity. A clear understanding of the facility's noncompliance with requirements (i.e., deficient practices) is essential to determine how the deficient practice(s) relates to any actual harm or potential for harm to the resident.

Noncompliance with Tag F325 may include (but is not limited to) one or more of the following, including failure to:

- Accurately and consistently assess a resident's nutritional status on admission and as needed thereafter;

- Identify a resident at nutritional risk and address risk factors for impaired nutritional status, to the extent possible;

- Identify, implement, monitor, and modify interventions (as appropriate), consistent with the resident's assessed needs, choices, goals, and current standards of practice, to maintain acceptable parameters of nutritional status;

- Notify the physician as appropriate in evaluating and managing causes of the resident's nutritional risks and impaired nutritional status;

- Identify and apply relevant approaches to maintain acceptable parameters of residents' nutritional status; and

- Provide a therapeutic diet when indicated.

Potential Tags for Additional Investigation

If noncompliance with 42 CFR 483.25(i) has been identified, the survey team may have determined during the investigation of Tag F325 that concerns may also be present with related process and/or structure requirements. Examples of related process and/or structure requirements related to noncompliance with Tag F325 may include the following:

- 42 CFR 483.10, Tag F150, Resident Rights [**Editor's Note**: Tag F150 should state Tag F151.]

  o Determine if the resident's preferences related to nutrition and food intake were considered.

- 42 CFR §483.20(b)(1), Tag F272, Comprehensive Assessments

  o Determine if the facility assessed the resident's nutritional status and the factors that put the resident at risk for failure to maintain acceptable parameters of nutritional status.

- 42 CFR §483.20(k), Tag F279, Comprehensive Care Plans

  o Determine if the facility developed a comprehensive care plan for each resident that includes measurable objectives, interventions/services, and time frames to meet the resident's needs as identified in the resident's assessment and provided a therapeutic diet when indicated.

- 42 CFR §483.20(k)(2)(iii), Tag F280, Comprehensive Care Plan Revision

  o Determine if the care plan was periodically reviewed and revised as necessary by qualified persons after each assessment to maintain acceptable parameters of nutritional status and provided a therapeutic diet when indicated.

- 42 CFR 483.20(k)(3)(ii), Tag F282, Provision of Care in Accordance with the Care Plan

  o Determine if the services provided or arranged by the facility were provided by qualified persons in accordance with the resident's written plan of care.

- 42 CFR 483.25(j), Tag F327, Hydration

  o Determine if the facility took measures to maintain proper hydration.

- 42 CFR 483.25(k)(2), F328, Special Needs

  o Determine if the facility took measures to provide proper treatment and care for Parenteral and Enteral Fluids.

- 42 CFR 483.25, Tag F329, Unnecessary Medicines

  o Determine if food and medication interactions are impacting the residents' dietary intake.

- 42 CFR 483.30(a), Tag F353, Sufficient Staff

  o Determine if the facility had qualified staff in sufficient numbers to provide necessary care and services, including supervision, based upon the comprehensive assessment and care plan.

- 42 CFR 483.35(a)(1)(2), F361, Dietary Services – Staffing

  o Determine if the facility employs or consults with a qualified dietitian. If not employed full-time, determine if the director of food service receives scheduled consultation from the dietitian concerning storage, preparation, distribution and service of food under sanitary conditions.

- 42 CFR 483.35(b), F362, Standard Sufficient Staff

  o Determine if the facility employs sufficient support personnel competent to carry out the functions of the dietary service.

- 42 CFR 483.40(a)(1)(2), Tag F385, Physician Services – Physician Supervision

  o Determine if a physician supervised the medical aspects of care of each resident, as indicated, as they relate to medical conditions that affect appetite and nutritional status.

- 42 CFR 483.75(h)(2)(ii), Tag F500, Use of Outsider resources

  o If the facility does not employ a qualified dietitian, determine if the professional services of a dietitian are furnished by an outside resource, meet professional standards and principles, and are timely.

- 42 CFR 483.75(i)(2)(i)(ii), Tag F501, Medical Director

  o Determine if the medical director helped develop and implement resident care policies as they relate to maintaining acceptable parameters of nutritional status and the provision of therapeutic diets when indicated.

- 42 CFR 483.75(o), Tag F520, Quality Assessment and Assurance

  o Related concerns may have been identified that would suggest the need for a review of facility practices. Such activities may involve a review of policies, staffing and staff training, contracts, etc. and interviews with management, for example. If there is a pattern of residents who have not maintained acceptable parameters of nutritional status without adequate clinical justification, determine if quality assurance activities address the facility's approaches to nutrition and weight issues.

DEFICIENCY CATEGORIZATION (Part IV, Appendix P)

Once the team has completed its investigation, analyzed the data, reviewed the regulatory requirements, and determined that noncompliance exists, the team must determine the severity of each deficiency, based on the resultant effect or potential for harm to the resident.

The key elements for severity determination for Tag F325 are as follows:

1. Presence of harm/negative outcome(s) or potential for negative outcomes due to a failure of care and services. Actual or potential harm/negative outcomes for F325 may include, but are not limited to:

   - Significant unplanned weight change;

   - Inadequate food/fluid intake;

   - Impairment of anticipated wound healing;

   - Failure to provide a therapeutic diet;

   - Functional decline; and

   - Fluid/electrolyte imbalance.

2. Degree of harm (actual or potential) related to the noncompliance. Identify how the facility practices caused, resulted in, allowed, or contributed to the actual or potential for harm:

   - If harm has occurred, determine if the harm is at the level of serious injury, impairment, death, compromise, or discomfort; and

   - If harm has not yet occurred, determine how likely the potential is for serious injury, impairment, death, compromise or discomfort to occur to the resident.

3. The immediacy of correction required. Determine whether the noncompliance requires immediate correction in order to prevent serious injury, harm, impairment, or death to one or more residents.

The survey team must evaluate the harm or potential for harm based upon the following levels of severity for Tag F325. First, the team must rule out whether Severity Level 4, Immediate Jeopardy to a resident's health or safety exists by evaluating the deficient practice in relation to immediacy, culpability, and severity. (Follow the guidance in Appendix Q, "Guidelines for Determining Immediate Jeopardy.")

Severity Level 4 Considerations: Immediate Jeopardy to Resident Health or Safety

Immediate Jeopardy is a situation in which the facility's noncompliance:

- With one or more requirements of participation has caused/resulted in, or is likely to cause serious injury, harm, impairment, or death to a resident; and

- Requires immediate correction, as the facility either created the situation or allowed the situation to continue by failing to implement preventative or corrective measures.

NOTE: The death or transfer of a resident who was harmed as a result of facility practices does not remove a finding of immediate jeopardy. The facility is required to implement specific actions to correct the deficient practices which allowed or caused the immediate jeopardy.

Examples of avoidable actual or potential resident outcomes that demonstrate severity at Level 4 may include, but are not limited to:

- Continued weight loss and functional decline resulting from ongoing, repeated systemic failure to assess and address a resident's nutritional status and needs, and implement pertinent interventions based on such an assessment;

- Development of life-threatening symptom(s), or the development or continuation of severely impaired nutritional status due to repeated failure to assist a resident who required assistance with meals;

- Substantial and ongoing decline in food intake resulting in significant unplanned weight loss due to dietary restrictions or downgraded diet textures (e.g., mechanic soft, pureed) provided by the facility against the resident's expressed preferences; or

- Evidence of cardiac dysrhythmias or other changes in medical condition due to hyperkalemia, resulting from the facility's failure to provide a potassium restricted therapeutic diet that was ordered.

If immediate jeopardy has been ruled out based upon the evidence, then evaluate whether actual harm that is not immediate jeopardy exists at Severity Level 3 or the potential for more than minimal harm at Level 2 exists.

Severity Level 3 Considerations: Actual Harm that is not Immediate Jeopardy

Level 3 indicates noncompliance that results in actual harm that is not immediate jeopardy. The negative outcome can include, but may not be limited to clinical compromise, decline, or the resident's inability to maintain and/or reach his/her highest practicable level of well-being.

Examples of avoidable actual resident outcomes that demonstrate severity at Level 3 may include, but are not limited to:

- Significant unplanned weight change and impaired wound healing (not attributable to an underlying medical condition) due to the facility's failure to revise and/or implement the care plan to address the resident's impaired ability to feed him/herself;

- Loss of weight from declining food and fluid intake due to the facility's failure to assess and address the resident's use of medications that affect appetite and food intake;

- Unplanned weight change and declining food and/or fluid intake due to the facility's failure to assess the relative benefits and risks of restricting or downgrading diet and food consistency or to obtain or accommodate resident preferences in accepting related risks;

- Decline in function related to poor food/fluid intake due to the facility's failure to accommodate documented resident food dislikes and provide appropriate substitutes; or

- A resident with known celiac disease (damage to the small intestine related to gluten allergy) develops persistent gastrointestinal symptoms including weight loss, chronic diarrhea, and vomiting, due to the facility's failure to provide a gluten-free diet (i. e., one free of wheat, barley, and rye products) as prescribed by the physician.

NOTE: If Severity Level 3 (actual harm that is not immediate jeopardy) has been ruled out based upon the evidence, then evaluate as to whether Severity Level 2 (no actual harm with the potential for more than minimal harm) exists.

Severity Level 2 Considerations: No Actual Harm with Potential for more than Minimal Harm that is not Immediate Jeopardy

Level 2 indicates noncompliance that results in a resident outcome of no more than minimal discomfort and/or has the potential to compromise the resident's ability to maintain or reach his or her highest practicable level of well being. The potential exists for greater harm to occur if interventions are not provided.

For Level 2 severity, the resident was at risk for, or has experienced the presence of one or more outcome(s) (e.g., unplanned weight change, inadequate food/fluid intake, impairment of anticipated wound healing, functional decline, and/or fluid/electrolyte imbalance), due to the facility's failure to help the resident maintain acceptable parameters of nutritional status.

Examples of avoidable actual or potential resident outcomes that demonstrate severity at Level 2 may include, but are not limited to:

- Failure to obtain accurate weight(s) and to verify weight(s) as needed;

- Poor intake due to the facility's intermittent failure to provide required assistance with eating, however, the resident met identified weight goals;

- Failure to provide additional nourishment when ordered for a resident, however, the resident did not experience significant weight loss; and

- Failure to provide a prescribed sodium-restricted therapeutic diet (unless declined by the resident or the resident's representative or not followed by the resident); however, the resident did not experience medical complications such as heart failure related to sodium excess.

Severity Level 1: No Actual Harm with Potential for Minimal Harm

The failure of the facility to provide appropriate care and services to maintain acceptable parameters of nutritional status and minimize negative outcomes places residents at risk for more than minimal harm. Therefore, Severity Level 1 does not apply for this regulatory requirement.

F327

§483.25(j) Hydration

§483.25(j) Hydration. The facility must provide each resident with sufficient fluid intake to maintain proper hydration and health.

Intent §483.25(j)

The intent of this regulation is to assure that the resident receives sufficient amount of fluids based on individual needs to prevent dehydration.

Interpretive Guidelines §483.25(j)

This corresponds to MDS 2.0 sections G, K, I, J and L when specified for use by the State.

"Sufficient fluid" means the amount of fluid needed to prevent dehydration (output of fluids far exceeds fluid intake) and maintain health. The amount needed is specific for each resident, and fluctuates as the resident's condition fluctuates (e.g., increase fluids if resident has fever or diarrhea).

Risk factors for the resident becoming dehydrated are:

- Coma/decreased sensorium;

- Fluid loss and increased fluid needs (e.g., diarrhea, fever, uncontrolled diabetes);

- Fluid restriction secondary to renal dialysis;

- Functional impairments that make it difficult to drink, reach fluids, or communicate fluid needs (e.g., aphasia);

- Dementia in which resident forgets to drink or forgets how to drink;

- Refusal of fluids; and

- Did the MDS trigger RAPs on hydration? What action was taken based on the RAP?

Consider whether assessment triggers RAPs and are RAPs used to assess the causal factors for decline, potential for decline or lack of improvement.

A general guideline for determining baseline daily fluids needs is to multiply the resident's body weight in kg times 30cc (2.2 lbs = 1kg), except for residents with renal or cardiac distress. An excess of fluids can be detrimental for these residents.

Procedures §483.25(j)

Identify if resident triggers RAPs for dehydration/fluid maintenance, and cognitive loss.

Probes §483.25(j)

Do sampled residents show clinical signs of possible insufficient fluid intake (e.g., dry skin and mucous membranes, cracked lips, poor skin turgor, thirst, fever), abnormal laboratory values (e.g., elevated hemoglobin and hematocrit, potassium, chloride, sodium, albumin, transferrin, blood urea nitrogen (BUN), or urine specific gravity)?

Has the facility provided residents with adequate fluid intake to maintain proper hydration and health? If not:

- Did the facility identify any factors that put the resident at risk of dehydration?

- What care did the facility provide to reduce those risk factors and ensure adequate fluid intake (e.g., keep fluids next to the resident at all times and assisting or cuing the resident to drink)? Is staff aware of need for maintaining adequate fluid intake?

- If adequate fluid intake is difficult to maintain, have alternative treatment approaches been developed, attempt to increase fluid intake by the use of popsicles, gelatin, and other similar non-liquid foods?

F328

§483.25(k) Special Needs

The facility must ensure that residents receive proper treatment and care for the following special services.

Intent 483.25(k)

The intent of this provision is that the resident receives the necessary care and treatment including medical and nursing care and services when they need the specialized services as listed below.

Interpretive Guidelines §483.25(k)

This corresponds to MDS 2.0 section P when specified by for use by the State.

The non-availability of program funding does not relieve a facility of its obligation to ensure that its residents receive all needed services listed in §1819(b)(4)(A) of the Act for Medicare and §1919(b)(4)(A) of the Act for Medicaid. For services not covered, a facility is required to assist the resident in securing any available resources to obtain the needed services.

§483.25(k)(1) Injections

Probes §483.25(k)(1)

For sampled residents receiving one or more of these services within 7 days of the survey:

- Is proper administration technique used (i.e., maintenance of sterility; correct needle size, route)?

- Are there signs of redness, swelling, lesions from previous injections?

- If appropriate, is resident observed for adverse reaction after the injection?

- Are syringes and needles disposed of according to facility policy and accepted Practice (e.g., Centers for Disease Control and Prevention and Occupational Safety and Health Administration guidelines)?

- Do nursing notes indicate, as appropriate, the resident's response to treatment (e.g., side effects/adverse actions; problems at the injection site(s); relief of pain)?

§483.25(k)(2) Parenteral and Enteral Fluids

Probes §483.25(k)(2)

This corresponds to MDS 2.0 sections K5 and 6 and P1 when specified for use by the State.

For residents selected for a comprehensive review, or focused review as appropriate, receiving one or more of these services within 7 days of the survey:

- Are there signs of inflammation or infiltration at the insertion site?

- If the IV site, tubing, or bottle/bag is changed, is sterile technique maintained?

- Is the rate of administration that which is ordered by the Physician?

- Has the resident received the amount of fluid during the past 24 hours that he/she should have received according to the physician's orders (allow flexibility up to 150cc unless an exact fluid intake is critical for the resident)?

Procedures §483.25(k)(2)

See §483.25(g) for enteral feedings (includes gastrostomy).

§483.25(k)(3) Colostomy, Ureterostomy, or Ileostomy care

Procedures §483.25(k)(3)

This corresponds to MDS 2.0 sections G, H, and P when specified for use by the State.

Identify if resident triggers RAPs for urinary incontinence, nutritional status, pressure ulcers (skin care).

Probes §483.25(k)(3)

- If appropriate, is the resident provided with self-care instructions?

- Does the staff member observe and respond to any signs of resident's discomfort about the ostomy or its care?

- Is skin surrounding the ostomy free of excoriation (abrasion, breakdown)?

- If excoriation is present, does the clinical record indicate an onset and a plan of care to treat the excoriation?

§483.25(k)(4) Tracheostomy Care

Procedures §483.25(k)(4) (Includes care of the tracheostomy site)

This corresponds to MDS 2.0 sections M and P when specified for use by the State.

Observations for tracheostomy care are most appropriate for residents with new or relatively new tracheostomies, and may not be appropriate for those with tracheostomies of long standing.

Probes §483.25(k)(4) (Includes care of the tracheostomy site)

- Is the skin around the tracheostomy clean and dry? Are the dressing and the ties clean and dry, with the cannula secure?

- Does the resident have signs of an obstructed airway or need for suctioning (e.g., secretions draining from mouth or tracheotomy; unable to cough to clear chest; audible crackles or wheezes; dyspneic, restless or agitated)?

- If appropriate for a specific resident, is there a suction machine and catheter immediately available?

- Is there an extra cannula of the correct size at the bedside or other place easily accessible if needed in an emergency?

- For sampled residents receiving one or more of these services within 7 days of the survey:

- Is suction machine available for immediate use, clean, working, and available to a source of emergency power?

- Is there an adequate supply of easily accessible suction catheters?

§483.25(k)(5) Standard: Tracheal Suctioning

Probes §483.25(k)(5)

This corresponds to MDS 2.0 section P when specified for use by the State.

§483.25(k)(6) Standard: Respiratory Care

Procedures §483.25(k)(6)

This corresponds to MDS 2.0 section P when specified for use by the State.

Includes use of respirators/ventilators, oxygen, intermittent positive pressure breathing (IPPB) or other inhalation therapy, pulmonary care, humidifiers, and other methods to treat conditions of the respiratory tract.

Identify if resident triggers RAPs for delirium and dehydration/fluid maintenance.

Probes §483.25(k)(6)

For sampled residents receiving one or more of these services within 7 days of the survey:

- If oxygen is in use, are precautions observed (e.g., proper storage and handling of oxygen cylinders secured)? Secondary "No Smoking" signs are not required in facilities that prohibit smoking and have signs at all major entrances that the facility does not allow smoking.

- If the survey team observes a treatment being administered, is the resident encouraged and instructed on how to assist in the treatment?

- Is the staff following the facility's protocol and/or written procedures for ventilators (e.g., functioning alarms); frequency of staff monitoring; monitoring of resident response (e.g., use of accessory muscles to breathe, cleanliness of mouth, skin irritation), and availability of manual resuscitators?

- If the resident is ventilator dependent, is routine machine maintenance and care done (e.g., water changes/tubing changes, safety checks on alarms, and machine functioning checks)?

§483.25(k)(7) Foot Care

Procedures §483.25(k)(7)

This corresponds with MDS 2.0 sections G and M when specified for use by the State.

Includes treatment of foot disorders by qualified persons, e.g., podiatrist, Doctor of Medicine, Doctor of Osteopathy), including, but not limited, to corns, neuroma, calluses, bunions, heel spurs, nail disorders, preventive care, to avoid foot problems in diabetic residents and residents with circulatory disorders.

Probes §483.25(k)(7)

For residents selected for a comprehensive review, or focused review, as appropriate:

- Do nails, corns, calluses, and other foot problems appear unattended; do these foot problems interfere with resident mobility?

- Are residents able to see a qualified person when they want?

- What preventive foot care do staff provide diabetic residents?

§483.25(k)(8) Prostheses

Probes §483.25(k)(8)

MDS 2.0 sections D, G, L, M, and P when specified for use by the State.

Includes artificial limbs, eyes, teeth.

For residents selected for a comprehensive review, or focused review, as appropriate:

- Is resident able to put on the prosthesis by himself/herself or with some assistance?

- Are residents wearing their prostheses?

- Does the prosthesis fit correctly?

- Is skin/mucous membrane in contact with the prosthesis free of abrasions, wounds, irritation?

F329

(Rev. 22, Issued: 12-15-06, Effective/Implementation: 12-18-06)

§483.25(l) Unnecessary Drugs

1. General. Each resident's drug regimen must be free from unnecessary drugs. An unnecessary drug is any drug when used:

(i) In excessive dose (including duplicate therapy); or
(ii) For excessive duration; or
(iii) Without adequate monitoring; or
(iv) Without adequate indications for its use; or
(v) In the presence of adverse consequences which indicate the dose should be reduced or discontinued; or
(vi) Any combinations of the reasons above.

2. Antipsychotic Drugs. Based on a comprehensive assessment of a resident, the facility must ensure that:

(i) Residents who have not used antipsychotic drugs are not given these drugs unless antipsychotic drug therapy is necessary to treat a specific condition as diagnosed and documented in the clinical record; and

(ii) Residents who use antipsychotic drugs receive gradual dose reductions, and behavioral interventions, unless clinically contraindicated, in an effort to discontinue these drugs.

INTENT: §483.25(l) Unnecessary drugs

The intent of this requirement is that each resident's entire drug/medication regimen be managed and monitored to achieve the following goals:

- The medication regimen helps promote or maintain the resident's highest practicable mental, physical, and psychosocial well-being, as identified by the resident and/or representative(s) in collaboration with the attending physician and facility staff;

- Each resident receives only those medications, in doses and for the duration clinically indicated to treat the resident's assessed condition(s);

- Non-pharmacological interventions (such as behavioral interventions) are considered and used when indicated, instead of, or in addition to, medication;

- Clinically significant adverse consequences are minimized; and

- The potential contribution of the medication regimen to an unanticipated decline or newly emerging or worsening symptom is recognized and evaluated, and the regimen is modified when appropriate.

NOTE: This guidance applies to all categories of medications including antipsychotic medications.

Although the regulatory language refers to "drugs," the guidance in this document generally will refer to "medications," except in those situations where the term "drug" has become part of an established pharmaceutical term (e.g., adverse drug event, and adverse drug reaction or consequence).

For purposes of this guidance, references to "the pharmacist" mean the facility's licensed pharmacist, whether employed directly by the facility or through arrangement.

The surveyor's review of medication use is not intended to constitute the practice of medicine. However, surveyors are expected to investigate the basis for decisions and interventions affecting residents.

DEFINITIONS

Definitions are provided to clarify terminology related to medications and to the evaluation and treatment of residents.

- "Adverse consequence" is an unpleasant symptom or event that is due to or associated with a medication, such as impairment or decline in an individual's mental or physical condition or functional or psychosocial status. It may include various types of adverse drug reactions and interactions (e.g., medication-medication, medication-food, and medication-disease).

  NOTE: Adverse drug reaction (ADR) is a form of adverse consequences. It may be either a secondary effect of a medication that is usually undesirable and different from the therapeutic effect of the medication or any response to a medication that is noxious and unintended and occurs in doses for prophylaxis, diagnosis, or treatment. The term "side effect" is often used interchangeably with ADR; however, side effects are but one of five ADR categories, the others being hypersensitivity, idiosyncratic response, toxic reactions, and adverse medication interactions. A side effect is an expected, well-known reaction that occurs with a predictable frequency and may or may not constitute an adverse consequence.

- "Anticholinergic side effect" is an effect of a medication that opposes or inhibits the activity of the parasympathetic (cholinergic) nervous system to the point of causing symptoms such as dry mouth, blurred vision, tachycardia, urinary retention, constipation, confusion, delirium, or hallucinations.

- "Behavioral interventions" are individualized non-pharmacological approaches (including direct care and activities) that are provided as part of a supportive physical and psychosocial environment, and are directed toward preventing, relieving, and/or accommodating a resident's distressed behavior.

- "Clinically significant" refers to effects, results, or consequences that materially affect or are likely to affect an individual's mental, physical, or psychosocial well-being either positively by preventing, stabilizing, or improving a condition or reducing a risk, or negatively by exacerbating, causing, or contributing to a symptom, illness, or decline in status.

- "Distressed behavior" is behavior that reflects individual discomfort or emotional strain. It may present as crying, apathetic or withdrawn behavior, or as verbal or physical actions such as: pacing, cursing, hitting, kicking, pushing, scratching, tearing things, or grabbing others.

- "Dose" is the total amount/strength/concentration of a medication given at one time or over a period of time. The individual dose is the amount/strength/concentration received at each administration. The amount received over a 24-hour period may be referred to as the daily dose.

  o "Excessive dose" means the total amount of any medication (including duplicate therapy) given at one time or over a period of time that is greater than the amount recommended by the manufacturer's label, package insert, current standards of practice for a resident's age and condition, or clinical studies or evidence-based review articles that are published in medical and/or pharmacy journals and that lacks evidence of:

    – A review for the continued necessity of the dose;

    – Attempts at, or consideration of the possibility of, tapering a medication; and

    – A documented clinical rationale for the benefit of, or necessity for, the dose or for the use of multiple medications from the same pharmacological class.

- "Duplicate therapy" refers to multiple medications of the same pharmacological class/category or any medication therapy that substantially duplicates a particular effect of another medication that the individual is taking.

- "Duration" is the total length of time the medication is being received.

  o "Excessive Duration" means the medication is administered beyond the manufacturer's recommended time frames or facility-established stop order policies, beyond the length of time advised by current standards of practice, clinical practice guidelines, clinical studies or evidence-based review articles, and/or without either evidence of additional therapeutic benefit for the resident or clinical evidence that would warrant the continued use of the medication.

- "Extrapyramidal symptoms (EPS)" are neurological side effects that can occur at any time from the first few days of treatment to years later. EPS includes various syndromes such as:

  o Akathisia, which refers to a distressing feeling of internal restlessness that may appear as constant motion, the inability to sit still, fidgeting, pacing, or rocking.

  o Medication-induced Parkinsonism, which refers to a syndrome of Parkinson-like symptoms including tremors, shuffling gait, slowness of movement, expressionless face, drooling, postural unsteadiness and rigidity of muscles in the limbs, neck and trunk.

  o Dystonia, which refers to an acute, painful, spastic contraction of muscle groups (commonly the neck, eyes and trunk) that often occurs soon after initiating treatment and is more common in younger individuals.

- "Gradual Dose Reduction (GDR)" is the stepwise tapering of a dose to determine if symptoms, conditions, or risks can be managed by a lower dose or if the dose or medication can be discontinued.

- "Indications for use" is the identified, documented clinical rationale for administering a medication that is based upon an assessment of the resident's condition and therapeutic goals and is consistent with manufacturer's recommendations and/or clinical practice guidelines, clinical standards of practice, medication references, clinical studies or evidence-based review articles that are published in medical and/or pharmacy journals.

- "Insomnia" is the inability to sleep characterized by difficulty falling asleep, difficulty staying asleep, early waking, or non-restorative sleep, which may result in impaired physical, social, or cognitive function.

- "Medication Interaction" is the impact of another substance (such as another medication, nutritional supplement including herbal products, food, or substances used in diagnostic studies) upon a medication. The interactions may alter absorption, distribution, metabolism, or elimination. These interactions may decrease the effectiveness of the medication or increase the potential for adverse consequences.

- "Medication Regimen Review" (MRR) is a thorough evaluation of the medication regimen by a pharmacist, with the goal of promoting positive outcomes and minimizing adverse consequences associated with medication. The review includes preventing, identifying, reporting, and resolving medication-related problems, medication errors, or other irregularities in collaboration with other members of the interdisciplinary team.[51]

- "Monitoring" is the ongoing collection and analysis of information (such as observations and diagnostic test results) and comparison to baseline data in order to:

  o Ascertain the individual's response to treatment and care, including progress or lack of progress toward a therapeutic goal;

  o Detect any complications or adverse consequences of the condition or of the treatments; and

  o Support decisions about modifying, discontinuing, or continuing any interventions.

- "Neuroleptic Malignant Syndrome" (NMS) is a syndrome related to the use of medications, mainly antipsychotics, that typically presents with a sudden onset of diffuse muscle rigidity, high fever, labile blood pressure, tremor, and notable cognitive dysfunction. It is potentially fatal if not treated immediately, including stopping the offending medications.

- "Non-pharmacological interventions" refers to approaches to care that do not involve medications, generally directed towards stabilizing or improving a resident's mental, physical or psychosocial well-being.

- "Psychopharmacological medication" is any medication used for managing behavior, stabilizing mood, or treating psychiatric disorders.

- "Serotonin Syndrome" is a potentially serious clinical condition resulting from overstimulation of serotonin receptors. It is commonly related to the use of multiple serotonin-stimulating medications (e.g., SSRIs, SNRIs, triptans, certain antibiotics). Symptoms may include restlessness, hallucinations, confusion, loss of coordination, fast heart beat, rapid changes in blood pressure, increased body temperature, overactive reflexes, nausea, vomiting and diarrhea.

- "Tardive dyskinesia" refers to abnormal, recurrent, involuntary movements that may be irreversible and typically present as lateral movements of the tongue or jaw, tongue thrusting, chewing, frequent blinking, brow arching, grimacing, and lip smacking, although the trunk or other parts of the body may also be affected.

OVERVIEW

Medications are an integral part of the care provided to residents of nursing facilities. They are administered to try to achieve various outcomes, such as curing an illness, diagnosing a disease or condition, arresting or slowing a disease process, reducing or eliminating symptoms, or preventing a disease or symptom.

A study of 33,301 nursing facility residents found that an average of 6.7 medications were ordered per resident, with 27 percent of residents taking nine or more medications.[52] Analysis of antipsychotic use by 693,000 Medicare nursing home residents revealed that 28.5 percent of the doses received were excessive and 32.2 percent lacked appropriate indications for use.[53]

Proper medication selection and prescribing (including dose, duration, and type of medication(s)) may help stabilize or improve a resident's outcome, quality of life and functional capacity. Any medication or combination of medications—or the use of a medication without adequate indications, in excessive dose, for an excessive duration, or without adequate monitoring—may increase the risk of a broad range of adverse consequences such as medication interactions, depression, confusion, immobility, falls, and related hip fractures.

Intrinsic factors including physiological changes accompanying the aging process, multiple comorbidities, and certain medical conditions may affect the absorption, distribution, metabolism or elimination of medications from the body and may also increase an individual's risk of adverse consequences.

While assuring that only those medications required to treat the resident's assessed condition are being used, reducing the need for and maximizing the effectiveness of medications are important considerations for all residents. Therefore, as part of all medication management (including antipsychotics), it is important for the interdisciplinary team to consider non-pharmacological approaches. Educating facility staff and providers in addition to implementing non-pharmacological approaches to resident conditions prior to, and/or in conjunction with, the use of medications may minimize the need for medications or reduce the dose and duration of those medications.[54]

Examples of non-pharmacological interventions may include:

- Increasing the amount of resident exercise, intake of liquids and dietary fiber in conjunction with an individualized bowel regimen to prevent or reduce constipation and the use of medications (e.g., laxatives and stool softeners);

- Identifying, addressing, and eliminating or reducing underlying causes of distressed behavior such as boredom and pain;

- Using sleep hygiene techniques and individualized sleep routines;

- Accommodating the resident's behavior and needs by supporting and encouraging activities reminiscent of lifelong work or activity patterns, such as providing early morning activity for a farmer used to awakening early;

- Individualizing toileting schedules to prevent incontinence and avoid the use of incontinence medications that may have significant adverse consequences (e.g., anticholinergic effects);

- Developing interventions that are specific to resident's interests, abilities, strengths and needs, such as simplifying or segmenting tasks for a resident who has trouble following complex directions;

- Using massage, hot/warm or cold compresses to address a resident's pain or discomfort; or

- Enhancing the taste and presentation of food, assisting the resident to eat, addressing food preferences, and increasing finger foods and snacks for an individual with dementia, to improve appetite and avoid the unnecessary use of medications intended to stimulate appetite.

The indications for initiating, withdrawing, or withholding medication(s), as well as the use of non-pharmacological approaches, are determined by assessing the resident's underlying condition, current signs and symptoms, and preferences and goals for treatment. This includes, where possible, the identification of the underlying cause(s), since a diagnosis alone may not warrant treatment with medication.

Orders from multiple prescribers can increase the resident's chances of receiving unnecessary medications. Many residents receive orders for medications from several practitioners, for example, attending and on-call physicians, consultants, and nurse practitioner(s). It is important that the facility clearly identify who is responsible for prescribing and identifying the indications for use of medication(s), for providing and administering the medication(s), and for monitoring the resident for the effects and potential adverse consequence of the medication regimen. This is also important when care is delivered or ordered by diverse sources such as consultants, providers, or suppliers (e.g., hospice or dialysis programs).

Staff and practitioner access to current medication references and pertinent clinical protocols helps to promote safe administration and monitoring of medications. One of the existing mechanisms to warn prescribers about risks associated with medications is the Food and Drug Administration (FDA) requirement that manufacturers include within the medication labeling warnings about adverse reactions and potential safety hazards identified both before and after approval of a medication, and what to do if they occur (Visit: www.fda.gov/medwatch/safety.htm). Manufacturers are required to update labels to warn about newly identified safety hazards—regardless of whether causation has been proven and whether the medication is prescribed for a disease or condition that is not included in the "Indications and Usage" section of the labeling (so-called "off-label" or unapproved use). The FDA may require manufacturers to place statements about serious problems in a prominently displayed box (so-called boxed or "black box" warnings), which indicates a need to closely evaluate and monitor the potential benefits and risks of that medication.

The facility's pharmacist is a valuable source of information about medications. Listings or descriptions of most significant risks, recommended doses, medication interactions, cautions, etc. can be found in widely available, standard references, and computer software and systems that provide up-to-date information. It is important to note that some of the medication information found in many of these references is not specific to older adults or institutionalized individuals.

Clinical standards of practice and clinical guidelines established by professional groups are useful to guide clinicians. Some of the recognized clinical resources available for understanding the overall treatment and management of medical problems, symptoms and medication consequences and precautions include the:

- American Geriatrics Society **www.americangeriatrics.org** and **www.geriatricsatyourfingertips.org**;

- American Medical Directors Association **www.amda.com**;

- American Psychiatric Association **www.psych.org**;

- American Society of Consultant Pharmacists **www.ASCP.com**;

- Agency for Healthcare Research and Quality (AHRQ) **www.ahrq.gov**;

- American Association for Geriatric Psychiatry **www.aagp.org**;

- Association for Practitioners in Infection Control and Epidemiology **www.apic.org**;

- CMS Sharing Innovations in Quality Web-site maintained at: **http://siq.air.org**;

- National Guideline Clearinghouse **www.guideline.gov**;

- Quality Improvement Organizations, Medicare Quality Improvement Community Initiatives **www.medqic.org**;

- U.S. Department of Health and Human Services, Food and Drug Administration Web site **www.fda.gov/medwatch/safety.htm**;

- U.S. Department of Health and Human Services, National Institute of Mental Health Web site, which includes publications and clinical research information **www.nimh.nih.gov**;

- Mace N, Rabins P. The 36-Hour Day: A Family Guide to Caring for Persons with Alzheimer Disease, Related Dementing Illnesses, and Memory Loss in Later Life; and

- "Bathing without a battle" **www.bathingwithoutabattle.unc.edu**.

NOTE: References to non-CMS sources or sites on the Internet included above or later in this document are provided as a service and do not constitute or imply endorsement of these organizations or their programs by CMS or the U.S. Department of Health and Human Services. CMS is not responsible for the content of pages found at these sites. URL addresses were current as of the date of this publication.

Although these guidelines generally emphasize the older adult resident, adverse consequences can occur in anyone at any age; therefore, these requirements apply to residents of all ages.

MEDICATION MANAGEMENT

Medication management is based in the care process and includes recognition or identification of the problem/need, assessment, diagnosis/cause identification, management/treatment, monitoring, and revising interventions, as warranted. The attending physician plays a key leadership role in medication management by developing, monitoring, and modifying the medication regimen in conjunction with residents and/or representative(s) and other professionals and direct care staff (the interdisciplinary team).

When selecting medications and non-pharmacological interventions, members of the interdisciplinary team participate in the care process to identify, assess, address, advocate for, monitor, and communicate the resident's needs and changes in condition.

This guidance is intended to help the surveyor determine whether the facility's medication management supports and promotes:

- Selection of medications(s) based on assessing relative benefits and risks to the individual resident;

- Evaluation of a resident's signs and symptoms, in order to identify the underlying cause(s), including adverse consequences of medications;

- Selection and use of medications in doses and for the duration appropriate to each resident's clinical conditions, age, and underlying causes of symptoms;

- The use of non-pharmacological interventions, when applicable, to minimize the need for medications, permit use of the lowest possible dose, or allow medications to be discontinued; and

- The monitoring of medications for efficacy and clinically significant adverse consequences.

The resident's clinical record documents and communicates to the entire team the basic elements of the care process. Information about aspects of the care process related to medications may be found in various locations within the record, such as: hospital discharge summaries and transfer notes, progress notes and interdisciplinary notes, history and physical examination, Resident Assessment Instrument (RAI), plan of care, laboratory reports, professional consults, medication orders, Medication Regimen Review (MRR) reports, and Medication Administration Records (MAR).

Resident Choice – A resident and/or representative(s) has the right to be informed about the resident's condition; treatment options, relative risks and benefits of treatment, required monitoring, expected outcomes of the treatment; and has the right to refuse care and treatment. If a resident refuses treatment, the facility staff and physician should inform the resident about the risks related to the refusal, and discuss appropriate alternatives such as offering the medication at another time or in another dosage form, or offer an alternative medication or non-pharmacological approach, if available.

Advance Directives – A resident may have written or verbal directions related to treatment choices (or a decision has been made by the resident's surrogate or representative) in accordance with state law. An advance directive is a means for the resident to communicate his or her wishes, which may include withdrawing or withholding medications. Whether or not a resident has an advanced directive, the facility is responsible for giving treatment, support, and other care that is consistent with the resident's condition and applicable care instructions.

NOTE: Choosing not to be resuscitated (reflected in a "Do Not Resuscitate" (DNR) order) indicates that the resident should not be resuscitated if respirations and/or cardiac function cease. A DNR order by itself does not indicate that the resident has declined other appropriate treatment and services.

Under these regulations, medication management includes consideration of:

I. Indications for use of medication (including initiation or continued use of antipsychotic medication);

II. Monitoring for efficacy and adverse consequences;

III. Dose (including duplicate therapy);

IV. Duration;

V. Tapering of a medication dose/gradual dose reduction for antipsychotic medications; and

VI. Prevention, identification, and response to adverse consequences.

I. Indications for Use of Medication (including Initiation or Continued Use of an Antipsychotic Medication)

An evaluation of the resident helps to identify his/her needs, comorbid conditions, and prognosis to determine factors (including medications and new or worsening medical conditions) that are affecting signs, symptoms, and test results. This evaluation process is important when making initial medication/intervention selections and when deciding whether to modify or discontinue a current medication intervention. Regarding "as needed" (PRN) medications, it is important to evaluate and document the indication(s), specific circumstance(s) for use, and the desired frequency of administration. As part of the evaluation, gathering and analyzing information helps define clinical indications and provide baseline data for subsequent monitoring. The evaluation also clarifies:

- Whether other causes for the symptoms (including behavioral distress that could mimic a psychiatric disorder) have been ruled out;

- Whether the signs, symptoms, or related causes are persistent or clinically significant enough (e.g., causing functional decline) to warrant the initiation or continuation of medication therapy;

- Whether non-pharmacological interventions are considered;

- Whether a particular medication is clinically indicated to manage the symptom or condition; and

- Whether the intended or actual benefit is sufficient to justify the potential risk(s) or adverse consequences associated with the selected medication, dose, and duration.

The content and extent of the evaluation may vary with the situation and may employ various assessment instruments and diagnostic tools. Examples of information to be considered and evaluated may include, but are not limited to, the following:

- An appropriately detailed evaluation of mental, physical, psychosocial, and functional status, including comorbid conditions and pertinent psychiatric symptoms and diagnoses and a description of resident complaints, symptoms, and signs (including the onset, scope, frequency, intensity, precipitating factors, and other important features);

- Each resident's goals and preferences;

- Allergies to medications and foods and potential for medication interactions;

- A history of prior and current medications and non-pharmacological interventions (including therapeutic effectiveness and any adverse consequences);

- Recognition of the need for end-of-life or palliative care; and

- The refusal of care and treatment, including the basis for declining it, and the identification of pertinent alternatives.

NOTE: The Resident Assessment Protocols (RAPs), an integral part of the comprehensive resident assessment, help identify some possible categories of causes of various symptoms including: behavioral symptoms of distress, delirium, and changes in functional status. Refer to 42 CFR 483.20 and the Minimum Data Set (MDS) and RAPs.

Circumstances that warrant evaluation of the resident and medication(s) may include:

- Admission or re-admission;

- A clinically significant change in condition/status;

- A new, persistent, or recurrent clinically significant symptom or problem;

- A worsening of an existing problem or condition;

- An unexplained decline in function or cognition;

- A new medication order or renewal of orders; and

- An irregularity identified in the pharmacist's monthly medication regimen review.

Specific considerations related to these circumstances may include the following:

- **Admission (or Readmission)** – Some residents may be admitted on medications for an undocumented chronic condition or without a clear indication as to why a medication was begun or should be continued. It is expected that the attending physician, pharmacist, and staff subsequently determine if continuing the medication is justified by evaluating the resident's clinical condition, risks, existing medication regimen, and related factors. If the indications for continuing the medication are unclear, or if the resident's symptoms could represent a clinically significant adverse consequence, additional consideration of the rationale for the medication(s) is warranted.

- **Multiple prescribers** – Regardless of who the prescribers are, the continuation of a medication needs to be evaluated to determine if the medication is still warranted in the context of the resident's other medications and comorbidities. Medications prescribed by a specialist or begun in another care setting, such as the hospital, need to have a clinically pertinent documented rationale.

- **New medication order as an emergency measure** – When a resident is experiencing an acute medical problem or psychiatric emergency (e.g., the resident's behavior poses an immediate risk to the resident or others), medications may be required. In these situations, it is important to identify and address the underlying causes of the problem or symptoms. Once the acute phase has stabilized, the staff and prescriber consider whether medications are still relevant. Subsequently, the medication is reduced or discontinued as soon as possible or the clinical rationale for continuing the medication is documented.

  When psychopharmacological medications are used as an emergency measure, adjunctive approaches, such as behavioral interventions and techniques should be considered and implemented as appropriate. Longer term management options should be discussed with the resident and/or representative(s).

- **Psychiatric disorders or distressed behavior** – As with all symptoms, it is important to seek the underlying cause of distressed behavior, either before or while treating the symptom. Examples of potential causes include:

  o Delirium;

  o Pain;

  o Chronic psychiatric illness such as schizophrenia or schizoaffective disorder;

  o Acute psychotic illness such as brief reactive psychosis;

  o Substance intoxication or withdrawal;

  o Environmental stressors (e.g., excessive heat, noise, overcrowding);

  o Psychological stressors (e.g., disruption of the resident's customary daily routine, grief over nursing home admission or health status, abuse, taunting, intimidation);

  o Neurological illnesses such as Huntington's disease or Tourette's syndrome; or

  o Medical illnesses such as Alzheimer's disease, Lewy body disease, vascular dementia, or frontotemporal dementia.

See Table I below in these guidelines for key issues related to indications for use of antipsychotic agents, monitoring, and adverse consequences.

II. Monitoring for Efficacy and Adverse Consequences

The information gathered during the initial and ongoing evaluations is essential to:

- Incorporate into a comprehensive care plan that reflects appropriate medication related goals and parameters for monitoring the resident's condition, including the likely medication effects and potential for adverse consequences. Examples of this information may include the FDA boxed warnings or adverse consequences that may be rare, but have sudden onset or that may be irreversible. If the facility has established protocols for monitoring specific medications and the protocols are accessible for staff use, the care plan may refer staff to these protocols;

- Optimize the therapeutic benefit of medication therapy and minimize or prevent potential adverse consequences;

- Establish parameters for evaluating the ongoing need for the medication; and

- Verify or differentiate the underlying diagnoses or other underlying causes of signs and symptoms.

The key objectives for monitoring the use of medications are to track progress towards the therapeutic goal(s) and to detect the emergence or presence of any adverse consequences. Effective monitoring relies upon understanding the indications and goals for using the medication, identifying relevant baseline information, identifying the criteria for evaluating the benefit(s) of the medication, and recognizing and evaluating adverse consequences. Monitoring parameters are based on the resident's condition, the pharmacologic properties of the medication being used and its associated risks, individualized therapeutic goals, and the potential for clinically significant adverse consequences.

Adverse consequences related to medications are common enough to warrant serious attention and close monitoring. For example, a study reported that 338 (42%) of 815 adverse drug events were judged preventable, and that common omissions included inadequate monitoring and either lack of response or a delayed response to signs, symptoms, or laboratory evidence of medication toxicity.[55]

Sources of information to facilitate defining the monitoring criteria or parameters may include cautions, warnings, and identified adverse consequences from:

- Manufacturers' package inserts and black-box warnings;

- Facility policies and procedures;

- Pharmacists;

- Clinical practice guidelines or clinical standards of practice;

- Medication references; and

- Clinical studies or evidence-based review articles that are published in medical and/or pharmacy journals.

Monitoring of the resident's response to any medication(s) is essential to evaluate the ongoing benefits as well as risks of various medications. It is important, for example, to monitor the effectiveness of medications used to address behavioral symptoms (e.g., behavioral monitoring) or to treat hypertension (e.g., periodic pulse and blood pressure).

Monitoring for adverse consequences involves ongoing vigilance and may periodically involve objective evaluation (e.g., assessing vital signs may be indicated if a medication is known to affect blood pressure, pulse rate and rhythm, or temperature). Using quantitative and qualitative monitoring parameters facilitates consistent and objective collection of information by the facility.

Examples of tools that may be used by facility staff, practitioners, or consultants to determine baseline status as well as to monitor for effectiveness and potential adverse consequences may include, but are not limited to the following:

Common Conditions/ Symptoms	Examples of Tools	Potential Applications	Source/Reference
Diabetes	Blood glucose, Hemoglobin A1C	Diagnose diabetes and determine diabetic control	www.endocrineweb.com/diabetes/diagnosis.html www.diabetes.org/home.jsp www.diabetes.niddk.nih.gov/ www.diabetestoolbox.com/HbA1c.asp
Alzheimer's Disease / Dementia	Mini Mental Status Exam (MMSE)	Determine degree of cognitive impairment	www.emedicine.com/med/topic3358.htm www.fpnotebook.com/NEU75.htm
Functional Decline	Instrumental Activities of Daily Living (IADL)	Assess functional capabilities	www.cdc.gov/nchs/datawh/nchsdefs/iadl.htm www.fpnotebook.com/GER3.htm
	Resident Assessment Instrument (RAI)	Assess aspects of nursing home resident's behavior and function	www.apadiv20.phhp.ufl.edu/fries.htm www.careplans.com/pages/library/RAI_user_guide.pdf
	Functional Alzheimer's Screening Test (FAST)	Assess level of function in individuals with dementia	http://geriatrics.uthscsa.edu/educational/med_students/fastscale_admin.htm
Delirium	Confusion Assessment Method (CAM)	Screen for cognitive impairment and delirium	www.hartfordign.org/publications/trythis/issue13.pdf http://elderlife.med.yale.edu/pdf/The%20Confusion%20Assessment%20Method.pdf
Bipolar Disorder	Mania Rating Scale	Assess severity of mania	www.psychiatryinpractice.com/AssessmentTools/default.aspx?11=3&12=3&13=&13= www.brainexplorer.org/factsheets/Psychiatry%20Rating%20Scales.pdf
Pain	List of pain scales	Assess pain characteristics (e.g., intensity, impact, timing)	www.chcr.brown.edu/pcoc/Physical.htm

Common Conditions/ Symptoms	Examples of Tools	Potential Applications	Source/Reference
Depression	Geriatric Depression Scale	Screen or monitor individuals at risk for depression	www.assessmentpsychology.com/geriatricscales.htm www.hartfordign.org/publications/trythis/issue04.pdf www.merck.com/mrkshared/mmg/tables/33t4.jsp
	Cornell Depression in Dementia Scale	Screen or monitor for depression in individuals with cognitive impairment	www.emoryhealthcare.org/departments/fuqua/CornellScale.pdf
Abnormal Movements	Abnormal Involuntary Movement Scales (AIMS)	Assess presence and severity of involuntary movements that may be due to disease or medications	www.carepaths.com/pages/Instruments_AIMS.asp www.mhsip.org/library/pdfFiles/abnormalinvoluntarymovementscale.pdf
Behavioral Symptoms associated with Dementia	Neuro-psychiatric Inventory-Nursing Home Version (NPI-NH)	Screen or monitor for behavior associated with dementia (e.g., hallucinations, agitation or anxiety)	www.alzheimer-insights.com/insights/vol2no3/vol2no3.htm
	Behavioral Pathology in Alzheimer's Disease Rating Scale (Behave AD)	Provide a global rating of non-cognitive symptoms.	www.alzforum.org/dis/dia/tes/neuropsychological.asp
	Cohen-Mansfield Agitation Inventory (CMAI)	Assess/rate distressed behavior in older individuals	www.researchinstituteonaging.org/assessment.html www.geriatrictimes.com/g010533.html

Monitoring involves several steps, including:

- **Identifying the essential information and how it will be obtained and reported.** It is important to consider who is responsible for obtaining the information, which information should be collected, and how the information will be documented. The information that is collected depends on therapeutic goals, detection of potential or actual adverse consequences, and consideration of risk factors, such as:

  o   Medication-medication, medication-food interactions;

  o   Clinical condition (for example renal disease);

  o   Properties of the medication;

  o   Black-box warnings; and

  o   History of adverse consequences related to a similar medication.

- **Determining the frequency of monitoring**. The frequency and duration of monitoring needed to identify therapeutic effectiveness and adverse consequences will depend on factors such as clinical standards of practice, facility policies and procedures, manufacturer's specifications, and the resident's clinical condition. Monitoring involves three aspects:

  o   Periodic planned evaluation of progress toward the therapeutic goals;

  o   Continued vigilance for adverse consequences; and

  o   Evaluation of identified adverse consequences.

  For example, when monitoring all psychopharmacological medications and sedative/hypnotics, the facility should review the continued need for them, at least quarterly (i.e., a 3 month period), and document the rationale for continuing the medication, including evidence that the following had been evaluated:

  - The resident's target symptoms and the effect of the medication on the severity, frequency, and other characteristics of the symptoms;

  - Any changes in the resident's function during the previous quarter (e.g., as identified in the Minimum Data Set); and

  - Whether the resident experienced any medication-related adverse consequences during the previous quarter.

  An important aspect of the review would include whether the pharmacological management of the resident's medical and/or psychiatric disorder is consistent with recommendations from relevant clinical practice guidelines, current standards of practice, and/or manufacturer's specifications.

- **Defining the methods for communicating, analyzing, and acting upon relevant information.** The monitoring process needs to identify who is to communicate with the prescriber, what information is to be conveyed, and when to ask the prescriber to evaluate and consider modifying the medication regimen.

  It is important to consider whether a resident's medications are promoting or maintaining a resident's highest practicable level of function. If the therapeutic goals are not being met or the resident is experiencing adverse consequences, it is essential for the prescriber in collaboration with facility staff and pharmacist to consider whether current medications and doses continue to be appropriate or should be reduced, changed, or discontinued.

- **Re-evaluating and updating monitoring approaches.** Modification of monitoring may be necessary when the resident experiences changes, such as:

  o   Acute onset of signs or symptoms or worsening of chronic disease;

o Decline in function or cognition;

o Addition or discontinuation of medications and/or non-pharmacological interventions;

o Addition or discontinuation of care and services such as enteral feedings; and

o Significant changes in diet that may affect medication absorption or effectiveness or increase adverse consequences.

Additional examples of circumstances that may indicate a need to modify the monitoring include: changes in manufacturer's specifications, FDA warnings, pertinent clinical practice guidelines, or other literature about how and what to monitor.

III. Dose (Including Duplicate Therapy)

A prescriber orders medication(s) based on a variety of factors including the resident's diagnoses, signs and symptoms, current condition, age, coexisting medication regimen, review of lab and other test results, input from the interdisciplinary team about the resident, the type of medication(s), and therapeutic goals being considered or used.

Factors influencing the appropriateness of any dose include the resident's clinical response, possible adverse consequences, and other resident and medication-related variables. Often, lab test results such as serum medication concentrations are only a rough guide to dosing. Significant adverse consequences can occur even when the concentration is within the therapeutic range. Serum concentrations alone may not necessarily indicate a need for dose adjustments, but may warrant further evaluation of a dose or the medication regimen.

The route of administration influences a medication's absorption and ultimately the dose received. Examples of factors that can affect the absorption of medications delivered by transdermal patches include skin temperature and moisture, and the integrity of the patch. Similarly, the flow rate of intravenous solutions affects the amount received at a given time.

Duplicate therapy is generally not indicated, unless current clinical standards of practice and documented clinical rationale confirm the benefits of multiple medications from the same class or with similar therapeutic effects. Some examples of potentially problematic duplicate therapy include:

- Use of more than one product containing the same medication can lead to excessive doses of a medication, such as concomitant use of acetaminophen/hydrocodone and acetaminophen, which may increase the risk of acetaminophen toxicity;

- Use of multiple laxatives to improve or maintain bowel movements, which may lead to abdominal pain or diarrhea;

- Concomitant use of multiple benzodiazepines such as lorazepam for anxiety and temazepam for sleep, which may increase fall risk; or

- Use of medications from different therapeutic categories that have similar effects or properties, such as multiple medications with anticholinergic effects (e.g., oxybutynin and diphenhydramine), which may increase the risk of delirium or excessive sedation.

Documentation is necessary to clarify the rationale for and benefits of duplicate therapy and the approach to monitoring for benefits and adverse consequences. This documentation may be found in various areas of the resident's clinical record.

IV. Duration

Many conditions require treatment for extended periods, while others may resolve and no longer require medication therapy. For example:

- Acute conditions such as cough and cold symptoms, upper respiratory condition, nausea and/or vomiting, acute pain, psychiatric or behavioral symptoms;

- Proton pump inhibitors (PPIs)/H2 blockers used for prophylaxis during the acute phase of a medical illness should be tapered and possibly discontinued after the acute phase of the illness has resolved, unless there is a valid clinical indication for prolonged use.

Periodic re-evaluation of the medication regimen is necessary to determine whether prolonged or indefinite use of a medication is indicated. The clinical rationale for continued use of a medication(s) may have been demonstrated in the clinical record, or the staff and prescriber may present pertinent clinical reasons for the duration of use. Common considerations for appropriate duration may include:

- A medication initiated as a result of a time-limited condition (for example, delirium, pain, infection, nausea and vomiting, cold and cough symptoms, or itching) is then discontinued when the condition has resolved, or there is documentation indicating why continued use is still relevant. Failure to review whether the underlying cause has resolved may lead to excessive duration.

- A medication is discontinued when indicated by facility stop order policy or by the prescriber's order, unless there is documentation of the clinical justification for its extended use. A medication administered beyond the stop date established in the prescriber's order or by facility policy, without evidence of clinical justification for continued use of the medication, may be considered excessive duration.

V. Tapering of a Medication Dose/Gradual Dose Reduction (GDR)

The requirements underlying this guidance emphasize the importance of seeking an appropriate dose and duration for each medication and minimizing the risk of adverse consequences. The purpose of tapering a medication is to find an optimal dose or to determine whether continued use of the medication is benefiting the resident. Tapering may be indicated when the resident's clinical condition has improved or stabilized, the underlying causes of the original target symptoms have resolved, and/or non-pharmacological interventions, including behavioral interventions, have been effective in reducing the symptoms.

There are various opportunities during the care process to evaluate the effects of medications on a resident's function and behavior, and to consider whether the medications should be continued, reduced, discontinued, or otherwise modified. Examples of these opportunities include:

- During the monthly medication regimen review, the pharmacist evaluates resident-related information for dose, duration, continued need, and the emergence of adverse consequences for all medications;

- When evaluating the resident's progress, the practitioner reviews the total plan of care, orders, the resident's response to medication(s), and determines whether to continue, modify, or stop a medication; and

- During the quarterly MDS review, the facility evaluates mood, function, behavior, and other domains that may be affected by medications.

Sometimes, the decision about whether to continue a medication is clear; for example, someone with a history of multiple episodes of depression or recurrent seizures may need an antidepressant or anticonvulsant medication indefinitely. Often, however, the only way to know whether a medication is needed indefinitely and whether the dose remains appropriate is to try reducing the dose and to monitor the resident closely for improvement, stabilization, or decline.

The time frames and duration of attempts to taper any medication depend on factors including the coexisting medication regimen, the underlying causes of symptoms, individual risk factors, and pharmacologic characteristics of the medications. Some medications (e.g., antidepressants, sedative/hypnotics, opioids) require more gradual tapering so as to minimize or prevent withdrawal symptoms or other adverse consequences.

NOTE: If the resident's condition has not responded to treatment or has declined despite treatment, it is important to evaluate both the medication and the dose to determine whether the medication should be discontinued or the dosing should be altered, whether or not the facility has implemented GDR as required, or tapering

Considerations Specific to Antipsychotics. The regulation addressing the use of antipsychotic medications identifies the process of tapering as a "gradual dose reduction (GDR)" and requires a GDR, unless clinically contraindicated.

Within the first year in which a resident is admitted on an antipsychotic medication or after the facility has initiated an antipsychotic medication, the facility must attempt a GDR in two separate quarters (with at least one month between the attempts), unless clinically contraindicated. After the first year, a GDR must be attempted annually, unless clinically contraindicated.

For any individual who is receiving an antipsychotic medication to treat behavioral symptoms related to dementia, the GDR may be considered clinically contraindicated if:

- The resident's target symptoms returned or worsened after the most recent attempt at a GDR within the facility; and

- The physician has documented the clinical rationale for why any additional attempted dose reduction at that time would be likely to impair the resident's function or increase distressed behavior.

For any individual who is receiving an antipsychotic medication to treat a psychiatric disorder other than behavioral symptoms related to dementia (for example, schizophrenia, bipolar mania, or depression with psychotic features), the GDR may be considered contraindicated, if:

- The continued use is in accordance with relevant current standards of practice and the physician has documented the clinical rationale for why any attempted dose reduction would be likely to impair the resident's function or cause psychiatric instability by exacerbating an underlying psychiatric disorder; or

- The resident's target symptoms returned or worsened after the most recent attempt at a GDR within the facility and the physician has documented the clinical rationale for why any additional attempted dose reduction at that time would be likely to impair the resident's function or cause psychiatric instability by exacerbating an underlying medical or psychiatric disorder.

Attempted Tapering Relative to Continued Indication or Optimal Dose

As noted, attempted tapering is one way to determine whether a specific medication is still indicated, and whether target symptoms and risks can be managed with a lesser dose of a medication. As noted, many medications in various categories can be tapered safely. The following examples of tapering relate to two common categories of concern: sedatives/hypnotics and psychopharmacologic medications (other than antipsychotic and sedatives/hypnotics medications).

Tapering Considerations Specific to Sedatives/Hypnotics.

For as long as a resident remains on a sedative/hypnotic that is used routinely and beyond the manufacturer's recommendations for duration of use, the facility should attempt to taper the medication quarterly unless clinically contraindicated. Clinically contraindicated means:

- The continued use is in accordance with relevant current standards of practice and the physician has documented the clinical rationale for why any attempted dose reduction would be likely to impair the resident's function or cause psychiatric instability by exacerbating an underlying medical or psychiatric disorder; or

- The resident's target symptoms returned or worsened after the most recent attempt at tapering the dose within the facility and the physician has documented the clinical rationale for why any additional attempted dose reduction at that time would be likely to impair the resident's function or cause psychiatric instability by exacerbating an underlying medical or psychiatric disorder.

Considerations Specific to Psychopharmacological Medications (Other Than Antipsychotics and Sedative/Hypnotics).

During the first year in which a resident is admitted on a psychopharmacological medication (other than an antipsychotic or a sedative/hypnotic), or after the facility has initiated such medication, the facility should attempt to taper the medication during at least two separate quarters (with at least one month between the attempts), unless clinically contraindicated. After the first year, a tapering should be attempted annually, unless clinically contraindicated. The tapering may be considered clinically contraindicated, if:

- The continued use is in accordance with relevant current standards of practice and the physician has documented the clinical rationale for why any attempted dose reduction would be likely to impair the resident's function or cause psychiatric instability by exacerbating an underlying medical or psychiatric disorder; or

- The resident's target symptoms returned or worsened after the most recent attempt at tapering the dose within the facility and the physician has documented the clinical rationale for why any additional attempted dose reduction at that time would be likely to impair the resident's function or cause psychiatric instability by exacerbating an underlying medical or psychiatric disorder.

VI. Adverse Consequences

Any medication or combination of medications (for example interactions between multiple medications with sedative or anticholinergic effects) can cause adverse consequences. Some adverse consequences occur quickly or abruptly, while others are more insidious and develop over time. Adverse consequences may become evident at any time after the medication is initiated, e.g., when there is a change in dose or after another medication has been added.

When reviewing medications used for a resident, it is important to be aware of the medication's recognized safety profile, tolerability, dosing, and potential medication interactions. Although a resident may have an unanticipated reaction to a medication that is not always preventable, many ADRs can be anticipated, minimized, or prevented. Some adverse consequences may be avoided by:

- Following relevant clinical guidelines and manufacturer's specifications for use, dose, administration, duration, and monitoring of the medication;

- Defining appropriate indications for use; and

- Determining that the resident:

  o Has no known allergies to the medication;

  o Is not taking other medications, nutritional supplements including herbal products, or foods that would be incompatible with the prescribed medication; and

  o Has no condition, history, or sensitivities that would preclude use of that medication.

Published studies have sought to identify the frequency, severity, and preventability of adverse consequences. Neuropsychiatric, hemorrhagic, gastrointestinal, renal/electrolyte abnormalities and metabolic/endocrine complications were the most common overall and preventable adverse consequences identified in two nursing home studies. Specifically, a study of 18 community-based nursing homes reported that approximately 50 percent (276/546) of all the adverse consequences—and 72 percent of those characterized as fatal, life-threatening, or serious—were considered preventable.[56] A second study of two academic-based nursing homes reported that inadequate monitoring, failure to act on the monitoring, and errors in ordering, including wrong dose, wrong medication, and medication-medication interactions were the most frequent causes for the preventable adverse consequences.[57]

The risk for adverse consequences increases with both the number of medications being taken regularly and with medications from specific pharmacological classes, such as anticoagulants, diuretics, antipsychotics, anti-infectives, and anticonvulsants.[58,59] See Tables I and II for classes of medications that are associated with frequent or severe adverse consequences. Adverse consequences can range from minimal harm to functional decline, hospitalization, permanent injury, and death.

Delirium (i.e., acute confusional state) is a common medication-related adverse consequence. In many facilities, a majority of the residents have dementia. Individuals who have dementia may be more sensitive to medication effects and may be at greater risk for delirium.[60] Delirium may result from treatable underlying causes including medical conditions and the existing medication regimen. The presence of delirium is associated with higher morbidity and mortality. Some of the classic signs of delirium may be difficult to recognize and may be mistaken for the natural progression of dementia, particularly in the late stages of dementia. Careful observation of the resident (including mental status and level of consciousness), review of the potential causes (e.g., medications, fluid and electrolyte imbalance, infections) of the mental changes and distressed behavior, and appropriate and timely management of delirium are essential.

[**Editor's Note:** See page 390 for endnotes pertaining to this section.]

TABLE I

MEDICATION ISSUES OF PARTICULAR RELEVANCE

This table lists alphabetically, examples of some categories of medications that have the potential to cause clinically significant adverse consequences, that may have limited indications for use, require specific monitoring, and which warrant careful consideration of relative risks and benefit. Inclusion of a medication in this table does not imply that it is contraindicated for every resident. Medications are identified by generic rather than trade names.

NOTE: This table is based on review of a variety of pharmaceutical references. It does not include all categories of medications or all medications within a category, and does not address all issues or considerations related to medication use, such as dosages. Medications other than those listed in this table may present significant issues related to indications, dosage, duration, monitoring, or potential for clinically significant adverse consequences.

Since medication issues continue to evolve and new medications are being approved regularly, it is important to refer to a current authoritative source for detailed medication information such as indications and precautions, dosage, monitoring, or adverse consequences.

The listed doses for psychopharmacological medications are applicable to older individuals. The facility is encouraged to initiate therapy with lower doses and, when necessary, only gradually increase doses. The facility may exceed these doses if it provides evidence to show why higher doses were necessary to maintain or improve the resident's function and quality of life.

Medication	Issues and Concerns
Analgesics	
acetaminophen	**Dosage/Adverse Consequences** • Daily doses greater than 4 grams/day from all sources (alone or as part of combination products) may increase risk of liver toxicity. **Monitoring** • For doses greater than the maximum recommended daily dose, documented assessment should reflect periodic monitoring of liver function and indicate that benefits outweigh risks.
Non-Steroidal Anti-Inflammatory Drugs (NSAIDs) Non-selective NSAIDs, e.g., • aspirin • diclofenac • diflunisal • ibuprofen • indomethacin • ketorolac • meclofenamate • naproxen • piroxicam • salicylates • tolmetin	**Indications** • NSAID, including COX-2 inhibitors, should be reserved for symptoms and/or inflammatory conditions for which lower risk analgesics (e.g., acetaminophen) have either failed, or are not clinically indicated. **Exception:** Use of low dose aspirin (81–325 mg/day) as prophylactic treatment for cardiovascular events such as myocardial infarct or stroke may be appropriate. **Interactions** • Aspirin may increase the adverse effects of COX-2 inhibitors on the gastrointestinal (GI) tract. • Some NSAIDS (e.g., ibuprofen) may reduce the cardioprotective effect of aspirin.

Medication	Issues and Concerns
Cyclooxygenase-II (COX-2) inhibitors, e.g., • celecoxib	**Monitoring** • Monitor closely for bleeding when ASA > 325 mg/day is being used with another NSAID or when NSAIDS are used with other platelet inhibitors or anticoagulants (See See 42 CFR 483.60(c) F428 for Table of Common Medication-Medication Interactions in Long Term Care). **Adverse Consequences** • May cause gastrointestinal (GI) bleeding in anyone with a prior history of, or with increased risk for, GI bleeding. Compared to nonselective NSAIDs, COX-2 inhibitors may reduce—but do not eliminate—risk of gastrointestinal bleeding. • May cause bleeding in anyone who is receiving warfarin, heparin, other anticoagulants, or platelets inhibitors (e.g., ticlopidine, clopidogrel, and dipyridamole). • Any NSAID may cause or worsen renal failure, increase blood pressure, or exacerbate heart failure. • Prolonged use of indomethacin, piroxicam, tolmetin, and meclofenamate should be avoided because of central nervous system side effects, e.g., headache, dizziness, somnolence, confusion.

Opioid analgesics
 	
Short-acting, e.g.,
    • codeine
    • fentanyl
    • hydrocodone
    • hydromorphone
    • meperidine
    • morphine
    • oxycodone
 	
Long-acting, e.g.,
    • fentanyl, transdermal
    • methadone
    • morphine sustained release
    • oxycodone, sustained release
	Indications
	
	• The initiation of longer-acting opioid analgesics is not recommended unless shorter-acting opioids have been tried unsuccessfully, or titration of shorter-acting doses has established a clear daily dose of opioid analgesic that can be provided by using a long-acting form.
	
	• Meperidine is not an effective oral analgesic in doses commonly used in older individuals.
	
	Adverse Consequences
	
	• May cause constipation, nausea, vomiting, sedation, lethargy, weakness, confusion, dysphoria, physical and psychological dependency, hallucinations and unintended respiratory depression, especially in individuals with compromised pulmonary function. These can lead to other adverse consequences such as falls.
	
	• Meperidine use (oral or injectable) may cause confusion, respiratory depression even with therapeutic analgesic doses.
	
	• Active metabolite of meperidine (normerperidine) accumulates with repeated use and has been associated with seizures.

pentazocine	**Indications** • Limited effectiveness because it is a partial opiate agonist-antagonist; is not recommended for use in older individuals.

Medication	Issues and Concerns
	Adverse Consequences • This opioid analgesic causes central nervous system side effects (including confusion and hallucinations) more commonly than other opioid analgesics. • May cause dizziness, lightheadedness, euphoria, sedation, hypotension, tachycardia, syncope.
propoxyphene and combination products with aspirin or acetaminophen	**Indications** • Offers few analgesic advantages over acetaminophen, yet has the adverse effects, including addiction risk, of other opioid medications; is not recommended for use in older individuals. **Adverse Consequences** • May cause hypotension and central nervous system effects (e.g., confusion, drowsiness, dizziness) that can lead to other adverse consequences such as falls.
Antibiotics	
All antibiotics	**Indications** • Use of antibiotics should be limited to confirmed or suspected bacterial infection. **Adverse Consequences** • Any antibiotic may cause diarrhea, nausea, vomiting, anorexia, and hypersensitivity/allergic reactions. • Antibiotics are non-selective and may result in the eradication of beneficial microorganisms and the emergence of undesired ones, causing secondary infections such as oral thrush, colitis, and vaginitis.
Parenteral vancomycin and aminoglycosides, e.g., • amikacin • gentamycin/gentamicin • tobramycin	**Monitoring** • Use must be accompanied by monitoring of renal function tests (which should be compared with the baseline) and by serum medication concentrations. • Serious adverse consequences may occur insidiously if adequate monitoring does not occur. **Exception:** Single dose administration prophylaxis. **Adverse Consequences** • May cause or worsen hearing loss and renal failure.

Medication	Issues and Concerns
nitrofurantoin	**Indications** • It is not the anti-infective/antibiotic of choice for treatment of acute urinary tract infection or prophylaxis in individuals with impaired renal function (CrCl <60 ml/min) because of ineffectiveness and the high risk of serious adverse consequences. **Adverse Consequences** • May cause pulmonary fibrosis (e.g., symptoms including dyspnea, cough) and peripheral neuropathy.
Fluoroquinolones, e.g., • ciprofloxacin • levofloxacin • moxifloxacin • ofloxacin	**Indications** • Use should be avoided in individuals with prolonged QTc intervals or who are receiving antiarrhythmic agents in class Ia (e.g., procainamide), class Ic (e.g., flecainide) or class III (e.g., amiodarone). **Adverse Consequences** • May cause prolonged QTc interval. • May increase risk of hypo- or hyperglycemia in individuals age 65 or older, and in individuals with diabetes mellitus, renal insufficiency (CrCl < 60 ml/min), or those receiving other glucose-altering medications. • May increase risk of acute tendonitis.
Anticoagulants	
warfarin	**Monitoring** • Use must be monitored by Prothrombin Time (PT)/International Normalization Ratio (INR), with frequency determined by clinical circumstances, duration of use, and stability of monitoring results. **Adverse Consequences** • Multiple medication interactions exist (See 42 CFR 483.60(c) F428 for Table of Common Medication-Medication Interactions in Long Term Care), which may: o Significantly increase PT/INR results to levels associated with life-threatening bleeding, or o Decrease PT/INR results to ineffective levels, or o Increase or decrease the serum concentration of the interacting medication.
Anticonvulsants	
All anticonvulsants, e.g., • carbamazepine • gabapentin • lamotrigine	**Indications** • In addition to seizures, may also be used to treat other disorders, such as bipolar disorder, schizoaffective disorder, chronic neuropathic pain, and for prophylaxis of migraine headaches.

Medication	Issues and Concerns
<ul><li>levetiracetam</li><li>oxcarbazepine</li><li>phenobarbital</li><li>phenytoin</li><li>primidone</li><li>valproic acid</li></ul>	• Need for indefinite continuation should be based on confirmation of the condition (for example, distinguish epilepsy from isolated seizure due to medical cause or distinguish migraine from other causes of headaches) and its potential causes (medications, electrolyte imbalance, hypocalcemia, etc.). **Duration** • If used to manage behavior, stabilize mood, or treat a psychiatric disorder, refer to Section V – Tapering of a Medication Dose/Gradual Dose Reduction (GDR) in the guidance. **Monitoring** • Serum medication concentration monitoring is not required or available for all anticonvulsants. Only the following anticonvulsants should be monitored with periodic serum concentrations: phenytoin, phenobarbital, primidone, divalproex sodium (as valproic acid), and carbamazepine. • Serum medication concentrations may help identify toxicity, but significant signs and symptoms of toxicity can occur even at normal or low serum concentrations. • When anticonvulsants are used for conditions other than seizure disorders (e.g., as mood stabilizers), the same concerns exist regarding the need for monitoring for effectiveness and side effects; but evaluation of symptoms—not serum concentrations—should be used to adjust doses. High or toxic serum concentrations should, however, be evaluated and considered for dosage adjustments. • Symptom control for seizures or behavior can occur with subtherapeutic serum medication concentrations. **Adverse Consequences** • May cause liver dysfunction, blood dyscrasias, and serious skin rashes requiring discontinuation of treatment. • May cause nausea/vomiting, dizziness, ataxia, somnolence/lethargy, incoordination, blurred or double vision, restlessness, toxic encephalopathy, anorexia, headaches. These effects can increase the risk for falls.
Antidepressants	

All antidepressants classes, e.g.,
Alpha-adrenoceptor antagonist, e.g.,
   • mirtazapine
Dopamine-reuptake blocking compounds, e.g.,
   • bupropion
	Indications
	
	• Agents usually classified as "antidepressants" are prescribed for conditions other than depression including anxiety disorders, post-traumatic stress disorder, obsessive compulsive disorder, insomnia, neuropathic pain (e.g., diabetic peripheral neuropathy), migraine headaches, urinary incontinence, and others.

Medication	Issues and Concerns
Monoamine oxidase inhibitors (MAOIs) Serotonin (5-HT 2) antagonists, e.g., • nefazodone • trazodone Selective serotonin-norepinephrine reuptake inhibitors (SNRIs), e.g., • duloxetine, • venlafaxine Selective serotonin reuptake inhibitors (SSRIs), e.g., • citalopram • escitalopram • fluoxetine • fluvoxamine • paroxetine • sertraline Tricyclic (TCA) and related compounds	**Dosage** • Use of two or more antidepressants simultaneously may increase risk of side effects; in such cases, there should be documentation of expected benefits that outweigh the associated risks and monitoring for any increase in side effects. **Duration** • Duration should be in accordance with pertinent literature, including clinical practice guidelines. • Prior to discontinuation, many antidepressants may need a gradual dose reduction or tapering to avoid a withdrawal syndrome (e.g., SSRIs, TCAs). • If used to manage behavior, stabilize mood, or treat a psychiatric disorder, refer to Section V – Tapering of a Medication Dose/Gradual Dose Reduction (GDR) in the guidance. **Monitoring** • All residents being treated for depression with any antidepressant should be monitored closely for worsening of depression and/or suicidal behavior or thinking, especially during initiation of therapy and during any change in dosage. **Interactions/Adverse Consequences** • May cause dizziness, nausea, diarrhea, anxiety, nervousness, insomnia, somnolence, weight gain, anorexia, or increased appetite. Many of these effects can increase the risk for falls. • Bupropion may increase seizure risk and be associated with seizures in susceptible individuals. • SSRIs in combination with other medications affecting serotonin (e.g., tramadol, St. John's Wort, linezolid, other SSRI's) may increase the risk for serotonin syndrome and seizures.
Monoamine oxidase inhibitors (MAOIs), e.g., • isocarboxazid • phenelzine • tranylcypromine	**Indications/Contraindications** • Should not be administered to anyone with a confirmed or suspected cerebrovascular defect or to anyone with confirmed cardiovascular disease or hypertension. • Should not be used in the presence of pheochromocytoma. • MAO Inhibitors are rarely utilized due to their potential interactions with tyramine or tryptophan-containing foods, other medications, and their profound effect on blood pressure.

Medication	Issues and Concerns
	Adverse Consequences • May cause hypertensive crisis if combined with certain foods, cheese, wine **Exception:** Monoamine oxidase inhibitors such as selegiline (MAO-B inhibitors) utilized for Parkinson's Disease, unless used in doses greater than 10 mg per day. **Interactions** • Should not be administered together or in rapid succession with other MAO inhibitors, tricyclic antidepressants, bupropion, SSRIs, buspirone, sympathomimetics, meperidine, triptans, and other medications that affect serotonin or norepinephrine.

Tricyclic antidepressants (TCAs), e.g.,
 	
• amitriptyline
• amoxapine
• doxepin
• combination products, e.g.,
 	
   o amitriptyline and chlordiazepoxide
 	
   o amitripytline and perphenazine
	Indications
	
	• Because of strong anticholinergic and sedating properties, TCAs and combination products are rarely the medication of choice in older individuals.
	
	Exception: Use of TCAs may be appropriate if:
	
	   o The resident is being treated for neurogenic pain (e.g., trigeminal neuralgia, peripheral neuropathy), based on documented evidence to support the diagnosis; and
	
	   o The relative benefits outweigh the risks and other, safer agents including non-pharmacological interventions or alternative therapies are not indicated or have been considered, attempted, and failed.
	
	Adverse Consequences
	
	• Compared to other categories of antidepressants, TCAs cause significant anticholinergic side effects and sedation (nortriptyline and desipramine are less problematic).

Antidiabetic medications	
Insulin and oral hypoglycemics, e.g., • acarbose • acetohexamide • chlorpropamide • glimepiride • glipizide • glyburide • metformin • repaglinide • rosiglitazone • tolazamide • tolbutamide	**Monitoring** • Use of anti-diabetic medications should include monitoring (for example, periodic blood sugars) for effectiveness based on desired goals for that individual and to identify complications of treatment such as hypoglycemia, impaired renal function. **NOTE:** Continued or long-term need for sliding scale insulin for non-emergency coverage may indicate inadequate blood sugar control.

Medication	Issues and Concerns

Including combination products, e.g.,
 	
• rosiglitazone/metformin
• glyburide/metformin
• glipizide/metformin
• pioglitazone/metformin
	• Residents on rosiglitazone should be monitored for visual deterioration due to new onset and/or worsening of macular edema in diabetic patients.
	
	Adverse Consequences
	
	• Metformin has been associated with the development of lactic acidosis (a potentially life threatening metabolic disorder), which is more likely to occur in individuals with:
	
	  o serum creatinine $\geq$ 1.5 mg/dL in males or $\geq$ 1.4 mg/dL in females.
	
	  o abnormal creatinine clearance from any cause, including shock, acute myocardial infarction, or septicemia.
	
	  o age $\geq$ 80 years unless measurement of creatinine clearance verifies normal renal function.
	
	  o radiologic studies in which intravascular iodinated contrast materials are given.
	
	  o congestive heart failure requiring pharmacological management.
	
	  o acute or chronic metabolic acidosis with or without coma (including diabetic ketoacidosis).
	
	• Rosiglitazone and pioglitazone have been associated with edema and weight gain; therefore, their use should be avoided in residents with Stage III or Stage IV heart failure.
	
	• Sulfonylureas can cause the syndrome of inappropriate antidiuretic hormone (SIADH) and result in hyponatremia.

chlorpropamide glyburide	**Indications** • Chlorpropamide and glyburide are not considered hypoglycemic agents of choice in older individuals because of the long half-life and/or duration of action and increased risk of hypoglycemia. **Adverse Consequences** • May cause prolonged and serious hypoglycemia (with symptoms including tachycardia, palpitations, irritability, headache, hypothermia, visual disturbances, lethargy, confusion, seizures, and/or coma).
Antifungals	
Imidazoles for systemic use, e.g., • fluconazole • itraconazole • ketoconazole	**Indications** • Should be used in lowest possible dose for shortest possible duration, especially in anyone receiving other medications known to interact with these medications.

Medication	Issues and Concerns

	Interactions/Adverse Consequences
	
	• Interaction with warfarin can cause markedly elevated PT/INR, increasing bleeding risk.
	
	• Multiply potentially significant medication interactions may occur, for example:
	
	  o These medications when administered concurrently may increase the effect or toxicity of phenytoin, theophylline, sulfonylureas (hypoglycemics).
	
	  o Other medications such as rifampin and cimetidine may decrease the effect of these antifungals.
	
	• May cause hepatotoxicity, headaches, GI distress.
	
	Monitoring
	
	• Enhanced monitoring may be required to identify and minimize adverse consequences when these antifungals are given with the following:
	
	  o warfarin (PT/INR)
	
	  o phenytoin (serum phenytoin levels)
	
	  o theophylline (serum theophylline levels)
	
	  o sulfonylureas (fasting blood glucose)

Antimanic medications	
Lithium	**Indications** • Should generally not be given to individuals with significant renal or cardiovascular disease, severe debilitation, dehydration, or sodium depletion. **Monitoring** • Toxic levels are very close to therapeutic levels. Serum lithium concentration should be monitored periodically, and dosage adjusted accordingly. **Interactions/Adverse Consequences** • May cause potentially dangerous sodium imbalance. • Adverse consequences may occur at relatively low serum concentrations (1–1.5 mEq/L). • Serum lithium concentration levels can be affected by many other medications, e.g., thiazide diurectics, ACE inhibitors, NSAIDs.

Medication	Issues and Concerns
Antiparkinson medications	
All classes, e.g., Catechol-O-Methyl Transferase (COMT) Inhibitors, e.g., • entacapone Dopamine agonists, e.g., • bromocriptine • ropinirole • pramipexole MAO inhibitors, e.g., • selegiline Others, e.g., • amantadine Various dopaminergic combinations, e.g., • carbidopa/levodopa • carbidopa/levodopa/entacapone	**Adverse Consequences** • May cause significant confusion, restlessness, delirium, dyskinesia, nausea, dizziness, hallucinations, agitation. • Increased risk of postural hypotension and falls, especially when given in conjunction with antihypertensive medications.
Antipsychotic medications	
All classes, e.g., First generation (conventional) agents, e.g. • chlorpromazine • fluphenazine • haloperidol • loxapine • mesoridazine • molindone • perphenazine • promazine • thioridazine • thiothixene • trifluoperazine • triflupromazine Second generation (atypical) agents, e.g. • aripiprazole • clozapine • olanzapine • quetiapine • risperidone • ziprasidone	**Indications** • An antipsychotic medication should be used only for the following conditions/diagnoses as documented in the record and as meets the definition(s) in the Diagnostic and Statistical Manual of Mental Disorders, Fourth Edition, Training Revision (DSM-IV TR) or subsequent editions): o Schizophrenia o Schizo-affective disorder o Delusional disorder o Mood disorders (e.g. mania, bipolar disorder, depression with psychotic features, and treatment refractory major depression) o Schizophreniform disorder o Psychosis NOS o Atypical psychosis o Brief psychotic disorder o Dementing illnesses with associated behavioral symptoms o Medical illnesses or delirium with manic or psychotic symptoms and/or treatment-related psychosis or mania (e.g., thyrotoxicosis, neoplasms, high dose steroids)

Medication	Issues and Concerns

	• In addition, the use of an antipsychotic must meet the criteria and applicable, additional requirements listed below:
	
	1. Criteria:
	
	   o Since diagnoses alone do not warrant the use of antipsychotic medications, the clinical condition must also meet at least one of the following criteria (A or B or C):
	
	      A. The symptoms are identified as being due to mania or psychosis (such as: auditory, visual, or other hallucinations; delusions (such as paranoia or grandiosity)); OR
	
	      B. The behavioral symptoms present a danger to the resident or to others; OR
	
	      C. The symptoms are significant enough that the resident is experiencing one or more of the following: inconsolable or persistent distress (e.g., fear, continuously yelling, screaming, distress associated with end-of-life, or crying); a significant decline in function; and/or substantial difficulty receiving needed care (e.g., not eating resulting in weight loss, fear and not bathing leading to skin breakdown or infection).
	
	2. Additional Requirements:
	
	   o Acute Psychiatric Situations
	
	     When an antipsychotic medication is being initiated or used to treat an acute psychiatric emergency (i.e., recent or abrupt onset or exacerbation of symptoms) related to one or more of the aforementioned conditions/diagnoses, that use must meet one of the above criteria and all of the following additional requirements:
	
	      A. The acute treatment period is limited to seven days or less; and
	
	      B. A clinician in conjunction with the interdisciplinary team must evaluate and document the situation within 7 days, to identify and address any contributing and underlying causes of the acute psychiatric condition and verify the continuing need for antipsychotic medication; and
	
	      C. Pertinent non-pharmacological interventions must be attempted, unless contraindicated, and documented following the resolution of the acute psychiatric situation.

Medication	Issues and Concerns
	o Enduring Psychiatric Conditions

Continuing:

o   Enduring Psychiatric Conditions

Antipsychotic medications may be used to treat an enduring (i.e., non-acute, chronic, or prolonged) condition, if the clinical condition/diagnosis meets the criteria in #1 above. In addition, before initiating or increasing an antipsychotic medication for enduring conditions, the target behavior must be clearly and specifically identified and monitored objectively and qualitatively, in order to ensure the behavioral symptoms are:

A. Not due to a medical condition or problem (e.g., headache or joint pain, fluid or electrolyte imbalance, pneumonia, hypoxia, unrecognized hearing or visual impairment) that can be expected to improve or resolve as the underlying condition is treated; and

B. Persistent or likely to reoccur without continued treatment; and

C. Not sufficiently relieved by non-pharmacological interventions; and

D. Not due to environmental stressors (e.g., alteration in the resident's customary location or daily routine, unfamiliar care provider, hunger or thirst, excessive noise for that individual, inadequate or inappropriate staff response, physical barriers) that can be addressed to improve the psychotic symptoms or maintain safety; and

E. Not due to psychological stressors (e.g., loneliness, taunting, abuse), or anxiety or fear stemming from misunderstanding related to his or her cognitive impairment (e.g., the mistaken belief that this is not where he/she lives or inability to find his or her clothes or glasses) that can be expected to improve or resolve as the situation is addressed.

•   After initiating or increasing the dose of an antipsychotic medication, the behavioral symptoms must be reevaluated periodically to determine the effectiveness of the antipsychotic and the potential for reducing or discontinuing the dose.

Exception: When antipsychotic medications are used for behavioral disturbances related to Tourette's disorder, or for non-psychiatric indications such as movement disorders associated with Huntington's disease, hiccups, nausea and vomiting associated with cancer or cancer chemotherapy, or adjunctive therapy at end of life.

Medication	Issues and Concerns
	Inadequate Indications • In many situations, antipsychotic medications are not indicated. They should not be used if the only indication is one or more of the following: 1) wandering; 2) poor self-care; 3) restlessness; 4) impaired memory; 5) mild anxiety; 6) insomnia; 7) unsociability; 8) inattention or indifference to surroundings; 9) fidgeting; 10) nervousness; 11) uncooperativeness; or 12) verbal expressions or behavior that are not due to the conditions listed under "Indications" and do not represent a danger to the resident or others.
	Dosage • Doses for acute indications (for example, delirium) may differ from those used for long-term treatment, but should be the lowest possible to achieve the desired therapeutic effects.
	Daily Dose Thresholds for Antipsychotic Medications Used to Manage Behavioral Symptoms Related to Dementing Illnesses Generic Medication / Dosage table below

Generic Medication	Dosage
First Generation	
chlorpromazine	75 mg
fluphenazine	4 mg
haloperidol	2 mg
loxapine	10 mg
molindone	10 mg
perphenazine	8 mg
pimozide	*
prochloroperazine	*
thioridazine	75 mg
thiothixene	7 mg
trifluoperazine	8 mg
Second Generation	
aripiprazole	10 mg
clozapine	50 mg
olanzapine	7.5 mg
quetiapine	150 mg
risperidone	2 mg
ziprasidone	*

* Not customarily used for the treatment of behavioral symptoms.

References:

Katz, I.R. (2004). Optimizing atypical antipsychotic treatment strategies in the elderly. Journal of the American Geriatrics Society, 52, pp. 272-277.

Schneider, L.S. (2005). Risk of death with atypical antipsychotic drug treatment for dementia. Meta-analysis of randomized placebo controlled trials. Journal of the American Medical Association, 294, pp. 1934-1943.

Saltz, B.L., Woerner, M.G., Robinson, D.G., & Kane, J.M. (2000). Side effects of antipsychotic drugs: Avoiding and minimizing their impact in elderly patients. Postgraduate Medicine, 107, pp. 169-178.

Medication	Issues and Concerns
	Duration • If used to manage behavior, stabilize mood, or treat a psychiatric disorder, refer to Section V – Tapering of a Medication Dose/Gradual Dose Reduction (GDR) in the guidance.

	Monitoring/Adverse Consequences
	
	• The facility assures that residents are being adequately monitored for adverse consequences such as:
	
	  o anticholinergic effects (see Table II) o increase in total cholesterol and triglycerides
	  o akathisia o parkinsonism
	  o neuroleptic malignant syndrome (NMS) o blood sugar elevation (including diabetes mellitus)
	  o cardiac arrhythmias o orthostatic hypotension
	  o death secondary to heart-related events (e.g., heart failure, sudden death) o cerebrovascular event (e.g., stroke, transient ischemic attack (TIA)) in older individuals with dementia
	  o falls o tardive dyskinesia
	  o lethargy o excessive sedation
	
	When antipsychotics are used without monitoring they may be considered unnecessary medications because of inadequate monitoring.

Anxiolytics	

All Anxiolytics
 	
Benzodiazepines, Short-acting, e.g.,
• alprazolam
• estazolam
• lorazepam
• oxazepam
• temazepam
 	
Benzodiazepines, Long acting, e.g.,
• chlordiazepoxide
• clonazepam
• clorazepate
• diazepam
• flurazepam
• quazepam.
 	
buspirone
 	
Other antidepressants except bupropion.
	Indications
	
	• Anxiolytic medications should only be used when:
	
	  o Use is for one of the following indications as defined in the Diagnostic and Statistical Manual of Mental Disorders, Fourth Edition, Training Revision (DSM-IV TR) or subsequent editions:
	
	  a. Generalized anxiety disorder
	  b. Panic disorder
	  c. Symptomatic anxiety that occurs in residents with another diagnosed psychiatric disorder
	  d. Sleep disorders (See Sedatives/Hypnotics)
	  e. Acute alcohol or benzodiazepine withdrawal
	  f. Significant anxiety in response to a situational trigger

Medication	Issues and Concerns

	g. Delirium, dementia, and other cognitive disorders with associated behaviors that:
	
	  – Are quantitatively and objectively documented;
	
	  – Are persistent;
	
	  – Are not due to preventable or correctable reasons; and
	
	  – Constitute clinically significant distress or dysfunction to the resident or represent a danger to the resident or others.
	
	• Evidence exists that other possible reasons for the individual's distress have been considered; and
	
	• Use results in maintenance or improvement in the individual's mental, physical or psychosocial well-being (e.g., as reflected on the MDS or other assessment tools); or
	
	• There are clinical situations that warrant the use of these medications such as:
	
	  – a long-acting benzodiazepine is being used to withdraw a resident from a short-acting benzodiazepine
	
	  – used for neuromuscular syndromes (e.g., cerebral palsy, tardive dyskinesia, restless leg syndrome or seizure disorders)
	
	  – symptom relief in end of life situations
	
	Dosage
	
	• Dosage is less than, or equal to, the following listed total daily doses unless higher doses (as evidenced by the resident's response and/or the resident's clinical record) are necessary to maintain or improve the resident's function.
	
	Total Daily Dose Thresholds for Anxiolytic Medications
	
	<table><tr><th>Generic Medication</th><th>Dosage</th></tr><tr><td>flurazepam</td><td>15 mg</td></tr><tr><td>chlordiazepoxide</td><td>20 mg</td></tr><tr><td>clorazepate</td><td>15 mg</td></tr><tr><td>diazepam</td><td>5 mg</td></tr><tr><td>clonazepam</td><td>1.5 mg</td></tr><tr><td>quazepam</td><td>7.5 mg</td></tr><tr><td>estazolam</td><td>0.5 mg</td></tr><tr><td>alprazolam</td><td>0.75 mg</td></tr><tr><td>oxazepam</td><td>30 mg</td></tr><tr><td>lorazepam</td><td>2 mg</td></tr></table>

Medication	Issues and Concerns
	Duration • If used to manage behavior, stabilize mood, or treat a psychiatric disorder, refer to Section V – Tapering of a Medication Dose/Gradual Dose Reduction (GDR) in the guidance. **Adverse Consequences** • May increase risk of confusion, sedation, and falls.
diphenhydramine and hydroxyzine	**Indications** • Not appropriate for use as an anxiolytic.
meprobamate	**Indications** • Highly addictive and sedating medication; not indicated for use in older individuals. **Dosage/Duration** • Those who have used meprobamate for prolonged periods may be physically and/or psychologically dependent and may need to be withdrawn slowly.
Cardiovascular medications (including antihypertensives)	
All antiarrhythmics	**Adverse Consequences** • Cardiac antiarrhythmics can have serious adverse effects in older individuals, including impaired mental function, falls, appetite, behavior, and heart function.
amiodarone	**Indications** • Only approved indication for use is to treat documented life-threatening recurrent ventricular arrhythmias that do not respond to other antiarrhythmic agents or when alternative agents are not tolerated. • Common off-label use to treat atrial fibrillation; however, literature suggests that in many higher risk individuals, alternative approaches to managing atrial fibrillation (rate control and anticoagulation) are equally effective and less toxic.* * Goldschlager, N., Epstein, A.E., Naccarelli, G., Olshansky, B., & Singh, B. (2000). Practical guidelines for clinicians who treat patients with amiodarone. Archives of Internal Medicine, 160, pp. 1741-1748. * Denus, S., Sanoski, C.A., Carlson, J., Opolski, G., & Spinler, S.A. (2005). Rate vs rhythm control in patients with atrial fibrillation: A meta-analysis. Archives of Internal Medicine, 165, pp. 258-262.

Medication	Issues and Concerns
	Dosage/Monitoring • It is critical to carefully consider risks and benefits, to use the lowest possible dose for the shortest possible duration, to closely monitor individuals receiving long-term amiodarone, and to seek and identify adverse consequences. **Interactions/Adverse Consequences** • May cause potentially fatal toxicities, including pulmonary toxicity (hypersensitivity pneumonitis or interstitial/alveolar pneumonitis) and hepatic injury. May cause hypothyroidism, exacerbate existing arrhythmia, and worsen heart failure. Can also impair mental function and behavior. • May cause clinically significant medication interactions; for example, with digoxin and warfarin. Toxicity increases with higher doses and longer duration of use.
disopyramide	**Adverse Consequences** • Disopyramide has potent negative inotropic effects (decreased force of heart contraction), which may induce heart failure in older individuals, and is also strongly anticholinergic.
All antihypertensives	**Dosage/Monitoring** • Doses of individual antihypertensives may require modification in order to achieve desired effects while minimizing adverse consequences, especially when multiple antihypertensives are prescribed simultaneously. • When discontinuing some antihypertensives (e.g., clonidine, beta blockers), gradual tapering may be required to avoid adverse consequences caused by abrupt cessation **Interactions/Adverse Consequences** • May cause dizziness, postural hypotension, fatigue, and an increased risk for falls. • Many other medications may interact with antihypertensives to potentiate their effect (e.g., levodopa, nitrates).
Alpha blockers, e.g., • alfuzosin • doxazosin • prazosin • tamsulosin • terazosin	**Adverse Consequences** • Doxazosin, prazosin, and terazosin can cause significant hypotension and syncope during the first few doses. Therefore, these medications should be initiated at bedtime with a slow titration of dose. • Prazosin can cause more CNS side effects and generally should be avoided in older individuals.

Medication	Issues and Concerns
Angiotensin converting enzyme (ACE) inhibitors, e.g., • benazepril • captopril • enalapril • fosinopril • lisinopril • ramipril Angiotensin II receptor blockers, e.g., • candesartan • eprosartan • irbesartan • losartan • olmesartan • valsartan	**Monitoring** • Monitoring of serum potassium is necessary especially in individuals receiving ACE inhibitors with potassium, or potassium sparing diuretics. **Adverse Consequences** • May cause angioedema (signs and symptoms of immediate hypersensitivity), chronic persistent nonproductive cough, or may worsen renal failure. • Potential for life-threatening elevation of serum potassium concentrations when used in combination with potassium supplements, potassium-sparing diuretics including spironolactone.

Beta adrenergic blockers, e.g.,
 	
Nonselective, e.g.,
 	
• propranolol
 	
Cardioselective, e.g.,
 	
• atenolol
• esmolol
• metoprolol
• nadolol
• timolol
	Adverse Consequences
	
	• May cause or exacerbate:
	
	   o Bradycardia, especially in individuals receiving other medications that affect cardiac conduction (e.g., calcium channel blockers);
	
	   o Dizziness, fatigue; depression, bronchospasm (especially, but not exclusively, propranolol); or
	
	   o Cardiac decompensation that may require adjusting dose in residents with acute heart failure.
	
	• May mask tachycardia associated with symptomatic hypoglycemia.
	
	• May have increased effect or may accumulate in individuals with hepatic impairment.

Calcium channel blockers, e.g., • nifedipine • isradipine • amlodipine • nisoldipine • diltiazem • verapamil	**Adverse consequences** • May cause clinically significant constipation. • May cause peripheral edema. • Some agents may cause generalized aching, headache, muscle pain. • Short acting/immediate release nifedipine increases the risk of cardiac complications and should not be used.
methyldopa Including combination products such as methyldopa/ hydrochlorothiazide	**Indications** • Alternate treatments for hypertension are preferred. **Adverse Consequences** • May cause bradycardia and excessive sedation; may exacerbate depression in older individuals.

Medication	Issues and Concerns
digoxin	**Indications** • Digoxin is indicated only for the following diagnoses: congestive heart failure, atrial fibrillation, paroxysmal supraventricular tachycardia, or atrial flutter. • Should be used with caution in individuals with impaired renal function. **Dosage** • Daily doses in older individuals should ordinarily not exceed 0.125 mg/day except when used to control atrial arrhythmia and ventricular rate. **Monitoring** • Must be used cautiously in individuals with renal failure or fluid and electrolyte imbalance, with close monitoring for adverse consequences and monitoring, as indicated, of both renal function and serum medication concentration ("digoxin level"). • Adverse consequences may occur even with therapeutic serum concentration, especially in older individuals. **Interactions/Adverse Consequences** • May interact with many other medications, possibly resulting in digoxin toxicity or elevated serum concentrations of other medications. • May cause significant bradycardia, especially when used in individuals taking other medications affecting cardiac conduction. • Toxicity may cause fatigue, nausea, vomiting, anorexia, delirium, cardiac arrhythmia.
Diuretics, e.g., • bumetanide • ethacrynic acid • furosemide • hydrochlorothiazide • metolazone • spironolactone • torsemide • triamterene	**Adverse Consequences** • May cause fluid and electrolyte imbalance (hypo/hypernatremia, hypo/hyperkalemia, dehydration, etc.), hypotension; may precipitate or exacerbate urinary incontinence, falls.
Nitrates, e.g., • isosorbide mononitrate • isosorbide dinitrate • nitroglycerin	**Adverse Consequences** • May cause headaches, dizziness, lightheadedness, faintness, or symptomatic orthostatic hypotension, especially when initially started or when taken in combination with antihypertensive medications.

Medication	Issues and Concerns
Cholesterol lowering medications	
HMG-CoA Reductase Inhibitors ("statins"), e.g., • atorvastatin • fluvastatin • lovastatin • pravastatin • rosuvastatin • simvastatin	**Monitoring** • Liver function monitoring should be performed consistent with manufacturer's recommendations, generally accepted as: o Prior to initiation of therapy, at 12 weeks following both initiation of therapy and any increase in dose, and periodically (e.g., semiannually) thereafter. **Adverse Consequences** • May impair liver function; liver function tests should be monitored as indicated above. • May cause muscle pain, myopathy, and rhabdomyolysis (breakdown of skeletal muscle) that can precipitate kidney failure especially in combination with other cholesterol lowering medications.
cholestyramine	**Interactions** • May reduce the absorption of other medications being taken concurrently. Other medications, including diuretics, beta-blockers, corticosteroids, thyroid hormones, digoxin, valproic acid, NSAIDs, sulfonylureas, and warfarin should be administered one hour before or four hours after cholestyramine administration to avoid this interaction. **Adverse Consequences** • May cause constipation, dyspepsia, nausea or vomiting, abdominal pain.
fibrates, e.g., • fenofibrate • clofibrate	**Monitoring** • Fenofibrate and clofibrate require regular monitoring of liver tests as well as evaluating the complete blood count (CBC) prior to and after initiation.
niacin	**Monitoring** • Monitor glucose and liver function tests regularly. **Adverse Consequences** • Interferes with glucose control and can aggravate diabetes. • Can exacerbate active gallbladder disease and gout. • Flushing is common.

Medication	Issues and Concerns
Cognitive Enhancers	
Cholinesterase inhibitors, e.g., • donepezil • galantamine • rivastigmine	**Indications** • As the underlying disorder progresses into advanced stages, the continued use of the medication should be reevaluated. **Adverse Consequences** • May affect cardiac conduction, especially in individuals who already have a cardiac conduction disorder or who are taking other medications that affect heart rate. • May cause insomnia, dizziness, nausea, vomiting, diarrhea, anorexia, and weight loss. • Should be used with caution in individuals with severe asthma or obstructive pulmonary disease.
NMDA receptor antagonists, e.g., • memantine	**Indications** • As the underlying disorder progresses into advanced stages, the continued use of the medication should be reevaluated. **Adverse Consequences** • May cause restlessness, distress, dizziness, somnolence, hypertension, headache, hallucinations, or increased confusion.
Cough, cold, and allergy medications	
All cough, cold, allergy medications	**Indications/Duration** • Should be used only for a limited duration (less than 14 days) unless there is documented evidence of enduring symptoms that cannot otherwise be alleviated and for which a cause cannot be identified and corrected.
Antihistamine H-1 blockers, e.g., • chlorpheniramine • cyproheptadine • diphenhydramine • hydroxyzine • meclizine • promethazine	**Indications** • H-1 blocker antihistamines have strong anticholinergic properties and are not considered medications of choice in older individuals. • If appropriate and effective, topical instead of oral diphenhydramine should be considered for allergic reactions involving the skin.

Medication	Issues and Concerns
	Dosage/Duration • Should be used in the smallest possible dosage for the shortest possible duration, especially in individuals who are susceptible to anticholinergic side effects or who are receiving other medications with anticholinergic properties (see Table II). **Adverse Consequences** May cause excessive sedation, confusion, cognitive impairment, distress, dry mouth, constipation, urinary retention. These may lead to other adverse consequences such as falls.
Oral decongestants, e.g., • pseudoephedrine	**Adverse Consequences** • May cause dizziness, nervousness, insomnia, palpitations, urinary retention, elevated blood pressure. • Should be used with caution in individuals who have insomnia or hypertension.
Gastrointestinal medications	
Phenothiazine-related antiemetics, e.g., • prochlorperazine • promethazine	**Indications** • Use with caution in individuals with Parkinson's disease, narrow-angle glaucoma, BPH, seizure disorder. **Adverse Consequences** • May cause sedation, dizziness, drowsiness, postural hypotension, and neuroleptic malignant syndrome. • May lower seizure threshold . • Promethazine and prochlorperazine may cause anticholinergic effects, such as constipation, dry mouth, blurred vision, urinary retention. • May cause extrapyramidal symptoms, including medication-induced parkinsonism, acute dystonic reactions, akathisia, and tardive dyskinesia. • May alter cardiac conduction or induce arrhythmias.
trimethobenzamide	**Adverse Consequences** • Relatively ineffective antiemetic that can cause significant extrapyramidal side effects in addition to lethargy, sedation, confusion. **Exception:** May be indicated in patients with Parkinson's Disease taking apomorphine.

Medication	Issues and Concerns
metoclopramide	**Indications** • High-risk medication with limited clinical indication and limited demonstrated effectiveness.* • Not recommended for first-line treatment of gastroesophageal reflux disease, especially in older individuals. • When used for diabetic gastroparesis, or other indications, relative benefits and risks should be assessed and documented. * Lata, P.F., Pigarelli, D.L. (2003). Chronic metoclopramide therapy for diabetic gastroparesis. Ann Pharmacotherapy, 37(1), pp. 122-126. **Adverse Consequences** • Especially in older individuals, metoclopramide may cause restlessness, drowsiness, insomnia, depression, distress, anorexia, and extrapyramidal symptoms, and may lower the seizure threshold. • May increase seizures in individuals with seizure disorders or exacerbate symptoms in individuals with Parkinson's Disease. **Monitoring** • It is essential to closely monitor at-risk individuals for adverse consequences.
Proton pump inhibitors (PPI), e.g., • esomeprazole • lansoprazole • omeprazole • rabeprazole H-2 antagonists, e.g., • cimetidine • famotidine • ranitidine	**Indications** • Indication for use should be based on clinical symptoms and/or endoscopic findings. • When used to treat or prevent NSAID-induced gastritis or esophagitis, documentation should exist that other, less GI-toxic analgesics have been tried or were not indicated. **Duration** • If used for greater than 12 weeks, clinical rationale for continued need and/or documentation should support an underlying chronic disease (e.g., GERD) or risk factors (e.g., chronic NSAID use). **Dosage** • Dosing of histamine-H2 antagonists should be based on renal function. **Interactions** • Cimetidine has higher incidence of medication interactions and should be avoided in older individuals.

Medication	Issues and Concerns
	Adverse Consequences • May cause or exacerbate headache, nausea, vomiting, flatulence, dysphagia, abdominal pain, diarrhea, or other gastrointestinal symptoms. • H-2 antagonists may cause confusion . PPIs may increase the risk of clostridium difficile colitis.
Glucocorticoids	
All glucocorticoids (except topical or inhaled dosage forms), e.g., • dexamethasone • hydrocortisone • methylprednisolone • prednisone	**Duration/Monitoring** • Necessity for continued use should be documented, along with monitoring for and management of adverse consequences. **Adverse Consequences** • Intermediate- or longer-term use may cause hyperglycemia, psychosis, edema, insomnia, hypertension, osteoporosis, mood lability, or depression.
Hematinics	
Erythropoiesis stimulants, e.g., • darbepoetin • erythropoietin	**Indications** • Assessment of causes and categories of anemia should precede or accompany the use of this medication. **Monitoring** • Use must be monitored according to specific manufacturer's instructions including blood pressure, baseline serum iron or ferritin level, and frequent complete blood count (CBCs) to permit tapering or discontinuation when hemoglobin/hematocrit reaches or exceeds target ranges. **Adverse Consequences** • May cause or worsen hypertension. • Excessive dose or duration can lead to polycythemia, dangerous thrombotic events including myocardial infarction and stroke.
Iron	**Indications** • Iron therapy is not indicated in anemia of chronic disease when iron stores and transferrin levels are normal or elevated. **Dosage/Duration** • Clinical rationale should be documented for long-term use (greater than two months) or administration more than once daily for greater than a week, because of side effects and the risk of iron accumulation in tissues.

Medication	Issues and Concerns
	Monitoring • Baseline serum iron or ferritin level and periodic CBC or hematocrit/ hemoglobin . **Adverse Consequences** • May cause constipation, dyspepsia. . Can accumulate in tissues and cause multiple complications if given chronically despite normal or high iron stores.
Laxatives	
All categories including bulk producing laxatives, hyperosmolar agents, saline laxatives, stimulant laxatives, emollient laxatives.	**Adverse Consequences** • May cause flatulence, bloating, abdominal pain. • Bulk forming laxatives and stool softeners may cause accumulation of stool and possible bowel obstruction, if not used with adequate fluids or in individuals with other causes of impaired bowel motility.
Muscle relaxants	
All muscle relaxants, e.g., • baclofen • carisoprodol • chlorzoxazone • cyclobenzaprine • dantrolene • metaxalone • methocarbamol • orphenadrine	**Indications/Adverse Consequences** • Most are poorly tolerated by older individuals due to anticholinergic side effects (see Table II), sedation, or weakness. • Long-term use in individuals with complications due to multiple sclerosis, spinal cord injuries, cerebral palsy, and other select conditions may be indicated, although close monitoring is still warranted. • Abrupt cessation of some muscle relaxants may cause or predispose individuals to seizures or hallucinations. **Exception:** Periodic use (once every three months) for a short duration (not more than seven days) may be appropriate, when other interventions or alternative medications are not effective or not indicated.
Orexigenics (appetite stimulants)	
All appetite stimulants, e.g., • megesterol acetate • oxandrolone • dronabinol	**Indications** • Use should be reserved for situations where assessment and management of underlying correctable causes of anorexia and weight loss is not feasible or successful, and after evaluating potential benefits/risks. **Monitoring** • Appetite and weight should be monitored at least monthly and agent should be discontinued if there is no improvement.

Medication	Issues and Concerns
	Adverse Consequences • Megesterol acetate may cause fluid retention, adrenal suppression, and symptoms of adrenal insufficiency. • Oxandrolone may cause virilization of females and feminization of males, excessive sexual stimulation, and fluid retention. Dronabinol may cause tachycardia, orthostatic hypotension, dizziness, dysphoria, and impaired cognition, which may lead to falls.
Osteoporosis medications	
Bisphosphonates, e.g., • alendronate • ibandronate • risedronate	**Dosage** • These medications must be taken according to very specific directions, including time of day, position, and timing relative to other medications and food. **Monitoring** • Individuals receiving these medications should be monitored closely for gastrointestinal complications, including esophageal or gastric erosion . **Adverse Consequences** • Potential to cause gastrointestinal symptoms including dysphagia, esophagitis, gastritis, or esophageal and gastric ulcers, especially when given to individuals who are also taking oral corticosteroids, aspirin or other nonsteroidal anti-inflammatory drugs (NSAIDs).
Platelet inhibitors	
All platelet inhibitors, e.g., • dipyridamole • dipyridamole extended-release and aspirin (as fixed-dose combination) • aspirin • clopidogrel	**Interactions/Adverse Consequences** • May cause thrombocytopenia and increase risk of bleeding. • Common side effects include headache, dizziness, and vomiting. • See discussion at NSAIDs regarding aspirin. • Concurrent use with warfarin or NSAIDs may increase risk of bleeding.
ticlopidine	**Indications** • Use may be appropriate in individuals who have had a previous stroke or have evidence of stroke precursors (i.e., transient ischemic attacks (TIAs)), and who cannot tolerate aspirin or another platelet inhibitor. **Adverse Consequences** • Associated with more severe side effects and considerably more toxic than other platelet inhibitors; use should be avoided in older individuals.

Medication	Issues and Concerns
	• Most serious side effects involve the hematologic system, including potentially life-threatening neutropenia. • May also cause nausea, vomiting, and diarrhea.
Respiratory medications	
theophylline	**Interactions** • Potentially significant interactions with many other medications may occur, especially various antibiotics, seizure medications, and cardiac medications. **Monitoring/Adverse Consequences** • There should be monitoring for signs and symptoms of toxicity, such as arrhythmia, seizure, GI upset, diarrhea, nausea/vomiting, abdominal pain, nervousness, headache, insomnia, distress, dizziness, muscle cramp, tremor. • Periodic monitoring of serum concentrations helps identify or verify toxicity.

Inhalant medications classes, e.g.,
 	
Anticholinergic, e.g.,
  • ipratropium
  • tiotropium
 	
Beta 2 agonists, e.g.,
  • albuterol
  • formoterol
  • pirbuterol acetate
  • salmeterol
 	
Corticosteroids, e.g.,
  • beclomethasone
  • budesonide
  • flunisolide
  • fluticasone
  • triamcinolone acetonide
 	
Miscellaneous, e.g.,
  • cromolyn
  • nedocromil sodium
	Adverse Consequences
	
	• Inhaled anticholinergics can cause xerostomia (dry mouth).
	
	• Inhaled beta agonists can cause restlessness, increased heart rate, and anxiety.
	
	• Inhaled steroids can cause throat irritation and oral candidiasis, especially if the mouth is not rinsed after administration.

Medication	Issues and Concerns
Sedatives/Hypnotics (sleep medications)	

All hypnotics
 	
Benzodiazepine hypnotics, e.g.,
 	
   • estazolam
   • flurazepam
   • quazepam
   • temazepam
   • triazolam
 	
Non-benzodiazepine hypnotics, e.g.,
 	
   • eszopiclone
   • zaleplon
   • zolpidem
 	
Melatonin receptor agonists, e.g.,
 	
   • ramelteon
 	
Other hypnotics, e.g.,
 	
   • chloral hydrate
 	
Miscellaneous agents used for sleep, e.g.,
 	
   • sedating antidepressants (e.g., trazodone)
   • sedating antihistamines (e.g., hydroxyzine)
	Indications
	
	• Most cases of insomnia are associated with underlying conditions (secondary or co-morbid insomnia) such as psychiatric disorders (e.g., depression), cardiopulmonary disorders (e.g., COPD, CHF), urinary frequency, pain, obstructive sleep apnea, and restless leg syndrome. Insomnia may be further described by the duration of symptoms.
	
	• Before initiating medications to treat insomnia, other factors potentially causing insomnia should be evaluated, including, for example:
	
	  o environment, such as excessive heat, cold, or noise; lighting
	
	  o inadequate physical activity
	
	  o facility routines that may not accommodate residents' individual needs (e.g., time for sleep, awakening, toileting, medication treatments)
	
	  o provision of care in a manner that disrupts sleep
	
	  o caffeine or medications known to disrupt sleep
	
	  o pain and discomfort
	
	  o underlying conditions (secondary or co-morbid insomnia) such as psychiatric disorders (e.g., depression), cardiopulmonary disorders (e.g., COPD, CHF), urinary frequency, pain, obstructive sleep apnea, and restless leg syndrome
	
	• It is expected that interventions (such as sleep hygiene approaches, individualizing the sleep and wake times to accommodate the person's wishes and prior customary routine, and maximizing treatment of any underlying conditions) are implemented to address the causative factor(s).
	
	• These guidelines apply to any medication that is being used to treat insomnia. Initiation of medications to induce or maintain sleep should be preceded or accompanied by other interventions to try to improve sleep. All sleep medications should be used in accordance with approved product labeling; for example, timing and frequency of administration relative to anticipated waking time.
	
	• The use of sedating medications for individuals with diagnosed sleep apnea requires careful assessment, documented clinical rationale, and close monitoring.

Medication	Issues and Concerns
	Exceptions: • Use of a single dose sedative for dental or medical procedures. • During initiation of treatment for depression, pain or other comorbid condition(s), short-term use of a sleep medication may be necessary until symptoms improve or the underlying aggravating factor can be identified and/or effectively treated.
	Dosage **Daily Dose Thresholds For Sedative-Hypnotic Medications** *(table below)* * These medications are not considered medications of choice for the management of insomnia, especially in older individuals. Reference: www.ahrq.gov/downloads/pub/evidence/pdf/insomnia/insomnia.pdf
	Duration • If used to induce sleep or treat a sleep disorder, refer to Section V – Tapering of a Medication Dose/Gradual Dose Reduction (GDR) in the guidance.
Barbiturates, e.g., • amobarbital • butabarbital • pentobarbital • secobarbital • phenobarbital • amobarbital-secobarbital • barbiturates with other medications	**NOTE:** Refers to barbiturates used to induce sleep or treat anxiety disorder. **Indications** • Barbiturates should not be initiated in any dose for any individuals to treat anxiety or insomnia; as they are highly addictive and cause numerous adverse effects, especially in older individuals **Exception:** These guidelines do not apply to the use of phenobarbital to treat seizure disorders (see Anticonvulsant section).

Generic Medication	Oral Dosage
chloral hydrate*	500 mg
diphenhydramine*	25 mg
estazolam	0.5 mg
eszopiclone	1 mg
flurazepam*	15 mg
hydroxyzine*	50 mg
lorazepam	1 mg
oxazepam	15 mg
quazepam*	7.5 mg
ramelteon	8 mg
temazepam	15 mg
triazolam*	0.125 mg
zaleplon	5 mg
zolpidem IR	5 mg
zolpidem CR	6.25 mg

Medication	Issues and Concerns
	Interactions/Adverse Consequences • May increase the metabolism of many medications (e.g., anticonvulsants, antipsychotics), which may lead to decreased effectiveness and subsequent worsening of symptoms or decreased control of underlying illness. • May cause hypotension, dizziness, lightheadedness, "hangover" effect, drowsiness, confusion, mental depression, unusual excitement, nervousness, headache, insomnia, nightmares, and hallucinations. • May increase the risk for falls
Thyroid medications	
All thyroid medications, e.g., • levothyroxine • triiodothryonine	**Interactions** • Many clinically significant medication interactions have been identified; therefore, re-evaluation of medication doses is indicated. **Dosage** • Initiation of thyroid supplementation should occur at low doses and be increased gradually to avoid precipitating cardiac failure or adrenal crisis. **Monitoring** • Assessment of thyroid function (e.g., TSH, serum T4 or T3) should occur prior to initiation and periodically thereafter, including when new signs and symptoms of hypo- or hyperthyroidism are present.
Urinary incontinence medications	
Urinary Incontinence Types and Agents, e.g., Urge incontinence: Anticholinergics, e.g., • darifenacin • oxybutynin • tolterodine • trospium Tricyclic antidepressants, e.g., • desipramine • imipramine Stress incontinence: Alpha adrenergic agonists, e.g., • pseudoephedrine	**Indications** • Before or soon after initiating medication(s) to manage urinary incontinence, assessment of underlying causes and identification of the type/category of urinary incontinence needs to be documented. • These medications have specific, limited indications based on the cause and type/category of incontinence. **Monitoring** • Ongoing assessments of the effects of the medication on the individual's urinary incontinence as well as lower urinary tract symptoms should be done periodically. **Adverse Consequences** • Anticholinergics and TCAs may cause anticholinergic effects (see Table II).

Medication	Issues and Concerns
Mixed incontinence, e.g., • estrogen replacement agents • imipramine Overflow incontinence, e.g., • alpha adrenergic antagonists (see antihypertensives) • bethanechol chloride	• Estrogen Replacement Agents: oral agents may cause systemic side effects and increased risks (e.g., deep venous thrombosis, breast cancer); therefore, topical agents may be preferred. • Bethanechol may cause hypotension, increased sweating and salivation, headache, cramps, diarrhea, nausea and vomiting, and worsening of asthma.

TABLE II

MEDICATIONS WITH SIGNIFICANT ANTICHOLINERGIC PROPERTIES

Table II lists common medications with significant anticholinergic properties and potential adverse consequences, but is not all-inclusive. Any of the following signs and symptoms may be caused by any of the medications in the lists below, alone or in combination, as well as by other medications not listed here that have anticholinergic properties.

This table is provided because: 1) Medications in many categories have anticholinergic properties; 2) The use of multiple medications with such properties may be particularly problematic because of the cumulative effects; and 3) Anticholinergic side effects are particularly common and problematic, especially in the older individual.[61, 62]

Examples of Medications with Anticholinergic Properties	
ANTIHISTAMINES (H-1 BLOCKERS) chlorpheniramine cyproheptadine diphenhydramine hydroxyzine	**CARDIOVASCULAR MEDICATIONS** furosemide digoxin nifedipine disopyramide

ANTIDEPRESSANTS
 	
amoxapine   amitriptyline
clomipramine   desipramine
doxepin   imipramine
nortriptyline   protriptyline
paroxetine
	GASTROINTESTINAL MEDICATIONS
	
	Antidiarrheal Medications
	  diphenoxylate atropine
	
	Antispasmodic Medications
	  belladonna clidinium chlordiazepoxide
	  dicyclomine hyoscyamine propantheline
	
	Antiulcer Medications
	  cimetidine ranitidine

ANTIPARKINSON MEDICATIONS amantadine benztropine biperiden trihexyphenidyl	**ANTIPSYCHOTIC MEDICATIONS** chlorpromazine clozapine olanzapine thioridazine
MUSCLE RELAXANTS cyclobenzaprine dantrolene orphenadrine	**URINARY INCONTINENCE** oxybutynin probantheline solifenacin tolterodine trospium
ANTIVERTIGO MEDICATIONS meclizine scopolamine	**PHENOTHIAZINE ANTIEMETICS** prochlorperazine promethazine
Potential Adverse Consequences of Medications with Anticholinergic Properties	
Blood pressure, increased	Breathing difficulty, changes
Clumsiness or unsteadiness	Convulsions

Digestive system changes, e.g.,
 	
  Bloating
  Bowel motility, decreased
	Mental status/behavior changes, e.g.,
	
	    Distress, excitement, nervousness
	    Attention, impaired

Constipation Ileus, paralytic/adynamic Nausea or vomiting Swallowing difficulty with dry mouth	Cognitive decline Confusion/disorientation Hallucinations Memory loss Restlessness or irritability
Delirium	Dizziness
Drowsiness	Fever
Headache	Heart rate, increased
Lethargy, fatigue	Mucous membrane dryness: mouth, nose
Muscle weakness, severe	Speech, slurring

Skin, changes
    Dryness   Sweating, decreased
    Flushing   Warmth, excessive
	Vision impairment, changes in acuity
	    Blurring Glaucoma, worsening
	    Eye pain Light sensitivity

Urinary retention or difficulty	

[**Editor's Note:** See page 390 for endnotes pertaining to this section.]

INVESTIGATIVE PROTOCOL
UNNECESSARY MEDICATIONS - MEDICATION REGIMEN REVIEW

Because they are closely related, the investigations of the requirements for medication regimen review and the review for unnecessary medications have been merged.

Objectives

- To determine whether each resident receives or is provided:

  o Only those medications that are clinically indicated in the dose and for the duration to meet his or her assessed needs;

  o Non-pharmacological approaches when clinically indicated, in an effort to reduce the need for or the dose of a medication; and

  o Gradual dose reduction attempts for antipsychotics (unless clinically contraindicated) and tapering of other medications, when clinically indicated, in an effort to discontinue the use or reduce the dose of the medication.

- To determine if the facility in collaboration with the prescriber:

  o Identifies the parameters for monitoring medication(s) or medication combinations (including antipsychotics) that pose a risk for adverse consequences; and for monitoring the effectiveness of medications (including a comparison with therapeutic goals); and

  o Recognizes and evaluates the onset or worsening of signs or symptoms, or a change in condition to determine whether these potentially may be related to the medication regimen; and follows-up as necessary upon identifying adverse consequences.

- To determine if the pharmacist:

  o Performed the monthly medication regimen review, and identified any existing irregularities regarding indications for use, dose, duration, and the potential for, or the existence of adverse consequences or other irregularities; and

  o Reported any identified irregularities to the attending physician and director of nursing.

- To determine whether the facility and/or practitioner acted on the report of any irregularity.

Use

Use this protocol during every initial and standard survey. In addition, this protocol may be used on revisits or abbreviated survey (complaint investigation) as necessary.

NOTE: This review is not intended to direct medication therapy. However, surveyors are expected to review factors related to the implementation, use, and monitoring of medications.

The surveyor is not expected to prove that an adverse consequence was directly caused by a medication or combination of medications, but rather that there was a failure in the care process related to considering and acting upon such possibilities.

If during the course of this review, the surveyor needs to contact the attending physician regarding questions related to the medication regimen, it is recommended that the facility's staff have the opportunity to provide the necessary information about the resident and the concerns to the physician for his/her review prior to responding to the surveyor's inquiries.

Procedures

Review the medications (prescription, over-the-counter medications, and nutritional supplements such as herbal products) currently ordered and/or discontinued by the prescriber at least back to the most recent signed recapitulation/reorder of all medications. Obtain a copy of the current orders if necessary. Gather information regarding the resident's mental, physical, functional, and psychosocial status and the medication-related therapeutic goals identified in the care plan as the basis for further review.

1. Observation and Record Review

Use the table below to guide observations, record review, and interviews with the resident or representative and relevant staff. Observe whether the medication-related interventions are consistently implemented over time and across various shifts. Note deviations from the care plan as well as potential medication-related adverse consequences. Verify observations by gathering additional information; for example, additional record reviews and/or interviews with the resident or representative, relevant staff, and practitioners.

SYMPTOMS, SIGNS, AND CONDITIONS THAT MAY BE ASSOCIATED WITH MEDICATIONS	REVIEW FOR HOW FACILITY MANAGED MEDICATIONS FOR THE RESIDENT

Determine if the resident has been transferred to acute care since the last survey and/or has recently (e.g., the previous 3 months) experienced a change in condition or currently has signs and symptoms, such as:
 	
• Anorexia and/or unplanned weight loss, or weight gain
• Behavioral changes, unusual behavior patterns (including increased distressed behavior)
• Bleeding or bruising, spontaneous or unexplained
• Bowel dysfunction including diarrhea, constipation and impaction
• Dehydration, fluid/electrolyte imbalance
• Depression, mood disturbance
• Dysphagia, swallowing difficulty
• Falls, dizziness, or evidence of impaired coordination
• Gastrointestinal bleeding
• Headaches, muscle pain, generalized or nonspecific aching or pain
• Mental status changes, (e.g., new or worsening confusion, new cognitive decline, worsening of dementia (including delirium))
• Rash, pruritus
• Respiratory difficulty or changes
• Sedation (excessive), insomnia, or sleep disturbance
• Seizure activity
• Urinary retention or incontinence
 	
If observations or record review indicate symptoms or changes in condition that may be related to medications (refer to Tables I and II, supplemented with current medication references), determine whether the facility considered medications as a potential cause of the change or symptom.
	Review the record (including the care plan, comprehensive assessment, and other parts of the record as appropriate) to determine whether it reflects the following elements related to medication management for the resident:
	
	• Clinical indications for use of the medication
	• Consideration of non-pharmacological interventions
	• Dose, including excessive dose and duplicate therapy
	• Duration, including excessive duration
	• Consideration of potential for tapering/GDR or rationale for clinical contraindication
	• Monitoring for and reporting of:
	  o Response to medications and progress toward therapeutic goals
	  o Emergence of medication-related adverse consequences
	• Adverse consequences, if present and potentially medication-related, note if there was:
	  o Recognition, evaluation, reporting, and management by the facility
	  o Physician action regarding potential medication-related adverse consequences

2. Interview

Interview the resident and or family/responsible party, to the extent possible, to determine:

- His/her participation in care planning and decision making, including discussions of the goals related to the use of medications;

- Whether approaches other than medications (as indicated) were discussed; and

- His/her evaluation of the results of the medication therapy and other approaches (such as decreasing symptoms of pain, improving functional ability).

If during the review, you identify concerns about the lack of indication for use; the dose or duration of a medication; lack of monitoring; failure to implement the care plan; or condition changes or functional decline that may be related to the medication regimen, interview knowledgeable staff to determine:

- Whether the resident has experienced any changes in the functioning or amount of activity that he/she is able to do;

- The clinical rationale for the use of the medication, dose or duration and how the interdisciplinary team is monitoring the resident's response to the medication;

- What process is in place to assure the care plan interventions for medication use are being implemented;

- Whether they were aware that the signs and symptoms may be adverse consequences related to the medication regimen;

- Whether the staff had contacted the attending physician to discuss the signs and symptoms and the current medication regimen;

- Whether and how the physician responded when informed of suspected adverse medication consequences; and

- Whether the pharmacist performed a medication regimen review and identified related signs and symptoms, or the staff informed the pharmacist of them if they occurred after the last pharmacist visit.

Interview the physician, as appropriate, to determine:

- Whether staff notified him/her of potential medication-related issues and concerns;

- His/her assessment of the significance of medication-related issues and concerns; and

- Rationale for his/her management of the resident's medications and/or medication-related issues or concerns.

3. Medication Regimen Review (MRR)

Review for compliance with the MRR requirements at F428. Determine:

- If the pharmacist had identified and reported to the director of nursing and attending physician any irregularities with the medication regimen such as:

  o The emergence or existence of clinically significant adverse consequences;

  o Excess dose or duration, lack of monitoring, lack of indication for use, lack of GDR (as indicated) or behavioral interventions for residents receiving antipsychotics, medication interactions potentially affecting the medication's effectiveness; and

- Whether the attending physician and the director of nursing acted on any irregularities identified in the report. The responses from the attending physician could include the following:

  o Changed the medication regimen in response to the concern raised in the report (or after additional review of the situation);

  o Provided a clinically pertinent rationale that is relevant to that specific resident's signs and symptoms, prognosis, test results, etc., documenting or indicating why the benefit of the medication(s) or dose(s) outweighed the risks of the adverse consequence;

  o Provided a clinically pertinent rationale for why any gradual dose reduction (for antipsychotic medications) and/or tapering (for other medications) is contraindicated, even for a trial period; or

  o Provided a clinically pertinent rationale for why a particular medication, dose, or duration is appropriate for a resident despite its risks (for example, the resident has had recurrent seizures unless he/she receives anticonvulsant dosing that exceeds the usual recommended serum medication concentration level or therapeutic range, and the attending physician and facility have been monitoring for and addressing adverse consequences).

- If the pharmacist identified a suspected adverse consequence, and the attending physician did not respond, determine if staff followed up with the attending physician.

  NOTE: If the staff and pharmacist identify a medication that they believe may be causing a serious adverse consequence or a risk of clinically significant adverse consequences for the resident, and the attending physician did not address the risks or harm to the resident, determine what steps staff took; e.g., contacting the medical director to review the situation and address the issue with the attending physician, as necessary. See guidance at 42 CFR 483.75(i) Medical Director (F501) for additional guidance.

If problems are identified with the MRR, interview the pharmacist, as indicated, to determine:

- How he/she conducts the MRR, including the frequency and extent of the medication review and under what circumstances a review might be conducted more often than monthly;

- How the facility communicates with him/her regarding medication-related issues in specific residents; and

- How he/she approaches the MRR process for short stay residents.

DETERMINATION OF COMPLIANCE (Task 6, Appendix P)

Synopsis of Regulation (F329)

The unnecessary medication requirement has six aspects in order to assure that medication therapy is appropriate for the individual resident. The facility must assure that medication therapy (including antipsychotic agents) is based upon:

- An adequate indication for use;

- Use of the appropriate dose;

- Provision of behavioral interventions and gradual dose reduction for individuals receiving antipsychotics (unless clinically contraindicated) in an effort to reduce or discontinue the medication;

- Use for the appropriate duration;

- Adequate monitoring to determine whether therapeutic goals are being met and to detect the emergence or presence of adverse consequences; and

- Reduction of dose or discontinuation of the medication in the presence of adverse consequences, as indicated.

Criteria for Compliance

Compliance with 42 CFR 483.25(l), F329, Unnecessary Medications

For a resident who has been, or is, receiving medication(s), the facility is in compliance if they, in collaboration with the prescriber:

- Assessed the resident to ascertain, to the extent possible, the causes of the condition or symptoms requiring treatment, including recognizing, evaluating, and determining whether the condition or symptoms may have reflected an adverse medication consequence;

- Based on the assessment, determined that medication therapy was indicated and identified the therapeutic goals for the medication;

- Utilized only those medications in appropriate doses for the appropriate duration, which are clinically necessary to treat the resident's assessed condition(s);

- Implemented a gradual dose reduction and behavioral interventions for each resident receiving antipsychotic medications unless clinically contraindicated;

- Monitored the resident for progress towards the therapeutic goal(s) and for the emergence or presence of adverse consequences, as indicated by the resident's condition and the medication(s); and

- Adjusted or discontinued the dose of a medication in response to adverse consequences, unless clinically contraindicated.

If not, cite F329.

Noncompliance for F329

After completing the investigation, determine whether or not compliance with the regulation exists. Noncompliance for F329 may include:

- **Inadequate Indications for Use** – Examples of noncompliance related to a medication being used without adequate indications include, but are not limited to:

  o Failure to document a clinical reason or demonstrate a clinically pertinent rationale, verbally or in writing, for using medication(s) for a specific resident.

  o Prescribing or administering a medication despite an allergy to that medication, or without clarifying whether a true allergy existed as opposed to other reactions (e.g., idiosyncratic reaction or other side effect).

  o Failure to provide a clear clinical rationale for continuing a medication that may be causing an adverse consequence.

  o Initiation of an antipsychotic medication to manage distressed behavior without considering a possible underlying medical cause (e.g., UTI, congestive heart failure)or environmental or psychosocial stressor.

  o Initiation of a medication presenting clinically significant risks without considering relative risks and benefits or potentially lower risk medications.

  o Concomitant use of two or more medications in the same pharmacological class without a clinically pertinent explanation.

- **Inadequate Monitoring** – Examples of noncompliance related to inadequate monitoring include, but are not limited to:

  o Failure to monitor the responses to or effects of a medication and failure to respond when monitoring indicates a lack of progress toward the therapeutic goal (e.g., relief of pain or normalization of thyroid function) or the emergence of an adverse consequence.

  o Failure to monitor a medication consistent with the current standard of practice or manufacturer's guidelines.

  o Failure to carry out the monitoring that was ordered or failure to monitor for potential clinically significant adverse consequences. For example, use of warfarin in conjunction with:

      – Inadequate or absent monitoring of PT/INR during treatment; and/or

      – Failure to recognize and monitor the increased risk of adverse consequences when the resident is receiving other medications that are known to increase the risk of bleeding or to interact with warfarin and increase PT/INR.

- **Excessive Dose (including duplicate therapy)** – Examples of noncompliance related to excessive dose include, but are not limited to:

  o Giving a total amount of any medication at one time or over a period of time that exceeds the amount recommended by the manufacturer's recommendations, clinical practice guidelines, evidence-based studies from medical/pharmacy journals, or standards of practice for a resident's age and condition, without a documented clinically pertinent rationale.

  o Failure to consider periodically the continued necessity of the dose or the possibility of tapering a medication.

  o Failure to provide and/or document a clinical rationale for using multiple medications from the same pharmacological class.

- **Excessive Duration** – Examples of noncompliance related to excessive duration include, but are not limited to:

  o Continuation beyond the manufacturer's recommended time frames, the stop date or duration indicated on the medication order, facility-established stop order policies, or clinical practice guidelines, evidence-based studies from medical/pharmacy journals, or current standards of practice, without documented clinical justification.

  o Continuation of a medication after the desired therapeutic goal has been achieved without evaluating whether the medication can offer any additional benefit, for example:

      – Use of an antibiotic beyond the recommended clinical guidelines or the facility policy without adequate reassessment of the resident and determination of continuing need.

      – Failure to re-evaluate the rationale for continuing antipsychotic medication initiated in an emergency after the acute phase has stabilized.

- **Adverse Consequences** – Examples of noncompliance related to adverse consequences include, but are not limited to:

  o Failure to act upon (i.e., discontinue a medication or reduce the dose or provide clinical justification for why the benefit outweighs the adverse consequences) a report of the risk for or presence of clinically significant adverse consequence(s);

  o Failure to respond to actual or potentially clinically significant adverse consequences related to the use of warfarin when the PT/INR exceeds the target goal.

- **Antipsychotic Medications without Gradual Dose Reduction and Behavioral Interventions unless Clinically Contraindicated** – Examples of noncompliance related to this requirement include, but are not limited to:

  o Failure to attempt GDR in the absence of identified and documented clinical contraindications.

  o Prolonged or indefinite antipsychotic use without attempting gradual dose reductions.

  o Failure to implement behavioral interventions to enable attempts to reduce or discontinue an antipsychotic medication.

Potential Tags for Additional Investigation

If noncompliance with 483.25(l) has been identified, then concerns with additional requirements may also have been identified. The surveyor is cautioned to investigate these related additional requirements before determining whether noncompliance with the additional requirements may be present. Examples of some of the related requirements that may be considered when noncompliance has been identified include the following:

- 42 CFR 483.10(b)(11), F157, Notification of Changes

  o Review whether the facility contacted the attending physician regarding a significant change in the resident's condition in relation to a potential adverse consequence of a medication, or if the resident has not responded to medication therapy as anticipated and/or indicated.

- 42 CFR 483.10 (b)(3) and (4), F154, F155, Notice of Rights and Services and (d)(2) Free Choice

  o Determine whether the resident was advised of her/his medical condition and therapy and was informed about her/his treatment including medications and the right to refuse treatments.

- 42 CFR 483.20(b), F272, Comprehensive Assessments

  o Review whether the facility's initial and periodic comprehensive assessments include an assessment of the resident's medication regimen.

- 42 CFR 483.20(k)(1) and (2), F279, F280, Comprehensive Care Plans

  o Review whether the resident's comprehensive care plan: a) was based on the assessment of the resident's conditions, risks, needs, and behavior; b) was consistent with the resident's therapeutic goals; (c) considered the need to monitor for effectiveness based on those therapeutic goals and for the emergence or presence of adverse consequences; and (d) was revised as needed to address medication-related issues.

- 42 CFR 483.25(a)(1), F310, Decline in ADL

  o Review whether the facility had identified, evaluated, and responded to a new or rapidly progressive decline in function, development or worsening of movement disorders, increased fatigue and activity intolerance that affected the resident's ADL ability in relation to potential medication adverse consequences.

- 42 CFR 483.25(d), F315, Urinary Incontinence

  o Review whether the facility had identified, evaluated, and responded to a change in urinary function or continence status in relation to potential medication adverse consequences.

- 42 CFR 483.25(f)(1)&(2), F319, F320, Mental and Psychosocial Functioning

  o Review whether the facility had identified, evaluated, and responded to a change in behavior and/or psychosocial changes, including depression or other mood disturbance, distress, restlessness, increasing confusion, or delirium in relation to potential medication adverse consequences.

- 42 CFR 483.25(i)(1), F325, Nutritional Parameters

    o   Review if the facility had identified, evaluated, and responded to a change in nutritional parameters, anorexia or unplanned weight loss, dysphagia, and/or swallowing disorders in relation to potential medication adverse consequences.

- 42 CFR 483.25(j), F327, Hydration

    o   Review if the facility had identified, evaluated, and responded to a change in hydration or fluid or electrolyte balance (for example, high or low sodium or potassium) in relation to potential medication adverse consequences.

- 42 CFR 483.40(a), F385, Physician Supervision

    o   Review if the attending physician supervised the resident's medical treatment, including assessing the resident's condition and medications, identifying the clinical rationale, and monitoring for and addressing adverse consequences.

- 42 CFR 483.40(b), F386, Physician Visits

    o   Review if the attending physician or designee reviewed the resident's total program of care and wrote, signed, and dated progress notes covering pertinent aspects of the medication regimen and related issues.

- 42 CFR 483.60(c), F428, Medication Regimen Review

    o   Review whether the licensed pharmacist has provided consultation regarding the integrity of medication-related records (e.g., MAR, physician order sheets, telephone orders), and potential or actual medication irregularities.

- 42 CFR 483.75(i), F501, Medical Director.

    o   Review whether the medical director, when requested by the facility, interacted with the attending physician regarding a failure to respond or an inadequate response to identified or reported potential medication irregularities and adverse consequences; and whether the medical director collaborated with the facility to help develop, implement, and evaluate policies and procedures for the safe and effective use of medications in the care of residents.

IV. DEFICIENCY CATEGORIZATION (Part IV, Appendix P)

Once the team has completed its investigation, analyzed the data, reviewed the regulatory requirement, and identified any deficient practice(s) that demonstrate that noncompliance with the regulation at F329 exists, the team must determine the severity of each deficiency, based on the resultant harm or potential for harm to the resident.

The key elements for severity determination for F329 are as follows:

1. **Presence of potential or actual harm/negative outcome(s) due to a failure related to unnecessary medications.**

    Examples of actual or potential harm/negative outcomes for F329 may include, but are not limited to:

- Potential for life-threatening toxicity from excessive dose or lack of indication for the use of digoxin.

- Complications (such as diarrhea with life threatening fluid loss, nephrotoxicity, hearing loss, or anaphylactic shock) from use of an antibiotic when no clear indication for use has been established or response to the use has not been monitored.

- Fractures or falls with injury resulting from the continuing use of medications (e.g., hypnotics/sedatives, antipsychotics, antidepressants, antihypertensives) in the presence of predisposing risks or adverse consequences such as persistent dizziness or recurrent falling without intervening or reevaluating the need for and dose of the medication believed to be the cause of the gait instability.

2. **Degree of potential or actual harm/negative outcome(s) due to a failure related to unnecessary medications.**

Identify how the facility practices caused, resulted in, allowed, or contributed to the actual or potential for harm:

- If harm has occurred, determine if the harm is at the level of serious injury, impairment, death, compromise, or discomfort; or

- If harm has not yet occurred, determine how likely is the potential for serious injury, impairment, death, compromise, or discomfort to occur to the resident.

3. **The immediacy of correction required.**

Determine whether the noncompliance requires immediate correction in order to prevent serious injury, harm, impairment, or death to one or more residents.

The survey team must evaluate the harm or potential for harm based upon the following levels of severity for tag F329. First, the team must rule out whether Severity Level 4, Immediate Jeopardy to a resident's health or safety, exists by evaluating the deficient practice in relation to immediacy, culpability, and severity. (Follow the guidance in Appendix Q.)

NOTE: The death or transfer of a resident who was harmed or injured as a result of facility noncompliance does not remove a finding of immediate jeopardy. The facility is required to implement specific actions to remove the jeopardy and correct the noncompliance which allowed or caused the immediate jeopardy.

Severity Level 4 Considerations: Immediate Jeopardy to Resident Health or Safety

Immediate Jeopardy is a situation in which the facility's noncompliance with one or more requirements of participation:

- Has allowed, caused, or resulted in, or is likely to allow, cause, or result in serious injury, harm, impairment, or death to a resident; and

- Requires immediate correction, as the facility either created the situation or allowed the situation to continue by failing to implement preventative or corrective measures.

Examples may include, but are not limited to:

- Failure to assess or respond appropriately for a resident taking warfarin who had an elevated INR of 9 or greater with or without bleeding, or the elevated INR persisted without assessment/follow-up.

- Failure to monitor PT/INR for a resident on anticoagulant therapy in accordance with current standards of practice and to recognize and/or respond to a life threatening adverse consequence related to anticoagulation.

- Failure to recognize developing serotonin syndrome (e.g., confusion, motor restlessness, tremor) in a resident receiving a SSRI, leading to the addition of medications with additive serotonin effect or medication to suppress the symptoms.

- Failure to recognize and respond to signs and symptoms of neuroleptic malignant syndrome (NMS).

- In the presence of gastrointestinal bleeding, the failure to recognize medication therapies (such as NSAIDs or COX-2 inhibitors, bisphosphonates) as potentially causing or contributing to the gastrointestinal bleed, resulting in the continued administration of the medication, until the resident required hospitalization for severe bleeding.

NOTE: If immediate jeopardy has been ruled out based upon the evidence, then evaluate whether actual harm that is not immediate jeopardy exists at Severity Level 3.

Severity Level 3 Considerations: Actual Harm that is Not Immediate Jeopardy

Level 3 indicates noncompliance that resulted in actual harm, and may include, but is not limited to, clinical compromise, decline, or the resident's inability to maintain and/or reach his/her highest practicable well-being. Examples may include, but are not limited to:

- Facility failure to take appropriate action (e.g., suspending administration of the anticoagulant) in response to an INR greater than 4 and less than 9 for a resident who is receiving warfarin until spontaneous bruising or frank bleeding occurs, resulting in the need to transfuse or hospitalize the resident.

- Facility failure to evaluate the medication regimen as a potential cause of seizure activity resulting in the addition of anticonvulsants to treat recent-onset seizures that can be adverse consequences of medications.

- Facility failure to implement a GDR that was not contraindicated in a resident receiving prolonged, continuous antipsychotic therapy resulting in functional decline, somnolence, lethargy, tremors, increased falling, or impaired ambulation.

NOTE: If Severity Level 3 (actual harm that is not immediate jeopardy) has been ruled out based upon the evidence, then evaluate as to whether Severity Level 2 (no actual harm with the potential for more than minimal harm) exists.

Severity Level 2 Considerations: No Actual Harm with Potential for More Than Minimal Harm that is Not Immediate Jeopardy

Level 2 indicates noncompliance that resulted in a resident outcome of no more than minimal discomfort and/or has the potential to compromise the resident's ability to maintain or reach his or her highest practicable level of well-being. The potential exists for greater harm to occur if interventions are not provided. Examples may include, but are not limited to:

- Facility failure to take appropriate action (e.g., change or suspend administration of the warfarin dose) for a resident who has an INR greater than 4 and less than 9 without any bleeding.

- Failure to monitor INR for a resident who has been stabilized on warfarin, but who has not had bleeding.

- Facility failure to identify and act upon minor symptoms of allergic response to medications, such as a rash.

- Facility failure to monitor for response to therapy or for the emergence or presence of adverse consequences before the resident has experienced an adverse consequence or decline in function (e.g., monitoring periodically for symptoms of behavioral distress in someone receiving psychopharmacological medication; monitoring thyroid function at least annually in an individual receiving thyroid hormone replacement; and monitoring hydration status and basic metabolic profile for a resident receiving diuretics or ACE inhibitors, who had a change in mental status after the onset of diarrhea).

Severity Level 1: No Actual Harm with Potential for Minimal Harm

The failure of the facility to provide appropriate care and services to manage the resident's medication regimen to avoid unnecessary medications and minimize negative outcome places residents at risk for more than minimal harm. Therefore, Severity Level 1 does not apply for this regulatory requirement.

F332 and F333

§483.25(m) Medication Errors

The facility must ensure that--

[F332] §483.25(m)(1) It is free of medication error rates of five percent or greater; and

[F333] §483.25(m)(2) Residents are free of any significant medication errors.

Interpretive Guidelines §483.25(m)

Medication Error -- The observed preparation or administration of drugs or biologicals which is not in accordance with:

1. Physician's orders;

2. Manufacturer's specifications (not recommendations) regarding the preparation and administration of the drug or biological;

3. Accepted professional standards and principles which apply to professionals providing services. Accepted professional standards and principles include the various practice regulations in each State, and current·commonly accepted health standards established by national organizations, boards, and councils.

"Significant medication error" means one which causes the resident discomfort or jeopardizes his or her health and safety. Criteria for judging significant medication errors as well as examples are provided under significant and non-significant medication errors. Discomfort may be a subjective or relative term used in different ways depending on the individual situation. (Constipation that is unrelieved by an ordered laxative that results in a drug error that is omitted for one day may be slightly uncomfortable or perhaps not uncomfortable at all. When the constipation persists for greater than three days, the constipation may be more significant. Constipation causing obstruction or fecal impaction can jeopardize the resident's health and safety.)

"Medication error rate" is determined by calculating the percentage of errors. The numerator in the ratio is the total number of errors that the survey team observes, both significant and nonsignificant. The denominator is called "opportunities for errors" and includes all the doses the survey team observed being administered plus the doses ordered but not administered. The equation for calculating a medication error rate is as follows:

Medication Error Rate = Number of Errors Observed divided by the Opportunities for Errors (doses given plus doses ordered but not given) X 100.

"Medication error rate" -- A medication error rate of 5% or greater includes both significant and nonsignificant medication errors. It indicates that the facility may have systemic problems with its drug distribution system and a deficiency should be written.

The error rate must be 5% or greater. Rounding of a lower rate (e.g., 4.6%) to a 5% rate is not permitted.

Significant and Nonsignificant Medication Errors

"Determining Significance" -- The relative significance of medication errors is a matter of professional judgment. Follow three general guidelines in determining whether a medication error is significant or not:

"Resident Condition" -- The resident's condition is an important factor to take into consideration. For example, a fluid pill erroneously administered to a dehydrated resident may have serious consequences, but if administered to a resident with a normal fluid balance may not. If the resident's condition requires rigid control, a single missed or wrong dose can be highly significant.

"Drug Category" -- If the drug is from a category that usually requires the resident to be titrated to a specific blood level, a single medication error could alter that level and precipitate a reoccurrence of symptoms or toxicity. This is especially important with a drug that has a Narrow Therapeutic Index (NTI) (i.e., a drug in which the therapeutic dose is very close to the toxic dose). Examples of drugs with NTI are as follows: Anticonvulsant: phenytoin (Dilantin),carbamazepine (Tegretol), Anticoagulants: warfarin (Coumadin) Antiarrhythmic (digoxin)Lanoxin) Antiasthmatics: theophylline (TheoDur) Antimanic Drugs: lithium salts (Eskalith, Lithobid).

"**Frequency of Error**" -- If an error is occurring with any frequency, there is more reason to classify the error as significant. For example, if a resident's drug was omitted several times, as verified by reconciling the number of tablets delivered with the number administered, classifying that error as significant would be more in order. This conclusion should be considered in concert with the resident's condition and the drug category.

"**Examples of Significant and Non-Significant Medication Errors**" -- Some of these errors are identified as significant. This designation is based on expert opinion without regard to the status of the resident. Most experts concluded that the significance of these errors, in and of themselves, have a high potential for creating problems for the typical long term care facility resident. Those errors identified as nonsignificant have also been designated primarily on the basis of the nature of the drug. Resident status and frequency of error could classify these errors as significant.

Examples of Medication Errors Detected

Omissions Examples (Drug ordered but not administered at least once):

Drug Order	Significance
Haldol 1mg BID	NS
Motrin 400mg TID	NS
Quinidine 200mg TID	S**
Tearisol Drops 2 both eyes TID	NS
Metamucil one packet BID	NS
Multivitamin one daily	NS
Mylanta Susp. one oz., TID AC	NS
Nitrol Oint. one inch	S

* Not Significant

**Significant

Unauthorized Drug Examples (Drugs administered without a physician's order):

Drug Order	Significance
Feosol	NS
Coumadin 4mg	S
Zyloprim 100mg	NS
Tylenol 5 gr	NS
Motrin 400mg	NS

Wrong Dose Examples:

Drug Order	Administered	Significance
Timoptic 0.25% one drop in the left eye TID	Three drops in each eye	NS
Digoxin 0.125mg everyday	0.25mg	S
Amphojel 30ml QID	15ml	NS
Dilantin 125 SUSP 12ml	2ml	S

Wrong Route of Administration Examples:

Drug Order	Administered	Significance
Cortisporin Ear Drops 4 to 5 left ear QID	Left Eye	S

Wrong Dosage Form Examples:

Drug Order	Administered	Significance
Colace Liquid 100mg BID	Capsule	NS
Mellaril Tab 10mg	Liquid Concentrate	NS*
Dilantin Kapseals 100 mg three Kapseals p.o. HS	Prompt Phenytoin 100 mg three capsules p.o. HS	S**

* If correct dose was given.
** Parke Davis Kapseals have an extended rate of absorption. Prompt phenytoin capsules do not.

Wrong Drug Examples:

Drug Order	Administered	Significance
Tums	Oscal	NS
Vibramycin	Vancomycin	S

Wrong Time Examples:

Drug Order	Administered	Significance
Digoxin 0.25mg daily at 8 a.m.	At 9:30 am	NS
Percocet 2 Tabs 20 min. before painful treatment	2 Tabs given 3 after treatment	S

Medication Errors Due to Failure to Follow Manufacturers Specifications' or Accepted Professional Standards

The following situations in drug administration may be considered medication errors:

- Failure to "Shake Well": The failure to "shake" a drug product that is labeled "shake well." This may lead to an under dose or over dose depending on the drug product and the elapsed time since the last "shake." The surveyor should use common sense in determining the adequacy of the shaking of the medication. Some drugs, for example dilantin, are more critical to achieve correct dosage delivery than others.

- Insulin Suspensions: Also included under this category is the failure to "mix" the suspension without creating air bubbles. Some individuals "roll" the insulin suspension to mix it without creating air bubbles. Any motion used is acceptable so long as the suspension is mixed and does not have air bubbles in it prior to the administration.

- Crushing Medications that should not be Crushed: Crushing tablets or capsules that the manufacturer states "do not crush."

Exceptions to the "Do Not Crush" rule:

- If the prescriber orders a drug to be crushed which the manufacturer states should not be crushed, the prescriber or the pharmacist must explain, in the clinical record, why crushing the medication will not adversely affect the resident. Additionally, the pharmacist should inform the facility staff to observe for pertinent adverse effects.

- If the facility can provide literature from the drug manufacturer or from a reviewed health journal to justify why modification of the dosage form will not compromise resident care.

- Adequate Fluids with Medications: The administration of medications without adequate fluid when the manufacturer specifies that adequate fluids be taken with the medication. For example:

  o   Bulk laxatives (e.g., Metamucil, Fiberall, Serutan, Konsyl, Citrucel);

o   Nonsteroidal Anti-Inflammatory Drugs (NSAIDs) should be administered with adequate fluid. Adequate fluid is not defined by the manufacturer but is usually four to eight ounces. The surveyor should count fluids consumed during meals or snacks (such as coffee, juice, milk, soft drinks, etc.) as fluids taken with the medication, as long as they have consumed within a reasonable time of taking the medication (e.g., within approximately 30 minutes). If the resident refuses to take adequate fluid, the facility should not be at fault so long as they made a good faith effort to offer fluid, and provided any assistance that may be necessary to drink the fluid. It is important that the surveyor not apply this rule to residents who are fluid restricted; and

o   Potassium supplements (solid or liquid dosage forms) such as: Kaochlor, Klorvess, Kaon, K-Lor, K-Tab, K-Dur, K-Lyte, Slow K, Klotrix, Micro K, or Ten K should be administered with or after meals with a full glass (e.g., approximately 4 - 8 ounces of water or fruit juice). This will minimize the possibility of gastrointestinal irritation and saline cathartic effect. If the resident refuses to take adequate fluid, the facility should not be at fault so long as they made a good faith effort to offer fluid, and provided any assistance that may be necessary to drink the fluid. It is important that the surveyor not apply this rule to residents who are fluid restricted.

• Medications that Must be Taken with Food or Antacids: The administration of medications without food or antacids when the manufacturer specifies that food or antacids be taken with or before the medication is considered a medication error. The most commonly used drugs that should be taken with food or antacids are the Nonsteroidal Anti-Inflammatory Drugs (NSAIDs). There is evidence that elderly, debilitated persons are at greater risk of gastritis and GI bleeds, including silent GI bleeds. Determine if the time of administration was selected to take into account the need to give the medication with food.

Examples of commonly used NSAIDs are as follows:

Generic Name	Brand Name
Diclofenac	Voltaren, Cataflam
Diflunisal	Dolobid
Etodolac	Lodine
Fenoprofen	Nalfon
Ibuprofen	Motrin, Advil
Indomethacin	Indocin
Ketoprofen	Orudis, Oruvail
Mefenamic Acid	Ponstel
Nabumetone	Relafen
Naproxen	Naprosyn, Aleve
Piroxicam	Feldene
Sulindac	Clinoril
Tolmetin	Tolectin

• Medications Administered with Enteral Nutritional Formulas: Administering medications immediately before, immediately after, or during the administration of enteral nutritional formulas (ENFs) without achieving the following minimum objectives:

o   Check the placement of the naso-gastric or gastrostomy tube in accordance with the facility's policy on this subject. **NOTE:** If the placement of the tube is not checked, this is not a medication error; it is a failure to follow accepted professional practice and should be evaluated under Tag F281 requiring the facility to meet professional standards of quality.

o   Flush the enteral feeding tube with at least 30 ml of preferably warm water before and after medications are administered. While it is noted that some facility policies ideally adopt flushing the tube after each individual medication is given, as opposed to after the group of multiple medications is given, unless there are known compatibility problems between medicines being mixed together, a minimum of one flushing before and after giving the medications is all the surveyor need review. There may be cases where flushing with 30 ml after each single medication is given may overload an individual with fluid, raising the risk of discomfort or stress on body functions. Failure to flush, before and after, would be counted as one medication error and would be included in the calculation for medication errors exceeding 5 percent.

o   The administration of enteral nutrition formula and administration of dilantin should be separated to minimize interaction. The surveyor should look for appropriate documentation and monitoring if the two are administered simultaneously. If the facility is not aware that there is a potential for an interaction between the two when given together, and is not monitoring for outcome of seizures or unwanted side effects of dilantin, then the surveyor should consider simultaneous administration a medication error.

- Medications Instilled into the Eye: The administration of eye drops without achieving the following critical objectives:

o   **Eye Contact**: The eye drop, but not the dropper, must make full contact with the conjunctival sac and then be washed over the eye when the resident closes the eyelid; and

o   **Sufficient Contact Time**: The eye drop must contact the eye for a sufficient period of time before the next eye drop is instilled. The time for optimal eye drop absorption is approximately 3 to 5 minutes. (It should be encouraged that when the procedures are possible, systemic effects of eye medications can be reduced by pressing the tear duct for one minute after eye drop administration or by gentle eye closing for approximately three minutes after the administration.)

- Allowing Resident to Swallow Sublingual Tablets: If the resident persists in swallowing a sublingual tablet (e.g., nitroglycerin) despite efforts to train otherwise, the facility should endeavor to seek an alternative dosage form for this drug.

- Medication Administered Via Metered Dose Inhalers (MDI): The use of MDI in other than the following ways (this includes use of MDI by the resident). This is an error if the person administering the drug did not do all the following:

o   Shake the container well;

o   Position the inhaler in front of or in the resident's mouth. Alternatively a spacer may be used;

o   For cognitively impaired residents, many clinicians believe that the closed mouth technique is easier for the resident and more likely to be successful. However, the open mouth technique often results in better and deeper penetration of the medication into the lungs, when this method can be used; and

o   If more than one puff is required, (whether the same medication or a different medication) wait approximately a minute between puffs.

NOTE: If the person administering the drug follows all the procedures outlined above, and there is a failure to administer the medication because the resident can't cooperate (for example, a resident with dementia may not understand the procedure), this should not be called a medication error. The surveyor should evaluate the facility's responsibility to assess the resident's circumstance, and possibly attempt other dosage forms such as oral dosage forms or nebulizers.

Determining Medication Errors

Timing Errors -- If a drug is ordered before meals (AC) and administered after meals (PC), always count this as a medication error. Likewise, if a drug is ordered PC and is given AC, count as a medication error. Count a wrong time error if the drug is administered 60 minutes earlier or later than its scheduled time of administration, BUT ONLY IF THAT WRONG TIME ERROR CAN CAUSE THE RESIDENT DISCOMFORT OR JEOPARDIZE THE RESIDENT'S HEALTH AND SAFETY. Counting a drug with a long half-life (e.g., digoxin) as a wrong time error when it is 15 minutes late is improper because this drug has a long half-life (beyond 24 hours) and 15 minutes has no significant impact on the resident. The same is true for many other wrong time errors (except AC AND PC errors).

To determine the scheduled time, examine the facility's policy relative to dosing schedules. The facility's policy should dictate when it administers a.m. doses, or when it administers the first dose in a 4-times-a-day dosing schedule.

Prescriber's Orders -- The latest recapitulation of drug orders is sufficient for determining whether a valid order exists provided the prescriber has signed the "recap." The signed "recap," if the facility uses the "recap" system and subsequent orders constitute a legal authorization to administer the drug.

Procedures §483.25(m)

Medication Error Detection Methodology -- Use an observation technique to determine medication errors. The survey team should observe the administration of drugs, on several different drug "passes," when necessary. Record what is observed; and reconcile the record of observation with the prescriber's drug orders to determine whether or not medication errors have occurred.

Do not rely solely on a paper review to determine medication errors. Detection of blank spaces on a medication administration record does not constitute the detection of actual medication errors. Paper review only identifies possible errors in most cases. In some cases paper review can help identify actual errors but research has shown that the procedure is time consuming for the number of actual errors detected.

Observation Technique --The survey team must know without doubt, what drugs, in what strength, and dosage forms, are being administered. This is accomplished prior to drug administration and may be done in a number of ways depending on the drug distribution system used (e.g. unit dose, vial system, punch card).

1. Identify the drug product. There are two principal ways to do this. In most cases, they are used in combination:

   - Identify the product by its size, shape, and color. Many drug products are identifiable by their distinctive size, shape, or color. This technique is problematic because not all drugs have distinctive sizes, shapes, or color.

   - Identify the product by observing the label. When the punch card or the unit dose system is used, the survey team can usually observe the label and adequately identify the drug product. When the vial system is used, observing the label is sometimes more difficult. Ask the nurse to identify the medication being administered.

2. Observe and record the administration of drugs ("pass"). Follow the person administering drugs and observe residents receiving drugs (e.g., actually swallowing oral dosage forms). Be neutral and as unobtrusive as possible during this process.

   - Make every effort to observe residents during several different drug "passes," if possible, so the survey team will have an assessment of the entire facility rather than one staff member on one drug pass.

   - Identifying residents can present a problem. The surveyor should ask appropriate staff to explain the facility policy or system for the identification of residents.

3. Reconcile the surveyor's record of observation with physician's orders. Compare the record of observation with the most current orders for drugs. This comparison involves two distinct activities:

   - For each drug on the surveyor's list: Was it administered according to the prescriber's orders? For example, in the correct strength, by the correct route? Was there a valid order for the drug? Was the drug the correct one?

- For drugs not on the surveyor's list: Are there orders for drugs that should have been administered, but were not? Examine the record for drug orders that were not administered and should have been. Such circumstances may represent omitted doses, one of the most frequent types of errors.

- Ask the person administering drugs, if possible, to describe the system for administering the drugs given. Occasionally, a respiratory therapist may administer inhalers, a designated treatment person may only administer topical treatments, a hospice nurse may administer hospice medications, another person may administer eye drops or as needed drugs, etc. Sometimes people may share medication carts. Under these circumstances, these individuals should be interviewed about the omitted dose, if they were involved, if possible. When persons that were actually responsible for administering the drugs are not available, ask their supervisor for clarification.

  The surveyor should now have a complete record of what was observed and what should have occurred according to the prescribers' orders. Determine the number of errors by adding the errors on each resident. Before concluding for certain that an error has occurred, discuss the apparent error with the person who administered the drugs if possible. There may be a logical explanation for an apparent error. For example, the surveyor observed that a resident had received Lasix 20 mg, but the order was for 40 mg. This was an apparent error in dosage. But the nurse showed the surveyor another more recent order which discontinued the 40 mg order and replaced it with a 20 mg order.

4. Reporting Errors -- Describe to the facility each error that the survey team detects (e.g., Mary Jones received digoxin in 0.125 instead of 0.25 mg). The survey team is not required to analyze the errors and come to any conclusions on how the facility can correct them. Do not attempt to categorize errors into various classifications (e.g., wrong dose, wrong resident). Stress that an error occurred and that future errors must be avoided.

5. Observe Many Individuals Administering Medications. Strive to observe as many individuals administering medications as possible. This provides a better picture of accuracy of the facility's entire drug distribution system.

Dose Reconciliation Technique Supplement to the Observation Technique -- When an omission error has been detected through the observation technique, the dose reconciliation technique can sometimes enable the survey team to learn how frequently an error has occurred in the past. Learning about the frequency of an error can assist in judging the significance of the error. (See Significant and Non Significant Medication Errors above.) The dose reconciliation technique requires a comparison of the number of doses remaining in a supply of drugs with the number of days the drug has been in use and the directions for use. For example, if a drug were in use for 5 days with direction to administer the drug 4 times a day, then 20 doses should have been used. If a count of the supply of that drug shows that only 18 doses were used (i.e., two extra doses exist) and no explanation for the discrepancy exists (e.g., resident refused the dose, or resident was hospitalized), then two omission errors may have occurred.

Use the dose reconciliation technique in facilities that indicate the number of drugs received, and the date and the specific "pass" when that particular drug was started. Unless this information is available, do not use this technique. If this information is not available, there is no Federal authority under which the survey team may require it, except for controlled drugs.

F334

§483.25(n) Influenza and pneumococcal immunizations---

(1) Influenza. The facility must develop policies and procedures that ensure that—

(i)   Before offering the influenza immunization, each resident or the resident's legal representative receives education regarding the benefits and potential side effects of the immunization;

(ii)   Each resident is offered an influenza immunization October 1 through March 31 annually, unless the immunization is medically contraindicated or the resident has already been immunized during this time period;

(iii)   The resident or the resident's legal representative has the opportunity to refuse immunization; and

(iv)   The resident's medical record includes documentation that indicates, at a minimum, the following:

(A)   That the resident or resident's legal representative was provided education regarding the benefits and potential side effects of influenza immunization; and

(B)   That the resident either received the influenza immunization or did not receive the influenza immunization due to medical contraindications or refusal.

(2) Pneumococcal disease. The facility must develop policies and procedures that ensure that—

(i)   Before offering the pneumococcal immunization, each resident or the resident's legal representative receives education regarding the benefits and potential side effects of the immunization;

(ii)   Each resident is offered an pneumococcal immunization, unless the immunization is medically contraindicate or the resident has already been immunized;

(iii) The resident or the resident's legal representative has the opportunity to refuse immunization; and

(iv)   The resident's medical record includes documentation that indicates, at a minimum, the following:

(A)   That the resident or resident's legal representative was provided education regarding the benefits and potential side effects of pneumococcal immunization; and

(B)   That the resident either received the pneumococcal immunization or did not receive the pneumococcal immunization due to medical contraindication or refusal.

(v)   Exception. As an alternative, based on an assessment and practitioner recommendation, a second pneumococcal immunization may be given after 5 years following the first pneumococcal immunization, unless medically contraindicated or the resident or the resident's legal representative refuses the second immunization.

Intent:

The intent of this requirement is to:

- Minimize the risk of residents acquiring, transmitting, or experiencing complications from influenza and pneumococcal pneumonia by assuring that each resident:

  o   Is informed about the benefits and risks of immunizations; and

  o   Has the opportunity to receive, unless medically contraindicated or refused or already immunized, the influenza and pneumococcal vaccine; and

- Assure documentation in the resident's medical record of the information/education provided regarding the benefits and risks of immunization and the administration or the refusal of or medical contraindications to the vaccine(s).

Definitions

Medical contraindication – A condition or risk that precludes the administration of a treatment or intervention because of the substantial probability that harm to the individual may occur.

Precaution - A condition in a potential recipient that might increase the risk for a serious adverse reaction or that might compromise the vaccine's induction of immunity. However, the risk for this happening is less than expected with a contraindication. For example, as a result of the resident's condition, complications could result, or a person might experience a more severe reaction to the vaccine than would have otherwise been expected; however, the risk for this happening is less than expected with medical contraindications.

Overview

Receipt of vaccinations is essential to the health and well-being of long term care residents. Establishing an immunization program facilitates achievement of this objective. Flu outbreaks place both the residents and the nursing facility staff at risk of infection. Pneumococcal pneumonia, a type of bacterial pneumonia, is a common cause of hospitalization and death in older people. People 65 years or older, are two to three times more likely than the younger population to get pneumococcal infections.

According to the Centers for Disease Control and Prevention (CDC),
(see http://www.cdc.gov/mmwr/preview/mmwrhtml/rr54e713a1.htm) "the primary option for reducing the effect of influenza is immuno-prophylaxis with vaccine. Inactivated (i.e., killed virus) influenza vaccine and live, attenuated influenza vaccine are available for use in the United States. Vaccinating persons at high risk for complications and their contacts each year before seasonal increases in influenza virus circulation is the most effective means of reducing the effect of influenza. When vaccine and epidemic strains are well-matched, achieving increased vaccination rates among persons living in closed settings (e.g., nursing homes and other chronic-care facilities) and among staff can reduce the risk for outbreaks by inducing herd immunity. Vaccination of health-care workers and other persons in close contact with persons at increased risk for severe influenza illness can also reduce transmission of influenza and subsequent influenza-related complications. Antiviral drugs used for chemoprophylaxis or treatment of influenza are a key adjunct to vaccine …However, antiviral medications are not a substitute for vaccination."

Because of the clinically complex conditions of most nursing home residents, it is especially important for the facility to have a program in place for the prevention of disease. The Long Term Care regulations at 42 CFR 483.65 (Tag F441) Infection Control, requires that each "facility must establish and maintain an infection control program designed to provide a safe, sanitary, and comfortable environment and to help prevent the development and transmission of disease and infection." The regulation for immunization complements this existing infection control regulation in the areas of prevention of the development and transmission of disease. (For more information on immunizations programs, see http://www.cdc.gov/nip/publications/long-term-care.pdf.)

An effective immunization program involves collaborating with the medical director to develop resident care policies for immunization(s) that reflect current standards of practice and that include:

- Physician approved policies for orders for influenza and pneumococcal polysaccharide vaccines (administration must be based on an assessment of each resident for possible medical contraindications – See Tag F386 for physician orders for vaccinations);

- Identification, of each resident's immunization status, including assessment for potential medical contraindications and record of vaccination;

- The vaccination schedule including mechanisms for recording and monitoring for administration of both influenza and pneumococcal pneumonia vaccines; and

- How pertinent information will be provided to residents. The facility may wish to use educational resources such as those provided by the U. S. Centers for Disease Control (CDC):

  o For trivalent inactivated vaccine (TIV): http://www.cdc.gov/nip/publications/VIS/vis-flu.pdf;

  o For live attenuated vaccine (LAIV)LAIV: http://www.cdc.gov/nip/publications/VIS/vis-flulive.pdf; and o **For pneumococcal polysaccharide vaccine; http://www.cdc.gov/nip/publications/vis/vis-ppv.pdf.**

For information on the influenza vaccines, the following site contains information on the background, types of vaccines, medical contraindications and other information: http://www.cdc.gov/mmwr/preview/mmwrhtml/rr54e713a1.htm.

Provision of Immunizations

In order for a resident to exercise his or her right to make informed choices, it is important for the facility to provide the resident with education regarding the benefits and potential side effects of immunizations. Facilities are required by 42 CFR 483.25(n)(1)(iv) and 42 CFR 483.25(n)(2)(iv) to document the provision of this education and the administration or refusal of the immunization or the medical contraindication of the immunization. There may be clinical indications or other reasons that a resident may not have received immunizations. Examples may include, but are not limited to the following:

- A decision may have been made to delay vaccination for a resident because a precaution is present. According to the CDC, "under normal circumstances, vaccinations should be deferred when a precaution is present. However, a vaccination might be indicated in the presence of a precaution because the benefit of protection from the vaccine outweighs the risk for an adverse reaction. The presence of a moderate or severe acute illness with or without a fever is a precaution to administration of all vaccines;"

- A resident may be in the end stages of a terminal illness and receiving care that is limited to comfort or palliative measures only. Vaccination decisions for residents in the end stages of a terminal illness should be made jointly by the physician and resident;

- A resident may have medical contraindications for live attenuated influenza vaccine (LAIV) that, according to the Centers for Disease Control and Prevention (www.cdc.gov/flu/professionals/vaccination/shouldnotlaiv.htm) include,but are not limited to:

    o Persons who are 50 years of age or older, have asthma, reactive airway disease, or other chronic disorders of the pulmonary or cardiovascular systems;

    o Persons with underlying medical conditions, including such metabolic diseases such as diabetes, renal dysfunction, and hemoglobinopathies;

    o Persons with known or suspected immunodeficiency diseases or who are receiving immuno-suppressive therapies; and

    o Persons with a history of hypersensitivity, including anaphylaxis, to any of the components of LAIV or to eggs;

- A resident may have already received the influenza vaccine for this season; and the pneumococcal immunization status is current; and

- The resident refused the immunization.

NOTE: Inactivated influenza vaccine contains noninfectious killed viruses and cannot cause influenza. Since there is a delay in developing antibodies after vaccination, the resident may develop influenza if there was exposure prior to receiving the vaccine. Coincidental respiratory disease unrelated to influenza vaccination can occur at any time after vaccination.

Following vaccination with inactivated vaccine a person may experience local reaction and/or systemic reactions. Local reactions typically include soreness at the vaccination site and body aches. Systemic reactions include fever, malaise and myalgia and persons who have had no previous exposure to the influenza virus antigens in the vaccine are most often affected.

Other reactions as identified by the CDC, which may occur immediately, presumably allergic reactions (e.g., hives, angioedema, allergic asthma, and systemic anaphylaxis) rarely are due to the influenza component of the vaccination, but probably result from hypersensitivity to other vaccine components; the majority of reactions probably are caused by residual egg protein. Persons who have had hives or swelling of the lips or tongue, or who have experienced acute respiratory distress or collapse after eating eggs should consult a physician for appropriate evaluation to help determine if vaccine should be administered. Persons who have documented immunoglobulin E (IgE)-mediated hypersensitivity to eggs, including those who have had occupational asthma or other allergic responses to egg protein, might also be at increased risk for allergic reactions to influenza vaccine, and consultation with a physician should be considered.

The following resource contains information on side effects of influenza vaccines:

> http://www.cdc.gov/mmwr/preview/mmwrhtml/rr54e713a1.htm

The resident's record should show vaccination administration to the resident unless the record contains documentation as to why vaccine was not administered, including but not limited to:

- Precautions necessitating delay in administering the vaccination;

- Medical contraindications to the use of the vaccines;

- The eligible resident refused the vaccine; or

- The resident has already been immunized.

NOTE: The influenza vaccine is given seasonally. Although the vaccines usually are representative of the influenza viruses likely to circulate during the flu season, occasionally the vaccine may not be as closely representative. The CDC indicates that administering the vaccine during October or November is generally most effective. However, residents admitted late in the influenza season, February or March, should be offered the influenza vaccine as late season outbreaks do occur. If a resident was admitted outside the influenza season (which is October 1 through March 31), the facility is not expected to offer the influenza vaccine to the resident, but they may, at their discretion.

There should be documentation in the medical record if there is reason to believe that the pneumococcal vaccine was given previously but the date cannot be verified and this had an impact upon the decision regarding administration of the vaccine.

According to the CDC, "Pneumococcal polysaccharide vaccine generally is considered safe based on clinical experience since 1977, when the pneumococcal polysaccharide vaccine was licensed in the United States. Approximately half of persons who receive pneumococcal vaccine develop mild, local side effects (e.g., pain at the injection site, erythema, and swelling). These reactions usually persist for less than 48 hours. Moderate systemic reactions (e.g., fever and myalgia) and more severe local reactions (e.g., local induration) are rare. Intradermal administration may cause severe local reactions and is inappropriate. Severe systemic adverse effects (e.g., anaphylactic reactions) rarely have been reported after administration of pneumococcal vaccine. For more information for the pneumococcal vaccine, see **http://www.cdc.gov/mmwr/preview/mmwrhtml/00047135.htm.**

The pneumococcal vaccine does not prevent or lessen the impact of other types of pneumonia, such as aspiration, fungal, or viral.

Investigative Protocol

Immunizations for Influenza and Pneumococcal Pneumonia

Objectives:

- To determine if the facility's immunization program has been implemented and assures that residents are offered vaccines, and that residents or legal representatives receive related education;

- To determine if education regarding the benefits and potential side effects of immunization(s) was provided to the resident or legal representative each time a vaccine was offered; and

- To determine if each resident received the influenza and/or pneumococcal immunization(s) unless medically contraindicated, refused, or already immunized, or because of circumstances outside of the facility's control, such as vaccine production delays.

Sampling:

For surveys during influenza season (October 1-March 31), follow the Procedure below for all residents who are selected for Comprehensive Reviews in Task 5C – Resident Review. If this number is below 5 residents, select additional residents from the Phase 1 Focused Review sample residents to meet the minimum number of 5 residents.

For surveys conducted outside influenza season, select 5 residents from the list the facility provided (see Task 2 – Entrance Conference) of all current residents who were in the facility during the previous influenza season. Give precedence in selection to those residents whom the survey team has selected as Phase 1 sample residents.

Procedure:

For all residents selected for this review, determine the following:

For the provision of Pneumococcal Pneumonia Vaccine, review all selected residents for:

- The provision of education related to the vaccine; and

- Either documentation of the administration of the vaccine; or

- If not provided, documentation as to why the vaccine was not provided, such as medical contraindications, refusal, or vaccine was already given prior to admission.

For the provision of Influenza Vaccine:

- For surveys occurring outside of influenza season, review selected residents for the provision of influenza education and immunization during the previous influenza season.

- For surveys occurring during influenza season, review all selected residents for the provision of influenza education and immunization during the current influenza season.

  Review residents for:

  o The provision of education for the vaccine; and

  o The administration of the vaccine, or if the vaccine was not provided, the reason why the vaccine was not provided, such as medical contraindications, refusal, unavailability of the vaccine, or vaccine was already given prior to admission.

NOTE: (For surveys occurring during influenza season) - Unavailability of the influenza vaccine can be a valid reason why a facility has not implemented the influenza vaccine program, especially during the early weeks of the influenza season. It is also likely that a facility surveyed during October may not have administered the vaccine, yet. In these instances, ask the facility to demonstrate that:

- The vaccine has been ordered and the facility received either the vaccine or a confirmation of the order indicating that the vaccine has been shipped or that the product is not available but will be shipped when the supply is available;

- Plans are developed on how and when the vaccines are to be administered;

- Residents have been screened to determine how many and which residents are eligible and wish to receive the vaccine; and

- Education regarding immunizations has been implemented.

For surveys occurring during influenza season, review the facility's immunization program if:

- There has been no shortage or lack of availability of the vaccines and residents have not refused the vaccine, but the residents have not yet been vaccinated;

- The resident(s), have not been evaluated for vaccination status, or

- The resident(s) has not received information/education about the benefits and potential risks of the immunizations.

For all facilities, determine if the facility developed influenza and pneumococcal vaccine policies and procedures including, but not limited to the following:

- The type of information/education provided to the resident prior to administration of the immunization(s);

- How the influenza vaccine program is implemented during the influenza season (October through March), including physician orders and standing orders (if standing orders are used);

- How the pneumococcal vaccine will be provided (i.e., throughout the calendar year);

- How residents and families are educated about the benefits and risks of the vaccines;

- Processes to address issues that are out of the facility's control such as non-availability of vaccines due to production delay or distribution problems, or the presence of a precaution in a resident that may warrant a delay in vaccine;

- The identification and tracking/monitoring of a resident's vaccination status (including medical contraindications or delayed administrations); and

- The location of documentation of education and administration of the vaccines.

If there are significant discrepancies between the facility's policies and procedures and the follow through for the vaccine program, ask the person responsible for implementing the procedures to explain the discrepancies.

Determination of Compliance (Task 6, Appendix P)

Synopsis of Regulation (F334)

The influenza and pneumococcal vaccination requirement has five aspects:

1. The resident is provided education regarding the benefits and potential side effects of the vaccinations;

2. The facility must offer each resident influenza and pneumococcal immunizations unless the immunization is medically contraindicated, or the resident's immunization status is current;

3. The resident, or the resident's legal representative, has the right to refuse the vaccinations;

4. Each eligible resident is administered the influenza and pneumococcal vaccine (unless refused or contraindicated or the resident has already been immunized); and

5. The facility must document that education was provided and that the resident either received the vaccine(s) or, if not received, that the vaccines(s) was (were) refused or medically contraindicated or the resident had already been immunized.

Criteria for Compliance

- Compliance with 42 CFR 483.25 (n), F334, Influenza and Pneumococcal Immunizations

  o The facility is in compliance with this requirement:

    - If each resident receives education regarding the benefits and potential side effects of the vaccine(s);

    - If each resident has been evaluated for eligibility to receive the vaccine(s);

    - If each resident is offered, unless medically contraindicated or already vaccinated, an influenza vaccine October 1 through March 31 annually, and a pneumococcal vaccine;

    - If the resident has the opportunity to refuse; and

    - If the record includes documentation that indicates, at a minimum:

      - The resident was provided education regarding the benefits and potential side effects; and

      - That the resident received the immunizations, refused the vaccination(s), or did not receive the vaccine(s) because of already being immunized, or as a result of a medical contraindication (including the nature of the resident's medical contraindications), unavailability, or a precaution that delayed the administration and a later date for administration has been planned.

If the facility is not in compliance with each of these aspects of the requirement, cite F334.

Non-compliance for F334

After completing the investigative protocol, determine whether noncompliance with the regulation exists. Noncompliance for F334 may include, but is not limited to, one or more of the following:

- An eligible resident did not receive either the influenza and/or the pneumococcal vaccines without a valid reason;.

- The facility did not evaluate to identify potential medical contraindications to the vaccines;

- The facility administered either of the vaccines to a resident who had refused them;

- The facility administered the influenza vaccine to a resident with medical contraindications, without physician involvement and/or approval;

- The facility administered the vaccine(s) to a resident who had an identified precaution, such as moderate or severe acute illness with or without fever, without physician involvement and/or approval;

- The facility administered the live attenuated influenza vaccine without physician approval to a resident who has a medical contraindication for live attenuated influenza vaccine;

- The facility failed to provide the pertinent information regarding the immunizations to the resident;

- The facility failed to document that the resident or resident's legal representative was provided education regarding the benefits and potential side effects of the influenza and, as applicable, the pneumococcal immunization; and

- The facility failed to document that the resident either received the vaccine(s) or did not receive the vaccine(s) due to medical contraindications or refusal.

Potential Tags for Additional Investigation

During the investigation of F334, the surveyor may have identified concerns with additional requirements related to outcome, process, and/or structure requirements. The surveyor is cautioned to investigate these related requirements before determining whether non-compliance may be present. Examples of some of the related requirements that may be considered when non-compliance F334 has been identified include the following:

- 42 CFR 483.20(b), F272, Comprehensive Assessments

    o   Review whether the resident's comprehensive assessment documented whether the influenza and/or pneumococcal vaccines were administered in the facility, including the reason(s) why a vaccine may not have been received in the facility.

- 42 CFR 483.65, F441, Infection Control Program

    o   Review whether the facility's program for infection control includes the prevention of the development and transmission of disease and infections including influenza and pneumococcal pneumonia.

- 42 CFR 483.75(i)(2), F501, Medical Director

    o   Determine whether the medical director has collaborated with the facility to develop policies and procedures based on current standards of practice for an immunization program, including the assessment of the resident, identification of medical contraindications/precautions and emergency medical interventions in the case of allergic reactions to the vaccines.

IV. DEFICIENCY CATEGORIZATION (Part IV, Appendix P)

Once the team has completed its investigation, analyzed the data, reviewed the regulatory requirement, and identified any deficient practice(s) that demonstrate that non-compliance with the regulation at F334 exists, the team must determine the severity of the deficient practice(s) and the resultant harm or potential for harm to the resident. The key elements for severity determination for F334 are as follows:

1. **Presence of harm/negative outcome(s) or potential for negative outcomes because of lack of appropriate treatment and care.**

Non-compliance related to an actual or potential harm/negative outcome for F334 may include, but is not limited to:

- A resident who is not eligible to receive the vaccines is administered the vaccine and has a reaction;

- A resident who is eligible for the vaccine refuses the immunization, however, the resident is administered the vaccine; or

- The facility fails to implement the immunization program and the residents experience an outbreak of influenza.

2. Degree of harm (actual or potential) related to the non-compliance. Identify how the facility practices caused, resulted in, allowed, or contributed to the actual or potential for harm:

- If harm has occurred, determine if the harm is at the level of serious injury, impairment, death, compromise, or discomfort; or

- If harm has not yet occurred, determine how likely is the potential for serious injury, impairment, death, or compromise or discomfort to occur to the resident.

3. The immediacy of correction required.

Determine whether the non-compliance requires immediate correction in order to prevent serious injury, harm, impairment, or death to one or more residents.

The survey team must evaluate the harm or potential for harm based upon the following levels of severity for Tag F334. First, the team must rule out whether Severity Level 4, Immediate Jeopardy to a resident's health or safety, exists by evaluating the deficient practice in relation to immediacy, culpability, and severity. (Follow the guidance in Appendix Q.)

NOTE: The death or transfer of a resident who was harmed or injured as a result of facility non-compliance does not remove a finding of immediate jeopardy. The facility is required to implement specific actions to correct the non-compliance which allowed or caused the immediate jeopardy.

Severity Level 4 Considerations: Immediate Jeopardy to Resident Health or Safety

Immediate Jeopardy is a situation in which the facility's non-compliance with one or more requirements of participation:

- Has allowed/caused/resulted in, or is likely to cause/allow/result in serious injury, harm, impairment, or death to a resident; and

- Requires immediate correction as the facility either created the situation or allowed the situation to continue by failing to implement preventative or corrective measures.

Examples of the facility's non-compliance that may cause or contribute to negative outcomes at severity level 4 include:

- A resident who is not eligible to receive the vaccine due to medical contraindications is administered the vaccine and experiences a life threatening reaction, such as anaphylactic shock; or

- Residents who were eligible to receive vaccines did not receive them as a result of the facility's failure to have any program for vaccinating residents.

NOTE: If immediate jeopardy has been ruled out based upon the evidence, then evaluate whether actual harm that is not immediate jeopardy exists at severity level 3.

Severity Level 3 Considerations: Actual Harm that is not Immediate Jeopardy

Level 3 indicates non-compliance that results in actual harm, and can include, but may not be limited to clinical compromise, decline, or the resident's ability to maintain and/or reach his/her highest practicable well-being. Examples of negative outcomes may include, but are not limited to:

- A resident who was not eligible to receive the vaccine due to medical contraindications receives the vaccine and experiences a reaction that is not life threatening, but requires treatment; or

- Because of an unwarranted delay (e.g., several weeks after it is available to the facility) in administering the influenza vaccine despite its availability, an eligible resident who has agreed to receive the influenza vaccine develops influenza.

NOTE: If severity level 3 (actual harm that is not immediate jeopardy) has been ruled out based upon the evidence, then evaluate as to whether level 2 (no actual harm with the potential for more than minimal harm) exists.

Severity Level 2 Considerations: No Actual Harm with Potential for more than Minimal Harm that is not Immediate Jeopardy

Level 2 indicates non-compliance that results in a resident outcome of no more than minimal discomfort and/or has the potential to compromise the resident's ability to maintain or reach his or her highest practicable level of well being. The potential exists for greater harm to occur if interventions are not provided. Examples of outcomes may include, but are not limited to:

- An eligible resident did not receive the vaccine, but did not develop symptoms of influenza;

- An eligible resident received two doses of the pneumococcal vaccine, due to a failure to document the receipt of the first dose, but did not experience any untoward reactions; or

- The staff did not assess for medical contraindications prior to providing the vaccines, but there were no reactions to the vaccine.

Severity Level 1: No Actual Harm with Potential for Minimal Harm

- The facility failed to document that information/education was provided to the resident prior to administering the immunizations.

[This page intentionally left blank]

F353 – F356

§483.30 — Nursing Services

F353

§483.30 Nursing Services

The facility must have sufficient nursing staff to provide nursing and related services to attain or maintain the highest practicable physical, mental, and psychosocial well-being of each resident, as determined by resident assessments and individual plans of care.

Intent §483.30

To assure that sufficient qualified nursing staff are available on a daily basis to meet residents' needs for nursing care in a manner and in an environment which promotes each resident's physical, mental and psychosocial well-being, thus enhancing their quality of life.

Procedures §483.30

§483.30(a) and (b) are to be reviewed during the standard survey whenever quality of care problems have been discovered (see Appendix P, Survey Protocol, Task 4, for further information and Task 5C for the investigative protocol to complete this review). In addition, fully review requirements of nursing services during an extended survey or when a waiver of RN and/or licensed nurse (RN/LPN) staffing has been requested or granted. Except as licensed nursing personnel are specifically required by the regulation (e.g., an RN for 8 consecutive hours a day, 7 days a week), the determination of sufficient staff will be made based on the staff's ability to provide needed care to residents that enable them to reach their highest practicable physical, mental and psychosocial well-being. The ability to meet the requirements of §§483.13, 483.15(a), 483.20, 483.25 and 483.65 determines sufficiency of nurse staffing.

§483.30(a) Sufficient Staff

§483.30(a)(1) The facility must provide services by sufficient numbers of each of the following types of personnel on a 24-hour basis to provide nursing care to all residents in accordance with resident care plans:

(i) Except when waived under paragraph (c) of this section, licensed nurses; and
(ii) other nursing personnel.

§483.30(a)(2) Except when waived under paragraph (c) of this section, the facility must designate a licensed nurse to serve as a charge nurse on each tour of duty.

For Interpretive Guidelines and Probes on §483.30(a) see Tag F354.

F354

§483.30(b) Registered Nurse

§483.30(b)(1) Except when waived under paragraph (c) or (d) of this section, the facility must use the services of a registered nurse for at least 8 consecutive hours a day, 7 days a week.

§483.30(b)(2) Except when waived under paragraph (c) or (d) of this section, the facility must designate a registered nurse to serve as the director of nursing on a full time basis.

§483.30(b)(3) The director of nursing may serve as a charge nurse only when the facility has an average daily occupancy of 60 or fewer residents.

Interpretive Guidelines §483.30(a) and (b)

At a minimum, "**staff**" is defined as licensed nurses (RNs and/or LPNs/LVNs), and nurse aides. Nurse aides must meet the training and competency requirements described in §483.75(e).

"**Full-time**" is defined as working 35 or more hours a week.

Except for licensed staff noted above, the determining factor in sufficiency of staff (including both numbers of staff and their qualifications) will be the ability of the facility to provide needed care for residents. A deficiency concerning staffing should ordinarily provide examples of care deficits caused by insufficient quantity and quality of staff. If, however, inadequate staff (either the number or category) presents a clear threat to residents reaching their highest practicable level of well-being, cite this as a deficiency. Provide specific documentation of the threat.

The facility is required to designate an RN to serve as DON on a full time basis. This requirement can be met when RNs share the position. If RNs share the DON position, the total hours per week must equal 40. Facility staff must understand the shared responsibilities. The facility can only be waived from this requirement if it has a waiver under subsection (c) or (d).

Probes §483.30(a) and (b)

Determine nurse staffing sufficiency for each unit:

- Is there adequate staff to meet direct care needs, assessments, planning, evaluation, supervision?

- Do work loads for direct care staff appear reasonable?

- Do residents, family, and ombudsmen report insufficient staff to meet resident needs?

- Are staff responsive to residents' needs for assistance, and call bells answered promptly?

- Do residents call out repeatedly for assistance?

- Are residents, who are unable to call for help, checked frequently (e.g., each half hour) for safety, comfort, positioning, and to offer fluids and provision of care?

- Are identified care problems associated with a specific unit or tour of duty?

- Is there a licensed nurse that serves as a charge nurse (e.g., supervises the provision of resident care) on each tour of duty (if facility does not have a waiver of this requirement)?

- What does the charge nurse do to correct problems in nurse staff performance?

- Does the facility have the services of an RN available 8 consecutive hours a day, 7 days a week (if this requirement has not been waived)?

- How does the facility assure that each resident receives nursing care in accordance with his/her plan of care on weekends, nights, and holidays?

- How does the sufficiency (numbers and categories) of nursing staff contribute to identified quality of care, resident rights, quality of life, or facility practices problems?

F355 – Nursing Waivers

§483.30(c) Nursing Facilities

Waiver of requirement to provide licensed nurses on a 24-hour basis.

To the extent that a facility is unable to meet the requirements of paragraphs (a)(2) and (b)(1) of this section, a State may waive such requirements with respect to the facility if--

(1) The facility demonstrates to the satisfaction of the State that the facility has been unable, despite diligent efforts (including offering wages at the community prevailing rate for nursing facilities), to recruit appropriate personnel;

(2) The State determines that a waiver of the requirement will not endanger the health or safety of individuals staying in the facility;

(3) The State finds that, for any periods in which licensed nursing services are not available, a registered nurse or a physician is obligated to respond immediately to telephone calls from the facility;

(4) A waiver granted under the conditions listed in paragraph (c) of this section is subject to annual State review;

(5) In granting or renewing a waiver, a facility may be required by the State to use other qualified, licensed personnel;

(6) The State agency granting a waiver of such requirements provides notice of the waiver to the State long term care ombudsman (established under section 307 (a)(12) of the Older Americans Act of 1965) and the protection and advocacy system in the State for the mentally ill and mentally retarded; and

(7) The nursing facility that is granted such a waiver by a State notifies residents of the facility (or, where appropriate, the guardians or legal representatives of such residents) and members of their immediate families of the waiver.

Intent §483.30(c)

To give the facility flexibility, in limited circumstances, when the facility cannot meet nurse staffing requirements.

Interpretive Guidelines §483.30(c)

The facility may request a waiver of the RN requirement, and/or the 24-hour licensed nurse requirement. If the facility is Medicaid-certified only, the State has the authority to grant the waiver. If the facility is dually-participating, CMS has the delegated authority to grant the waiver. (See guidelines for §483.30(d).)

A survey of Nursing Services must be conducted if a waiver has been granted or requested.

Probes §483.30(c)

Before granting a continuation of this waiver, or during the annual review, at a minimum, determine:

- Is a continuing effort being made to obtain licensed nurses?
- How does the facility ensure that residents' needs are being met?
- Are all nursing policies and procedures followed on each shift during times when licensed services are waived?
- Is there a qualified person to assess, evaluate, plan and implement resident care?
- Is care being carried out according to professional practice standards on each shift?

- Can the survey team ensure the State that the absence of licensed nurses will NOT endanger the health or safety of residents?

- Are there trends in the facility, which might be indicators of decreased quality of care as a result of insufficient staffing to meet resident needs (e.g., increases in incident reports, the infection rate, hospitalizations)?

- Are there increases in loss of function, pressure sores, tube feedings, catheters, weight loss, mental status?

- Is there evidence that preventive measures (e.g., turning, ambulating) are taken to avoid poor quality of care outcomes and avoidable sudden changes in health status?

- Is there evidence that sudden changes in resident health status and emergency needs are being properly identified and managed by appropriate facility staff and in a timely manner?

- If the facility has a waiver of the requirement to provide licensed nurses on a 24-hour basis, have they notified the ombudsman, residents, surrogates or legal representatives, and members of their immediate families of the waiver, and are there services residents need that are not provided because licensed nurses are not available?

- Is there an increase in hospitalizations because licensed personnel are not available to provide appropriate services?

- Does the facility meet all applicable requirements to continue to receive a waiver?

- Does the staff indicate that an RN or physician is available to respond immediately to telephone calls when licensed nurses are not available?

§483.30(d) SNFs

Waiver of the requirement to provide services of a registered nurse for more than 40 hours a week.

§483.30(d)(1) The Secretary may waive the requirement that a SNF provide the services of a registered nurse for more than 40 hours a week, including a director of nursing specified in paragraph (b) of this section, if the Secretary finds that--

(i) The facility is located in a rural area and the supply of skilled nursing facility services in the area is not sufficient to meet the needs of individuals residing in the area;

(ii) The facility has one full-time registered nurse who is regularly on duty at the facility 40 hours a week; and

(iii) The facility either--

(A) Has only patients whose physicians have indicated (through physicians' orders or admission notes) that they do not require the services of a registered nurse or a physician for a 48-hours period or;

(B) Has made arrangements for a registered nurse or a physician to spend time at the facility, as determined necessary by the physician, to provide necessary skilled nursing services on days when the regular full-time registered nurse is not on duty;

(iv) The Secretary provides notice of the waiver to the State long term care ombudsman (established under section 307(a)(12) of the Older Americans Act of 1965) and the protection and advocacy system in the State for the mentally ill and mentally retarded; and

(v) The facility that is granted such a waiver notifies residents of the facility (or, where appropriate, the guardians or legal representatives of such residents) and members of their immediate families of the waiver.

(2) A waiver of the registered nurse requirement under paragraph (d)(1) of this section is subject to annual renewal by the Secretary.

Interpretive Guidelines §483.30(d)

CMS is delegated the waiver authority for SNFs, including dually-participating facilities (SNF/NFs). The Medicare waiver authority is far more limited than is the States' authority under Medicaid since a State may waive any element of the nurse staffing requirement, whereas the Secretary may waive only the RN requirement. The requirements that a registered nurse provide services for 8 hours a day, 7 days a week (more than 40 hours a week), and that there be an RN designated as director of nursing on a full-time basis, may be waived by the Secretary in the following circumstances:

- The facility is located in a rural area with an inadequate supply of SNF services to meet area needs. Rural is defined as "all areas not delineated as `urban` by the Bureau of Census, based on the most recent census;

- The facility has one full-time registered nurse regularly working 40 hours a week. This may be the same individual, or part-time individuals. This nurse may or may not be the DON, and may perform some DON and some clinical duties if the facility so desires; **and either**;

- The facility has only residents whose physicians have noted, in writing, do not need RN or physician care for a 48 hour period. This does not relieve the facility from responsibility for providing for emergency availability of a physician, when necessary, nor does it relieve the facility from being responsible for meeting all needs of the residents during those 48 hours;

OR

- A physician or RN will spend the necessary time at the facility to provide care residents need during the days that an RN is not on duty. This requirement refers to clinical care of the residents that need skilled nursing services.

- If a waiver of this requirement has been granted, conduct a survey of nursing services during each certification survey. Dually-participating facilities must meet the waiver provisions of the SNF.

Probes §483.30(d)

If the SNF has a waiver of the more than 40 hours a week RN requirement:

- Is there an RN on duty 40 hours a week?

- If more than one RN provides the 40 hour per week coverage, how is information exchanged that maintains continuity of resident care?

- Does each clinical record have documentation by the physician that the resident does not need services of a physician or an RN for a 48 hour period each week.

- Are there any emergency or routine services that should be, but are not, provided to residents during the days that a registered nurse is not on duty?

- If specific skilled care is necessary for a resident during the time that an RN is not on duty, does an RN or physician provide that service on an "as needed" basis?

- Did the facility notify residents (or their legal guardians) and their immediate families about the waiver and the ombudsman?

See also probes at §483.30(c).

If the SNF requests continuation of the waiver to provide the services of a registered nurse for more than 40 hours a week, the survey team is to provide the Secretary with information needed to grant this continuation.

- Does the SNF meet all requirements necessary for continuation of the waiver?

Procedures §483.30(a)-(d)

If the facility has an approved nurse staffing waiver, it is **not** considered a deficiency. The facility does not need to submit a POC.

The following procedure should be used to document that a facility has a waiver of nurse staffing requirements.

When a facility does not meet the nurse staffing requirements, cite the appropriate tag. If the facility does have a waiver, reference the tag number based on the type of facility. The type of facility (SNF, NF, or SNF/NF) determines what type of waiver is granted:

- For SNFs and SNF/NFs which may be waived from the requirement to provide more than 40 hours of registered nurse services a week, and for NFs which have been granted a waiver from the 56 hour registered nurse requirement, cite Tag F354;

- For NFs that have a waiver of the 24-hour licensed nursing requirement, cite F353, or

- Both facility types could be waived for the requirement to designate a registered nurse as the director of nursing on a full-time basis. Cite F355.

When the Form CMS-2567 is entered into OSCAR, code the waived tag as a "W." Enter the tag number, leave the correction date blank, and enter a "W" in the CP field. This will indicate that this is not a deficiency--that the requirement has been waived.

F356

§483.30(e) Nurse Staffing Information—

(1) Data requirements. The facility must post the following information on a daily basis:

(i) Facility name.

(ii) The current date.

(iii) The total number and the actual hours worked by the following categories of licensed and unlicensed nursing staff directly responsible for resident care per shift:

(A) Registered nurses.

(B) Licensed practical nurses or licensed vocational nurses (as defined under State law).

(C) Certified nurse aides.

(iv) Resident census.

(2) Posting requirements.

(i) The facility must post the nurse staffing data specified in paragraph (e)(1) of this section on a daily basis at the beginning of each shift.

(ii) Data must be posted as follows:

(A)   **Clear and readable format.**

(B)   **In a prominent place readily accessible to residents and visitors.**

(3) **Public access to posted nurse staffing data. The facility must, upon oral or written request, make nurse staffing data available to the public for review at a cost not to exceed the community standard.**

(4) **Facility data retention requirements. The facility must maintain the posted daily nurse staffing data for a minimum of 18 months, or as required by State law, whichever is greater.**

[This page intentionally left blank]

F360 – F373

§483.35 — Dietary Services

F360

§483.35 Dietary Services

The facility must provide each resident with a nourishing, palatable, well-balanced diet that meets the daily nutritional and special dietary needs of each resident.

F361

§483.35(a) Staffing

The facility must employ a qualified dietitian either full-time, part-time, or on a consultant basis.

§483.35(a)(1) If a qualified dietitian is not employed full-time, the facility must designate a person to serve as the director of food service who receives frequently scheduled consultation from a qualified dietitian.

§483.35(a)(2) A qualified dietitian is one who is qualified based upon either registration by the Commission on Dietetic Registration of the American Dietetic Association, or on the basis of education, training, or experience in identification of dietary needs, planning, and implementation of dietary programs.

Intent §483.35(a)

The intent of this regulation is to ensure that a qualified dietitian is utilized in planning, managing and implementing dietary service activities in order to assure that the residents receive adequate nutrition.

A director of food services has no required minimum qualifications, but must be able to function collaboratively with a qualified dietitian in meeting the nutritional needs of the residents.

Interpretive Guidelines §483.35(a)

A dietitian qualified on the basis of education, training, or experience in identification of dietary needs, planning and implementation of dietary programs has experience or training which includes:

- Assessing special nutritional needs of geriatric and physically impaired persons;

- Developing therapeutic diets;

- Developing"regular diets" to meet the specialized needs of geriatric and physically impaired persons;

- Developing and implementing continuing education programs for dietary services and nursing personnel;

- Participating in interdisciplinary care planning;

- Budgeting and purchasing food and supplies; and

- Supervising institutional food preparation, service and storage.

Procedures §483.35(a)

If resident reviews determine that residents have nutritional problems, determine if these nutritional problems relate to inadequate or inappropriate diet nutrition/assessment and monitoring. Determine if these are related to dietitian qualifications.

Probes §483.35(a)

If the survey team finds problems in resident nutritional status:

- Do practices of the dietitian or food services director contribute to the identified problems in residents' nutritional status? If yes, what are they?

- What are the educational, training, and experience qualifications of the facility's dietitian?

F362

§483.35 (b) Standard Sufficient Staff

The facility must employ sufficient support personnel competent to carry out the functions of the dietary service.

Interpretive Guidelines §483.35(b)

"**Sufficient support personnel**" is defined as enough staff to prepare and serve palatable, attractive, nutritionally adequate meals at proper temperatures and appropriate times and support proper sanitary techniques being utilized.

Procedures §483.35(b)

For residents who have been triggered for a dining review, do they report that meals are palatable, attractive, served at the proper temperatures and at appropriate times?

Probes §483.35(b)

Sufficient staff preparation:

- Is food prepared in scheduled timeframes in accordance with established professional practices?

Observe food service:

- Does food leave kitchen in scheduled timeframes? Is food served to residents in scheduled timeframes?

F363

§483.35(c) Menus and Nutritional Adequacy

Menus must:

(1) Meet the nutritional needs of residents in accordance with the recommended dietary allowances of the Food and Nutrition Board of the National Research Council, National Academy of Sciences;

Intent §483.35(c)(1)(2)(3)

The intent of this regulation is to assure that the meals served meet the nutritional needs of the resident in accordance with the recommended dietary allowances (RDAs) of the Food and Nutrition Board of the National Research Council, of the National Academy of Sciences. This regulation also assures that there is a prepared menu by which nutritionally adequate meals have been planned for the resident and followed.

Procedures §483.35(c)(1)

For sampled residents who have a comprehensive review or a focused review, as appropriate, observe if meals served are consistent with the planned menu and care plan in the amounts, types and consistency of foods served.

If the survey team observes deviation from the planned menu, review appropriate documentation from diet card, record review, and interviews with food service manager or dietitian to support reason(s) for deviation from the written menu.

Probes §483.35(c)(1)

Are residents receiving food in the amount, type, consistency and frequency to maintain normal body weight and acceptable nutritional values?

If food intake appears inadequate based on meal observations, or resident's nutritional status is poor based on resident review, determine if menus have been adjusted to meet the caloric and nutrient-intake needs of each resident.

If a food group is missing from the resident's daily diet, does the facility have an alternative means of satisfying the resident's nutrient needs? If so, does the facility perform a follow-up?

Menu adequately provides the daily basic food groups:

- Does the menu meet basic nutritional needs by providing daily food in the groups of the food pyramid system and based on individual nutritional assessment taking into account current nutritional recommendations?

NOTE: A standard meal planning guide (e.g., food pyramid) is used primarily for menu planning and food purchasing. It is not intended to meet the nutritional needs of all residents. This guide must be adjusted to consider individual differences. Some residents will need more due to age, size, gender, physical activity, and state of health. There are many meal planning guides from reputable sources, i.e., American Diabetes Association, American Dietetic Association, American Medical Association, or U.S. Department of Agriculture, that are available and appropriate for use when adjusted to meet each resident's needs.

§483.35(c)(2) and (3) Menus and Nutritional Adequacy

§483.35(c)(2) Be prepared in advance; and

Probes §483.35(c)(2)

Menu prepared in advance:

Are there preplanned menus for both regular and therapeutic diets?

§483.35(c)(3) Be followed.

Probes §483.35(c)(3)

Menu followed:

- Is food served as planned? If not, why? There may be legitimate and extenuating circumstances why food may not be available on the day of the survey and must be considered before a concern is noted.

F364

§483.35(d) Food

Each resident receives and the facility provides:

(1) Food prepared by methods that conserve nutritive value, flavor, and appearance;

(2) Food that is palatable, attractive, and at the proper temperature;

Intent §483.35(d)(1)(2)

The intent of this regulation is to assure that the nutritive value of food is not compromised and destroyed because of prolonged food storage, light, and air exposure; prolonged cooking of foods in a large volume of water and prolong holding on steam table, and the addition of baking soda. Food should be palatable, attractive, and at the proper temperature as determined by the type of food to ensure resident's satisfaction. Refer to §483.15(e) and/or §483.15(a).

Interpretive Guidelines §483.35(d)(1)

"Food-palatability" refers to the taste and/or flavor of the food.

"Food attractiveness" refers to the appearance of the food when **served** to residents.

Procedures §483.35(d)(1)

Evidence for palatability and attractiveness of food, from day to day and meal to meal, may be strengthened through sources such as: additional observation, resident and staff interviews, and review of resident council minutes. Review nutritional adequacy in §483.25(i)(l).

Probes §483.35(d)(1)(2)

Does food have a distinctly appetizing aroma and appearance, which is varied in color and texture?

Is food generally well seasoned (use of spices, herbs, etc.) and acceptable to residents?

Conserves nutritive value:

- Is food prepared in a way to preserve vitamins? Method of storage and preparation should cause minimum loss of nutrients.

Food temperature:

- Is food served at preferable temperature (hot foods are served hot and cold foods are served cold) as discerned by the resident and customary practice? Not to be confused with the proper holding temperature.

F365

§483.35(d)(3) Food prepared in a form designed to meet individual needs; and

F366

§483.35(d)(4) Substitutes offered of similar nutritive value to residents who refuse food served.

Therapeutic diets must be prescribed by the attending physician. [**Editor's Note**: This sentence was inserted incorrectly. This sentence should be inserted at §483.35(e).]

Procedures §483.35(d)(3)(4)

Observe trays to assure that food is appropriate to resident according to assessment and care plan. Ask the resident how well the food meets their taste needs. Ask if the resident is offered or is given the opportunity to receive substitutes when refusing food on the original menu.

Probes §483.35(d)(3)(4)

Is food cut, chopped, or ground for individual resident's needs?

Are residents who refuse food offered substitutes of similar nutritive value?

Interpretive Guidelines §483.35(d)(4)

A food substitute should be consistent with the usual and ordinary food items provided by the facility. For example, if a facility never serves smoked salmon, they would not be required to serve this as a food substitute; or the facility may, instead of grapefruit juice, substitute another citrus juice or vitamin C rich juice that the resident likes.

F367

§483.35(e) Therapeutic Diets

Therapeutic diets must be prescribed by the attending physician.

Intent §483.35(e)

The intent of this regulation is to assure that the resident receives and consumes foods in the appropriate form and/or the appropriate nutritive content as prescribed by a physician and/or assessed by the interdisciplinary team to support the treatment and plan of care.

Interpretive Guidelines §483.35(e)

"Therapeutic Diet" is defined as a diet ordered by a physician as part of treatment for a disease or clinical condition, or to eliminate or decrease specific nutrients in the diet, (e.g., sodium) or to increase specific nutrients in the diet (e.g., potassium), or to provide food the resident is able to eat (e.g., a mechanically altered diet).

"Mechanically altered diet" is one in which the texture of a diet is altered. When the texture is modified, the type of texture modification must be specific and part of the physicians' order.

Procedures §483.35(e)

If the resident has inadequate nutrition or nutritional deficits that manifests into and/or are a product of weight loss or other medical problems, determine if there is a therapeutic diet that is medically prescribed.

Probes §483.35(e)

Is the therapeutic diet that the resident receives prescribed by the physician?

Also, see §483.25(i), Nutritional Status.

F368

§483.35(f) Frequency of Meals

(1) Each resident receives and the facility provides at least three meals daily, at regular times comparable to normal mealtimes in the community.

(2) There must be no more than 14 hours between a substantial evening meal and breakfast the following day, except as provided in (4) below.

(3) The facility must offer snacks at bedtime daily.

(4) When a nourishing snack is provided at bedtime, up to 16 hours may elapse between a substantial evening meal and breakfast the following day if a resident group agrees to this meal span, and a nourishing snack is served.

Intent §483.35(f)(1-4)

The intent of this regulation is to assure that the resident receives his/her meals at times most accepted by the community and that there are not extensive time lapses between meals. This assures that the resident receives adequate and frequent meals.

Interpretive Guidelines §483.35(f)(1-4)

A "**substantial evening meal**" is defined as an offering of three or more menu items at one time, one of which includes a high-quality protein such as meat, fish, eggs, or cheese. The meal should represent no less than 20 percent of the day's total nutritional requirements.

"**Nourishing snack**" is defined as a verbal offering of items, single or in combination, from the basic food groups. Adequacy of the "nourishing snack" will be determined both by resident interviews and by evaluation of the overall nutritional status of residents in the facility, (e.g., Is the offered snack usually satisfying?)

Procedures §483.35(f)(1-4)

Observe meal times and schedules and determine if there is a lapse in time between meals. Ask for resident input on meal service schedules, to verify if there are extensive lapses in time between meals.

F369

§483.35(g) Assistive Devices

The facility must provide special eating equipment and utensils for residents who need them.

Intent §483.35(g)

The intent of this regulation is to provide residents with assistive devices to maintain or improve their ability to eat independently. For example, improving poor grasp by enlarging silverware handles with foam padding, aiding residents with impaired coordination or tremor by installing plate guards, or providing postural supports for head, trunk, and arms.

Procedures §483.35(g)

Review sampled residents comprehensive assessment for eating ability. Determine if recommendations were made for adaptive utensils and if they were, determine if these utensils are available and utilized by resident. If recommended but not used, determine if this is by resident's choice. If utensils are not being utilized, determine when these were recommended and how their use is being monitored by the facility and if the staff is developing alternative recommendations.

F373

(Rev. 26; Issued: 08-17-07; Effective/Implementation Dates: 08-17-07)

§483.35(h) Paid Feeding Assistants-

(1) **State-approved training course.** A facility may use a paid feeding assistant, as defined in §488.301 of this chapter, if—

    (i)   The feeding assistant has successfully completed a State-approved training course that meets the requirements of §488.160 before feeding residents; and

    (ii)   The use of feeding assistants is consistent with State law.

(2) **Supervision.**

    (i)   A feeding assistant must work under the supervision of a registered nurse (RN) or licensed practical nurse (LPN).

    (ii)   In an emergency, a feeding assistant must call a supervisory nurse for help on the resident call system.

(3) **Resident Selection criteria.**

    (i)   A facility must ensure that a feeding assistant feeds only residents who have no complicated feeding problems.

    (ii)   Complicated feeding problems include, but are not limited to, difficulty swallowing, recurrent lung aspirations, and tube or parenteral/IV feedings.

    (iii)   The facility must base resident selection on the charge nurse's assessment and the resident's latest assessment and plan of care.

NOTE: One of the specific features of the regulatory requirement for this tag is that paid feeding assistants must complete a training program with the following minimum content as specified at §483.160:

    a.   Minimum training course contents. A State-approved training course for paid feeding assistants must include, at a minimum, 8 hours of training in the following:

    (1) Feeding techniques;
    (2) Assistance with feeding and hydration;
    (3) Communication and interpersonal skills;
    (4) Appropriate responses to resident behavior;
    (5) Safety and emergency procedures, including the Heimlich maneuver;
    (6) Infection control;
    (7) Resident rights; and
    (8) Recognizing changes in residents that are inconsistent with their normal behavior and the importance of reporting those changes to the supervisory nurse.

b. Maintenance of records. A facility must maintain a record of all individuals, used by the facility as feeding assistants, who have successfully completed the training course for paid feeding assistants.

Intent: §483.35(h)

The intent of this regulation is to ensure that employees who are used as paid feeding assistants are:

- Properly trained (in accordance with the requirements at §483.160, including maintenance of records);

- Adequately supervised;

- Assisting only those residents without complicated feeding problems and who have been selected as eligible to receive these services from a paid feeding assistant; and

- Providing assistance in accordance with the resident's needs, based on individualized assessment and care planning.

Definitions

."Paid feeding assistant" is defined in the regulation at 42 CFR 488.301 as"an individual who meets the requirements specified at 42 CFR 483.35(h)(1)(i) of this chapter and who is paid to feed residents by a facility, or who is used under an arrangement with another agency or organization."

NOTE: The regulation uses the term,"paid feeding assistant." While we are not using any other term, facilities and States may use whatever term they prefer, such as dining assistant, meal assistant, resident assistant, nutritional aide, etc. in order to convey more respect for the resident. Facilities may identify this position with other titles; however, the facility must be able to identify those employees who meet the requirements under the paid feeding assistant regulation. These requirements do not apply to family and/or volunteers who may be providing the resident with assistance.

."Resident call system," for the purposes of this requirement includes not only the standard hard-wired call system, but other means in an emergency situation by which a paid feeding assistant can achieve timely notification of a supervisory nurse (when not present in the room).

OVERVIEW

The intent behind the use of paid feeding assistants by nursing homes is to provide nutrition and hydration support to residents who may be at risk for unplanned weight loss and dehydration. These are residents with no complicated problems associated with eating or drinking, who cannot or do not eat independently due to physical or cognitive disabilities, or those who simply need cueing or encouragement to eat. The use of paid feeding assistants is intended to supplement certified nurse aides, not substitute for nurse aides or licensed nursing staff. Use of paid feeding assistants is an option for nursing homes if their state approves the use of paid feeding assistants and establishes a mechanism to approve training programs for paid feeding assistants.

Interpretive Guidelines §483.35(h)

NOTE: The regulation at §483.30(a)(2) requires that"Except when waived under paragraph (c) of this section, the facility must designate a licensed nurse to service as a charge nurse on each tour of duty." In the paid feeding assistant regulation, the term charge nurse is used to identify who is responsible for assessing the eligibility of a resident to be assisted by a paid feeding assistant. The regulation also states that a paid feeding assistant must work under the supervision of an RN or LPN, and they must call the supervisory nurse in case of an emergency. Therefore, a facility that has received a waiver and does not have either an RN or LPN available in the building cannot use paid feeding assistants during those times.

Charge Nurse Assessment of Resident Eligibility for Feeding Assistance

The facility must base resident selection on the charge nurse's (RN, or LPN if allowed by State law) current assessment of the resident's condition and the resident's latest comprehensive assessment and plan of care. Charge nurses may wish to consult with interdisciplinary team members, such as speech-language pathologists or other professionals, when making their decisions.

Paid feeding assistants are permitted to assist only those residents who have no complicated eating or drinking problems. This includes residents who are dependent in eating and/or those who have some degree of dependence, such as needing cueing or partial assistance, as long as they do not have complicated eating or drinking problems.

Paid feeding assistants are not permitted to assist residents who have complicated eating problems, such as (but not limited to) difficulty swallowing, recurrent lung aspirations, or who receive nutrition through parenteral or enteral means. Nurses or nurse aides must continue to assist residents to eat or drink who require the assistance of staff with more specialized training.

Facilities may use paid feeding assistants to assist eligible residents to eat and drink at meal times, snack times, or during activities or social events as needed, whenever the facility can provide the necessary supervision.

Supervision (by RN/LPN) of Paid Feeding Assistants

A paid feeding assistant must work under the supervision of an RN or LPN. While we are not prescribing the exact means by which facility RNs and LPNs assert their supervisory responsibilities, we expect that facilities will do so in a way that avoids negative outcomes for their residents. If a facility chooses to use paid feeding assistants, it is the facility's responsibility to ensure that adequate supervisory nursing staff are available to supervise these assistants.

The supervisory nurse should monitor the provision of the assistance provided by paid feeding assistants to evaluate on an ongoing basis:

- Their use of appropriate feeding techniques;

- Whether they are assisting assigned residents according to their identified eating and drinking needs;

- Whether they are providing assistance in recognition of the rights and dignity of the resident; and

- Whether they are adhering to safety and infection control practices.

Adequate supervision by a supervising nurse does not necessarily mean constant visual contact or being physically present during the meal/snack time, especially if a feeding assistant is assisting a resident to eat in his or her room. However, whatever the location, the feeding assistant must be aware of and know how to access the supervisory nurse immediately in the event that an emergency should occur. Should an emergency arise, a paid feeding assistant must immediately call a supervisory nurse for help on the resident call system.

The charge nurse and the supervisory nurse may or may not be the same individuals.

Resident Call System

The regulatory language at this Tag states that,"in an emergency, a feeding assistant must call a supervisory nurse for help on the resident call system." Residents may be receiving assistance in eating or drinking in various locations throughout the facility, such as dining areas, activity rooms, or areas such as patios or porches in which a resident call system is not readily available. The resident call system requirement at §483.70(f), F463, only specifies that the call system be available in the residents rooms and bathrooms. Regardless of where a resident is being assisted to eat or drink, in the case of an emergency, the facility needs to have a means for a paid feeding assistant to obtain timely help of a supervisory nurse. Therefore, for the purposes of this requirement, a "resident call system" includes not only the standard hard-wired or wireless call system, but other means in an emergency situation by which a paid feeding assistant can achieve timely notification of a supervisory nurse.

Use of Existing Staff as Paid Feeding Assistants

Facilities may use their existing staff to assist eligible residents to eat and drink. These employees must have successfully completed a State-approved training course for paid feeding assistants, which has a minimum of 8 hours of training as required in §483.160. Staff may include, for example, administrative, clerical, housekeeping, dietary staff, or activity specialists. Employees used as paid feeding assistants, regardless of their position, are subject to the same training and supervisory requirements as any other paid feeding assistant.

Maintenance of Training Records

The facility must maintain a record of all employees used by the facility as paid feeding assistants. The record should include verification that they have successfully completed a State-approved training course for paid feeding assistants.

INVESTIGATIVE PROTOCOL

Use of Paid Feeding Assistants

Objectives

The objectives of this protocol are to determine, for a facility that uses paid feeding assistants:

- If individuals used as paid feeding assistants successfully completed a State-approved training course;

- If sampled residents who were selected to receive assistance from paid feeding assistants were assessed by the charge nurse and determined to be eligible to receive these services based on the latest assessment and plan of care; and

- If the paid feeding assistants are supervised by an RN or LPN.

Use

This protocol is used when a surveyor identifies concerns through observation; interview with residents, family, or staff; or record review, that the facility may not be following the requirements regarding paid feeding assistants, including proper training and supervision of feeding assistants, and proper selection of residents for feeding assistance.

Procedures

Briefly review the comprehensive assessment and interdisciplinary care plan to guide observations to be made. The team coordinator assigns one surveyor to obtain the facility's records of all employees, used by the facility as paid feeding assistants, for review for completion of the training course for paid feeding assistants.

Observations

If the concern was discovered through resident or family interview, observe the resident while they are being assisted to eat and drink by a paid feeding assistant. Determine if the assistant is using proper feeding technique and is providing the type of assistance specified in the resident's care plan. Note the resident's condition and observe for the presence of complicated feeding problems.

If the concern was discovered through observations that were already made, only conduct additional observations if necessary to complete the investigation.

Interviews

Resident and Family Interviews

If a resident is selected for this protocol through surveyor observation that they are having difficulties in eating or drinking and they are being assisted by a paid feeding assistant, interview the resident if the resident is interviewable. Ask questions to gain information about why the resident is receiving these services and the resident's experience with receiving assistance to eat and drink. If concerns are identified, inquire if they have reported these problems to a nurse. If the resident is not interviewable, ask these questions of a family member.

If the concern was discovered through resident or family interviews already conducted as part of Task 5D, focus any additional interview on questions specific to the investigation.

Paid Feeding Assistant Interviews

Interview the paid feeding assistant who was assisting the selected resident. Determine whether there are concerns with the paid feeding assistant's training, supervision, or the selection of the resident such as:

- What training did you successfully complete in providing feeding assistance?

- What information did you receive about this resident's needs for assistance (type of assistance needed, any precautions)?

- In what manner and by whom are you supervised while assisting residents?

- What issues/problems do you report (such as coughing, choking, changes in the resident's usual responses, or level of alertness) and to whom do you report?

- What would you do if an emergency occurred while you were assisting a resident to eat or drink? Who would you contact and how would you contact them if you are not near the resident call system?

Charge Nurse Interview

Interview the charge nurse who is responsible for assessing this resident as eligible to receive assistance by a paid feeding assistant. Ask:

- How they determined that this resident has no complicated feeding problems and is eligible to be assisted by a paid feeding assistant;

- How they determine that each eligible resident remains free of emergent complicated feeding problems;

- Who supervises paid feeding assistants and how is the supervision accomplished;

- Describe the processes in place to handle emergencies when a supervisor is not present in the area where paid feeding assistants are assisting residents.

Supervisory Nurse Interview

Interview the nurse who is supervising the resident during the meal or other times when the paid feeding assistant is assisting the resident to eat or drink. Ask how they supervise paid feeding assistants.

Review of Assessment of Eligibility to Receive Assistance from a Paid Feeding Assistant

Determine whether the charge nurse based her/his assessment of the resident's ongoing eligibility to be assisted by a paid feeding assistant on identification of the current condition of the resident and any additional or new risk factors or condition changes that may impact on the resident's ability to eat or drink. This information may be contained in the RAI or in other supporting documents such as progress notes, etc. The assessment of eligibility to receive assistance from a paid feeding assistant is ongoing and should be in place from the day of admission.

Requirements for Training of Paid Feeding Assistants

Determine how the facility identifies that paid feeding assistants have successfully completed a State-approved training course that meets the requirements at 42 CFR 483.160 before they are allowed to assist eligible residents with eating and drinking.

If the facility uses temporary (agency) staff as paid feeding assistants, request documentation that these staff have met the minimum training requirements specified by the State.

DETERMINATION OF COMPLIANCE (TASK 6, APPENDIX P)

The information below should be used by the survey team for their deficiency determination at Task 6 in Appendix P. The survey team must evaluate the evidence documented during the survey to determine if a deficiency exists due to a failure to meet a requirement, and if there are any negative resident outcomes or potential for negative outcomes due to the failure.

Synopsis of Regulation (42 CFR 483.35)

The paid feeding assistant requirement has five aspects:

- Staff who are used as paid feeding assistants must have completed a State-approved training course;

- The facility must base resident selection to be fed by a paid feeding assistant on the charge nurse's assessment and resident's latest assessment and care plan;

- Paid feeding assistants must work under the supervision of an RN or LPN, and, in an emergency, must call a supervisory nurse for help on the resident call system;

- Paid feeding assistants assist only residents who have no complicated health problems related to eating or drinking that make them ineligible for these services; and

- The facility must maintain a record of all individuals used by the facility as paid feeding assistants, and must maintain documentation of successful completion of a State-approved training course by these individuals.

Criteria for Compliance

Compliance with 42 CFR 483.35(h), F373, Paid Feeding Assistants

The facility is in compliance with this requirement if all the following are met:

- The facility only employs paid feeding assistants who have successfully completed a State-approved training course before providing assistance;

- The facility selected qualified residents based on the charge nurse's ongoing assessment and the latest assessment and plan of care;

- The facility provides supervision by an RN or LPN;

- The facility provides in cases of emergency a working call system (and other means for areas without a call system) for the paid feeding assistant to summon help in an emergency;

- The facility ensures that the paid feeding assistant only assists residents who have no complicated health problems related to eating or drinking that make them ineligible for these services; and

- The facility maintains a record of all individuals used by the facility as paid feeding assistants, and maintains documentation of each paid feeding assistant's successful completion of a State-approved training course.

    If not, cite F373.

Non-compliance for F373

After completing the investigative protocol, determine whether or not noncompliance with the regulation exists. Noncompliance for F373 may include, but is not limited to, one or more of the following:

- An employee of the facility (permanent or temporary) who has not successfully completed the State-approved training course is assisting a resident to eat/drink;

- The facility allowed an employee who has completed a course that is not State-approved to assist a resident to eat or drink;

- A paid feeding assistant was observed assisting a resident in a location without a call system available or other means of emergency notification;

- A resident who was assessed by the charge nurse as ineligible for services due to complicated eating/drinking problems, or a resident who has not been assessed for eligibility, is being assisted by a paid feeding assistant;

- A paid feeding assistant was not being supervised by a RN or LPN;

- RN or LPN staff members assigned to supervise paid feeding assistants were observed to be unavailable (e.g., not in reach of contact);

- The clinical record of a resident being assisted by a paid feeding assistant did not show evidence that the resident was eligible to receive assistance from a paid feeding assistant;

- The facility did not maintain records of paid feeding assistants working in the facility; or

- The facility did not maintain documentation of a paid feeding assistant's successful completion of a State-approved paid feeding training course.

Potential Tags for Additional Investigation

During the investigation of F373, the surveyor may have identified concerns with additional requirements related to outcome, process, and/or structure requirements. The surveyor is cautioned to investigate these related requirements before determining whether non-compliance may be present at these other tags. Examples of some of the related requirements that may be considered when non-compliance has been identified include the following (but are not limited to):

- 42 CFR 483.15(a), F241, Dignity

  - Determine if staff are attentive and responsive to the resident's requests, and if they provide assistance to eat in a manner that respects the resident's dignity, meets needs in a timely manner, and minimizes potential feelings of embarrassment, humiliation, and/or isolation related to inability to assist themselves with food or fluid intake.

- 42 CFR 483.20(b), F272, Comprehensive Assessments

  - Review whether the facility initially and periodically conducted a comprehensive, accurate assessment of the resident's ability to eat and drink with or without assistance and/or identified a condition that makes the resident ineligible for this service.

- 42 CFR 483.20(k)(1), F279, Comprehensive Care Plans

  - Review whether the facility developed a comprehensive care plan that was based on the assessment of the resident's conditions, needs, and behaviors, and was consistent with the resident's goals in order to provide assistance with nutrition and hydration as necessary.

- 42 CFR 483.20(k)(2)(iii), F280, Comprehensive Care Plan Revision

  - Determine if the care plan was reviewed and revised periodically, as necessary, related to eligibility to eat and drink with assistance of a paid feeding assistant.

- 42 CFR 483.25(i)(1), F325, Nutritional Parameters

  - Review if the facility had identified, evaluated, and responded to a change in nutritional parameters, anorexia, or unplanned weight loss, dysphagia, and/or swallowing disorders in relation to the resident's ability to eat.

- 42 CFR 483.25(i)(2), F327, Hydration [**Editor's Note:** The correct tag number for 42 CFR 483.25(i)(2) is F326 and the correct regulation number for F327, Hydration is 42 CFR 483.25(j).

  o Review if the facility had identified, evaluated, and responded to a change in the resident's ability to swallow liquids.

- 42 CFR 483.25 (a)(3) F312, ADL Assistance for Dependent Residents

  o Determine if staff identified and implemented appropriate measures to provide food and fluids for the resident who cannot perform relevant activities of daily living.

- 42 CFR 483.30(a), F353, Sufficient Staff

  o Determine if the facility has qualified staff in sufficient numbers to provide assistance to eat or drink to those residents who require such assistance. For residents who are not eligible to receive assistance from paid feeding assistants, determine if there are sufficient CNAs to provide this assistance to these residents in a timely fashion.

- 42 CFR 483.75(i)(2), F501, Medical Director

  o Determine whether the medical director collaborates with the facility to help develop, implement, and evaluate resident care policies and procedures based on current standards of practice, e.g., the use of paid feeding assistants, their supervision, and the criteria for determining which residents are eligible to receive assistance to eat or drink from paid feeding assistants.

IV. DEFICIENCY CATEGORIZATION (Part IV, Appendix P)

Once the team has completed its investigation, analyzed the data, reviewed the regulatory requirement, and identified any deficient practice(s) that demonstrate that non-compliance with the regulation at F373 exists, the team must determine the severity of the deficient practice(s) and the resultant harm or potential for harm to the resident. The key elements for severity determination for F373 are as follows:

1. **Presence of harm/negative outcome(s) or potential for negative outcomes because of lack of appropriate use of paid feeding assistants.**

    Non-compliance related to an actual or potential harm/negative outcome for F373 may include, but is not limited to:

    - A resident who is not eligible to receive these services is assisted by a paid feeding assistant; or

    - A resident who is eligible to receive these services is assisted by a paid feeding assistant and develops coughing and/or choking episodes related to the paid feeding assistant using poor techniques indicating lack of appropriate supervision

2. **Degree of harm (actual or potential) related to the non-compliance:**

    Identify how the facility practices caused, resulted in, allowed, or contributed to the actual or potential for harm:

    - If harm has occurred, determine if the harm is at the level of serious injury, impairment, death, compromise, or discomfort; or

    - If harm has not yet occurred, determine how likely is the potential for serious injury, impairment, death, or compromise or discomfort to occur to the resident.

3. **The immediacy of correction required:**

    Determine whether the non-compliance requires immediate correction in order to prevent serious injury, harm, impairment, or death to one or more residents.

The survey team must evaluate the harm or potential for harm based upon the following levels of severity for tag F373. First, the team must rule out whether Severity Level 4, Immediate Jeopardy to a resident's health or safety exists by evaluating the deficient practice in relation to immediacy, culpability, and severity. (Follow the guidance in Appendix Q, Guidelines for Determining Immediate Jeopardy.)

NOTE: The death or transfer of a resident who was harmed or injured as a result of facility non-compliance does not remove a finding of immediate jeopardy. The facility is required to implement specific actions to correct the non-compliance which allowed or caused the immediate jeopardy.

Severity Level 4 Considerations: Immediate Jeopardy to Resident Health or Safety

Immediate Jeopardy is a situation in which the facility's non-compliance with one or more requirements of participation:

- Has allowed/caused/resulted in, or is likely to cause/allow/result in serious injury, harm, impairment, or death to a resident; and

- Requires immediate correction as the facility either created the situation or allowed the situation to continue by failing to implement preventative or corrective measures.

Examples of the facility's non-compliance that may cause or contribute to negative outcomes at severity level 4 include, but are not limited to:

- An eligible resident in an activity room who is being improperly assisted to eat by a paid feeding assistant, experiences choking, there was no call system readily available, and/or the supervising nurse was not available to assist, and the resident expired;

- A resident who is not eligible to receive these services due to complicated feeding problems is assisted by a paid feeding assistant, whether or not the resident has experienced negative outcomes.

NOTE: If immediate jeopardy has been ruled out based upon the evidence, then evaluate whether actual harm that is not immediate jeopardy exists at severity level 3.

Severity Level 3 Considerations: Actual Harm that is not Immediate Jeopardy

Level 3 indicates non-compliance that results in actual harm, and can include but may not be limited to clinical compromise, decline, or the failure to maintain and/or reach the resident's highest practicable well-being.

Examples of the facility's non-compliance that may cause or contribute to negative outcomes at severity level 3 include, but are not limited to:

- An eligible resident who was assessed to have the potential to improving their eating ability was assisted to eat by a paid feeding assistant. The assistant provided too much food, too quickly and the resident was pocketing the food in her cheeks. The resident experienced choking and coughing and subsequently vomited. As a result, the resident became fearful, refused solid foods, and would only consume liquid dietary supplements.

NOTE: If severity level 3 (actual harm that is not immediate jeopardy) has been ruled out based upon the evidence, then evaluate as to whether level 2 (no actual harm with the potential for more than minimal harm) exists.

Severity Level 2 Considerations: No Actual Harm with potential for more than minimal harm that is Not Immediate Jeopardy

Level 2 indicates non-compliance that results in a resident outcome of no more than minimal discomfort and/or has the potential to compromise the resident's ability to maintain or reach his or her highest practicable level of well being. The potential exists for greater harm to occur if interventions are not provided.

Examples of the facility's non-compliance that may cause or contribute to negative outcomes at severity level 2 include, but are not limited to:

- Paid feeding assistants are assisting eligible residents to eat in an area with no call system, and the supervising nurses are not nearby, but there have been no resident outcomes; and

- Eligible residents are being assisted to eat by employees who have not successfully completed a State-approved paid feeding assistant training course and who otherwise by State law would not be allowed to feed residents (such as RNs, LPNs or CNAs), and there were no resident negative outcomes.

Severity Level 1: No actual harm with potential for minimal harm

Level 1 is a deficiency that has the potential for causing no more than a minor negative impact on the resident(s).

Examples of the facility's non-compliance that may cause or contribute to negative outcomes at severity level 1 include, but are not limited to:

- Facility did not maintain a record of employees who had completed a State approved paid feeding assistant training program and were used by the facility as paid feeding assistants.

F371

(Rev. 48; Issued: 06-12-09; Effective/Implementation Date: 06-12-09)

§483.35(i) Sanitary Conditions

The facility must –

§483.35(i)(1) Procure food from sources approved or considered satisfactory by Federal, State or local authorities; and

§483.35(i)(2) Store, prepare, distribute and serve food under sanitary conditions.

INTENT: (Tag F371) 42 CFR 483.35(i) Sanitary Conditions

The intent of this requirement is to ensure that the facility:

- Obtains food for resident consumption from sources approved or considered satisfactory by Federal, State or local authorities; and

- Follows proper sanitation and food handling practices to prevent the outbreak of foodborne illness. Safe food handling for the prevention of foodborne illnesses begins when food is received from the vendor and continues throughout the facility's food handling processes.

DEFINITIONS

Definitions are provided to clarify terms related to sanitary conditions and the prevention of foodborne illness.

- **"Cross-contamination"** refers to the transfer of harmful substances or disease-causing microorganisms to food by hands, food contact surfaces, sponges, cloth towels, or utensils which are not cleaned after touching raw food, and then touch ready-to-eat foods. Cross-contamination can also occur when raw food touches or drips onto cooked or ready-to-eat foods.[1]

- **"Danger Zone"** refers to temperatures above 41 degrees Fahrenheit (F) and below 135 degrees F that allow the rapid growth of pathogenic microorganisms that can cause foodborne illness. Potentially Hazardous Foods (PHF) or Time/Temperature Control for Safety (TCS) Foods held in the danger zone for more than 4 hours (if being prepared from ingredients at ambient temperature) or 6 hours (if cooked and cooled) may cause a foodborne illness outbreak if consumed.

- **"Dry Storage"** refers to storing/maintaining dry foods (canned goods, flour, sugar, etc.) and supplies (disposable dishware, napkins, and kitchen cleaning supplies).

- **"Food Contamination"** refers to the unintended presence of potentially harmful substances, including, but not limited to microorganisms, chemicals or physical objects in food.[2]

- **"Food Preparation"** refers to the series of operational processes involved in getting foods ready for serving, such as: washing, thawing, mixing ingredients, cutting, slicing, diluting concentrates, cooking, pureeing, blending, cooling, and reheating.

- **"Food Service/Distribution"** refers to the processes involved in getting food to the resident. This may include holding foods hot on the steam table or under refrigeration for cold temperature control, dispensing food portions for individual residents, family style and dining room service, or delivering trays to residents' rooms or units, etc.

- **"Foodborne Illness"** refers to illness caused by the ingestion of contaminated food or beverages.

- **"Highly Susceptible Population"** refers to persons who are more likely than the general population to experience foodborne illness because of their susceptibility to becoming ill if they ingest microorganisms or toxins. Increased susceptibility may be associated with immuno-compromised health status, chronic disease and advanced age.

- **"Pathogen"** refers to an organism capable of causing a disease (e.g., pathogenic bacteria or viruses).

- **"Potentially Hazardous Food (PHF)" or"Time/Temperature Control for Safety (TCS) Food"** refers to food that requires time/temperature control for safety to limit the growth of pathogens or toxin formation.

- **"Ready-to -Eat Food"** refers to food that is edible with little or no preparation to achieve food safety. It includes foods requiring minimal preparation for palatability or culinary purposes, such as mixing with other ingredients (e.g., meat type salads such as tuna, chicken, or egg salad).

- **"Storage"** refers to the retention of food (before and after preparation) and associated dry goods.

- **"Toxins"** refer to poisonous substances that are produced by living cells or organisms (e.g., pathogenic bacteria) that cause foodborne illness when ingested.

OVERVIEW

Nursing home residents risk serious complications from foodborne illness as a result of their compromised health status. Unsafe food handling practices represent a potential source of pathogen exposure for residents. Sanitary conditions must be present in health care food service settings to promote safe food handling.

Effective food safety systems involve identifying hazards at specific points during food handling and preparation, and identifying how the hazards can be prevented, reduced or eliminated. It is important to focus attention on the risks that are associated with foodborne illness by identifying critical control points (CCPs) in the food preparation processes that, if not controlled, might result in food safety hazards. Some operational steps that are critical to control in facilities to prevent or eliminate food safety hazards are thawing, cooking, cooling, holding, reheating of foods, and employee hygienic practices.

Web sites for additional information regarding safe food handling to minimize the potential for foodborne illness include:

- National Food Safety Information Network's Gateway to Government Food Safety Information at www.FoodSafety.gov;

- United States Food & Drug Administration Food Code Web site at http://www.cfsan.fda.gov/~dms/primecon.html;

- United States Food & Drug Administration Hazard Analysis Critical Control Point http://www.cfsan.fda.gov/~dms/hret2toc.html, (Operator's Manual) and http://www.cfsan.fda.gov/~dms/hret3toc.html (Regulator's manual).

NOTE: References to non-CMS sources or sites on the Internet are provided as a service and do not constitute or imply endorsement of these organizations or their programs by CMS or the U.S. Department of Health and Human Services. CMS is not responsible for the content of pages found at these sites. The uniform resource locator addresses were current as of the date of this publication.

TYPES OF FOOD CONTAMINATION

Food contaminants fall into 3 categories: biological, chemical, and physical.

Biological Contamination

Biological contaminants are pathogenic bacteria, viruses, toxins, and spores that contaminate food. The two most common types of disease producing organisms are bacteria and viruses. Parasites may also contaminate food, but are less common.

- **Pathogenic Bacteria** - Not all bacteria in food cause illness in humans. For example, live cultures of Lactobacillus bacteria are added to yogurt to enhance digestion. However, some bacteria can be pathogenic and thus may cause illness or death (e.g., some strains of Escherichia Coli). It is vital to control the growth of bacteria during food storage and preparation because raw or uncooked food may naturally contain pathogenic organisms (e.g., Salmonella in poultry).

  Several factors which may influence the growth of bacteria include:

  o Hazardous nature of the food. Although almost any food can be contaminated, certain foods are considered more hazardous than others and are called"potentially hazardous foods (PHF) or Time/Temperature Controlled for Safety (TCS)" food. Examples of PHF/TCS foods include ground beef, poultry, chicken, seafood (fish or shellfish), cut melon, unpasteurized eggs, milk, yogurt and cottage cheese;

  o Acidity (pH) of the food. More acidic food (i. e., pH < 5), such as pineapple, vinegar, and lemon juice, inhibits bacterial growth;

  o Water percentage of the food. Foods that have a high level of water (e.g., fruits and vegetables) encourage bacterial growth; and

  o Time and temperature control of the food. Time in conjunction with temperature controls is critical. The longer food remains in the danger zone, the greater the risks for growth of harmful pathogens. Bacteria multiply rapidly in a moist environment in the danger zone. Freezing does not kill bacteria. Rapid death of most bacteria occurs at 165 degrees F or above.

    NOTE: Some foods may be considered a TCS food needing time/temperature control for safety to limit pathogenic microorganism growth or toxin formation. Examples include foods held for later service (e.g., cooked rice, refried beans, grilled sautéed onions, or baked potatoes).

- **Viruses** - Viruses cannot reproduce without a living host (animal or human). While they cannot reproduce in or on food, viruses may survive long enough in or on a food to be transmitted to a new host. Two viruses that are well known for being spread by poor food handling practices are Hepatitis A and Norovirus (formerly known as Norwalk virus).

- **Toxins** - Toxins are poisonous substances that come from a variety of sources. Some pathogens (e.g., Staphylococcus aureus and Clostridium botulinum) produce toxins as a byproduct of their growth. Most toxins are not destroyed by high temperatures. A PHF/TCS food that is allowed to remain in the danger zone long enough for the bacteria to produce toxins will become unsafe to eat.

- **Spores** - A spore is an inactive form of an organism that is highly resistant to extreme temperatures, acidity, and dehydration. The organism is reactivated once conditions become favorable for its growth. Two common spore-forming pathogens are Bacillus cereus and Clostridium botulinum. Temperature control is the way to minimize the danger associated with spore-forming organisms.

Chemical Contamination

The most common chemicals that can be found in a food system are cleaning agents (such as glass cleaners, soaps, and oven cleaners) and insecticides. Chemicals used by the facility staff, in the course of their duties, may contaminate food (e.g., if a spray cleaner is used on a worktable surface while food is being prepared it becomes exposed to a chemical). An inadequately identified chemical may be mistaken for an ingredient used in food preparation. For example, incorrectly stored (e.g., dishwashing liquid stored in a syrup bottle) or unlabeled (e.g., white granulated cleaner that looks like salt) cleaning products may be inadvertently added to food and cause illness. It is recommended that chemical products including, but not limited to cleaning supplies, be stored separately from food items.

Physical Contamination

Physical contaminants are foreign objects that may inadvertently enter the food. Examples include but are not limited to staples, fingernails, jewelry, hair, glass, metal shavings from can openers, and pieces of bones.

FACTORS IMPLICATED IN FOODBORNE ILLNESSES

Many pathogens contribute to foodborne outbreaks in facilities. Several factors that cause pathogen growth include, but are not limited to:

- Poor Personal Hygiene - Employee health and hygiene are significant factors in preventing foodborne illness. This has been demonstrated in the population at large[3], commercial food service establishments[4], and in nursing facilities[5]. Foodborne illness in nursing homes has been associated with Norovirus. Because "infectious" individuals (persons capable of transmitting an infection or communicable disease whether they be colonized or infected) are a source of Norovirus, proper hand washing techniques and exclusion of infectious workers from handling food are critical for prevention of foodborne illness.

- Inadequate Cooking and Improper Holding Temperatures - Poorly cooked food promotes the growth of pathogens that may cause foodborne illness. The PHF/TCS foods require adequate cooking and proper holding temperatures to reduce the rapid and progressive growth of illness producing microorganisms, such as Salmonellae and Clostridium botulinum.

- Contaminated Equipment - Equipment can become contaminated in various ways including, but not limited to:

  o Poor personal hygiene;

  o Improper sanitation; and

  o Contact with raw food (e.g., poultry, eggs, seafood, and meat).

- Unsafe Food Sources - Unsafe food sources are sources not approved or considered satisfactory by Federal, State, or local authorities. Nursing homes are not permitted to use home-prepared or home-preserved (e.g., canned, pickled) foods for service to residents[3].

  NOTE: The food procurement requirements for facilities are not intended to restrict resident choice. All residents have the right to accept food brought to the facility by any visitor(s) for any resident.

Pathogenic Microorganisms and Strategies for their Control

The table below illustrates the more commonly identified ingestible items which have been associated with the listed illness - producing organisms. The primary agents are the organisms that have been associated with the ingestible food source[7]. Further, the primary control strategies list the preventive actions to inhibit the growth of these organisms.

Source of Contamination	Primary Agents of Concern	Primary Control Strategies
A. Hazards that are likely to occur - strategies that must be in place to prevent foodborne illness.		
Eggs, raw or unpasteurized	• Salmonella	• PHF/TCS • Cook to proper temperature • Prevention of cross-contamination to ready-to-eat foods
Poultry, raw	• Campylobacter • Salmonella	• PHF/TCS • Cook to proper temperature • Prevention of cross-contamination to ready-to-eat foods
	• Clostridium perfringens	• PHF/TCS • Cook to proper temperature
Meat, raw	• E. coli 0157:H7 • Salmonella • Campylobacter	• PHF/TCS • Cook to proper temperature • Prevention of cross-contamination to ready-to-eat foods
	• Clostridium perfringens	• PHF/TCS • Cook to proper temperature
Infectious food workers	• Norovirus • Hepatitis A virus • Shigella • Salmonella	• Exclusion of infectious food workers • Proper hand-washing procedures • Avoid bare-hand contact with ready-to-eat foods
	• Staphylococcus aureus	• PHF/TCS • Proper hand-washing procedures • Avoid bare-hand contact with ready-to-eat foods
B. Hazards that may occur as a result of adulteration of food products, and for which good food handling practices are needed to minimize the potential for foodborne illness transmission.		
Fruits and vegetables, fresh	• E. coli O157:H7 • Salmonella • Norovirus • Hepatitis A virus • Shigella	• Wash prior to use (unless pre-washed) • Keep cut and raw fruits and vegetables refrigerated
Ready-to-eat meat and poultry products	• Listeria monocytogenes	• Proper refrigeration during storage
Pasteurized dairy products	• Listeria monocytogenes	• Proper refrigeration during storage
Ice	• Norovirus	• Cleaning and sanitizing the internal components of the ice machine according to manufacturers' guidelines

SOM, Appendix PP, Guidance to Surveyors

PREVENTION OF FOODBORNE ILLNESS

Food Handling and Preparation

Proper food preparation, storage, and handling practices are essential in preventing foodborne illness. Education, training, and monitoring of all staff and volunteers involved in food service, as well as establishing effective infection control and quality assurance programs help maintain safe food handling practices.

Approaches to create a homelike environment or to provide accessible nourishments may include a variety of unconventional and non-institutional food services. Meals or snacks may be served at times other than scheduled meal times and convenience foods, ready-toeat foods, and pre -packaged foods may be stored and microwave heated on the nursing units. Whatever the approach, it is important that staff follow safe food handling practices.

Employee Health

Employees who handle food must be free of communicable diseases and infected skin lesions. (See the requirement at 42 CFR 483. 65(b)(2) regarding preventing the spread of infection.) Bare hand contact with foods is prohibited.

Hand Washing, Gloves, and Antimicrobial Gel

Since the skin carries microorganisms, it is critical that staff involved in food preparation consistently utilize good hygienic practices and techniques. Staff should have access to proper hand washing facilities with available soap (regular or anti-microbial), hot water, and disposable towels and/or heat/air drying methods. Antimicrobial gel (hand hygiene agent that does not require water) cannot be used in place of proper hand washing techniques in a food service setting[8].

The appropriate use of utensils such as gloves, tongs, deli paper and spatulas is essential in preventing foodborne illness. Gloved hands are considered a food contact surface that can get contaminated or soiled. Failure to change gloves between tasks can contribute to cross-contamination. Disposable gloves are a single use item and should be discarded after each use.

   NOTE: The use of disposable gloves is not a substitute for proper hand washing with soap and water.

Hair Restraints/Jewelry/Nail Polish

Dietary staff must wear hair restraints (e.g., hairnet, hat, and/or beard restraint) to prevent their hair from contacting exposed food. Dietary staff maintaining nails that are clean and neat, and wearing intact disposable gloves in good condition, and that are changed appropriately will also help reduce the spread of microorganisms. Since jewelry can harbor microorganisms, it is recommended that dietary staff keep jewelry to a minimum and cover hand jewelry with gloves when handling food[9].

Food Receiving and Storage

When food is brought into the nursing home, inspection for safe transport and quality upon receipt and proper storage helps ensure its safety. Keeping track of when to discard perishable foods and covering, labeling, and dating all foods stored in the refrigerator or freezer is indicated.

When food is brought into the facility from an of-site kitchen (any kitchen that is not operated by the facility) and the food preparation entity is approved or considered satisfactory by and is inspected by other federal, State, or local authorities, verify the last approved inspection of the supplier and continue to inspect the facility for safe food handling and storage and food quality.

*   **Dry Food Storage** - Dry storage may be in a room or area designated for the storage of dry goods, such as single service items, canned goods, and packaged or containerized bulk food that is not PHF/TCS. The focus of protection for dry storage is to keep non-refrigerated foods, disposable dishware, and napkins in a clean, dry area, which is free from contaminants. Controlling temperature, humidity, rodent and insect infestation helps prevent deterioration or contamination of the food. Dry foods and goods should be handled and stored to maintain the integrity of the packaging until they are ready to use. It is recommended that foods stored in bins (e.g., flour or sugar) be removed from their original packaging.

Keeping food of the floor and clear of ceiling sprinklers, sewer/waste disposal pipes, and vents can also help maintain food quality and prevent contamination. Desirable practices include managing the receipt and storage of dry food, removing foods not safe for consumption, keeping dry food products in closed containers, and rotating supplies.

- **Refrigerated Storage** - PHF/TCS foods must be maintained at or below 41 degrees F, unless otherwise specified by law. Frozen foods must be maintained at a temperature to keep the food frozen solid.

  Refrigeration prevents food from becoming a hazard by significantly slowing the growth of most microorganisms. Inadequate temperature control during refrigeration can promote bacterial growth. Adequate circulation of air around refrigerated products is essential to maintain appropriate food temperatures. Foods in a walk-in unit should be stored of the floor.

  Practices to maintain safe refrigerated storage include:

  o   Monitoring food temperatures and functioning of the refrigeration equipment daily and at routine intervals during all hours of operation;

  o   Placing hot food in containers (e.g., shallow pans) that permit the food to cool rapidly;

  o   Separating raw animal foods (e.g., beef, fish, lamb, pork, and poultry) from each other and storing raw meats on shelves below fruits, vegetables or other ready-to-eat foods so that meat juices do not drip onto these foods; and

  o   Labeling, dating, and monitoring refrigerated food, including, but not limited to leftovers, so it is used by its use-by date, or frozen (where applicable) or discarded.

  NOTE: Chemical products, including, but not limited to cleaning supplies, should be stored away from food items.

Safe Food Preparation

Many steps in safe food preparation must be controlled or monitored to prevent foodborne illness. Identification of potential hazards in the food preparation process and adhering to critical control points can reduce the risk of food contamination and thereby prevent foodborne illness.

Commercially pre-washed, pre-cut, and pre-packaged lettuce and other fruits and vegetables are considered edible without further preparation.

- **Cross-Contamination** - Cross-contamination can occur when harmful substances or disease-causing microorganisms are transferred to food by hands, food contact surfaces, sponges, cloth towels, or utensils that are not cleaned after touching raw food and then touch ready-to-eat goods. Cross-contamination can also occur when raw food touches or drips onto cooked or ready-to-eat foods. Examples of ways to reduce cross-contamination include, but are not limited to:

  o   Store raw meat (e.g., beef, pork, lamb, poultry, and seafood) separately and in drip-proof containers and in a manner that prevents crosscontamination of other food in the refrigerator;

  o   Between uses, store towels/cloths used for wiping surfaces during the kitchen's daily operation in containers filled with sanitizing solution at the appropriate concentration per manufacturer's specifications (see Manual Washing and Sanitizing section). Periodically testing the sanitizing solution helps assure that it maintains the correct concentration[10].

  o   Wash and sanitize cutting boards made of acceptable materials (e.g., hardwood, acrylic) between uses, consistent with applicable code[11], and

  o   Clean and sanitize work surfaces and food-contact equipment (e.g., food processors, blenders, preparation tables, knife blades, can openers, and slicers) between uses.

- **Thawing -** Thawing frozen foods is often the first step in food preparation. Thawing food at room temperature is not acceptable because the food is within the danger zone for rapid bacterial proliferation. Recommended methods to safely thaw frozen foods include:

  o Thawing in the refrigerator, in a drip -proof container, and in a manner that prevents cross-contamination;

  o Completely submerging the item under cold water (at a temperature of 70 degrees F or below) that is running fast enough to agitate and float of loose ice particles;

  o Thawing the item in a microwave oven, then cooking and serving it immediately afterward; or

  o Thawing as part of a continuous cooking process.

- **Final Cooking Temperatures -** Cooking is a critical control point in preventing foodborne illness. Cooking to heat all parts of food to the temperature and for the time specified below will either kill dangerous organisms or inactivate them sufficiently so that there is little risk to the resident if the food is eaten promptly after cooking. Monitoring the food's internal temperature for 15 seconds determines when microorganisms can no longer survive and food is safe for consumption. Foods should reach the following internal temperatures:

  o Poultry and stuffed foods - 165 degrees F;

  o Ground meat (e.g., ground beef, ground pork), ground fish, and eggs held for service - at least 155 degrees F;

  o Fish and other meats - 145 degrees F for 15 seconds;

  o Unpasteurized eggs when cooked to order in response to resident request and to be eaten promptly after cooking; - 145 degrees F for 15 seconds; until the white is completely set and the yolk is congealed; and

  o When cooking raw animal foods in the microwave, foods should be rotated and stirred during the cooking process so that all parts of the food are heated to a temperature of at least 165 degrees F, and allowed to stand covered for at least 2 minutes after cooking to obtain temperature equilibrium.

NOTE: Fresh, frozen, or canned fruits and vegetables that are cooked do not require the same level of microorganism destruction as raw animal foods. Cooking to a hot holding temperature (135 degrees F) prevents the growth of pathogenic bacteria that may be present in or on these foods.

- **Reheating Foods -** Reheated cooked foods present a risk because they have passed through the danger zone multiple times during cooking, cooling, and reheating. The PHF/TCS food that is cooked and cooled must be reheated so that all parts of the food reach an internal temperature of 165 degrees F for at least 15 seconds before holding for hot service. Ready-to-eat foods that require heating before consumption are best taken directly from a sealed container (secured against the entry of microorganisms) or an intact package from an approved food processing source and heated to at least 135 degrees F for holding for hot service.

  Although proper reheating will kill most organisms of concern, some toxins, such as that produced by Staphylococcus aureus, cannot be inactivated by reheating food.

  NOTE: Using the steam table to reheat food is unacceptable since it does not bring the food to the proper temperature within acceptable timeframes.

- **Cooling -** Improper cooling is a major factor in causing foodborne illness. Taking too long to chill PHF/TCS foods has been consistently identified as one factor contributing to foodborne illness. Foods that have been cooked and held at improper temperatures promote the growth of disease-causing microorganisms that may have survived the cooking process (e.g., spore -formers). Cooled food items can be re-contaminated by unsanitary handling practices or cross-contaminated from other food products, utensils, and equipment.

SOM, Appendix PP, Guidance to Surveyors

Large or dense food items, such as roasts, turkeys, soups, stews, legumes, and chili may require interventions (e.g., placing foods in shallow pans, cutting roasts into smaller portions, utilizing ice water baths, and stirring periodically)in order to be chilled safely within an allowed time period. These foods take a long time to cool because of their volume and density. If the hot food container is tightly covered, the cooling rate may be slowed further, leading to longer cooling times during which the food remains in the danger zone. Cooked potentially hazardous foods that are subject to time and temperature control for safety are best cooled rapidly within 2 hours, from 135 to 70 degrees F, and within 4 more hours to the temperature of approximately 41 degrees F. The total time for cooling from 135 to 41 degrees F should not exceed 6 hours.

- **Modified Consistency** - Residents who require a modified consistency diet may be at risk for developing foodborne illness because of the increased number of food handling steps required when preparing pureed and other modified consistency foods. When hot pureed, ground, or diced food drop into the danger zone (below 135 degrees F), the mechanically altered food must be reheated to 165 degrees F for 15 seconds.

- **Pooled Eggs** - Pooled eggs are raw eggs that have been cracked and combined together. The facility should crack only enough eggs for immediate service in response to a resident's requests or as an ingredient immediately before baking. Salmonella infections associated with unpasteurized eggs can be prevented by using pasteurized shell eggs or egg products in foods that require pooling of eggs or foods that will not be thoroughly cooked, such as but not limited to Caesar dressing, Hollandaise or Béarnaise sauce and French toast.

The U.S. Department of Agriculture, Food Safety and Inspection Service, Salmonella Enteritidis (SE) Risk Assessment states"A partial list of persons with increased susceptibility to infectious agents includes persons with chronic diseases, and nursing home residents. The elderly are particularly susceptible to infectious agents such as SE for a number of reasons. The disproportionate impact of severe complications and death from Salmonellosis in the elderly is illustrated by epidemiologic evidence." Waivers to allow undercooked unpasteurized eggs for resident preference are not acceptable. Pasteurized shell eggs are available and allow for safe consumption of undercooked eggs.

NOTE: Raw eggs with damaged shells are also unsafe because of the potential for contamination.

Food Service and Distribution

Various systems are available for serving and distributing food items to residents. These include but are not limited to tray lines, portable steam tables transported to a unit or dining area, open shelved food transport carts with covered trays, or enclosed carts that have hot and cold compartments. Some systems incorporate a heating element (pellet) under each plate of hot food. The purpose of these systems is to provide safe holding and transport of the food to the resident's location. Food safety requires consistent temperature control from the tray line to transport and distribution to prevent contamination (e.g., covering food items). The length of time needed to transport trays is more critical when the food is simply covered and transported in open or closed carts without a heated and cooled environment.

- **Tray line and Alternative Meal Preparation and Service Area** - The tray line may include, but is not limited to the steam table where hot prepared foods are held and served, and the chilled area where cold foods are held and served. A resident's meal tray may consist of a combination of foods that require different temperatures. Food preparation or service area problems/risks to avoid include, but are not limited to:

    o Holding foods in danger zone temperatures which are between 41 degrees F and 135 degrees F;

    o Using the steam table to heat food;

    o Serving meals on soiled dishware and with soiled utensils; and

    o Handling food with bare hands or improperly handling equipment and utensils.

The maximum length of time that foods can be held on a steam table is a total of 4 hours. Monitoring of the temperature by food service workers while food is on the steam table is essential. Foods may be reheated (only once) to 165 degrees F. Reheated foods are best discarded if not eaten within two hours after reheating[12].

- **Food Distribution** - Dining locations include any area where one or more residents eat their meals. These can be located adjacent to the kitchen or a distance from the kitchen, such as residents' rooms and dining rooms in nursing units on other floors or wings of the building. Potential food handling problems/risks associated with food distribution include:

    o Staff distributing trays without first properly washing their hands; and

    o Serving food to residents after collecting soiled plates and food waste, without proper hand washing.

- **Snacks** - Snacks refer to those foods that are served between meals or at bed time. Temperature control and freedom from contamination are also important when ready-toeat or prepared food items for snacks are sent to the unit and are held for delivery; or stored at the nursing station, in a unit refrigerator or unit cupboards. Food handling risks associated with food stored on the units may include but are not limited to:

    o Food left on trays or countertops beyond safe time and/or temperature requirements;

    o Food left in refrigerators beyond safe "use by" dates (including, but not limited to foods that have been opened but were not labeled, etc.);

    o Food stored in a manner (open containers, without covers, spillage from one food item onto another, etc.) that allows cross-contamination; and

    o Failure to maintain refrigerated food temperatures at safe levels;

- **Special Events** - Facility-sponsored special events, such as cookouts and picnics where food may not be prepared in the facility's kitchen and is served outdoors or in other locations, require the same food safety considerations.

- **Transported Foods** - If residents take prepared foods with them out of the facility (e.g., bag lunches for residents attending dialysis, clinics, sporting events, or day treatment programs), the foods must be handled and prepared for them with the same safe and sanitary approaches used during primary food preparation in the facility. Appropriate food transport equipment or another approach to maintaining safe temperatures for food at special events can help prevent foodborne illness.

- **Ice** - Appropriate ice and water handling practices prevent contamination and the potential for waterborne illness. Ice must be made from potable water. Ice that is used to cool food items (e.g., ice in a pan used to cool milk cartons) is not to be used for consumption. Keeping the ice machine clean and sanitary will help prevent contamination of the ice. Contamination risks associated with ice and water handling practices may include, but are not limited to:

    o Staff who use poor hygiene, fail to wash hands adequately, or handle ice with their bare hands are not following appropriate infection control practices when dispensing water and ice; and

    o Unclean equipment, including the internal components of ice machines that are not drained, cleaned, and sanitized as needed and according to manufacturer's specifications.

- **Refrigeration** - A potential cause of foodborne illness is improper storage of PHF/TCS food. The refrigerator must be in good repair and keep foods at or below 41 degrees F. The freezer must keep frozen foods frozen solid. The following are methods to determine the proper working order of the refrigerators and freezers:

    o Document the temperature of external and internal refrigerator gauges as well as the temperature inside the refrigerator. Measure whether the temperature of a PHF/TCS food that has been inside for at least 24 hours is 41 degrees or less;

    o To make sure the cooling process is effective, measure the temperature of a PHF/TCS that has a prolonged cooling time (e.g., one in a large, deep, tightly covered container). Determine if it is in the danger zone;

    o Check for situations where potential for cross-contamination is high (e.g., raw meat stored over ready-to-eat items);

o Check the firmness of frozen food and inspect the wrapper to determine if it is intact enough to protect the food; and

o Interview food service personnel regarding the operation of the refrigerator and the freezer.

EQUIPMENT AND UTENSIL CLEANING AND SANITIZATION

A potential cause of foodborne outbreaks is improper cleaning (washing and sanitizing) of contaminated equipment. Protecting equipment from contamination via splash, dust, grease, etc. is indicated. Dishwashing machines, operated according to the manufacturer specifications, wash, rinse, and sanitize dishes and utensils using either heat or chemical sanitization. Manual dishwashing is often used for pots and pans, or when the dishwashing machine is not operational.

Machine Washing and Sanitizing

Dishwashing machines use either heat or chemical sanitization methods. The following are specifications according to the U.S. Department of Health and Human Services, Public Health Services, Food and Drug Administration Food Code (or according to manufacturer's directions) for each method.

- High Temperature Dishwasher (heat sanitization):

  o Wash   150-165 degrees F wash; and

  o Final Rinse   180 degrees F final rinse
                  (160 degrees F at the rack level/dish surface reflects 180 degrees F at the manifold, which is the area just before the final rinse nozzle where the temperature of the dish machine is measured); or

                  165 degrees F for a stationary rack, single temperature machine.

- Low Temperature Dishwasher (chemical sanitization):

  o Wash   120 degrees F wash; and

  o Final Rinse   50 ppm (parts per million) hypochlorite (chlorine) on dish surface in final rinse.

Manual Washing and Sanitizing

A 3-step process is used to manually wash, rinse, and sanitize dishware correctly. The first step is thorough washing using hot water and detergent after food particles have been scraped. The second is rinsing with hot water to remove all soap residues. The third step is sanitizing with either hot water or a chemical solution maintained at the correct concentration, based on periodic testing, and for the effective contact time according to manufacturer's guidelines.

After washing and rinsing, dishes and utensils are sanitized by immersion in either:

- Hot water (at least 171 degrees F) for 30 seconds; or

- A chemical sanitizing solution used according to manufacturer's instructions. Chemical sanitization requires greater controls than hot water sanitization. If explicit instructions are not provided by the manufacturer, the recommended sanitization concentrations are as follows:

  o Chlorine   50-100 ppm minimum 10 second contact time

  o Iodine   12.5 ppm minimum 30 second contact time

  o QAC space (Quaternary)   150-200 ppm concentration and contact time per Manufacturer's instructions (Ammonium Compound)

A high concentration of sanitation solutions may be potentially hazardous (see manufacturer's instructions). Improper test strips yield inaccurate results when testing for chemical sanitation.

Drying food preparation equipment and utensils with a towel or cloth may increase risks for cross contamination.

Cleaning Fixed Equipment

When cleaning fixed equipment (e.g., mixers, slicers, and other equipment that cannot readily be immersed in water), the removable parts are washed and sanitized and nonremovable parts are cleaned with detergent and hot water, rinsed, air-dried and sprayed with a sanitizing solution (at the effective concentration). Finally, the equipment is reassembled and any food contact surfaces that may have been contaminated during the process are re-sanitized (according to the manufacturer's instructions). Service area wiping cloths are cleaned and dried or placed in a chemical sanitizing solution of appropriate concentration.

[**Editor's Note:** See page 393 for endnotes pertaining to this section.]

INVESTIGATIVE PROTOCOL

SANITARY CONDITIONS

Objectives

- To determine if the facility obtained food safe for consumption from approved sources;

- To determine if the facility stores, prepares, distributes, and serves food in a sanitary manner to prevent foodborne illness;

- To determine if the facility has systems (e.g., policies, procedures, training, and monitoring) in place to prevent the spread of foodborne illness and minimize food storage, preparation and handling practices that could cause food contamination and could compromise food safety; and

- To determine if the facility utilizes safe food handling from the time the food is received from the vendor and throughout the food handling processes in the facility.

Use

Use this protocol to investigate compliance at F371 (§483.35(i)(1) and (2)).

Procedures

Adhere to sanitary requirements (e.g., proper washing hands when entering the kitchen and between tasks, use of hair restraints) when assessing the kitchen and meal service throughout the survey process. During the initial tour of the facility and throughout the survey, observe the kitchen(s) and food service area(s) and review planned menus to determine when to assess food preparation processes. Observe subsequent kitchen/food services during times when food is being stored, prepared, cooked, plated, transported, and distributed to determine if safe food handling practices are being followed. Corroborate observations through interview, record review, and other appropriate documentation.

> **NOTE:** When a facility receives food from an of-site kitchen (any kitchen not operated by the facility), determine whether the food was obtained from an approved source.

1. Observation

Conduct the following observations:

- Food procurement procedures:

  o Determine whether food meets safe and sanitary conditions related to when, where, and how the food was received for residents consumption.

  o Check invoices from food vendors when necessary to verify the source of food acquisition and the date of delivery.

- Food preparation procedures:

  o Observe staff food handling practices, such as proper hand washing, the appropriate use of utensils, glove, and hairnets;

  o Observe food labeling and dates (e.g., used by dates);

  o Observe food handling practices that have potential for crosscontamination (e.g., use of food contact surfaces and equipment to prepare various uncooked and ready-to-eat foods);

o   If the facility is cooking a PHF/TCS food, evaluate if the food reached the acceptable final cooking temperatures, by inserting the stem of a calibrated thermometer into the middle or thickest part of the food;

o   If a PHF/TCS food is prepared from ingredients at room temperature, determine if it was cooled to 41 degrees F within 4 hours. For example, when observing tuna or chicken salad preparation, determine when the salad was prepared, then measure the current temperature; and

o   Observe staff preparing modified consistency (e.g., pureed, mechanical soft) PHF/TCS foods to determine whether food safety was compromised.

Service of food during meal times –

•   Observe the staff measuring the temperature of all hot and cold menu items. Cold foods should be at or below 41 degrees F when served. Hot foods should be at 135 degrees F or above when served.

Service after meal times:

•   Observe whether facility personnel are operating the dish washing machine according to the manufacturer's specifications. Evaluate sanitization with a calibrated thermometer (for a high temperature machine), chlorine test tape (for a low temperature machine), or other manufacturer recommended method;

•   Check whether the facility has the appropriate equipment and supplies to evaluate the safe operation of the dish machine and the washing of pots and pans (e.g., maximum registering thermometer, appropriate chemical test strips, and paper thermometers);

•   Evaluate sanitization during manual pot and pan washing (3-step process). Test the final rinse water temperature if using hot water for sanitization or the concentration of chemical sanitizer being used. Determine if the appropriate test strip for that chemical is being utilized;

•   Observe stored dishes, utensils, pots/pans, and equipment for evidence of soiling. These items should be stored in a clean dry location and not exposed to splash, dust or other contamination; and

•   Evaluate whether proper hand washing is occurring between handling soiled and clean dishes to prevent cross-contamination of the clean dishes.

Storage of food:

•   Observe for evidence of pests, rodents and droppings and other sources of contamination in food storage areas;

•   Observe food labeling and dates (e.g., used by dates);

•   Observe that foods are stored off of the floor, and clear of ceiling sprinklers, sewer/waste disposal pipes and cleaning chemicals;

•   Observe whether the facility has canned goods that have a compromised seal (e.g., punctures); and

•   Observe whether staff access bulk foods without touching the food.

2.   Interview

During the course of the survey, interview the staff who performs the task about the procedures they follow to procure, store, prepare, distribute, and serve food to residents. Request clarification from the dietary supervisor/manager or qualified dietitian concerning the following:

•   What is the facility's practice for dealing with employees who come to work with symptoms of contagious illness (e.g., coughing, sneezing, diarrhea, vomiting) or open wounds;

- How does the facility identify problems with time and temperature control of PHF/TCS foods and what are the processes to address those problems;

- Whether the facility has, and follows, a cleaning schedule for the kitchen and food service equipment; and

- If there is a problem with equipment, how staff informs maintenance and follows up to see if the problem is corrected.

3. Record Review

In order to investigate identified food safety concerns, review supporting data, as necessary, including but not limited to:

- Any facility documentation, such as dietary policies and procedures, related to compliance with food sanitation and safety. Determine if the food service employees have received training related to such compliance;

- Food temperature records from the tray line, refrigerator/freezer temperature records, and dishwasher records;

- Maintenance records, such as work orders and manufacturer's specifications, related to equipment used to store, prepare, and serve food; and

- Facility infection control records regarding surveillance for foodborne illness and actions related to suspected or confirmed outbreaks of gastrointestinal illnesses.

4. Review of Facility Practices

Review of facility practices may include, but is not limited to, review of policies and procedures for sufficient staffing, staff training, and following manufacturer's recommendations as indicated. In order to establish if the facility has a process in place to prevent the spread of foodborne illness, interview the staff to determine how they:

- Monitor whether the facility appropriately procures, stores, prepares, distributes, and serves food;

- Identify and analyze pertinent issues and underlying causes of a food safety concern (e.g., refrigerator or dishwasher malfunction);

- Implement interventions that are pertinent and timely in relation to the urgency and severity of a concern; and

- Monitor the implementation of interventions and determine if additional modification is needed.

DETERMINATION OF COMPLIANCE (TASK 6, APPENDIX P)

Synopsis of Regulation (F371)

The sanitary conditions requirement has two aspects. The first aspect requires that the facility procures food from sources approved or considered satisfactory by Federal, State, or local authorities. The second aspect requires that the facility stores, prepares, distributes, and serves food under sanitary conditions to prevent foodborne illness.

Criteria for Compliance

The facility is in compliance with 42 CFR 483.35(i)(1)(2), Sanitary Conditions, if staff:

- Procures, stores, handles, prepares, distributes, and serve food to minimize the risk of foodborne illness;

- Maintains PHF/TCS foods at safe temperatures, cools food rapidly, and prevents contamination during storage;

- Cooks food to the appropriate temperature and holds PHF/TCS food at or below 41 degrees F or at or above 135 degrees F;

- Utilizes proper hand washing and personal hygiene practices to prevent food contamination; and

- Maintains equipment and food contact surfaces to prevent food contamination.

If not, cite at Tag F371.

Noncompliance for F371

After completing the Investigative Protocol, analyze the data in order to determine whether noncompliance with the regulation exists. Noncompliance for Tag F371 may include, but is not limited to, failure to do one or more of the following:

- Procure, store, handle, prepare, distribute, and serve food in accordance with the standards summarized in this guidance;

- Maintain PHF/TCS foods at safe temperatures, at or below 41 degrees F (for cold foods) or at or above 135 degrees F (for hot foods) except during preparation, cooking, or cooling, and ensure that PHF/TCS food plated for transport was not out of temperature control for more than four hours from the time it is plated;

- Store raw foods (e.g., meats, fish) in a manner to reduce the risk of contamination of cooked or ready-to-eat foods;

- Cook food to the appropriate temperature to kill pathogenic microorganisms that may cause foodborne illness;

- Cool food in a manner that prevents the growth of pathogenic microorganisms;

- Utilize proper personal hygiene practices (e.g., proper hand washing and the appropriate use of gloves) to prevent contamination of food; and

- Use and maintain equipment and food contact surfaces (e.g., cutting boards, dishes, and utensils) to prevent cross-contamination.

Potential Tags for Additional Investigation

During the investigation of 42 CFR §483.35(i)(1)(2), the surveyor may have identified concerns related to these requirements. The surveyor should investigate these requirements before determining whether noncompliance may be present. The following are related outcome, process, and structure requirements that may be considered:

- 42 CFR 483.25(g)(2), F322, Nasogastric Tubes

  o   Determine if residents have experienced nausea, vomiting, diarrhea, or other gastrointestinal symptoms as a result of the failure to store, handle, administer, or remove and discard tube feeding solutions in a safe and sanitary manner.

- 42 CFR 483.25(i), F325, Nutrition

  o   Determine if multiple residents have experienced nausea, vomiting, diarrhea, or other gastrointestinal symptoms related to foodborne illness, which may impact their nutritional status.

- 42 CFR 483.30(a)(b), F353 Sufficient Staffing

  o   Determine if the facility has sufficient staffing to meet the needs of the resident.

- 42 CFR 483.35(a)(1)(2), F361, Dietary Services – Staffing

  o   Determine if the facility employs or consults with a qualified dietitian. If not employed full-time, determine if the director of food service receives scheduled consultation from the dietitian concerning storage, preparation, distribution and service of food under sanitary conditions.

- 42 CFR 483.35(b), F362, Standard Sufficient Staff

    o   Determine if the facility employs sufficient support personnel competent to carry out the functions of the dietary service.

- 42 CFR 483.35(h) Paid Feeding Assistant

    o   Determine if the Feeding Assistant has successfully completed a State-approved training course that meets Federal requirements and that the Feeding Assistant is utilizing proper techniques to prevent foodborne illness.

- 42 CFR 483.65(a), F441, Infection Control

    o   Determine if the facility's infection control program included investigation, control, and prevention of foodborne illness.

- 42 CFR 483.65(b)(3), F444*, Handwashing Techniques *[**Editor's Note:** The tag number cited is incorrect. The correct tag number is F441.]

    o   Determine if the facility has practices in place to prevent the spread of infection, including proper hand washing techniques.

- 42 CFR 483.70(c)(2), F456, Maintain All Essential Equipment

    o   Determine if the equipment in the kitchen, such as refrigerators, food carts, tray line equipment, freezers, dishwashers, ovens, stoves, and ranges etc. is maintained in safe operating condition and according to manufacturers' specifications.

- 42 CFR 483. 70(h), F465, Other Environmental Conditions

    o   Determine if the kitchen physical environment, such as, floors, walls, ceilings, and vent hoods are safe, clean, and sanitary.

- 42 CFR 483.70(h)(4), F469, Effective Pest Control Program

    o   Determine if the facility has maintained an effective pest control program so that it remains free of pests and rodents. Determine whether there is evidence of roaches, ants, flies, mice, etc. in food storage, preparation and service areas.

- 42 CFR 483.70(o)(2)(i)(ii), F520, Quality Assessment and Assurance [**Editor's Note**: The reference cited should be 42 CFR 483.75(o)(2)(i)(ii), F520 Quality Assessment and Assurance.]

    o   Determine whether the quality assessment and assurance committee seeks and reviews concerns related to foodborne illness, and food safety and sanitation to develop and implement appropriate actions to correct identified quality deficiencies when indicated.

IV. DEFICIENCY CATEGORIZATION (PART IV, APPENDIX P)

Once the survey team has completed its investigation, analyzed the data, reviewed the regulatory requirements, and determined that noncompliance exists, the team must determine the severity of each deficiency, based on the resultant effect or potential for harm to the resident.

The key elements for severity determination for Tag F371 are as follows:

1. **Presence of harm/negative outcome(s) or potential for negative outcomes because of the presence of unsanitary conditions.** Actual or potential harm/negative outcome for Tag F371 may include, but is not limited to:

- Foodborne illness; or

- Ingestion or potential ingestion of food that was not procured from approved sources, and stored, prepared, distributed or served under sanitary conditions.

2. **Degree of harm (actual or potential) related to the noncompliance.** Identify how the facility's noncompliance caused, resulted in, allowed or contributed to the actual or potential for harm.

- If harm has occurred, determine if the harm is at the level of serious injury, impairment, death, compromise, or discomfort; or

- If harm has not yet occurred, determine the potential for serious injury, impairment, death, or compromise or discomfort to occur to the resident.

3. **The immediacy of correction required.** Determine whether the noncompliance requires immediate correction in order to prevent serious injury, harm, impairment, or death to one or more residents.

The survey team must evaluate the harm or potential for harm based upon the following levels of severity for Tag F371. First, the team must rule out whether Severity Level 4, Immediate Jeopardy to a resident's health or safety exists by evaluating the deficient practice in relation to immediacy, culpability, and severity. (Follow the guidance in Appendix Q.)

Severity Level 4 Considerations: Immediate Jeopardy to Resident Health or Safety

Immediate Jeopardy is a situation in which the facility's noncompliance with one or more requirements of participation:

- Has allowed/caused/resulted in or is likely to allow/cause/result in serious injury, harm, impairment, or death to a resident; and

- Requires immediate correction, as the facility either created the situation or allowed the situation to continue by failing to implement preventive or corrective measures.

  NOTE: The death or transfer of a resident who was harmed or injured as a result of facility noncompliance does not remove a finding of immediate jeopardy. The facility is required to implement specific actions to remove the jeopardy and correct the noncompliance, which allowed or caused the immediate jeopardy.

Examples of negative outcomes that occurred or have the potential to occur at Severity Level 4 as a result of the facility's deficient practices may include:

- A roast (raw meat) thawing on a plate in the refrigerator had bloody juices overflowing and dripping onto uncovered salad greens on the shelf below. The contaminated salad greens were not discarded and were used to make salad for the noon meal;

- The facility had a recent outbreak of Norovirus after the facility allowed a food worker who was experiencing vomiting and diarrhea to continue preparing food. Observations and interviews indicate that other food service staff with gastrointestinal illnesses are also permitted to prepare food; and

- The facility purchased unpasteurized shell eggs for all cooking purposes. The cook prepared and served sunny-side-up eggs with barely cooked yolks (i.e., not cooked to at least 145 degrees F for at least 15 seconds) for fourteen residents' breakfasts. Using unpasteurized, shell eggs to prepare undercooked eggs for eating increased the risk of residents being infected with Salmonella, which could lead to a life-threatening illness. The facility did not have a system in place to minimize foodborne illness in the preparation of undercooked unpasteurized eggs.

Severity Level 3 Considerations: Actual Harm that is Not Immediate Jeopardy

Severity Level 3 indicates noncompliance that results in actual harm that is not immediate jeopardy. The negative outcome can include but may not be limited to clinical compromise, decline, or the resident's inability to maintain and/or reach his/her highest practicable level of well-being. Therefore, a Level 3 deficiency is indicated when unsafe food handling and inadequate sanitary conditions result in actual harm to residents. Examples of avoidable actual or potential resident outcomes that demonstrate severity at Level 3 may include, but are not limited to:

- Outbreak of nausea and vomiting occurs in the facility related to the inadequate sanitizing of dishes and utensils; and

- Episode of food poisoning occurs because facility had an event in which tuna, chicken, and potato salads served in bulk were not kept adequately chilled and were still left out for eating after 5 hours.

Severity Level 2 Considerations: No Actual Harm with Potential for More Than Minimal Harm that is Not Immediate Jeopardy

Severity Level 2 indicates noncompliance that results in a resident outcome of no more than minimal discomfort and/or has the potential to compromise the resident's ability to maintain or reach his or her highest practicable level of well being. The potential exists for greater harm to occur if interventions are not provided.

As a result of the facility's noncompliance, the potential for food contamination and/or growth of pathogenic microorganisms exists. Examples of avoidable actual or potential resident outcomes that demonstrate severity at Level 2 may include, but are not limited to:

- Food service workers sliced roast pork on the meat slicer. The meat slicer was not washed, rinsed, and sanitized after usage. The facility failed to educate and train staff on how to clean and sanitize all kitchen equipment;

- During the initial tour of the kitchen, two food service workers were observed on the loading dock. One was smoking and the other employee was emptying trash. Upon returning to the kitchen, they proceeded to prepare food without washing their hands; and

- Upon inquiry by the surveyor, the food service workers tested the sanitizer of the dish machine, the chemical rinse of the pot-and -pan sink, and a stationary bucket used for wiping cloths. The facility used chlorine as the sanitizer. The sanitizer tested less than 50 ppm in all three locations. Staff interviewed stated they were unaware of the amount of sanitizer to use and the manufacturer's recommendations to maintain the appropriate ppm of available sanitizer.

Severity Level 1 Considerations: No Actual Harm with Potential for Minimal Harm

The failure of the facility to procure, prepare, store, distribute and handle food under sanitary conditions places this highly susceptible population at risk for more than minimal harm. Therefore, Severity Level 1 does not apply for this regulatory requirement.

F372

§483.35(i)(3) Dispose of Garbage and Refuse Properly

Interpretive Guidelines §483.35(i)(3)

The intent of this regulation is to assure that garbage and refuse be properly disposed.

Procedures §483.35(i)(3)

Garbage/refuse:

Observe garbage and refuse container construction, and outside storage receptacles.

Probes §483.35(i)(3)

Are garbage and refuse containers in good condition (no leaks) and is waste properly contained in dumpsters or compactors with lids or otherwise covered?

Are areas such as loading docks, hallways, and elevators used for both garbage disposal and clean food transport kept clean, free of debris and free of foul odors and waste fat?

Is the garbage storage area maintained in a saunter condition to prevent the harborage and feeding of pests?

Are garbage receptacles covered when being removed from the kitchen area to the dumpster?

[This page intentionally left blank]

F385 – F390

§483.40 — Physician Services

F385

§483.40 Physician Services

A physician must personally approve in writing a recommendation that an individual be admitted to a facility. Each resident must remain under the care of a physician.

§483.40(a) Physician Supervision

The facility must ensure that--

(1) The medical care of each resident is supervised by a physician; and

(2) Another physician supervises the medical care of residents when their attending physician is unavailable.

Intent §483.40

The intent of this regulation is to ensure the medical supervision of the care of nursing home residents by a personal physician.

Interpretive Guidelines §483.40

A physician's "personal approval" of an admission recommendation must be in written form. The physician's admission orders for the resident's immediate care as required in §483.20(a) will be accepted as "personal approval" of the admission.

"**Supervising the medical care of residents**" means participating in the resident's assessment and care planning, monitoring changes in resident's medical status, and providing consultation or treatment when called by the facility. It also includes, but is not limited to, prescribing new therapy, ordering a resident's transfer to the hospital, conducting required routine visits or delegating and supervising follow-up visits to nurse practitioners or physician assistants. Each resident should be allowed to designate a personal physician. (See §483.10(d)(1).) The facility's responsibility in this situation is to simply assist the resident, when necessary, in his or her efforts to obtain those services. For example, the facility could put the resident in touch with the county medical society for the purpose of obtaining referrals to practicing physicians in the area.

Facilities should share MDS and other assessment data with the physician.

Procedures §483.40

If there is a deficiency in §483.10, Resident Rights; §483.13, Resident Behavior and Facility Practices; §483.15, Quality of Life; or §483.25, Quality of Care, fully review all of the tags under this requirement.

Probes §483.40(a)

- How was the supervising physician involved in the resident's assessment and care planning?

- If staff reported a significant change in medical status to the supervising physician, did the physician respond?

- If the supervising physician was unavailable and could not respond, did the facility have a physician on call? Did this physician respond?

- Are residents sent to hospital emergency rooms routinely because the facility does not always have a physician on call?

F386

§483.40(b) Physician Visits

The physician must--

(1) Review the resident's total program of care, including medications and treatments, at each visit required by paragraph (c) of this section;

(2) Write, sign, and date progress notes at each visit; and

(3) Sign and date all orders with the exception of influenza and pneumococcal polysaccharide vaccines, which may be administered per physician-approved facility policy after an assessment for contraindications.

Intent §483.40(b)

The intent of this regulation is to have the physician take an active role in supervising the care of residents. This should not be a superficial visit, but should include an evaluation of the resident's condition and a review of and decision about the continued appropriateness of the resident's current medical regime.

Interpretive Guidelines §483.40(b)

Total program of care includes all care the facility provides residents to maintain or improve their highest practicable mental and physical functional status, as defined by the comprehensive assessment and plan of care. Care includes medical services and medication management, physical, occupational, and speech/language therapy, nursing care, nutritional interventions, social work and activity services that maintain or improve psychosocial functioning.

The physician records residents' progress and problems in maintaining or improving their mental and physical functional status. The physician need not review the total plan of care at each visit, but must review the total plan of care at visits required by §483.40(c). There is no requirement for physician renewal of orders.

In cases where facilities have created the option for a resident's record to be maintained by computer, rather than hard copy, electronic signatures are acceptable. See Guidelines for §483.75(l)(1) for information on facility safeguards concerning electronic signatures.

Physician orders may be transmitted by facsimile machine if the following conditions are met:

- The physician should have signed and retained the original copy of the order from which the facsimile was transmitted and be able to provide it upon request. Alternatively, the original may be sent to the facility at a later time and substituted for the facsimile.

- The facility should photocopy the faxed order since some facsimiles fade over time. The facsimile copy can be discarded after facility photocopies it.

- A facility using such a system should establish adequate safeguards to assure that it is not subject to abuse.

It is not necessary for a physician to re-sign the facsimile order when he/she visits the facility.

When rubber stamp signatures are authorized by the facility's management, the individual whose signature the stamp represents shall place in the administrative offices of the facility a signed statement to the effect that he/she is the only one who has the stamp and uses it. A list of computer codes and written signatures must be readily available and maintained under adequate safeguards.

Probes §483.40(b)

- Do services ordered by a physician show a pattern of care to maintain or improve the resident's level of independent functioning? For example, how do physician orders reflect the resident's nutritional status and needs?

- Does documentation reflect continuity of care in maintaining or improving a resident's mental and physical functional status? For example, do the attending physician's rehabilitation service orders show a pattern of consistent restorative programming?

F387

§483.40(c) Frequency of Physician Visits

(1) The residents must be seen by a physician at least once every 30 days for the first 90 days after admission, and at least once every 60 days thereafter.

(2) A physician visit is considered timely if it occurs not later than 10 days after the date the visit was required.

F388

§483.40(c)(3) Except as provided in paragraphs (c)(4) and (f) of this section, all required physician visits must be made by the physician personally.

§483.40(c)(4) At the option of the physician, required visits in SNFs, after the initial visit, may alternate between personal visits by the physician and visits by a physician assistant, nurse practitioner or clinical nurse specialist in accordance with paragraph (e) of this section.

Interpretive Guidelines §483.40(c)

"Must be seen" means that the physician must make actual face-to-face contact with the resident. There is no requirement for this type of contact at the time of admission, since the decision to admit an individual to a nursing facility (whether from a hospital or from the individual's own residence) generally involves physician contact during the period immediately preceding the admission.

After the initial physician visit in SNFs, where States allow their use, a qualified nurse practitioner (NP), clinical nurse specialist or physician assistant (PA) may make every other required visit. (See §483.40(e) Physician delegation of tasks in SNFs.)

In a NF, the physician visit requirement, in accordance with the State law, may be satisfied by NP, clinical nurse specialist or PA. (See §483.40(f).)

The timing of physician visits is based on the admission date of the resident. Visits will be made within the first 30 days, and then at 30 day intervals up until 90 days after the admission date. Visits will then be at 60 day intervals. Permitting up to 10 days slippage of a due date will not affect the next due date. However, do not specifically look at the timetables for physician visits unless there is indication of inadequate medical care. The regulation states that the physician (or his/her delegate) must visit the resident **at least** every 30 or 60 days. There is no provision for physicians to use discretion in visiting at intervals longer than those specified at §483.40(c).

Policy that allows an NP, clinical nurse specialist, or PA to make every other required visit, and that allows a 10 day slippage in the time of the visit, does not relieve the physician of the obligation to visit a resident when the resident's medical condition makes that visit necessary.

It is expected that visits will occur at the facility rather than the doctor's office unless office equipment is needed or a resident specifically requests an office visit. If the facility has established policy that residents leave the grounds for medical care, the resident does not object, and this policy does not infringe on his/her rights, there is no prohibition to this practice. The facility should inform the resident of this practice, in accordance with §483.10(b).

Probes §483.40(c)

- How does the scheduling and frequency of physician visits relate to any identified quality of care problems?

- When a PA, clinical nurse specialist, or NP performs a delegated physician visit, and determines that the resident's condition warrants direct contact between the physician and the resident, does the physician follow-up promptly with a personal visit?

F389

§483.40(d) Availability of Physicians for Emergency Care

The facility must provide or arrange for the provision of physician services 24 hours a day, in case of emergency.

Interpretive Guidelines §483.40(d)

If a resident's own physician is unavailable, the facility should attempt to contact that physician's designated referral physician before assuming the responsibility of assigning a physician. Arranging for physician services may include assuring resident transportation to a hospital emergency room/ward or other medical facility if the facility is unable to provide emergency medical care at the facility.

Probes §483.40(d)

- Does the facility have a physician on call for medical emergencies? Does this physician respond?

- For what reasons are residents sent to hospital emergency rooms?

- Did medical management of the emergency affect the resident's maintaining or improving their functional abilities?

- If the resident refused the physician's visit, what has the facility done to explain to the resident the results and alternatives that may be available?

F390

§483.40(e) Physician Delegation of Tasks in SNFs

(1) Except as specified in paragraph (e)(2) of this section, a physician may delegate tasks to a physician assistant, nurse practitioner, or clinical nurse specialist who--

(i) Meets the applicable definition in §491.2 of this chapter or, in the case of a clinical nurse specialist, is licensed as such by the State;

(ii) Is acting within the scope of practice as defined by State law; and

(iii) Is under the supervision of the physician.

(2) A physician may not delegate a task when the regulations specify that the physician must perform it personally, or when the delegation is prohibited under State law or by the facility's own policies.

Interpretive Guidelines §483.40(e)

"**Nurse practitioner**" is a registered professional nurse now licensed to practice in the State and who meets the State's requirements governing the qualifications of nurse practitioners.

"**Clinical nurse specialist**" is a registered professional nurse currently in practice in the State and who meets the State's requirements governing the qualifications of clinical nurse specialists.

"**Physician assistant**" is a person who meets the applicable State requirements governing the qualifications for assistants to physicians.

When **personal** performance of a particular task by a physician is specified in the regulations, performance of that task cannot be delegated to anyone else. The tasks of examining the resident, reviewing the resident's total program of care, writing progress notes, and signing orders may be delegated according to State law. The extent to which physician services are delegated to physician extenders in SNFs will continue to be determined by the provisions of §483.40(e), while the extent to which these services are performed by physician extenders in NFs will be determined by the individual States under §483.40(f).

Probes §483.40(e)

- Do the facility's attending physicians delegate to NPs, clinical nurse specialists, or PAs?

- Do NP/clinical nurse specialist/PA progress notes and orders follow the scope of practice allowed by State law?

- What evidence is there of physician supervision of NPs or PAs? For example, do physicians countersign NP/PA orders, if required by State law?

§483.40(f) Performance of Physician Tasks in NFs

At the option of State, any required physician task in a NF (including tasks which the regulations specify must be performed personally by the physician) may also be satisfied when performed by a nurse practitioner, clinical nurse specialist, or physician assistant who is not an employee of the facility but who is working in collaboration with a physician.

Interpretive Guidelines §483.40(f)

If delegation of physician tasks is permitted in your State and the physician extender does not meet the qualifications listed here, cite F388.

Procedures §483.40(f)

If a nurse practitioner, clinical nurse specialist, or physician assistant is performing required physician tasks in a NF, is this allowed by the State? Is this person an employee of the facility? (Facility employees are prohibited from serving in this capacity.)

Probes §483.40(f)

Is this person working in collaboration with the physician?

[This page intentionally left blank]

F406 – F407

§483.45 — Specialized Rehabilitative Services

§483.45 Specialized Rehabilitative Services

F406

§483.45(a) Provision of Services

If specialized rehabilitative services such as, but not limited to physical therapy, speech-language pathology, occupational therapy, and mental health rehabilitative services for mental illness and mental retardation, are required in the resident's comprehensive plan of care, the facility must--

(1) Provide the required services; or

(2) Obtain the required services from an outside resource (in accordance with §483.75(h) of this part) from a provider of specialized rehabilitative services.

Intent §483.45(a)(1)(2)

The intent of this regulation is to assure that residents receive necessary specialized rehabilitative services as determined by the comprehensive assessment and care plan, to prevent avoidable physical and mental deterioration and to assist them in obtaining or maintaining their highest practicable level of functional and psycho-social well-being.

"**Specialized rehabilitative services**" are differentiated from restorative services which are provided by nursing staff. Specialized rehabilitative services are provided by or coordinated by qualified personnel.

Specialized rehabilitative services are considered a facility service and are, thus, included within the scope of facility services. They must be provided by or coordinated by qualified personnel. They must be provided to residents who need them even when the services are not specifically enumerated in the State plan. No fee can be charged a Medicaid recipient for specialized rehabilitative services because they are covered facility services.

A facility is not obligated to provide specialized rehabilitative services if it does not have residents who require these services. If a resident develops a need for these services after admission, the facility must either provide the services, or, where appropriate, obtain the services from an outside resource.

For a resident with MI or MR to have his or her specialized needs met, the individual must receive all services necessary to assist the individual in maintaining or achieving as much independence and self-determination as possible. They are:

"**Specialized services for MI or MR**" refers to those services to be **provided by the State** which can only be delivered by personnel or programs other than those of the NF (e.g., outside the NF setting), because the overall level of NF services is not as intense as necessary to meet the individual's needs.

The Preadmission Screening and Annual Resident Review (PASARR) report indicates specialized services required by the resident. The State is required to list those services in the report, as well as provide or arrange for the provision of the services. If the State determines that the resident does not require specialized services, the facility is responsible to provide all services necessary to meet the resident's mental health or mental retardation needs.

"**Mental health rehabilitative services for MI and MR**" refers to those services of lesser frequency or intensity to be implemented by all levels of nursing facility staff who come into contact with the resident who is mentally ill or who has mental retardation. These services are necessary regardless of whether or not they are required to be subject to the PASARR process and whether or not they require additional services to be provided or arranged for by the State as specialized services.

The facility should provide interventions which complement, reinforce and are consistent with any specialized services (as defined by the resident's PASARR) the individual is receiving or is required to receive by the State. The individual's plan of care should specify how the facility will integrate relevant activities throughout all hours of the individual's day at the NF to achieve this consistency and enhancement of PASARR goals. The surveyor should see competent interaction by staff at all times, in both formal and informal settings in accordance with the individual's needs.

Mental health rehabilitative services for MI and MR may include, but are not limited to:

- Consistent implementation during the resident's daily routine and across settings, of systematic plans which are designed to change inappropriate behaviors;

- Drug therapy and monitoring of the effectiveness and side effects of medications which have been prescribed to change inappropriate behavior or to alter manifestations of psychiatric illness;

- Provision of a structured environment for those individuals who are determined to need such structure (e.g., structured socialization activities to diminish tendencies toward isolation and withdrawal);

- Development, maintenance and consistent implementation across settings of those programs designed to teach individuals the daily living skills they need to be more independent and self-determining including, but not limited to, grooming, personal hygiene, mobility, nutrition, vocational skills, health, drug therapy, mental health education, money management, and maintenance of the living environment;

- Crisis intervention service;

- Individual, group, and family psychotherapy;

- Development of appropriate personal support networks; and

- Formal behavior modification programs.

Procedures §483.45(a)(1)(2)

For sampled residents, whose comprehensive assessment indicates physical, psychosocial, and/or communications rehabilitation potential (See MDS 2.0, sections G, C, F, E), observe for unmet needs for rehabilitative services. Determine the extent of follow through with comprehensive care plan using probes outlined below. Verify from the chart that resident is receiving frequency and type of therapy as outlined in the care plan.

Probes §483.45(a)(1)(2)

1. For physical therapy

    a. What did the facility do to improve the resident's muscle strength? The resident's balance?

    b. What did the facility do to determine if as assistive device would enable the resident to reach or maintain his/her highest practicable level of physical function?

    c. If the resident has an assistive device, is he/she encouraged to use it on a regular basis?

    d. What did the facility do to increase the amount of physical activity the resident could do (for example, the number of repetitions of an exercise, the distance walked)?

    e. What did the facility do to prevent or minimize contractures, which could lead to decreased mobility and increased risk of pressure ulcer occurrence?

2. For occupational therapy

    a. What did the facility do to decrease the amount of assistance needed to perform a task?

    b. What did the facility do to decrease behavioral symptoms?

    c. What did the facility do to improve gross and fine motor coordination?

    d. What did the facility do to improve sensory awareness, visual-spatial awareness, and body integration?

    e. What did the facility do to improve memory, problem solving, attention span, and the ability to recognize safety hazards?

3. For speech-language pathology.

    a. What did the facility do to improve auditory comprehension such as understanding common, functional words, concepts of time and place, and conversation?

    b. What did the facility do to improve speech production?

    c. What did the facility do to improve the expressive behavior such as the ability to name common, functional items?

    d. What did the facility do to improve the functional abilities of residents with moderate to severe hearing loss who have received and audiologic evaluation? For example, did the facility instruct the resident how to effectively and independently use environmental controls to compensate for hearing loss such as eye contact, preferential seating, use of the better ear?

    e. For the resident who cannot speak, did the facility assess for a communication board or an alternate means of communication?

4. For health rehabilitative services for MI and MR

    a. What did the facility do to decrease incidents of inappropriate behaviors, for individuals with MR, or behavioral symptoms for persons with MI? To increase appropriate behavior?

    b. What did the facility do to identify and treat the underlying factors behind tendencies toward isolation and withdrawal?

    c. What did the facility do to develop and maintain necessary daily living skills?

    d. How has the facility modified the training strategies it uses with its residents to account for the special learning needs of its residents with MI or MR?

    e. Questions to ask individuals with MI or MR:

        (1) Who do you talk to when you have a problem or need something?

        (2) What do you do when you feel happy? Feel sad? Can't sleep at night?

        (3) In what activities are you involved, and how often?

F407

§483.45(b) Qualifications

Specialized rehabilitative services must be provided under the written order of a physician by qualified personnel.

Intent §485.45(b)

The intent of this regulation is to assure that the rehabilitative services are medically necessary as prescribed by a physician and provided by qualified personnel to maximize potential outcomes.

Specialized rehabilitative services are provided for individual's under a physician's order by a qualified professional. Once the assessment for specialized rehabilitative services is completed, a care plan must be developed, followed, and monitored by a licensed professional. Once a resident has met his or her care plan goals, a licensed professional can either discontinue treatment or initiate a maintenance program which either nursing or restorative sides will follow to maintain functional and physical status.

Interpretive Guidelines §483.45(b)

"Qualified personnel" means that professional staff are licensed, certified or registered to provide specialized therapy/rehabilitative services in accordance with applicable State laws.

Health rehabilitative services for MI and MR must be implemented consistently by all staff unless the nature of the services is such that they are designated or required to be implemented only by licensed or credentialed personnel.

Procedures §483.45(b)

Determine if there are any problems in quality of care related to maintaining or improving functional abilities. Determine if these problems are attributable in part to the qualifications of specialized rehabilitative services staff.

Determine from the care plan and record that rehabilitative services are provided under the written order of a physician and by qualified personnel. If a problem in a resident's rehabilitative care is identified that is related to the qualifications of the care providers, it may be necessary to validate the care providers qualification.

Probes §483.45(b)

If the facility does not employ professional staff who have experience working directly with or designing training or treatment programs to meet the needs of individuals with MI or MR, how has the facility arranged for the necessary direct or staff training services to be provided?

F411 – F412

§483.55 — Dental Services

F411

§483.55 Dental Services

The facility must assist residents in obtaining routine and 24-hour emergency dental care.

§483.55(a) Skilled Nursing Facilities

A facility--

(1) Must provide or obtain from an outside resource, in accordance with §483.75(h) of this part, routine and emergency dental services to meet the needs of each resident;

(2) May charge a Medicare resident an additional amount for routine and emergency dental services;

(3) Must if necessary assist the resident--

(i) In making appointments; and

(ii) By arranging for transportation to and from the dentist's office; and

(4) Promptly refer residents with lost or damaged dentures to a dentist.

Intent §483.55

The intent of this regulation is to ensure that the facility be responsible for assisting the resident in obtaining needed dental services, including routine dental services.

Interpretive Guidelines §483.55

This requirement makes the facility directly responsible for the dental care needs of its residents. The facility must ensure that a dentist is available for residents, i.e., employ a staff dentist or have a contract (arrangement) with a dentist to provide services.

For Medicare and private pay residents, facilities are responsible for having the services available, but they may impose an additional charge for the services.

For all residents of the facility, if they are unable to pay for needed dental services, the facility should attempt to find and alternative funding sources or alternative service delivery systems so that the resident is able to maintain his/her highest practicable level of well-being. (See §483.15(g).)

The facility is responsible for selecting a dentist who provides dental services in accordance with professional standards of quality and timeliness under §483.75(h)(2).

"Routine dental services" means an annual inspection of the oral cavity for signs of disease, diagnosis of dental disease, dental radiographs as needed, dental cleaning, fillings (new and repairs), minor dental plate adjustments, smoothing of broken teeth, and limited prosthodontic procedures, e.g., taking impressions for dentures and fitting dentures.

"Emergency dental services" includes services needed to treat an episode of acute pain in teeth, gums, or palate; broken, or otherwise damaged teeth, or any other problem of the oral cavity by a dentist that required immediate attention.

"**Prompt referral**" means, within reason, as soon as the dentures are lost or damaged. Referral does not mean that the resident must see the dentist at that time, but does mean that an appointment (referral) is made, or that the facility is aggressively working at replacing the dentures.

Probes §483.55

Do residents selected for comprehensive or focused reviews, as appropriate, with dentures use them?

Are residents missing teeth and may be in need of dentures?

Do sampled residents have problems eating and maintaining nutritional status because of poor oral health or oral hygiene?

Are resident's dentures intact? Proper fit?

F412

§483.55(b) Nursing Facilities

The facility--

(1) Must provide or obtain from an outside resource, in accordance with §483.75(h) of this part, the following dental services to meet the needs of each resident:

    (i) Routine dental services (to the extent covered under the State plan); and

    (ii) Emergency dental services;

(2) Must, if necessary, assist the resident--

    (i) In making appointments; and

    (ii) By arranging for transportation to and from the dentist's office; and

(3) Must promptly refer residents with lost or damaged dentures to a dentist.

Interpretive Guidelines §483.55(b)(1)(i)

For Medicaid residents, the facility must provide the resident, without charge, all emergency dental services, as well as those routine dental services that are covered under the State plan.

F425 – F431

§483.60 — Pharmacy Services

F425

(Rev. 22, Issued: 12-15-06, Effective/Implementation: 12-18-06)

§483.60 Pharmacy Services

The facility must provide routine and emergency drugs and biologicals to its residents, or obtain them under an agreement described in §483.75(h) of this part. The facility may permit unlicensed personnel to administer drugs if State law permits, but only under the general supervision of a licensed nurse.

(a) Procedures. A facility must provide pharmaceutical services (including procedures that assure the accurate acquiring, receiving, dispensing, and administering of all drugs and biologicals) to meet the needs of each resident.

(b) Service Consultation. The facility must employ or obtain the services of a licensed pharmacist who--

  (1) Provides consultation on all aspects of the provision of pharmacy services in the facility;

INTENT (F425) 42 CFR 483.60, 483.60(a) & (b)(1)

The intent of this requirement is that:

- In order to meet the needs of each resident, the facility accurately and safely provides or obtains pharmaceutical services, including the provision of routine and emergency medications and biologicals, and the services of a licensed pharmacist;

- The licensed pharmacist collaborates with facility leadership and staff to coordinate pharmaceutical services within the facility, and to guide development and evaluation of the implementation of pharmaceutical services procedures;

- The licensed pharmacist helps the facility identify, evaluate, and address/resolve pharmaceutical concerns and issues that affect resident care, medical care or quality of life such as the:

  o Provision of consultative services by a licensed pharmacist between the pharmacist's visits, as necessary; and

  o Coordination of the pharmaceutical services if multiple pharmaceutical service providers are utilized (e.g., pharmacy, infusion, hospice, prescription drug plans [PDP]); and

- The facility utilizes only persons authorized under state requirements to administer medications.

NOTE: Although the regulatory language refers to "drugs," the guidance in this document generally will refer to "medications," except in those situations where the term "drug" has become part of an established pharmaceutical term (e.g., adverse drug event, adverse drug reaction or consequence).

For purposes of this guidance, references to "the pharmacist" mean the licensed pharmacist, whether employed directly by the facility or through arrangement.

DEFINITIONS

Definitions are provided to clarify terminology related to pharmaceutical services and the management of each resident's medication regimen for effectiveness and safety.

- "Acquiring medication" is the process by which a facility requests and obtains a medication.

- "Administering medication" is the process of giving medication(s) to a resident.

- "Biologicals" are products isolated from a variety of natural sources—human, animal, or microorganism—or produced by biotechnology methods and other cutting-edge technologies. They may include a wide range of products such as vaccine, blood and blood components, allergenics, somatic cells, gene therapy, tissues, and recombinant therapeutic proteins.

- "Current standards of practice" refers to approaches to care, procedures, techniques, treatments, etc., that are based on research and/or expert consensus and that are contained in current manuals, textbooks, or publications, or that are accepted, adopted or promulgated by recognized professional organizations or national accrediting bodies.

- "Dispensing" is a process that includes the interpretation of a prescription; selection, measurement, and packaging or repackaging of the product (as necessary); and labeling of the medication or device pursuant to a prescription/order.

- "Disposition" is the process of returning, releasing and/or destroying discontinued or expired medications.

- "Pharmaceutical Services" refers to:

  o The process (including documentation, as applicable) of receiving and interpreting prescriber's orders; acquiring, receiving, storing, controlling, reconciling, compounding (e.g., intravenous antibiotics), dispensing, packaging, labeling, distributing, administering, monitoring responses to, using and/or disposing of all medications, biologicals, chemicals (e.g., povidone iodine, hydrogen peroxide);

  o The provision of medication-related information to health care professionals and residents;

  o The process of identifying, evaluating and addressing medication-related issues including the prevention and reporting of medication errors; and

  o The provision, monitoring and/or the use of medication-related devices.

- "Pharmacy assistant or technician" refers to the ancillary personnel who work under the supervision and delegation of the pharmacist, consistent with state requirements.

- "Receiving medication"—for the purpose of this guidance—is the process of accepting a medication from the facility's pharmacy or an outside source (e.g., vending pharmacy delivery agent, Veterans Administration, family member).

OVERVIEW

The provision of pharmaceutical services is an integral part of the care provided to nursing home residents. The management of complex medication regimens is challenging and requires diverse pharmaceutical services to minimize medication-related adverse consequences or events. The overall goal of the pharmaceutical services system within a facility is to ensure the safe and effective use of medications.

Preventable medication-related adverse consequences and events are a serious concern in nursing homes. Gurwitz and colleagues evaluated the incidence and preventability of adverse drug events in 18 nursing homes in Massachusetts noting that 51% of the adverse drug events were judged to be preventable including 171 (72%) of the 238 fatal, life threatening or serious events and 105 (34%) of the 308 significant events. If these findings are extrapolated to all US nursing homes, approximately 350,000 adverse drug events may occur annually among this patient population, including 20,000 fatal or life threatening events.[63, 64]

Factors that increase the risk of adverse consequences associated with medication use in the nursing home setting include complex medication regimens, numbers and types of medication used, physiological changes accompanying the aging process, as well as multiple comorbidities.

The consultative services of a pharmacist can promote safe and effective medication use. A pharmacist evaluates and coordinates all aspects of pharmaceutical services provided to all residents within a facility by all providers (e.g., pharmacy, prescription drug plan, prescribers). A pharmacist can also help in the development of medication-related documentation procedures, such as identification of abbreviations approved for use in the facility and can help guide the selection and use of medications in accordance with the authorized prescriber's orders, applicable state and federal requirements, manufacturers' specifications, characteristics of the resident population, and individual resident conditions.

Providing pharmaceutical consultation is an ongoing, interactive process with prospective, concurrent, and retrospective components. To accomplish some of these consultative responsibilities, pharmacists can use various methods and resources, such as technology, additional personnel (e.g., dispensing pharmacists, pharmacy technicians), and related policies and procedures.

Numerous recognized resources address different aspects of pharmaceutical services and medication utilization, such as:

- The American Society of Consultant Pharmacists (ASCP) www.ascp.com;

- The American Society of Health System Pharmacists (ASHP) www.ashp.com;

- The American Medical Directors Association (AMDA) www.amda.com;

- The National Coordinating Council for Medication Error Reporting and Prevention (NCCMERP) www.nccmerp.org;

- US Department of Health and Human Services (DHHS), Food and Drug Administration (FDA) www.fda.gov/cder; and

- The DHHS, CMS Sharing Innovations in Quality website at: http://siq.air.org.

NOTE: References to non-CMS sources or sites on the Internet are provided as a service and do not constitute or imply endorsement of these organizations or their programs by CMS or the U.S. Department of Health and Human Services. CMS is not responsible for the content of pages found at these sites. URL addresses were current as of the date of this publication.

PROVISION OF ROUTINE AND/OR EMERGENCY MEDICATIONS

The regulation at 42 CFR 483.60 (F425) requires that the facility provide or obtain routine and emergency medications and biologicals in order to meet the needs of each resident. Facility procedures and applicable state laws may allow the facility to maintain a limited supply of medications in the facility for use during emergency or after-hours situations. Whether prescribed on a routine, emergency, or as needed basis, medications should be administered in a timely manner. Delayed acquisition of a medication may impede timely administration and adversely affect a resident's condition. Factors that may help determine timeliness and guide acquisition procedures include:

- Availability of medications to enable continuity of care for an anticipated admission or transfer of a resident from acute care or other institutional settings;

- Condition of the resident including the severity or instability of his/her condition, a significant change in condition, discomfort, risk factors, current signs and symptoms, and the potential impact of any delay in acquiring the medications;

- Category of medication, such as antibiotics or analgesics;

- Availability of medications in emergency supply, if applicable; and

- Ordered start time for a medication.

SERVICES OF A LICENSED PHARMACIST

The facility is responsible for employing or contracting for the services of a pharmacist to provide consultation on all aspects of pharmaceutical services. The facility may provide for this service through any of several methods (in accordance with state requirements) such as direct employment or contractual agreement with a pharmacist. Whatever the arrangement or method employed, the facility and the pharmacist identify how they will collaborate for effective consultation regarding pharmaceutical services. The pharmacist reviews and evaluates the pharmaceutical services by helping the facility identify, evaluate, and address medication issues that may affect resident care, medical care, and quality of life.

The pharmacist is responsible for helping the facility obtain and maintain timely and appropriate pharmaceutical services that support residents' healthcare needs, that are consistent with current standards of practice, and that meet state and federal requirements. This includes, but is not limited to, collaborating with the facility and medical director to:

- Develop, implement, evaluate, and revise (as necessary) the procedures for the provision of all aspects of pharmaceutical services;

- Coordinate pharmaceutical services if and when multiple pharmaceutical service providers are utilized (e.g., pharmacy, infusion, hospice, prescription drug plans [PDP])

- Develop intravenous (IV) therapy procedures if used within the facility (consistent with state requirements) may include determining competency of staff, facility-based IV admixture procedures that address sterile compounding, dosage calculations, IV pump use, and flushing procedures;

- Determine (in accordance with or as permitted by state law) the contents of the emergency supply of medications and monitor the use, replacement, and disposition of the supply;

- Develop mechanisms for communicating, addressing, and resolving issues related to pharmaceutical services;

- Strive to assure that medications are requested, received, and administered in a timely manner as ordered by the authorized prescriber (in accordance with state requirements), including physicians, advanced practice nurses, pharmacists, and physician assistants;

- Provide feedback about performance and practices related to medication administration and medication errors;

- Participate on the interdisciplinary team to address and resolve medication-related needs or problems;

- Establish procedures for:
  - conducting the monthly medication regimen review (MRR) for each resident in the facility,
  - addressing the expected time frames for conducting the review and reporting the findings,
  - addressing the irregularities,
  - documenting and reporting the results of the review (See F428 for provision of the review.); and

- Establish procedures that address medication regimen reviews for residents who are anticipated to stay less than 30 days or when the resident experiences an acute change of condition as identified by facility staff.

  NOTE: Facility procedures should address how and when the need for a consultation will be communicated, how the medication review will be handled if the pharmacist is off-site, how the results or report of their findings will be communicated to the physician, expectations for the physician's response and follow up, and how and where this information will be documented.

In addition, the pharmacist may collaborate with the facility and medical director on other aspects of pharmaceutical services including, but not limited to:

- Developing procedures and guidance regarding when to contact a prescriber about a medication issue and/or adverse effects, including what information to gather before contacting the prescriber;

- Developing the process for receiving, transcribing, and recapitulating medication orders;

- Recommending the type(s) of medication delivery system(s) to standardize packaging, such as bottles, bubble packs, tear strips, in an effort to minimize medication errors;

- Developing and implementing procedures regarding automated medication delivery devices or cabinets, if automated devices or cabinets are used, including: the types or categories of medications, amounts stored, location of supply, personnel authorized to access the supply, record keeping, monitoring for expiration dates, method to ensure accurate removal of medications and the steps for replacing the supply when dosages are used, and monitoring the availability of medications within the system;

- Interacting with the quality assessment and assurance committee to develop procedures and evaluate pharmaceutical services including delivery and storage systems within the various locations of the facility in order to prevent, to the degree possible, loss or tampering with the medication supplies, and to define and monitor corrective actions for problems related to pharmaceutical services and medications, including medication errors;

- Recommending current resources to help staff identify medications and information on contraindications, side effects and/or adverse effects, dosage levels, and other pertinent information; and

- Identifying facility educational and informational needs about medications and providing information from sources such as nationally recognized organizations to the facility staff, practitioners, residents, and families.

  NOTE: This does not imply that the pharmacist must personally present educational programs.

PHARMACEUTICAL SERVICES PROCEDURES

The pharmacist, in collaboration with the facility and medical director helps develop and evaluate the implementation of pharmaceutical services procedures that address the needs of the residents, are consistent with state·and federal requirements, and reflect current standards of practice. These procedures address, but are not limited to, acquiring; receiving; dispensing; administering; disposing; labeling and storage of medications; and personnel authorized to access or administer medications.

Acquisition of Medications

Examples of procedures addressing acquisition of medications include:

- Availability of an emergency supply of medications, if allowed by state law, including the types or categories of medications; amounts, dosages/strengths to be provided; location of the supply; personnel authorized to access the supply; record keeping; monitoring for expiration dates; and the steps for replacing the supply when medications are used;

- When, how to, and who may contact the pharmacy regarding acquisition of medications and the steps to follow for contacting the pharmacy for an original routine medication order, emergency medication order, and refills;

- The availability of medications when needed, that is, the medication is either in the facility (in the emergency supply) or obtained from a pharmacy that can be reached 24 hours a day, seven days a week;

- The receipt, labeling, storage, and administration of medications dispensed by the physician, if allowed by state requirements;

- Verification or clarification of an order to facilitate accurate acquisition of a medication when necessary (e.g., clarification when the resident has allergies to, or there are contraindications to the medication being ordered);

- Procedure when delivery of a medication will be delayed or the medication is not or will not be available; and

- Transportation of medications from the dispensing pharmacy or vendor to the facility consistent with manufacturer's specifications, state and federal requirements, and standards of professional practice to prevent contamination, degradation, and diversion of medications.

Receiving Medication(s)

Examples of procedures addressing receipt of medications include:

- How the receipt of medications from dispensing pharmacies (and family members or others, where permitted by state requirements) will occur and how it will be reconciled with the prescriber's order and the requisition for the medication;

- How staff will be identified and authorized in accordance with applicable laws and requirements to receive the medications and how access to the medications will be controlled until the medications are delivered to the secured storage area; and

- Which staff will be responsible for assuring that medications are incorporated into the resident's specific allocation/storage area.

Dispensing Medication(s)

Examples of procedures to assure compatible and safe medication delivery, to minimize medication administration errors, and to address the facility's expectations of the in-house pharmacy and/or outside dispensing pharmacies include:

- Delivery and receipt;

- Labeling; and

- The types of medication packaging (e.g., unit dose, multi-dose vial, blister cards).

Administering Medications

Examples of procedures addressing administration of medications include:

- Providing continuity of staff to ensure that medications are administered without unnecessary interruptions;

- Reporting medication administration errors, including how and to whom to report;

- Authorizing personnel, consistent with state requirements, to administer the medications, including medications needing intravenous administration (see Authorized Personnel and Staff Qualifications section within this document);

- Assuring that the correct medication is administered in the correct dose, in accordance with manufacturer's specifications and with standards of practice, to the correct person via the correct route in the correct dosage form and at the correct time;

- Defining the schedules for administering medications to:

  o Maximize the effectiveness (optimal therapeutic effect) of the medication (for example, antibiotics, antihypertensives, insulins, pain medications);

  o Avoid potential significant medication interactions such as medication-food or medication-medication interactions; and

  o Recognize resident choices and activities, to the degree possible, consistent with the medical plan of care;

- Defining general guidelines for specific monitoring related to medications, when ordered or indicated, including specific item(s) to monitor (e.g., blood pressure, pulse, blood sugar, weight), frequency (e.g., weekly, daily), timing (e.g., before or after administering the medication), and parameters for notifying the prescriber;

- Defining pertinent techniques and precautions for administering medications through alternate routes such as eye, ear, buccal, injection, intravenous, atomizer/aerosol/ inhalation therapy, or enteral tubes;

- Documenting the administration of medications, including:

  o The administration of routine medication(s), and if not administered, an explanation of why not;

  o The administration of "as-needed" medications including the justification and response;

  o The route, if other than oral (intended route may be preprinted on MAR); and

  o Location of administration sites such as transdermal patches and injections;

- Providing accessible current information about medications (e.g., medication information references) and medication-related devices and equipment (e.g., user's manual);

- Clarifying any order that is incomplete, illegible, or presents any other concerns, prior to administering the medication; and

- Reconciling medication orders including telephone orders, monthly or other periodic recapitulations, medication orders to the pharmacy, and medication administration record (MAR), including who may transcribe prescriber's orders and enter the orders onto the MAR.

Disposition of Medications

Examples of procedures addressing the disposition of medications include:

- Timely identification and removal (from current medication supply) of medications for disposition;

- Identification of storage method for medications awaiting final disposition;

- Control and accountability of medications awaiting final disposition consistent with standards of practice;

- Documentation of actual disposition of medications to include: resident name, medication name, strength, prescription number (as applicable), quantity, date of disposition, and involved facility staff, consultant(s) or other applicable individuals; and

- Method of disposition consistent with applicable state and federal requirements, local ordinances, and standards of practice.

Labeling and Storage of Medications, including Controlled Substances

Examples of procedures addressing accurate labeling of the medications (including appropriate accessory and cautionary instructions) include:

- Labeling medications prepared by facility staff, such as IV solutions prepared in the facility;

- Requirements for labeling medications not labeled by a pharmacy, such as bulk supplies/bottles of over-the counter (OTC) medications (as permitted);

- Modifying labels due to changes in the medication orders or directions, in accordance with state and federal requirements; and

- Labeling multi-dose vials to assure product integrity, considering the manufacturer's specifications (e.g., modified expiration dates upon opening the multi-dose vial).

Examples of procedures addressing the safe storage of medications include:

- Location, security (locking), and authorized access to the medication rooms, carts and other storage areas;

- Temperatures and other environmental considerations of medication storage area(s) such as the medication room(s) and refrigerators; and

- Location, access, and security for discontinued medications awaiting disposal.

Examples of procedures addressing controlled medications include:

- Location, access, and security for controlled medications, including the separately locked permanently affixed compartment for those Schedule II medications or preparations with Schedule II medications needing refrigeration;

- A system of records of receipt and disposition of all controlled medications that accounts for all controlled medications; and

- Periodic reconciliation of controlled medications including the frequency, method, by whom, and pertinent documentation.

Authorized Personnel

The facility may permit unlicensed personnel to administer medications if state law permits, but only under the general supervision of a licensed nurse.

The facility assures that all persons administering medications are authorized according to state and federal requirements, oriented to the facility's procedures, and have access to current information regarding medications being used within the facility, including side effects of medications, contraindications, doses, etc.

Examples of procedures addressing authorized personnel include:

- How the facility assures ongoing competency of all staff (including temporary, agency, or on-call staff) authorized to administer medications and biologicals;

- Training regarding the operation, limitations, monitoring, and precautions associated with medication administration devices or other equipment, if used, such as:

  o IV pumps or other IV delivery systems including calculating dosage, infusion rates, and compatibility of medications to be added to the IV;

  o Blood glucose meters, including calibration and cleaning between individual residents; and

  o Using, maintaining, cleaning, and disposing of the various types of devices for administration including nebulizers, inhalers, syringes, medication cups, spoons, and pill crushers;

- Identifying pharmacy personnel in addition to the pharmacist (e.g., pharmacy technicians, pharmacist assistants) who are authorized under state and federal requirements to access medications and biologicals.

INVESTIGATIVE PROTOCOL

For investigating compliance with the requirements at 42 CFR 483.60 and 483.60(a) & (b), see State Operations Manual, Appendix P, II.B., The Traditional Standard Survey, Task 5, Sub-Task 5E Investigative Protocol: Medication Pass and Pharmacy Services.

DETERMINATION OF COMPLIANCE (Task 6, Appendix P)

Synopsis of Regulation (F425)

The Pharmaceutical Services, Procedures and Consultation requirement has four aspects. First, the facility must provide routine and/or emergency medications and biologicals or obtain them under an agreement described in 42 CFR 483.75(h). Second, the facility must have procedures for pharmaceutical services to meet the resident's needs. The procedures must assure accurate acquisition, receipt, dispensing, and administration of all medications and biologicals. Third, the facility must have a licensed pharmacist who provides consultation and oversees all aspects of the pharmaceutical services. Fourth, the facility must follow applicable laws and regulations about who may administer medications.

Criteria for Compliance

Compliance with 42 CFR 483.60, F425, Pharmaceutical Services

The facility is in compliance with this requirement, if they provide or arrange for:

- Each resident to receive medications and/or biologicals as ordered by the prescriber;

- The development and implementation of procedures for the pharmaceutical services;

- The services of a pharmacist who provides consultation regarding all aspects of pharmaceutical services; and

- Personnel to administer medications, consistent with applicable state law and regulations.

If not, cite F425.

Noncompliance for F425

After completing the Investigative Protocol, analyze the data and review the regulatory requirement in order to determine whether or not compliance with F425 exists. As the requirements for F425 include both process and structural components, a determination of noncompliance with F425 does not require a finding of harm to the resident. If the survey team identifies noncompliance at other tags which may be related to the roles and responsibilities of the pharmacist or the provision of pharmaceutical services, the team must also decide whether there is noncompliance with this requirement. Noncompliance for F425 may include (but is not limited to) the facility failure to:

- Utilize the services of a pharmacist;

- Ensure that only appropriate personnel administer medications;

- Provide medications and/or biologicals to meet the needs of the resident; and

- Develop or implement procedures for any of the following: acquiring, receiving, dispensing or accurately administering medications.

Potential Tags for Additional Investigation

If noncompliance with 42 CFR 483.60 and 483.60(a) & (b) has been identified, then concerns with additional requirements may also have been identified. The surveyor is cautioned to investigate these related additional requirements before determining whether noncompliance with the additional requirements may be present. Examples of some of the related requirements that should be considered when noncompliance has been identified include the following:

- 42 CFR 483.30(a), F353, Sufficient Staff

  o Determine if the facility had qualified staff in sufficient numbers to provide medications on a 24-hour basis to meet the needs of the residents, based upon the comprehensive assessment and care plan.

- 42 CFR 483.75(i)(2), F501, Medical Director

    o Determine whether the medical director, in collaboration with the facility and the pharmacist, and based on current standards of practice, helped the facility develop procedures for the safe and accurate provision of medications to meet the needs of the residents.

- 42 CFR 483.75 (o), F520, Quality Assessment and Assurance

    o Determine whether the quality assessment and assurance committee, if concerns regarding pharmaceutical services have been identified, has identified those concerns, responded to the concerns and, as appropriate, has developed, implemented, and monitored appropriate plans of action to correct identified quality deficiencies.

- 42 CFR 483.75(l)(1), F514, Clinical Records

    o Determine whether the facility has maintained clinical records, including medication administration, in accordance with accepted professional standards and practices that are complete, accurately documented, and readily accessible.

IV. DEFICIENCY CATEGORIZATION (Part IV, Appendix P)

Once the survey team has completed its investigation, reviewed the regulatory requirements, and determined that noncompliance exists, the team must determine the severity of each deficiency, based on the resultant harm or potential for harm to the resident.

The key elements for severity determination for F425 are as follows:

1. **Presence of potential or actual harm/negative outcome(s) due to a facility failure related to pharmaceutical services.**

    Identify actual or potential harm/negative outcomes for F425 which may include, but are not limited to:

- The facility's failure to involve a pharmacist in developing, implementing, and evaluating pharmaceutical procedures including procedures for accurately acquiring, receiving, storing, controlling, dispensing, and administering routine and emergency medications and biologicals resulted in the lack of specific procedures or in procedures that were not consistent with current standards of practice, for example:

    o Absent or inadequate IV infusion procedures led to a resident developing congestive heart failure as a result of an IV infusing too quickly.

- The facility's failure to provide medications needed by a resident in a timely manner resulted in continued pain or worsening symptoms.

- The use of unauthorized personnel to administer medications created the potential for harm.

2. **Degree of potential or actual harm/negative outcome(s) due to a facility failure related to pharmaceutical services.**

    Identify how the facility's practices caused, resulted in, allowed, or contributed to the actual or potential for harm:

- If harm has occurred, determine if the harm is at the level of serious injury, impairment, death, compromise, or discomfort.

- If harm has not yet occurred, determine how likely is the potential for serious injury, impairment, death, compromise, or discomfort to occur to the resident.

3. The immediacy of correction required.

Determine whether the noncompliance requires immediate correction in order to prevent serious injury, harm, impairment, or death to one or more residents.

The survey team must evaluate the harm or potential for harm based upon the following levels of severity for tag F425. First, the team must rule out whether Severity Level 4, Immediate Jeopardy to a resident's health or safety, exists by evaluating the deficient practice in relation to immediacy, culpability, and severity. (Follow the guidance in Appendix Q, Guidelines for Determining Immediate Jeopardy.)

NOTE: The death or transfer of a resident who was harmed or injured as a result of facility noncompliance does not remove a finding of immediate jeopardy. The facility is required to implement specific actions to remove the jeopardy and correct the noncompliance which allowed or caused the immediate jeopardy.

Severity Level 4 Considerations: Immediate Jeopardy to Resident Health or Safety

Immediate Jeopardy is a situation in which the facility's noncompliance with one or more requirements of participation:

- Has caused/resulted in, or is likely to cause, serious injury, harm, impairment, or death to a resident; and

- Requires immediate correction as the facility either created the situation or allowed the situation to continue by failing to implement preventative or corrective measures.

Examples may include, but are not limited to:

- Severity Level 4 (Immediate Jeopardy) deficiency at another tag (e.g., F309, F329, F332, F333, F428) and the noncompliance is related to a failure of the facility to provide or obtain the service of a pharmacist or to collaborate with the pharmacist to establish and implement procedures for using medications, resulting in the potential for significant adverse consequences.

- The facility, in collaboration with the pharmacist, failed to establish effective procedures to meet the needs of the residents, such as:

  o Assuring that pain medications were available to meet the needs of the resident. For example, failure to assure availability of pain medication for a recently admitted resident resulting in the resident complaining of excruciating pain (e.g., a pain score of 9 on a 10-point scale).

  o Assuring that devices used to administer medications (such as IV pumps) were working properly, leading to an adverse consequence at the immediate jeopardy level.

  o Identifying medication errors, for example, medications were being dispensed without a valid prescriber's order, resulting in a resident incorrectly receiving three medications over two consecutive months.

NOTE: If immediate jeopardy has been ruled out based upon the evidence, then evaluate whether actual harm that is not immediate jeopardy exists at Severity Level 3.

Severity Level 3 Considerations: Actual Harm that is Not Immediate Jeopardy

Level 3 indicates noncompliance that results in actual harm, and may include, but is not limited to, clinical compromise, decline, or the resident's inability to maintain and/or reach his/her highest practicable well-being. Examples may include, but are not limited to:

- Severity Level 3 deficiency at another tag (e.g., F309, F329, F332, F333, F428) and the noncompliance is related to a failure of the facility to provide or obtain the services of a pharmacist or to collaborate with the pharmacist to develop and implement procedures for monitoring medication therapy, resulting in a failure to monitor treatment and the resident experiencing actual harm.

- The facility in collaboration with the pharmacist failed to assure that procedures were developed and implemented, such as:

    o An effective procedure/mechanism to assure that all medication orders were processed consistently and accurately through the stages of ordering, receiving, and administering medications (including transfer orders, admission orders, telephone orders, order renewals, and the MAR). For example, a transcription error led to an incorrect dose of a medication being administered and the resident experiencing spontaneous bruising and epistaxis requiring medical intervention.

    o Provisions to assure that staff were trained or competent to use new medication-related devices (e.g., intravenous pump). This resulted in a resident receiving an excessive dose of medication requiring subsequent hospitalization or receiving a sub-therapeutic dose of medication with consequential exacerbation of a condition (e.g., infection), continuation of treatment beyond the expected time frame, and subsequent functional decline.

NOTE: If Severity Level 3 (actual harm that is not immediate jeopardy) has been ruled out based upon the evidence, then evaluate as to whether Severity Level 2 (no actual harm with the potential for more than minimal harm) exists.

Severity Level 2 Considerations: No Actual Harm with Potential for More Than Minimal Harm that is Not Immediate Jeopardy

Level 2 indicates noncompliance that results in a resident outcome of no more than minimal discomfort and/or has the potential to compromise the resident's ability to maintain or reach his or her highest practicable level of well-being. The potential exists for greater harm to occur if interventions are not provided. Examples may include, but are not limited to:

- A Severity Level 2 deficiency at another tag (e.g., F309, F329, F332, F333, F428) and the noncompliance is related to a failure of the facility to implement established medication administration procedures. For example, as a result of failure of licensed staff to supervise medication administration by authorized unlicensed personnel, errors occurred in providing timely oral antibiotic therapy.

- The facility failed to obtain or provide the services of a pharmacist or to collaborate with the pharmacist to assure that effective policies and procedures were established and implemented including, for example:

    o As a result of not reordering medications often enough to maintain an adequate supply, a resident did not receive medication for heartburn for seven days and had difficulty sleeping due to nocturnal heartburn. The level of discomfort did not interfere with the resident's participating in activities or performing activities of daily living.

    o As a result of failure to identify medications that should not be crushed for administration, a resident received a medication that was crushed, contrary to the manufacturer's specifications (e.g., an enteric coated aspirin). While the resident did not experience any harm, the potential for harm was present.

NOTE: If Severity Level 2 (no actual harm with potential for more than minimal harm that is not immediate jeopardy) has been ruled out based upon the evidence, then evaluate as to whether Severity Level 1 (no actual harm with the potential for minimal harm) exists.

Severity Level 1 Considerations: No Actual Harm with Potential for Minimal Harm

In order to cite no actual harm with potential for minimal harm at this tag, the surveyor must verify that no resident harm or potential for more than minimal harm identified at other requirements was related to lack of pharmaceutical services, absence of or failure to implement pharmaceutical procedures, or absence of oversight by the pharmacist.

Examples of noncompliance for Severity Level 1 may include:

- The facility and the pharmacist failed to collaborate to:

    o Implement pharmaceutical procedures, but there were no negative resident outcomes or potential for more than minimal negative outcomes as a result of that deficient practice.

- There is no pharmacist; and

    o There were no negative resident outcomes or potential for more than minimal negative outcomes related to pharmaceutical services; and

    o Pharmaceutical procedures were in place; and

    o The facility was actively seeking a new pharmacist.

    NOTE: If there is no pharmacist and there were negative outcomes, or procedures were not in place or if the facility was not looking for a replacement, cite at a Severity Level 2 or higher severity.

- There was a short term failure to provide medications that posed minimal risk to the resident, such as a routine order for a daily multivitamin.

F428

(Rev. 22, Issued: 12-15-06, Effective/Implementation: 12-18-06)

§483.60(c) Drug Regimen Review

(1) The drug regimen of each resident must be reviewed at least once a month by a licensed pharmacist.

(2) The pharmacist must report any irregularities to the attending physician, and the director of nursing, and these reports must be acted upon.

INTENT (F428) 42 CFR 483.60(c)(1)(2) Medication Regimen Review

The intent of this requirement is that the facility maintains the resident's highest practicable level of functioning and prevents or minimizes adverse consequences related to medication therapy to the extent possible, by providing:

- A licensed pharmacist's review of each resident's regimen of medications at least monthly; or

    o A more frequent review of the regimen depending upon the resident's condition and the risks or adverse consequences related to current medication(s);

- The identification and reporting of irregularities to the attending physician and the director of nursing; and

- Action taken in response to the irregularities identified.

NOTE: Although the regulatory language refers to "drugs," the guidance in this document generally will refer to "medications," except in those situations where the term "drug" has become part of an established pharmaceutical term (e.g., adverse drug event, and adverse drug reaction or consequence).

For purposes of this guidance, references to "the pharmacist" mean the licensed pharmacist, whether employed directly by the facility or through arrangement.

DEFINITIONS

Definitions are provided to clarify terminology related to pharmaceutical services and the management of each resident's medication regimen for effectiveness and safety.

- "Adverse consequence" refers to an unpleasant symptom or event that is due to or associated with a medication, such as impairment or decline in an individual's mental or physical condition or functional or psychosocial status. It may include various types of adverse drug reactions and interactions (e.g., medication-medication, medication-food, and medication-disease).

  NOTE: Adverse drug reaction (ADR) is a form of adverse consequence. It may be either a secondary effect of a medication that is usually undesirable and different from the therapeutic and helpful effects of the medication or any response to a medication that is noxious and unintended and occurs in doses used for prophylaxis, diagnosis, or therapy. The term "side effect" is often used interchangeably with ADR; however, side effects are but one of five ADR categories. The others are hypersensitivity, idiosyncratic response, toxic reactions, and adverse medication interactions. A side effect is an expected, well-known reaction that occurs with a predictable frequency and may or may not rise to the level of being an adverse consequence.

- "Clinically significant" means effects, results, or consequences that materially affect or are likely to affect an individual's mental, physical, or psychosocial well-being either positively by preventing, stabilizing, or improving a condition or reducing a risk, or negatively by exacerbating, causing, or contributing to a symptom, illness, or decline in status.

- "Dose" is the total amount/strength/concentration of a medication given at one time or over a period of time. The individual dose is the amount/strength/concentration received at each administration. The amount received over a 24-hour period may be referred to as the daily dose.

  o "Excessive dose" (including duplicate therapy) means the total amount of any medication given at one time or over a period of time that is greater than the amount recommended by the manufacturer's label, package insert, or current standards of practice for a resident's age and condition; without evidence of a review for the continued necessity of the dose or of attempts at, or consideration of the possibility of, tapering a medication; and there is no documented clinical rationale for the benefit of, or necessity for the dose or for the use of multiple medications from the same class.

- "Duration" is the total length of time the medication is being received.

  o "Excessive Duration" means the medication is administered beyond the manufacturer's recommended time frames or facility-established stop order policies, beyond the length of time advised by current standards of practice, and/or without either evidence of additional therapeutic benefit for the resident or clear clinical factors that would warrant the continued use of the medication.

- "Irregularity" refers to any event that is inconsistent with usual, proper, accepted, or right approaches to providing pharmaceutical services (see definition in F425), or that impedes or interferes with achieving the intended outcomes of those services.

- "Medication Interaction" is the impact of another substance (such as another medication, herbal product, food or substances used in diagnostic studies) upon a medication. The interactions may alter absorption, distribution, metabolism, or elimination. These interactions may decrease the effectiveness of the medication or increase the potential for adverse consequences.

- "Medication Regimen Review" (MRR) is a thorough evaluation of the medication regimen of a resident, with the goal of promoting positive outcomes and minimizing adverse consequences associated with medication. The review includes preventing, identifying, reporting, and resolving medication-related problems, medication errors, or other irregularities, and collaborating with other members of the interdisciplinary team.[65]

- "Monitoring" is the ongoing collection and analysis of information (such as observations and diagnostic test results) and comparison to baseline data in order to:

  o Ascertain the individual's response to treatment and care, including progress or lack of progress toward a therapeutic goal;

  o Detect any complications or adverse consequences of the condition or of the treatments; and

  o Support decisions about modifying, discontinuing, or continuing any interventions.

- "Pharmacy Assistant or Technician" refers to ancillary personnel who work under the supervision and delegation of the pharmacist as consistent with state requirements.

OVERVIEW

Many nursing home residents require multiple medications to address their conditions, leading to complex medication regimens. Medications are used for their therapeutic benefits in diagnosing, managing, and treating acute and/or chronic conditions, for maintaining and/or improving a resident's functional status, and for improving or sustaining the resident's quality of life. The nursing home population may be quite diverse and may include geriatric residents as well as individuals of any age with special needs, such as those who are immunocompromised or who have end stage renal disease or spinal cord or closed head injuries. Regardless, this population has been identified as being at high risk for adverse consequences related to medications. Some adverse consequences may mimic symptoms of chronic conditions, the aging process, or a newly emerging condition.

Transitions in care such as a move from home or hospital to the nursing home, or vice versa, increases the risk of medication-related issues. Medications may be added, discontinued, omitted, or changed. It is important, therefore, to review the medications. Currently, safeguards to help identify medication issues include:

- The physician providing and reviewing the orders and total program of care on admission and the prescriber reviewing at each visit;

- The nurse reviewing medications when transmitting the orders to the pharmacy and/or prior to administering medications;

- The interdisciplinary team reviewing the medications as part of the comprehensive assessment for the Resident Assessment Instrument (RAI) and/or care plan;

- The pharmacist reviewing the prescriptions prior to dispensing; and

- The pharmacist performing the medication regimen review at least monthly.

During the MRR, the pharmacist applies his/her understanding of medications and related cautions, actions and interactions as well as current medication advisories and information. The pharmacist provides consultation to the facility and the attending physician(s) regarding the medication regimen and is an important member of the interdisciplinary team. Regulations prohibit the pharmacist from delegating the medication regimen reviews to ancillary staff.

Some resources are available to facilitate evaluating medication concerns related to the performance of the MRR, such as:

- American Society of Consultant Pharmacists (ASCP) www.ascp.com;

- American Medical Directors Association (AMDA) www.amda.com;

- National Coordinating Council for Medication Error Reporting and Prevention (NCCMERP) www.nccmerp.org;

- American Geriatrics Society (AGS) www.americangeriatrics.org;

- U.S. Department of Health and Human Services, Food and Drug Administration (FDA) http://www.fda.gov/medwatch/safety.htm; and

- DHHS, CMS Sharing Innovations in Quality website at: http://siq.air.org.

NOTE: References to non-CMS sources or sites on the Internet are provided as a service and do not constitute or imply endorsement of these organizations or their programs by CMS or the U.S. Department of Health and Human Services. CMS is not responsible for the content of pages found at these sites. URL addresses were current as of the date of this publication.

This guidance is not intended to imply that all adverse consequences related to medications are preventable, but rather to specify that a system exists to assure that medication usage is evaluated on an ongoing basis, that risks and problems are identified and acted upon, and that medication-related problems are considered when the resident has a change in condition. This guidance will discuss the following aspects of the facility's MRR component of the pharmaceutical services systems:

- A pharmacist's review of the resident's medication regimen to identify and report irregularities; and

- Acting upon identified irregularities in order to minimize or prevent adverse consequences, to the extent possible.

NOTE: The surveyor's review of medication use is not intended to constitute the practice of medicine. However, surveyors are expected to investigate the basis for decisions and interventions affecting residents.

MEDICATION REGIMEN REVIEW (MRR)

The MRR is an important component of the overall management and monitoring of a resident's medication regimen. The pharmacist must review each resident's medication regimen at least once a month in order to identify irregularities; and to identify clinically significant risks and/or adverse consequences resulting from or associated with medications. It may be necessary for the pharmacist to conduct the MRR more frequently, for example weekly, depending on the resident's condition and the risks for adverse consequences related to current medications.

Generally, MRRs are conducted in the facility because important information about indications for use, potential medication irregularities or adverse consequences (such as symptoms of tardive dyskinesia, dizziness, anorexia, or falls) may be attainable only by talking to the staff, reviewing the medical record, and observing and speaking with the resident. However, electronic health and medication records and other available technology may permit the pharmacist to conduct some components of the review outside the facility.

Important aspects of the MRR include identification of irregularities, including medication-related errors and adverse consequences, location and notification of MRR findings, and response to identified irregularities. This guidance discusses these aspects and also provides some examples of clinically significant medication interactions.

Identification of Irregularities

An objective of the MRR is to try to minimize or prevent adverse consequences by identifying irregularities including, for example: syndromes potentially related to medication therapy, emerging or existing adverse medication consequences, as well as the potential for adverse drug reactions and medication errors. The resident's record may contain information regarding possible and/or actual medication irregularities. Possible sources to obtain this information include: the medication administration records (MAR); prescribers' orders; progress, nursing and consultants' notes; the Resident Assessment Instrument (RAI); laboratory and diagnostic test results, and other sources of information about behavior monitoring and/or changes in condition. The pharmacist may also obtain information from the Quality Measures/Quality Indicator reports, the attending physician, facility staff, and (as appropriate) from interviewing, assessing, and/or observing the resident.

The pharmacist's review considers factors such as:

- Whether the physician and staff have documented objective findings, diagnoses and/or symptom(s) to support indications for use;

- Whether the physician and staff have identified and acted upon, or should be notified about, the resident's allergies and/or potential side effects and significant medication interactions (such as medication-medication, medication-food, medication-disease, medication-herbal interactions);

- Whether the medication dose, frequency, route of administration, and duration are consistent with the resident's condition, manufacturer's recommendations, and applicable standards of practice;

- Whether the physician and staff have documented progress towards, or maintenance of, the goal(s) for the medication therapy;

- Whether the physician and staff have obtained and acted upon laboratory results, diagnostic studies, or other measurements (such as bowel function, intake and output) as applicable;

- Whether medication errors exist or circumstances exist that make them likely to occur; and

- Whether the physician and staff have noted and acted upon possible medication-related causes of recent or persistent changes in the resident's condition such as worsening of an existing problem or the emergence of new signs or symptoms. The following are examples of changes potentially related to medication use that could occur at any age, however, some of the changes are more common in the geriatric population and may be unrelated to medications:

  o Anorexia and/or unplanned weight loss, or weight gain;

  o Behavioral changes, unusual behavior patterns (including increased distressed behavior);

  o Bowel function changes including constipation, ileus, impaction;

  o Confusion, cognitive decline, worsening of dementia (including delirium) of recent onset;

  o Dehydration, fluid/electrolyte imbalance;

  o Depression, mood disturbance;

  o Dysphagia, swallowing difficulty;

  o Excessive sedation, insomnia, or sleep disturbance;

  o Falls, dizziness, or evidence of impaired coordination;

  o Gastrointestinal bleeding;

  o Headaches, muscle pain, generalized aching or pain;

  o Rash, pruritus;

  o Seizure activity;

  o Spontaneous or unexplained bleeding, bruising;

  o Unexplained decline in functional status (e.g., ADLs, vision); and

  o Urinary retention or incontinence.

Upon conducting the MRR, the pharmacist may identify and report concerns in one or more of the following categories:[i] (See F329 for additional discussion of irregularities relating to dose, duration, indications for use, monitoring, and adverse consequences.)

- The use of a medication without identifiable evidence of adequate indications for use;

- The use of a medication to treat a clinical condition without identifiable evidence that safer alternatives or more clinically appropriate medications have been considered;

- The use of an appropriate medication that is not helping attain the intended treatment goals because of timing of administration, dosing intervals, sufficiency of dose, techniques of administration, or other reasons;

- The use of a medication in an excessive dose (including duplicate therapy) or for excessive duration, thereby placing the resident at greater risk for adverse consequences or causing existing adverse consequences;

- The presence of an adverse consequence associated with the resident's current medication regimen;

- The use of a medication without evidence of adequate monitoring; i.e., either inadequate monitoring of the response to a medication or an inadequate response to the findings;

- Presence of medication errors or the risk for such errors;

- Presence of a clinical condition that might warrant initiation of medication therapy; and

  NOTE: The presence of a diagnosis or symptom does not necessarily warrant medication, but often depends on the consideration of many factors simultaneously.

- A medication interaction associated with the current medication regimen.

The following table provides examples of some problematic medication interactions in the long-term care population. These examples represent common interactions but are not meant to be all inclusive.

NOTE: Concomitant use of these medication combinations is not necessarily inappropriate and these examples are not intended to imply that the medications cannot be used simultaneously. Often, several medications with documented interactions can be given together safely. However, concomitant use of such medications warrants careful consideration of potential alternatives, possible need to modify doses, and diligent monitoring.

Common Medication-Medication Interactions in Long Term Care[67]

Medication 1	Medication 2	Impact
warfarin	NSAIDs such as ibuprofen, naproxen, COX-2 inhibitors	Potential for serious gastrointestinal bleeding
warfarin	sulfonamides such as trimethoprim/ sulfamethoxazole	Increased effects of warfarin, with potential for bleeding
warfarin	macrolides such as clarithromycin, erythromycin	Increased effects of warfarin, with potential for bleeding
warfarin	fluoroquinolones such as ciprofloxacin, levofloxacin, ofloxacin	Increased effects of warfarin, with potential for bleeding
warfarin	phenytoin	Increased effects of warfarin and/or phenytoin
ACE Inhibitors such as benazepril, captopril, enalapril, and lisinopril	potassium supplements	Elevated serum potassium levels
ACE Inhibitors such as benazepril, captopril, enalapril, and lisinopril	spironolactone	Elevated serum potassium levels
digoxin	amiodarone	digoxin toxicity
digoxin	verapamil	digoxin toxicity
theophylline	fluoroquinolones such as ciprofloxacin, levofloxacin, ofloxacin	theophylline toxicity

Location and Notification of Medication Regimen Review Findings

The pharmacist is expected to document either that no irregularity was identified or the nature of any identified irregularities. The pharmacist is responsible for reporting any identified irregularities to the attending physician and director of nursing. The timeliness of notification of irregularities depends on factors including the potential for or presence of serious adverse consequences; for example, immediate notification is indicated in cases of bleeding in a resident who is receiving anticoagulants or in cases of possible allergic reactions to antibiotic therapy. If no irregularities were identified during the review, the pharmacist includes a signed and dated statement to that effect. The facility and the pharmacist may collaborate to identify the most effective means for assuring appropriate notification. This notification may be done electronically.

The pharmacist does not need to document a continuing irregularity in the report each month if the pharmacist has deemed the irregularity to be clinically insignificant or evidence of a valid clinical reason for rejecting the pharmacist's recommendation was provided. In this situation, the pharmacist need only reconsider annually whether to report the irregularity again or make a new recommendation.

The pharmacist's findings are considered part of each resident's clinical record. If documentation of the findings is not in the active record, it is maintained within the facility and is readily available for review. The interdisciplinary team is encouraged to review the reports and to get the pharmacist's input on resident problems and issues. Establishing a consistent location for the pharmacist's findings and recommendations can facilitate communication with the attending physician, the director of nursing, the remainder of the interdisciplinary team, the medical director, the resident and his or her legal representative (in accord with 42 CFR 483.10(b)(2),(d)(2)), ombudsman (with permission of the resident in accord with 42 CFR 483.10(j)(3)), and surveyors.

Response to Irregularities Identified in the MRR

Throughout this guidance, a response from a physician regarding a medication problem implies appropriate communication, review, and resident management, but does not imply that the physician must necessarily order tests or treatments recommended or requested by the staff, unless the physician determines that those are medically valid and indicated.

For those issues that require physician intervention, the physician either accepts and acts upon the report and potential recommendations or rejects all or some of the report and provides a brief explanation of why the recommendation is rejected, such as in a dated progress note. It is not acceptable for a physician to document only that he/she disagrees with the report, without providing some basis for disagreeing.

If there is the potential for serious harm and the attending physician does not concur with or take action on the report, the facility and the pharmacist should contact the facility's medical director for guidance and possible intervention to resolve the issue. The facility should have a procedure to resolve the situation when the attending physician is also the medical director. For those recommendations that do not require a physician intervention, such as one to monitor vital signs or weights, the director of nursing or designated licensed nurse addresses and documents action(s) taken.

INVESTIGATIVE PROTOCOL

Refer to the Investigative Protocol at F329 for evaluation of medication regimen review.

DETERMINATION OF COMPLIANCE (Task 6, Appendix P)

Synopsis of regulation (F428)

This requirement has four aspects relating to the safety of the resident's medication regimen, including:

- A review by the pharmacist of each resident's medication regimen at least once a month or more frequently depending upon the resident's condition and the risks or adverse consequences related to current medication(s);

- The identification of any irregularities;

- Reporting irregularities to the attending physician and the director of nursing; and

- Action in response to irregularities reported.

Criteria for compliance

Compliance with 42 CFR 483.60(c)(1) and (2), F428, Medication Regimen Review

The facility is in compliance with this requirement if:

- The pharmacist has performed a medication regimen review on each resident at least once a month or more frequently depending upon the resident's condition and/or risks or adverse consequence associated with the medication regimen;

- The pharmacist has identified any existing irregularities;

- The pharmacist has reported any identified irregularities to the director of nursing and attending physician; and

- The report of any irregularities has been acted upon.

If not, cite F428.

Noncompliance for F428

After completing the Investigative Protocol, analyze the data in order to determine whether or not compliance with F428 exists. A determination of noncompliance with F428 does not require a finding of harm to the resident. Noncompliance may include (but is not limited to) one or more of the following:

- The pharmacist failed to conduct an MRR at least monthly (or more frequently, as indicated).

- The pharmacist failed to identify or report the absence of or inadequate indications for use of a medication, or a medication or medication combination with significant potential for adverse consequences or medication interactions.

- The pharmacist failed to identify or report medications in a resident's regimen that could (as of the review date) be causing or associated with new, worsening, or progressive signs and symptoms.

- The pharmacist failed to identify and report the absence of any explanation as to why or how the benefit of a medication(s) with potential for clinically significant adverse consequences outweighs the risk.

- The pharmacist failed to identify and report the lack of evidence or documentation regarding progress toward treatment goals.

- The facility failed to act upon a report of clinically significant risks or existing adverse consequences or other irregularities.

Potential Tags for Additional Investigation

If noncompliance with 483.60(c)(1) and (2) has been identified, then concerns with additional requirements may also have been identified. The surveyor is cautioned to investigate these related additional requirements before determining whether noncompliance with the additional requirements may be present. Examples of some of the related requirements that should be considered when noncompliance has been identified include the following:

- 42 CFR 483.10(b)(11), F157, Notification of Changes

  o Review whether the facility contacted the attending physician regarding a significant change in the resident's condition in relation to a potential adverse consequence of a medication, or a need to alter treatment significantly (i.e., a need to discontinue an existing form of treatment due to adverse consequences, or to commence a different form of treatment).

- 42 CFR 483.25(l), F329, Unnecessary Medications

  o Review whether the resident is receiving any medications without an indication for use, in excessive dose or duration, with inadequate monitoring, or in the presence of any adverse consequences that indicate that the dose should be reduced or discontinued.

- 42 CFR 483.40(a), F385, Physician Supervision

  o Review whether the attending physician supervised the resident's medical treatment, including assessing the resident's condition, identifying the need for and continuing use of medication to address the resident's needs, and identifying and addressing adverse consequences related to medications.

- 42 CFR 483.40(b), F386, Physician Visits

  o Review whether the attending physician or another designated practitioner reviewed the resident's total program of care including the beneficial and adverse effects of medications and treatment, and provided a relevant progress note at each visit.

- 42 CFR 483.60(a)(b)(1), F425, Pharmacy Services

  o Review whether the licensed pharmacist has provided consultation regarding all aspects of pharmaceutical services.

- 42 CFR 483.75(i), F501, Medical Director

  o Review whether the medical director, when requested by the facility, interacted with the attending physician regarding an inadequate response to identified or reported potential medication irregularities and adverse consequences.

IV. DEFICIENCY CATEGORIZATION (Part IV, Appendix P)

Once the survey team has completed its investigation, analyzed the data, reviewed the regulatory requirements, and determined that noncompliance exists, the team must determine the severity of each deficiency, based on the resultant harm or potential for harm to the resident. The survey team must identify whether noncompliance cited at other tags (e.g., F329, F332/333) was the direct result of or related to inadequate or absent MRR or response to notification regarding irregularities.

The key elements for severity determination for F428 are as follows:

1. **Presence of potential or actual harm/negative outcome(s) due to a facility failure related to the MRR.**

   Identify actual or potential harm/negative outcomes which for F428 may include, but are not limited to:

   - The resident experienced a clinically significant adverse consequence associated with a medication.

   - Irregularities within the medication regimen or inaccuracy of medication-related documents created the potential for adverse consequences such as overdose, respiratory depression, rash, or anorexia.

2. **Degree of potential or actual harm/negative outcome(s) due to a facility failure related to the MRR.**

   Identify to what degree the facility practices caused, resulted in, allowed, or contributed to the actual or potential harm:

   - If harm has occurred, determine if the harm is at the level of serious injury, impairment, death, compromise, or discomfort; or

   - If harm has not yet occurred, determine the potential for serious injury, impairment, death, compromise, or discomfort to occur to the resident.

3. **The immediacy of correction required.**

   Determine whether the noncompliance requires immediate correction in order to prevent serious injury, harm, impairment, or death to one or more residents.

The survey team must evaluate the harm or potential for harm based upon the following levels of severity for tag F428. First, the team must rule out whether Severity Level 4, Immediate Jeopardy, to a resident's health or safety, exists by evaluating the deficient practice in relation to immediacy, culpability, and severity. (Follow the guidance in Appendix Q, Guidelines for Determining Immediate Jeopardy.)

NOTE: The death or transfer of a resident who was harmed or injured as a result of facility noncompliance does not remove a finding of immediate jeopardy. The facility is required to implement specific actions to remove the jeopardy and correct the noncompliance which allowed or caused the immediate jeopardy.

Severity Level 4 Considerations: Immediate Jeopardy to Resident Health or Safety

Immediate Jeopardy is a situation in which the facility's noncompliance with one or more requirements of participation:

- Has allowed, caused, or resulted in, or is likely to allow, cause, or result in serious injury, harm, impairment, or death to a resident; and

- Requires immediate correction, as the facility either created the situation or allowed the situation to continue by failing to implement preventative or corrective measures.

Examples may include, but are not limited to:

- Despite identifying irregularities with the potential for serious harm or death, the pharmacist did not report the irregularities to the attending physician or no action was taken on the irregularities reported.

- Findings of noncompliance at Severity Level 4 at Tag(s) F309, F329, F332, or F333 that show evidence of process failures for conducting the MRR.

- Repeated or cumulative failures in multiple areas of the medication regimen review process (e.g., failure to identify, report, or act upon) that resulted in the resident(s) experiencing actual or potential harm.

NOTE: If immediate jeopardy has been ruled out based upon the evidence, then evaluate whether actual harm that is not immediate jeopardy exists at Severity Level 3.

Severity Level 3 Considerations: Actual Harm that is Not Immediate Jeopardy

Level 3 indicates noncompliance that resulted in actual harm, and may include, but is not limited to, clinical compromise, decline, or the resident's inability to maintain and/or reach his/her highest practicable well-being. Examples may include, but are not limited to:

- The pharmacist's MRR failed to identify the indication for continued use for opioid analgesics that had been prescribed for a resident's acute pain which had resolved. As a result of prolonged duration of use, the resident became more lethargic, withdrawn, and anorectic.

- The pharmacist's MRR identified that the staff were crushing medications that should not be crushed, based on inappropriate standing orders to crush all medications. As a result of facility failure to act upon the notification, the resident experienced clinically significant adverse consequences such as hypoglycemia or hypotension that required medical intervention.

- The pharmacist's MRR identified that medications were not being given as ordered (such as antiparkinsons or pain medications not given prior to physical therapy), which may have contributed to impaired function. The facility failed to take any action to adhere to the orders.

- The physician and/or director of nursing failed to act in response to the pharmacist's MRR which identified the indefinite continuation of an antidepressant in a resident who had no history of depression, who had been placed on the antidepressant without an evaluation to confirm presence of depression, and whose function and mood were not monitored while getting the medication for months. The resident experienced clinically significant adverse consequences such as falls, constipation, or change in weight.

- The pharmacist's MRR failed to identify and report the medication regimen as a possible cause of recurrent falling in a resident who was given increasing doses of anticonvulsants to treat behavioral symptoms related to dementia, resulting in serious injury.

- The pharmacist's MRR failed to identify and report clinically significant medication interactions in a resident who was started on warfarin, and who had also been receiving one or more of the following: digoxin, phenytoin, antibiotics, amiodarone, or an oral antifungal, resulting in a marked elevation in the INR with significant gastrointestinal bleeding or hematuria.

- Findings of noncompliance at Severity Level 3 at tag(s) F309, F329, F332, F333 that show evidence of process failures for conducting the MRR.

NOTE: If Severity Level 3 (actual harm that is not immediate jeopardy) has been ruled out based upon the evidence, then evaluate as to whether Severity Level 2 (no actual harm with the potential for more than minimal harm) exists.

Severity Level 2 Considerations: No Actual Harm with Potential for More Than Minimal Harm that is Not Immediate Jeopardy

Level 2 indicates noncompliance that resulted in a resident outcome of no more than minimal discomfort and/or has the potential to compromise the resident's ability to maintain or reach his or her highest practicable level of well-being. The potential exists for greater harm to occur if interventions are not provided. Examples include, but are not limited to:

- The facility failed to respond to the pharmacist's notification that the resident was not receiving all the medications ordered; however, there was no change in the resident condition.

- The pharmacist's MRR failed to identify and report a resident who is receiving multiple antihypertensive medications, but is not being monitored for postural hypotension, and who complains of lightheadedness especially while upright.

- The pharmacist's MRR failed to identify and report risks of hyperkalemia in a resident who has impaired renal function and is receiving an ACE inhibitor and potassium supplements.

- The pharmacist's MRR failed to evaluate and report on the potential adverse consequences of a medication known to cause anorexia for a resident with a recently decreased appetite, who had not yet experienced a significant unplanned weight loss.

- Findings of noncompliance at Severity Level 2 at tag(s) F309, F329, or F332, F333 that show evidence of process failures for conducting the MRR.

NOTE: If Severity Level 2 (no actual harm with potential for more than minimal harm that is not immediate jeopardy) has been ruled out based upon the evidence, then evaluate as to whether Severity Level 1 (no actual harm with the potential for minimal harm) exists.

Severity Level 1 Considerations: No Actual Harm with Potential for Minimal Harm

Level 1 indicates noncompliance that resulted in no harm to the resident, and the potential for no more than minimal harm. Examples may include, but are not limited to:

- The pharmacist conducted the medication review, identified an irregularity that has not resulted in a negative outcome and is of minimal consequence (such as a multi-vitamin not being given as ordered) and reported to the director of nursing and attending physician, but neither of them acted upon the report.

F431

(Rev. 22, Issued: 12-15-06, Effective/Implementation: 12-18-06)

§483.60(b) Service Consultation. The facility must employ or obtain the services of a licensed pharmacist who—

(2) Establishes a system of records of receipt and disposition of all controlled drugs in sufficient detail to enable an accurate reconciliation; and

(3) Determines that drug records are in order and that an account of all controlled drugs is maintained and periodically reconciled.

§483.60(d) Labeling of Drugs and Biologicals

Drugs and biologicals used in the facility must be labeled in accordance with currently accepted professional principles, and include the appropriate accessory and cautionary instructions, and the expiration date when applicable.

(e) Storage of Drugs and Biologicals

(1) In accordance with State and Federal laws, the facility must store all drugs and biologicals in locked compartments under proper temperature controls, and permit only authorized personnel to have access to the keys.

(2) The facility must provide separately locked, permanently affixed compartments for storage of controlled drugs listed in Schedule II of the Comprehensive Drug Abuse Prevention and Control Act of 1976 and other drugs subject to abuse, except when the facility uses single unit package drug distribution systems in which the quantity stored is minimal and a missing dose can be readily detected.

INTENT (F431) 42 CFR 483.60(b)(2)(3)(d) Labeling of Drugs and Biologicals & (e) Storage of Drugs and Biologicals

The intent of this requirement is that the facility, in coordination with the licensed pharmacist, provides for:

- Safe and secure storage (including proper temperature controls, limited access, and mechanisms to minimize loss or diversion) and safe handling (including disposition) of all medication;

- Accurate labeling to facilitate consideration of precautions and safe administration of medications;

- A system of medication records that enables periodic accurate reconciliation and accounting of all controlled medications; and

- Identification of loss or diversion of controlled medications so as to minimize the time between actual loss or diversion and the detection and determination of the extent of loss or diversion.

NOTE: For purposes of this guidance, references to "the pharmacist" mean the licensed pharmacist, whether employed directly by the facility or through arrangement.

DEFINITIONS (refer to F425 and F428 for additional definitions)

- "Adverse consequence" refers to an unpleasant symptom or event that is due to or associated with a medication, such as impairment or decline in an individual's mental or physical condition or functional or psychosocial status. It may include various types of adverse drug reactions and interactions (e.g., medication-medication, medication-food, and medication-disease).

- "Clinically significant" refers to effects, results, or consequences that materially affect or are likely to affect an individual's physical, mental, or psychosocial well-being either positively by preventing, stabilizing, or improving a condition or reducing a risk, or negatively by exacerbating, causing, or contributing to a symptom, illness, or decline in status.

OVERVIEW

Due to the number and types of medications that may be used and the vulnerable populations being served, the regulations require a long term care facility to have formal mechanisms to safely handle and control medications, and to maintain accurate and timely medication records. These regulations also require the facility to use a pharmacist to help establish and evaluate these mechanisms or systems. This guidance addresses those portions of the facility's pharmaceutical services related to medication access and storage, appropriate security and safeguarding of controlled medications, and labeling of medications to assure that they are stored safely and are provided to the residents accurately and in accordance with the prescriber's instructions.

MEDICATION ACCESS AND STORAGE

A facility is required to secure all medications in a locked storage area and to limit access to authorized personnel (for example, pharmacy technicians or assistants who have been delegated access to medications by the facility's pharmacist as a function of their jobs) consistent with state or federal requirements and professional standards of practice.

Storage areas may include, but are not limited to, drawers, cabinets, medication rooms, refrigerators, and carts. Depending on how the facility locks and stores medications, access to a medication room may not necessarily provide access to the medications (for example, medications stored in a locked cart, locked cabinets, a locked refrigerator, or locked drawers within the medication room). When medications are not stored in separately locked compartments within a storage area, only appropriately authorized staff may have access to the storage area.

Access to medications can be controlled by keys, security codes or cards, or other technology such as fingerprints. Schedule II medications must be maintained in separately locked, permanently affixed compartments. The access system (e.g. key, security codes) used to lock Schedule II medications and other medications subject to abuse, cannot be the same access system used to obtain the non-scheduled medications. The facility must have a system to limit who has security access and when access is used. Exception: Controlled medications and those subject to abuse may be stored with non-controlled medications as part of a single unit package medication distribution system, if the supply of the medication(s) is minimal and a shortage is readily detectable.

During a medication pass, medications must be under the direct observation of the person administering the medications or locked in the medication storage area/cart. In addition, the facility should have procedures for the control and safe storage of medications for those residents who can self-administer medications.

Safe medication storage includes the provision of appropriate environmental controls. Because many medications can be altered by exposure to improper temperature, light, or humidity, it is important that the facility implement procedures that address and monitor the safe storage and handling of medications in accordance with manufacturers' specifications, State requirements and standards of practice (e.g., United States Pharmacopeia (USP) standards).

CONTROLLED MEDICATIONS

Regulations require that the facility have a system to account for the receipt, usage, disposition, and reconciliation of all controlled medications. This system includes, but is not limited to:

- Record of receipt of all controlled medications with sufficient detail to allow reconciliation (e.g., specifying the name and strength of the medication, the quantity and date received, and the resident's name). However, in some delivery systems (e.g., single unit package medication delivery system or automated dispensing systems utilizing single-unit packages of medications that are not dispensed pursuant to a specific order), the resident's name may not be applicable;

     NOTE: The facility may store some controlled medications in an emergency medication supply in accordance with state requirements. The facility's policies and procedures must address the reconciliation and monitoring of this supply.

- Records of usage and disposition of all controlled medications with sufficient detail to allow reconciliation (e.g., the medication administration record [MAR], proof-of-use sheets, or declining inventory sheets), including destruction, wastage, return to the pharmacy/manufacturer, or disposal in accordance with applicable State requirements;

- Periodic reconciliation of records of receipt, disposition and inventory for all controlled medications (monthly or more frequently as defined by facility procedures or when loss is identified). The reconciliation identifies loss or diversion of controlled medications so as to minimize the time between the actual loss or diversion and the time of detection and follow-up to determine the extent of loss. Because diversion can occur at any time, the reconciliation should be done often enough to identify problems. Some State or other federal requirements may specify the frequency of reconciliation.

     o If discrepancies are identified during the reconciliation, the pharmacist and the facility develop and implement recommendations for resolving them.

     o If the systems have not been effective in preventing or identifying diversion or loss, it is important that the pharmacist and the facility review and revise related controls and procedures, as necessary, such as increasing the frequency of monitoring or the amount of detail used to document controlled substances.

NOTE: The pharmacist is not required by these regulations to perform the reconciliation, but rather to evaluate and determine that the facility maintains an account of all controlled medications and completes the reconciliation according to its procedures, consistent with State and federal requirements.

LABELING OF MEDICATIONS AND BIOLOGICALS

This section requires facility compliance with currently accepted labeling requirements, even though the pharmacies are responsible for the actual labeling. Labeling of medications and biologicals dispensed by the pharmacy must be consistent with applicable federal and State requirements and currently accepted pharmaceutical principles and practices. Although medication delivery systems may vary, the medication label at a minimum includes the medication name (generic and/or brand) and strength, the expiration date when applicable, and typically includes the resident's name, route of administration, appropriate instructions and precautions (such as shake well, with meals, do not crush, special storage instructions).

For medications designed for multiple administrations (e.g., inhalers, eye drops), the label is affixed in a manner to promote administration to the resident for whom it was prescribed.

When medications are prepared or compounded for intravenous infusion, the label contains the name and volume of the solution, resident's name, infusion rate, name and quantity of each additive, date of preparation, initials of compounder, date and time of administration, initials of person administering medication if different than compounder, ancillary precautions as applicable, and date after which the mixture must not be used.

For over-the-counter (OTC) medications in bulk containers (e.g., in states that permit bulk OTC medications to be stocked in the facility), the label contains the original manufacturer's or pharmacy-applied label indicating the medication name, strength, quantity, accessory instructions, lot number, and expiration date when applicable. If supplies of bulk OTC medications are used for a specific resident, the container identifies that resident by name and must contain the original manufacturer's or pharmacy-applied label.

The facility ensures that medication labeling in response to order changes is accurate and consistent with applicable state requirements.

INVESTIGATIVE PROTOCOL

For investigating compliance with the requirement at 483.60(d) & (e), see State Operations Manual, Appendix P, II.B. The Traditional Standard Survey, Task 5, Sub- Task 5E Investigative Protocol: Medication Pass and Pharmacy Services.

DETERMINATION OF COMPLIANCE (Task 6, Appendix P)

Synopsis of regulation (F431)

This requirement has several aspects. The pharmaceutical services must:

- Provide for the safe and secure storage of medications, i.e., medications must be stored at proper temperatures and locked at all times (except when under direct staff observation);

- Limit access to medications only to authorized staff;

- Label medications in accordance with Federal and State labeling requirements and accepted standards of practice; and

- Have safeguards and systems in place to control, account for, and periodically reconcile controlled medications.

Criteria for Compliance

Compliance with 42 CFR 483.60(b)(2)(3)(d)(e), F431, Labeling, Storage, and Controlled Medications.

The facility is in compliance if:

- The facility safeguards medications by locking the medications, limiting access, and disposing of medications appropriately;

- Medications are stored under proper temperature controls and in accordance with manufacturers' specifications;

- Medication labeling identifies, at a minimum, the medication's name, strength, expiration date when applicable, and lot number, and provides instructions as necessary for safe administration;

- Schedule II medications are stored in separately locked, permanently affixed compartments, except when the facility uses single unit medication distribution systems in which the quantity stored is minimal and a missing dose can be readily detected; and

- Controlled medications are reconciled accurately.

If not, cite F431.

Noncompliance for F431

After completing the investigation, determine whether compliance with the regulation exists. Noncompliance for F431 may include (but is not limited to) facility failure to:

- Store medications to preserve their integrity, for example allowing medications that should be stored between 40 and 86 degrees Fahrenheit to either reach temperatures below 32 degrees or above 100 degrees;

- Provide accurate labeling with appropriate accessory and cautionary instructions, thereby creating a potential for the wrong medication to be administered or for the correct medications to be given by the wrong route; and

- Accurately reconcile controlled medications.

IV. DEFICIENCY CATEGORIZATION (Part IV, Appendix P)

Once the survey team has completed its investigation, analyzed the data, reviewed the regulatory requirements, and determined that noncompliance exists, the team must determine the severity of each deficiency, based on the resultant harm or potential for harm to the resident.

The key elements for severity determination for F431 are as follows:

1. **Presence of actual or potential harm/negative outcome(s) due to a facility failure related to storage, labeling, or reconciliation of controlled medications.**

   Identify actual or potential harm/negative outcomes for F431 which may include, but are not limited to:

   - Accidental ingestion of medication(s) by a resident(s) as a result of failure to lock medications;

   - One or more residents received (or had the potential to receive) the wrong medication or dose or the correct medication by the wrong route as a result of inaccurate or incomplete labeling; or

   - Potential for a resident(s) to receive potentially ineffective medication(s) as a result of storing medications or vaccines at wrong temperatures, resulting in their potential inactivation.

2. **Degree of actual or potential harm/negative outcome(s) due to a facility failure related to storage, labeling, or reconciliation of controlled medications.**

   Identify how the facility practices caused, resulted in, allowed, or contributed to the actual or potential for harm:

   - If harm has occurred, determine if the harm is at the level of serious injury, impairment, death, compromise, or discomfort; or

   - If harm has not yet occurred, determine the potential for serious injury, impairment, death, compromise, or discomfort to occur to the resident.

3. **The immediacy of correction required.**

   Determine whether the noncompliance requires immediate correction in order to prevent serious injury, harm, impairment, or death to one or more residents.

The survey team must evaluate the harm or potential for harm based upon the following levels of severity for tag F431. First, the team must rule out whether Severity Level 4, Immediate Jeopardy, to a resident's health or safety, exists by evaluating the deficient practice in relation to immediacy, culpability, and severity. (Follow the guidance in Appendix Q, Guidelines for Determining Immediate Jeopardy.)

NOTE: The death or transfer of a resident who was harmed or injured as a result of facility noncompliance does not remove a finding of immediate jeopardy. The facility is required to implement specific actions to remove the jeopardy and correct the noncompliance which allowed or caused the immediate jeopardy.

Severity Level 4 Considerations: Immediate Jeopardy to Resident Health or Safety

Immediate Jeopardy is a situation in which the facility's noncompliance with one or more requirements of participation:

- Has caused/resulted in, or is likely to cause, serious injury, harm, impairment, or death to a resident; and

- Requires immediate correction as the facility either created the situation or allowed the situation to continue by failing to implement preventative or corrective measures.

Examples may include, but are not limited to:

- The facility failed to restrict access to medications resulting in serious injury or harm or death from ingestion of the medications (e.g., warfarin, digoxin, antibiotics, opioids, anticonvulsants, antipsychotics) or posed a significant risk to the health of the residents resulting in the potential for clinically significant adverse consequences such as kidney or liver failure, anaphylaxis, cardiac arrest, or death; or

- As a result of an incorrect label on the package, staff administered the wrong medication or wrong dose(s) of a medication (e.g., anticonvulsant, antihyperglycemic, benzodiazepine) with a potential for clinically significant adverse consequences, which resulted in or had the potential for serious harm or death (e.g., toxic levels of the medication, unresponsiveness, uncontrolled seizures).

NOTE: If immediate jeopardy has been ruled out based upon the evidence, then evaluate whether actual harm that is not immediate jeopardy exists at Severity Level 3.

Severity Level 3 Considerations: Actual Harm that is Not Immediate Jeopardy

Level 3 indicates noncompliance that resulted in actual harm, and can include but may not be limited to compromise, decline, or interference with the resident's ability to maintain and/or reach his/her highest practicable well-being. Examples may include, but are not limited to:

- Medication labeling was incomplete and lacked instructions that the medication was not to be given with specific foods (e.g., milk or milk-based products) resulting in altered effectiveness of the medication and worsening of the residents' symptoms, requiring medical intervention; or

- The facility failed to implement a system to reconcile controlled medications. As a result, medications were unavailable for residents for whom the medications were prescribed. Residents experienced moderate pain that compromised their ability to perform ADLs.

NOTE: If Severity Level 3 (actual harm that is not immediate jeopardy) has been ruled out based upon the evidence, then evaluate as to whether Severity Level 2 (no actual harm with the potential for more than minimal harm) exists.

Severity Level 2 Considerations: No Actual Harm with Potential for More Than Minimal Harm that is Not Immediate Jeopardy

Level 2 indicates noncompliance that resulted in a resident outcome of no more than minimal discomfort and/or the potential to compromise the resident's ability to maintain or reach his or her highest practicable level of well-being. The potential exists for greater harm to occur if interventions are not provided. Examples may include, but are not limited to:

- The facility's medication cart was not kept locked or under direct observation of authorized staff and a wandering resident with dementia ingested a medication that he/she had taken off the cart but did not suffer any adverse consequences; or

- As a result of inaccurate labeling, the resident received the wrong medication or dose or the correct medication by the wrong route and experienced discomfort but did not require any interventions.

NOTE: If Severity Level 2 (no actual harm with potential for more than minimal harm that is not immediate jeopardy) has been ruled out based upon the evidence, then evaluate as to whether Severity Level 1 (no actual harm with the potential for minimal harm) exists.

Severity Level 1 Considerations: No Actual Harm with Potential for Minimal Harm

Level 1 indicates noncompliance that resulted in no harm to the resident, and the potential for no more than minimal harm. Examples may include, but are not limited to:

- The facility failed to reconcile controlled medications but there was no negative resident outcome and no potential for more than minimal harm.

F441

§483.65 — Infection Control

F441

(Rev. 55, Issued: 12-02-09 Effective: 09-30-09, Implementation: 09-30-09)

§483.65 Infection Control

The facility must establish and maintain an Infection Control Program designed to provide a safe, sanitary and comfortable environment and to help prevent the development and transmission of disease and infection.

§483.65(a) Infection Control Program

The facility must establish an Infection Control Program under which it-

(1) Investigates, controls, and prevents infections in the facility;

(2) Decides what procedures, such as isolation should be applied to an individual resident; and

(3) Maintains a record of incidents and corrective actions related to infections.

§483.65(b) Preventing Spread of Infection

(1) When the Infection Control Program determines that a resident needs isolation to prevent the spread of infection, the facility must isolate the resident.

(2) The facility must prohibit employees with a communicable disease or infected skin lesions from direct contact with residents or their food, if direct contact will transmit the disease.

(3) The facility must require staff to wash their hands after each direct resident contact for which handwashing is indicated by accepted professional practice.

§483.65(c) Linens

Personnel must handle, store, process, and transport linens so as to prevent the spread of infection.

INTENT: (F441) 42CFR 483.65 Infection Control

The intent of this regulation is to assure that the facility develops, implements, and maintains an Infection Prevention and Control Program in order to prevent, recognize, and control, to the extent possible, the onset and spread of infection within the facility. The program will:

- Perform surveillance and investigation to prevent, to the extent possible, the onset and the spread of infection;

- Prevent and control outbreaks and cross-contamination using transmission-based precautions in addition to standard precautions;

- Use records of infection incidents to improve its infection control processes and outcomes by taking corrective actions, as indicated;

- Implement hand hygiene (hand washing) practices consistent with accepted standards of practice, to reduce the spread of infections and prevent cross-contamination; and

- Properly store, handle, process, and transport linens to minimize contamination.

DEFINITIONS

Definitions are provided to clarify terminology or terms related to infection control practices in nursing homes.

- **"Airborne precautions"** refers to actions taken to prevent or minimize the transmission of infectious agents/organisms that remain infectious over long distances when suspended in the air. These particles can remain suspended in the air for prolonged periods of time and can be carried on normal air currents in a room or beyond, to adjacent spaces or areas receiving exhaust air.[1]

- **"Alcohol-based hand rub"** (ABHR) refers to a 60-95 percent ethanol or isopropyl-containing preparation base designed for application to the hands to reduce the number of viable microorganisms.

- **"Antifungal"** refers to a medication used to treat a fungal infection such as athlete's foot, ringworm or candidiasis.

- **"Anti-infective"** refers to a group of medications used to treat infections.

- **"Antiseptic hand wash"** is "washing hands with water and soap or other detergents containing an antiseptic agent."[2]

- **"Cohorting"** refers to the practice of grouping residents infected or colonized with the same infectious agent together to confine their care to one area and prevent contact with susceptible residents (cohorting residents). During outbreaks, healthcare personnel may be assigned to a cohort of residents to further limit opportunities for transmission (cohorting staff).

- **"Colonization"** refers to the presence of microorganisms on or within body sites without detectable host immune response, cellular damage, or clinical expression.

- **"Communicable disease"** (also known as [a.k.a.] "Contagious disease") refers to an infection transmissible (as from person-to-person) by direct contact with an affected individual or the individual's body fluids or by indirect means (as by a vector).

- **"Community associated infections"** (formerly "Community Acquired Infections") refers to infections that are present or incubating at the time of admission, or generally develop within 72 hours of admission.

- **"Contact precautions"** are measures that are "intended to prevent transmission of infectious agents, including epidemiologically important microorganisms, which are spread by direct or indirect contact with the resident or the resident's environment."[3]

- **"Droplet precautions"** refers to actions designed to reduce/prevent the transmission of pathogens spread through close respiratory or mucous membrane contact with respiratory secretions.[4]

- **"Hand hygiene"** is a general term that applies to washing hands with water and either plain soap or soap/detergent containing an antiseptic agent; or thoroughly applying an alcohol-based hand rub (ABHR).

- **"Hand washing"** refers to washing hands with plain (i.e., nonantimicrobial) soap and water.

- **"Health care associated infection [HAI]"** (a.k.a. "nosocomial" and "facility-acquired" infection) refers to an infection that generally occurs after 72 hours from the time of admission to a health care facility.

- **"Infection"** refers the establishment of an infective agent in or on a suitable host, producing clinical signs and symptoms (e.g., fever, redness, heat, purulent exudates, etc).

- **"Infection prevention and control program"** refers to a program (including surveillance, investigation, prevention, control, and reporting) that provides a safe, sanitary and comfortable environment to help prevent the development and transmission of infection.

- **"Infection preventionist (IP)"** (a.k.a. infection control professional) refers to a person whose primary training is in either nursing, medical technology, microbiology, or epidemiology and who has acquired additional training in infection control.

- **"Isolation"** refers to the practices employed to reduce the spread of an infectious agent and/or minimize the transmission of infection.

- **"Isolation precautions"** see "Transmission-Based Precautions"

- **"Medical waste"** refers to any solid waste that is generated in the diagnosis, treatment, or immunization of human beings or animals, in research pertaining to, or in the production or testing of biologicals (e.g., blood-soaked bandages, sharps).

- **"Methicillin resistant staphylococcus aureus (MRSA)"** refers to Staphylococcus aureus bacteria that are resistant to treatment with semi-synthetic penicillins (e.g., Oxacillin/Nafcillin/Methicillin).

- **"Multi-Drug resistant organisms (MDROs)"** refers to microorganisms, predominantly bacteria, that are resistant to one or more classes of antimicrobial agents. Although the names of certain MDROs describe resistance to only one agent, these pathogens are frequently resistant to most available antimicrobial agents.[5]

- **"Outbreak"** is the occurrence of more cases of a particular infection than is normally expected, the occurrence of an unusual organism, or the occurrence of unusual antibiotic resistance patterns.[6]

- **"Personal protective equipment" (PPE)** refers to protective items or garments worn to protect the body or clothing from hazards that can cause injury.

- **"Standard precautions"** (formerly "Universal Precautions") refers to infection prevention practices that apply to all residents, regardless of suspected or confirmed diagnosis or presumed infection status. Standard Precautions is a combination and expansion of Universal Precautions and Body Substance Isolation (a practice of isolating all body substances such as blood, urine, and feces).[7]

- **"Surveillance"** refers to the ongoing, systematic collection, analysis, interpretation, and dissemination of data to identify infections and infection risks, to try to reduce morbidity and mortality and to improve resident health status.

- **"Transmission-based precautions"** (a.k.a. "Isolation Precautions") refers to the actions (precautions) implemented, in addition to standard precautions, that are based upon the means of transmission (airborne, contact, and droplet) in order to prevent or control infections.

- **"Vancomycin resistant enterococcus (VRE)"** refers to enterococcus that has developed resistance to vancomycin.

OVERVIEW

Infections are a significant source of morbidity and mortality for nursing home residents and account for up to half of all nursing home resident transfers to hospitals. Infections result in an estimated 150,000 to 200,000 hospital admissions per year at an estimated cost of $673 million to $2 billion annually. When a nursing home resident is hospitalized with a primary diagnosis of infection, the death rate can reach as high as 40 percent.

It is estimated that an average of 1.6 to 3.8 infections per resident occur annually in nursing homes. Urinary tract, respiratory (e.g., pneumonia and bronchitis), and skin and soft tissue infections (e.g., pressure ulcers) represent the most common endemic infections in residents of nursing homes.[8] Other common infections include conjunctivitis, gastroenteritis, and influenza.[9]

Confirming and managing an infectious outbreak can be costly and time consuming. An effective facility-wide infection prevention and control program can help to contain costs and reduce adverse consequences. An effective program relies upon the involvement, support, and knowledge of the facility's administration, the entire interdisciplinary team, residents, and visitors.

Critical aspects of the infection prevention and control program include recognizing and managing infections at the time of a resident's admission to the facility and throughout their stay, as well as following recognized infection control practices while providing care (e.g., hand hygiene, handling and processing of linens, use of standard precautions, and appropriate use of transmission-based precautions and cohorting or separating residents). It is important that residents' conditions be reassessed because older adults may have coexisting diseases that complicate the diagnosis of an infection (e.g., joint degeneration vs. infectious arthritis, COPD versus pneumonia), and they may also have atypical or non-specific signs and symptoms related to infections, such as altered mental status, function or behavior, and impaired fever response.

Because of the potential negative impact that a resident may experience as a result of the implementation of special precautions, the facility is challenged to promote the individual resident's rights and well-being while trying to prevent and control the spread of infections.

NOTE: It is important that all infection prevention and control practices reflect current Centers for Disease Control (CDC) guidelines.

INFECTION PREVENTION AND CONTROL PROGRAM

An effective infection prevention and control program is necessary to control the spread of infections and/or outbreaks.

Program Development and Oversight

Program development and oversight emphasize the prevention and management of infections. Program oversight involves establishing goals and priorities for the program, planning, and implementing strategies to achieve the goals, monitoring the implementation of the program (including the interdisciplinary team's infection control practices), and responding to errors, problems, or other identified issues. Additional activities involved in program development and oversight may include but are not limited to:

- Identifying the staff's roles and responsibilities for the routine implementation of the program as well as in case of an outbreak of a communicable disease, an episode of infection, or the threat of a bio-hazard attack;

- Developing and implementing appropriate infection control policies and procedures, and training staff on them;

- Monitoring and documenting infections, including tracking and analyzing outbreaks of infection as well as implementing and documenting actions to resolve related problems;

- Defining and managing appropriate resident health initiatives, such as:

  - The immunization program (influenza, pneumonia, etc); and

  - Tuberculosis screening on admission and following the discovery of a new case, and managing active cases consistent with State requirements;

- Providing a nursing home liaison to work with local and State health agencies; and

- Managing food safety, including employee health and hygiene, pest control, investigating potential food-borne illnesses, and waste disposal.

The facility identifies personnel responsible for overall program oversight, which may involve collaboration of the administrator, the medical director or his/her designee, the director of nursing, and other appropriate facility staff as needed. This group may define how and when the program is to be routinely monitored and situations that may trigger a focused review of the program. The group communicates the findings from collecting and analyzing data to the facility's staff and management, and directs changes in practice based on identified trends, government infection control advisories, and other factors.

Components of an Infection Prevention and Control Program

An effective infection prevention and control program incorporates, but is not limited to, the following components:

- Policies, procedures, and practices which promote consistent adherence to evidence-based infection control practices;

- Program oversight including planning, organizing, implementing, operating, monitoring, and maintaining all of the elements of the program and ensuring that the facility's interdisciplinary team is involved in infection prevention and control;

- Infection preventionist, a person designated to serve as coordinator of the infection prevention and control program;

- Surveillance, including process and outcome surveillance, monitoring, data analysis, documentation and communicable diseases reporting (as required by State and Federal law and regulation);

- Education, including training in infection prevention and control practices, to ensure compliance with facility requirements as well as State and Federal regulation; and

- Antibiotic review including reviewing data to monitor the appropriate use of antibiotics in the resident population.

Examples of activities related to the Infection Prevention and Control Program may include but are not limited to:

- Undertaking process and/or outcome surveillance activities to identify infections that are causing, or have the potential to cause an outbreak;

- Conducting data analysis to help detect unusual or unexpected outcomes and to determine the effectiveness of infection prevention and control practices;

- Documenting observations related to the causes of infection and/or infection trends; and

- Implementing measures to prevent the transmission of infectious agents and to reduce risks for device and procedure-related infections.

Policies and Procedures

Policies and procedures are the foundation of the facility's infection prevention and control program. Policies and procedures are reviewed periodically and revised as needed to conform to current standards of practice or to address specific facility concerns.

Written policies establish the program's expectations and parameters. For example, policies may specify the use of standard precautions facility-wide and use of transmission-based precautions when indicated, define the frequency and nature of surveillance activities, require that staff use accepted hand hygiene after each direct resident contact for which hand hygiene is indicated, or prohibit direct resident contact by an employee who has an infected skin lesion or communicable disease.

Procedures guide the implementation of the policies and performance of specific tasks. Procedures may include, for example, how to identify and communicate information about residents with potentially transmissible infectious agents, how to obtain vital signs for a resident on contact precautions and what to do with the equipment after its use, and essential steps and considerations (including choosing agents) for performing hand hygiene.

Infection Preventionist (IP)

A facility may designate an IP to serve as the coordinator of an Infection Prevention and Control Program. Responsibilities may include collecting, analyzing, and providing infection data and trends to nursing staff and health care practitioners; consulting on infection risk assessment, prevention, and control strategies; providing education and training; and implementing evidence-based infection control practices, including those mandated by regulatory and licensing agencies, and guidelines from the Centers for Disease Control and Prevention.

Surveillance

Essential elements of a surveillance system include use of standardized definitions and listings of the symptoms of infections, use of surveillance tools such as infection surveys and data collection templates, walking rounds throughout the facility,[10] identification of segments of the resident populations at risk for infection, identification of the processes or outcomes selected for surveillance, statistical analysis of data that can uncover an outbreak, and feedback of results to the primary caregivers so that they can assess the residents for signs of infection.

Two types of surveillance (process and outcome) can be implemented in facilities.

Process Surveillance

Process surveillance reviews practices directly related to resident care[10] in order to identify whether the practices comply with established prevention and control procedures and policies based on recognized guidelines. Examples of this type of surveillance include monitoring of compliance with transmission based precautions, proper hand hygiene,[11] and the use and disposal of gloves. Process surveillance determines, for example, whether the facility:

- Minimizes exposure to a potential source of infection;

- Uses appropriate hand hygiene prior to and after all procedures;[12]

- Ensures that appropriate sterile techniques are followed; for example, that staff:

- • Use sterile gloves, fluids, and materials, when indicated,[13] depending on the site and the procedure;[14]

- • Avoid contaminating sterile procedures;[15] and

- • Ensure that contaminated/non-sterile items are not placed in a sterile field.

- Uses Personal Protective Equipment (PPE) when indicated;[16]

- Ensures that reusable equipment is appropriately cleaned, disinfected, or reprocessed; and

- Uses single-use medication vials and other single use items appropriately (proper disposal after every single use). [17]

Outcome Surveillance

In contrast to process surveillance, outcome surveillance is designed to identify and report evidence of an infection. The outcome surveillance process consists of collecting/documenting data on individual cases and comparing the collected data to standard written definitions (criteria) of infections. The IP or other designated staff reviews data (including residents with fever or purulent drainage, and cultures or other diagnostic test results consistent with potential infections) to detect clusters and trends. Other sources of relevant data may include antibiotic orders, laboratory antibiograms (antibiotic susceptibility profiles), medication regimen review reports, and medical record documentation such as physician progress notes and transfer summaries accompanying newly admitted residents.[18] The facility's program should choose to either track the prevalence of infections (existing/current cases both old and new) at a specific point, or focus on regularly identifying new cases during defined time periods. When conducting outcome surveillance, the facility may choose to use one or more of the automated systems and authoritative resources that are available, and include definitions.

Documentation

Facilities may use various approaches to gathering, documenting, and listing surveillance data. The facility's infection control reports describe the types of infections and are used to identify trends and patterns. Descriptive documentation provides the facility with summaries of the observations of staff practices and/or the investigation of the causes of an infection and/or identification of underlying cause(s) of infection trends.

It is important that the infection prevention and control program define how often and by what means surveillance data will be collected, regardless of whether the facility creates its own forms, purchases preprinted forms, or uses automated systems.

Monitoring

Monitoring of the implementation of the program, its effectiveness, the condition of any resident with an infection, and the resolution of the infection and/or an outbreak is considered an integral part of nursing home infection surveillance. The facility monitors practices (e.g., dressing changes and transmission-based precaution procedures) to ensure consistent implementation of established infection prevention and control policies and procedures based on current standards of practice. All residents are monitored for current infections and infection risks.

Data Analysis

Determining the origin of infections helps the facility identify the number of residents who developed infections within the nursing home. Comparing current infection control surveillance data (including the incidence or prevalence of infections and staff practices) to past data enables detection of unusual or unexpected outcomes, trends, effective practices, and performance issues. The facility can then evaluate whether it needs to change processes or practices to enhance infection prevention and minimize the potential for transmission of infections.

It is important that surveillance reports be shared with appropriate individuals including, but not limited to, the director of nursing and medical director. In addition, it is important that the staff and practitioners receive reports that are relevant to their practices to help them recognize the impact of their care on infection rates and outcome.

Communicable Disease Reporting

It is important for each facility to have processes that enable them to consistently comply with State and local health department requirements for reporting communicable diseases.

Education

Both initial and ongoing infection control education help staff comply with infection control practices. Updated education and training are appropriate when policies and procedures are revised or when there is a special circumstance, such as an outbreak, that requires modification or replacement of current practices.[19] In addition to education regarding general infection control principles, some infection control training is discipline and task specific (e.g., insertion of urinary catheters, suctioning, intravenous care or blood glucose monitoring). Follow-up competency evaluations identify staff compliance.

Essential topics of infection control training include, but are not limited to routes of disease transmission, hand hygiene, sanitation procedures, MDROs, transmission-based precaution techniques, and the federally required OSHA education.

Antibiotic Review

Because of increases in MDROs, review of the use of antibiotics (including comparing prescribed antibiotics with available susceptibility reports) is a vital aspect of the infection prevention and control program. It is the physician's (or other appropriate authorized practitioner's) responsibility to prescribe appropriate antibiotics and to establish the indication for use of specific medications. As part of the medication regimen review, the consultant pharmacist can assist with the oversight by identifying antibiotics prescribed for resistant organisms or for situations with questionable indications, and reporting such findings to the director of nursing and the attending physician. See the Guidance at §483.65*, Tag F329 regarding use of a medication without adequate indication for use and at §483.65**, Tag F428 regarding medication regimen review.

*[**Editor's Note:** The section cited is incorrect. The correct section is §483.25(l).]
[Editor's Note:** The section cited is incorrect. The correct section is §483.60(c).]

PREVENTING THE SPREAD OF INFECTION

Factors Associated with the Spread of Infection in Nursing Homes

Many factors contribute to a substantial severity and frequency of infections and infectious diseases in nursing homes. These infections can arise from individual or institutional factors, or both. Modes of transmission of infection include, but are not limited to:

- Contact;
- Droplet; and
- Airborne.

Individual Factors

Examples of individual factors contributing to infections and the severity of the infection outcomes in facility residents include, but are not limited to the following:

- Medications affecting resistance to infection such as corticosteroids and chemotherapy;
- Limited physiologic reserve (e.g., decreased function of the heart, lungs, and kidneys);
- Compromised host defenses (e.g., decreased or absent cough reflex predisposing to aspiration pneumonia, thinning skin associated with pressure ulcers, decreased tear production predisposing to conjunctivitis, vascular insufficiency, and impaired immune function);

- Coexisting chronic diseases (e.g., diabetes, arthritis, cancer, COPD, anemia);

- Complications from invasive diagnostic procedures such as skin or bloodstream infections;

- Impaired responses to infection (e.g., cell mediated responses); and

- Increased frequency of therapeutic toxicity (e.g., declining kidney and liver function).

Institutional Factors

In addition to individual factors, institutional factors may also facilitate transmission of infections among residents, including but not limited to:

- Pathogen exposure in shared communal living space (e.g., handrails and equipment);

- Common air circulation;

- Direct/indirect contact with health care personnel/visitors/other residents;

- Direct/indirect contact with equipment used to provide care; and

- Transfer of residents to and from hospitals or other settings.

Residents can be exposed to potentially pathogenic organisms in several ways, including but not limited to the following:

- Improper hand hygiene;

- Improper glove use (e.g., utilizing a single pair of gloves for multiple tasks or multiple residents); and

- Improper food handling.

Direct Transmission (Person to Person)

Direct transmission occurs when microorganisms are transferred from an infected/colonized person to another person. Contaminated hands of healthcare personnel are often implicated in direct contact transmission. Agents that can be transmitted by direct contact include, but are not limited to MRSA, VRE, and Influenza.

Indirect Transmission

Indirect transmission involves the transfer of an infectious agent through a contaminated intermediate object. The following are examples of opportunities for indirect contact.

- Resident-care devices (e.g., electronic thermometers or glucose monitoring devices) may transmit pathogens if devices contaminated with blood or body fluids are shared without cleaning and disinfecting between uses for different residents; and

- Clothing, uniforms, laboratory coats, or isolation gowns used as PPE may become contaminated with potential pathogens after care of a resident colonized or infected with an infectious agent, (e.g., MRSA, VRE, and Clostridium difficile). Indirect contact may occur through toilets and bedpans. Examples of illnesses spread via a fecal-oral route include salmonella, shigella, and pathogenic strains of E. coli, norovirus, and symptomatic Clostridium difficile.

Reducing and/or preventing infections through indirect contact requires the decontamination (i.e., cleaning, sanitizing, or disinfecting an object to render it safe for handling) of resident equipment, medical devices, and the environment. Alternatively, the facility may also consider using single-use disposable devices. The choice of decontamination method depends on the risk of infection to the resident coming into contact with equipment or medical devices.

The CDC has adopted the Spaulding classification system that identifies three risk levels associated with medical and surgical instruments: critical, semi-critical and noncritical.[20] This includes:

- Critical items (e.g., needles, intravenous catheters, indwelling urinary catheters) are defined as those items which normally enter sterile tissue, or the vascular system, or through which blood flows. The equipment must be sterile when used, based on one of several accepted sterilization procedures;[20]

- Semi-critical items (e.g., thermometers, podiatry equipment, electric razors) are defined as those objects that touch mucous membranes or skin that is not intact. Such items require meticulous cleaning followed by high-level disinfection treatment using an FDA- approved chemo sterilizer agent, or they may be sterilized; and.

- Non-critical items (e.g., stethoscopes, blood pressure cuffs, over-bed tables) are defined as those that come into contact with intact skin or do not contact the resident. They require low level disinfection by cleaning periodically and after visible soiling, with an EPA disinfectant detergent or germicide that is approved for health care settings.

Single-use disposable equipment is an alternative to sterilizing reusable medical instruments. Devices labeled by the manufacturer for single use are never to be reused, even if they are reprocessed.

Prevention and Control of Transmission of Infection

Infectious organisms (e.g., bacteria, viruses, or parasites) may be transmitted by direct contact (e.g., skin to skin) or indirect contact (e.g., via air, water, inanimate objects). Healthcare personnel and resident care equipment often move from resident to resident and therefore may serve as a vehicle for transferring infectious organisms. Another potential challenge is that the transmission of infectious organisms within the facility may be facilitated by inadequate hand hygiene facilities, rinsing bed pans in inappropriate places (e.g., resident's sink), or inappropriate placement of colonized or infected residents (e.g., sharing a bathroom with a non- infected resident).

Airborne transmission can occur by inhaling pathogenic droplet nuclei (e.g., M Tuberculosis). Contaminated environmental surfaces are also potential reservoirs for infections. Infections caused by bacteria and viruses are especially common. Clostridium difficile can live on inanimate surfaces for up to 5 months[21] while the hepatitis B virus can last up to a week[22] and the influenza virus can survive on fomites (e.g., any inanimate object or substance capable of carrying infectious organisms and transferring them from one individual to another) for up to 8 hours. [23]

The appropriate disposal of waste helps minimize the potential transmission of infections. It is important for the facility to monitor safe handling of blood and body fluids and the disposal of contaminated waste.

General Approaches to Prevention and Control

A facility's infection control practices are important to preventing the transmission of infections. Infection control precautions used by the facility include two primary tiers: "Standard Precautions" and "Transmission-Based Precautions."

Standard Precautions

Standard precautions are based upon the principle that all blood, body fluids, secretions, excretions (except sweat), non-intact skin, and mucous membranes may contain transmissible infectious agents. Standard precautions are intended to be applied to the care of all persons in all healthcare settings, regardless of the suspected or confirmed presence of an infectious agent. Implementation of standard precautions constitutes the primary strategy for preventing healthcare-associated transmission of infectious agents among residents and healthcare personnel. Appropriate infection control measures should be used in each resident interaction.

Standard precautions include but are not limited to hand hygiene, safe injection practices, the proper use of PPE (e.g., gloves, gowns, and masks), resident placement, and care of the environment, textiles, and laundry. Also, equipment or items in the resident environment likely to have been contaminated with infectious fluids or other potentially infectious matter must be handled in a manner so as to prevent transmission of infectious agents, (e.g., wear gloves for handling soiled equipment, and properly clean and disinfect or sterilize reusable equipment before use on another resident).[24] In addition to proper hand hygiene, it is important for staff to use appropriate protective equipment as a barrier to exposure to any body fluids (whether known to be infected or not). For example, in situations identified as appropriate, gloves and other equipment such as gowns and masks are to be used as necessary to control the spread of infections. Standard precautions are also intended to protect residents by ensuring that healthcare personnel do not carry infectious agents to residents on their hands or via equipment used during resident care.

Disposal of waste is also handled as though all body fluids are infectious. Potentially contaminated articles are stored and disposed of in appropriate containers (e.g., sharps containers, biohazard bags, etc.), and the environment is cleaned using germicidal agents to reduce the risk of transmission of infection.

Hand Hygiene

Hand hygiene continues to be the primary means of preventing the transmission of infection. The following is a list of some situations that require hand hygiene:

- When coming on duty;

- When hands are visibly soiled (hand washing with soap and water);Before and after direct resident contact (for which hand hygiene is indicated by acceptable professional practice);

- Before and after performing any invasive procedure (e.g., fingerstick blood sampling);

- Before and after entering isolation precaution settings;

- Before and after eating or handling food (hand washing with soap and water);

- Before and after assisting a resident with meals;

- Before and after assisting a resident with personal care (e.g., oral care, bathing);

- Before and after handling peripheral vascular catheters and other invasive devices;

- Before and after inserting indwelling catheters;

- Before and after changing a dressing;

- Upon and after coming in contact with a resident's intact skin, (e.g., when taking a pulse or blood pressure, and lifting a resident);

- After personal use of the toilet (hand washing with soap and water);

- Before and after assisting a resident with toileting (hand washing with soap and water);

- After contact with a resident with infectious diarrhea including, but not limited to infections caused by norovirus, salmonella, shigella, and C. difficile (hand washing with soap and water);

- After blowing or wiping nose;

- After contact with a resident's mucous membranes and body fluids or excretions;

- After handling soiled or used linens, dressings, bedpans, catheters and urinals;

- After handling soiled equipment or utensils;

- After performing your personal hygiene (hand washing with soap and water);

- After removing gloves or aprons; and

- After completing duty.

Consistent use by staff of proper hygienic practices and techniques is critical to preventing the spread of infections. It is necessary for staff to have access to proper hand washing facilities with available soap (regular or anti-microbial), warm water, and disposable towels and/or heat/air drying methods. Alcohol based hand rubs (ABHR) cannot be used in place of proper hand washing techniques in a food service setting.[25]

Recommended techniques for washing hands with soap and water include wetting hands first with clean, running warm water, applying the amount of product recommended by the manufacturer to hands, and rubbing hands together vigorously for at least 15 seconds covering all surfaces of the hands and fingers; then rinsing hands with water and drying thoroughly with a disposable towel; and turning off the faucet on the hand sink with the disposable paper towel.

Except for situations where hand washing is specifically required, antimicrobial agents such as ABHR are also appropriate for cleaning hands and can be used for direct resident care. Recommended techniques for performing hand hygiene with an ABHR include applying product to the palm of one hand and rubbing hands together, covering all surfaces of hands and fingers, until the hands are dry. In addition, gloves or the use of baby wipes are not a substitute for hand hygiene.

Other Staff-Related Preventive Measures

Facility staff who have direct contact with residents or who handle food must be free of communicable diseases and open skin lesions, if direct contact will transmit the disease. It is important that the facility maintain documentation of how they handle staff with communicable infections or open skin lesions.

It is important that all staff involved in direct resident contact maintain fingernails that are clean, neat, and trimmed. Wearing intact disposable gloves in good condition and that are changed after each use helps reduce the spread of microorganisms. It is important for dietary staff to wear hair restraints (e.g., hairnet, hat, and/or beard restraint) while in the kitchen areas to prevent their hair from contacting exposed food. Since jewelry can harbor microorganisms, it is recommended by the FDA that dietary staff keep jewelry to a minimum and remove or cover hand jewelry when handling food.[26]

Transmission-based Precautions

Transmission-based precautions are used for residents who are known to be, or suspected of being infected or colonized with infectious agents, including pathogens that require additional control measures to prevent transmission. In nursing homes, it is appropriate to individualize decisions regarding resident placement (shared or private), balancing infection risks with the need for more than one occupant in a room, the presence of risk factors that increase the likelihood of transmission, and the potential for adverse psychological impact on the infected or colonized resident.[27]

It is essential both to communicate transmission-based precautions to all health care personnel, and for personnel to comply with requirements. Pertinent signage (i.e., isolation precautions) and verbal reporting between staff can enhance compliance with transmission-based precautions to help minimize the transmission of infections within the facility.

It is important to use the standard approaches, as defined by the CDC for transmission-based precautions: airborne, contact, and droplet precautions.[28] The category of transmission-based precaution determines the type of PPE to be used. Communication (e.g., verbal reports, signage) regarding the particular type of precaution to be utilized is important. When transmission-based precautions are in place, PPE should be readily available. Proper hand washing remains a key preventive measure, regardless of the type of transmission-based precaution employed.

Transmission-based precautions are maintained for as long as necessary to prevent the transmission of infection. It is appropriate to use the least restrictive approach possible that adequately protects the resident and others. Maintaining isolation longer than necessary may adversely affect psychosocial well-being. The facility should document in the medical record the rationale for the selected transmission-based precautions.

Airborne Precautions

Airborne precautions prevent the transmission of organisms that remain infectious when suspended in the air (e.g., varicella zoster (shingles) and M. tuberculosis). Resident health activities related to infection control include tuberculosis (TB) screening and management of active cases, consistent with State requirements. Management of some airborne infections such as active TB requires a single-resident airborne infection isolation room (AIIR) that is equipped with special air handling and ventilation capacity. Although not all residents with airborne infections will require an AIIR, residents with infections requiring an AIIR may need to be transported to an acute care setting unless the facility can place the resident in a private AIIR room with the door closed. In cases when AIIR is required it is important for the facility to have a plan in place to effectively manage a situation involving a resident with suspected or active TB while awaiting the resident's transfer to an acute care setting.

Personnel caring for residents on airborne precautions should wear a mask or respirator that is donned prior to room entry, depending on the disease-specific recommendations.[29] Depending on the condition, staff can use N95 or higher level respirators or wear masks if respirators are not available.

Contact Precautions

Contact transmission risk requires the use of contact precautions to prevent infections that are spread by person-to-person contact. Contact precautions require the use of appropriate PPE, including a gown and gloves upon entering the contact precaution room. Prior to leaving the contact precaution room the PPE is removed and hand hygiene is performed.

Depending on the situation, options for residents on contact precautions may include the following: a private room, cohorting, or sharing a room with a roommate with limited risk factors (e.g., without indwelling devices, without pressure ulcers and not immunocompromised).

Droplet Precautions

In contrast to contact transmission, respiratory droplets transmit infections directly from the respiratory tract of an infected individual to susceptible mucosal surfaces of the recipient. Since this generally occurs at close proximity, facial protection is necessary. Respiratory droplets are generated when an infected person coughs, sneezes, or talks; or during procedures such as suctioning, endotracheal intubation, cough induction by chest physiotherapy, and cardiopulmonary resuscitation. Studies have shown that respiratory viruses can enter the body via the nasal mucosa, conjunctivae and less frequently the mouth.[30] Examples of droplet-borne organisms that may cause infections include, but are not limited to influenza and mycoplasma.

The maximum distance for droplet transmission is currently unresolved, but the area of defined risk based on epidemiological findings is approximately 3-10 feet.[31] In contrast to airborne pathogens, droplet-borne pathogens are generally not transmitted through the air over long distances. Masks are to be used within approximately 6 to 10 feet of a resident or upon entry into a resident's room with respiratory droplet precautions. Residents with droplet precautions are placed in either a private room, cohorted, or share a room with a roommate with limited risk factors.

Implementation of Transmission-Based Precautions

It is important that facility staff clearly identify the type of precautions and the appropriate PPE to be used in the care of the resident. The PPE should be readily available near the entrance to the resident's room. Signage can be posted on the resident's door instructing visitors to see the nurse before entering.

It is not always possible to identify prospectively residents needing transmission-based precautions. The diagnosis of many infections is based on clinical signs and symptoms, but often requires laboratory confirmation. However, since laboratory tests (especially those that depend on culture techniques) may require two or more days to complete, transmission-based precautions may need to be implemented while test results are pending, based on the clinical presentation and the likely category of pathogens.[32] The use of appropriate transmission-based precautions when a resident develops symptoms or signs of a transmissible infection or arrives at a nursing home with symptoms of an infection (pending laboratory confirmation) reduces transmission opportunities. However, once it is confirmed that the resident is no longer a risk for transmitting the infection, removing transmission-based precautions avoids unnecessary social isolation.

Safe Water Precautions

Safe drinking water is also critical to controlling the spread of infections. The facility is responsible for maintaining a safe and sanitary water supply, by meeting nationally recognized standards set by the FDA for drinking water (<500 CFU/mL per heterotrophic plate count).

HANDLING LINENS TO PREVENT AND CONTROL INFECTION TRANSMISSION

It is important that all potentially contaminated linen be handled with appropriate measures to prevent cross-transmission. If the facility handles all used linen as potentially contaminated (i.e., using standard precautions), no additional separating or special labeling of the linen is recommended. No special precautions (i.e., double bagging) or categorizing is recommended for linen originating in isolation rooms. Double bagging of linen is only recommended if the outside of the bag is visibly contaminated or is observed to be wet through to the outside of the bag. Alternatively, leak-resistant bags are recommended for linens contaminated with blood or body substances. If standard precautions for contaminated linens are not used, then some identification with labels, color coding or other alternatives means of communication is important.

For the routine handling of contaminated laundry, minimum agitation is recommended, to avoid the contamination of air, surfaces, and persons. The risk of environmental contamination may be reduced by having personnel bag or contain contaminated linen at the point of use, and not sorting or pre-rinsing in resident care areas.

It is important that laundry areas have hand washing facilities and products, as well as appropriate PPE (i.e., gloves and gowns) available for workers to wear while sorting linens. Laundry equipment should be used and maintained according to the manufacturer's instructions to prevent microbial contamination of the system. It is recommended that damp linen is not left in machines overnight.

Detergent and water physically remove many microorganisms from the linen through dilution during the wash cycle. An effective way to destroy microorganisms in laundry items is through hot water washing at temperatures above 160°F (71°C) for 25 minutes.[33] Alternatively, low temperature washing at 71 to 77 degrees F (22-25 degrees C) plus a 125-part-per-million (ppm) chlorine bleach rinse has been found to be effective and comparable to high temperature wash cycles.[34]

If laundry chutes are used, it is recommended that they are properly designed and maintained so as to minimize dispersion of aerosols from contaminated laundry (e.g., no loose items in the chute and bags are closed before tossing into the chute).

If linen is sent off to a professional laundry, the facility should obtain an initial agreement between the laundry service and facility that stipulates the laundry will be hygienically clean and handled to prevent recontamination from dust and dirt during loading and transport.

Standard mattresses and pillows can become contaminated with body substances during resident care if the integrity of the covers of these items is compromised. A mattress cover is generally a fitted, protective material, the purpose of which is to prevent the mattress from becoming contaminated with body fluids and substances. A linen sheet placed on the mattress is not considered a mattress cover. Patches for tears and holes in mattress covers do not provide an impermeable surface over the mattress. Therefore it is recommended that mattress covers with tears or holes be replaced. It is recommended that moisture resistant mattress covers be cleansed and disinfected between residents with an EPA approved germicidal detergent to help prevent the spread of infections, and fabric mattress covers should be laundered between residents. Pillow covers and washable pillows should be laundered in a hot water laundry cycle between residents or when they become contaminated with body substances. Discarding mattresses if fluids have penetrated into the mattress fabric and washing pillows and pillow covers in a hot-water laundry cycle will also reduce the risk of indirect contact with infectious agents.[35]

RECOGNIZING AND CONTAINING OUTBREAKS

It is important that facilities know how to recognize and contain infectious outbreaks. An outbreak is typically one or more of the following:[36]

- One case of an infection that is highly communicable;

- Trends that are 10 percent higher than the historical rate of infection for the facility that may reflect an outbreak or seasonal variation and therefore warrant further investigation; or

- Occurrence of three or more cases of the same infection over a specified length of time on the same unit or other defined areas.

Once an outbreak has been identified, it is important that the facility take the appropriate steps to contain it. State health departments offer guidance and regulations regarding responding to and reporting outbreaks. This information is often received in advance of an outbreak and included in the infection prevention and control program. Plans for containing outbreaks usually include efforts to prevent further transmission of the infection while considering the needs of all residents and staff.[36]

PREVENTING SPREAD OF ILLNESS RELATED TO MDROs

The MDROs found in facilities include, but are not limited to MRSA, VRE, and clostridium difficile (C. difficile). Transmission-based precautions are employed for residents who are actively infected with multi-drug resistant organisms. Aggressive infection control measures and strict compliance by healthcare personnel can help minimize the spread of MDROs to other susceptible individuals.[37]

Staphylococcus is a common cause of infections in hospitals and nursing homes, and increasingly in the community. Common sites of MRSA colonization include the rectum, perineum, skin and nares.[38] Colonization may precede or endure beyond an acute infection. MRSA is transmitted person-to-person (most common), and on inanimate objects.

The MRSA infection is commonly treated with vancomycin, which in turn can lead to increased enterococcus antibiotic resistance. Therefore, preventing infection with MRSA and the limited use of antibiotics for individuals who are only colonized can also help prevent the development of VRE. Enterococcus is an organism that normally occurs in the colorectal tract. VRE infections have been associated with prior antibiotic use.

C. difficile is a bacterial species of the genus clostridium, which are gram-positive, anaerobic, spore-forming rods (bacilli). The organism normally lives benignly in the colon in spore form. When antibiotic use eradicates normal intestinal flora, the organism may become active and produce a toxin that causes symptoms such as diarrhea, abdominal pain, and fever. More severe cases can lead to additional complications such as intestinal damage and severe fluid loss. Treatment options include stopping antibiotics and starting specific anticlostridial antibiotics, e.g., metronidazole or oral vancomycin. If a resident has diarrhea due to C. difficile, large numbers of C. difficile organisms will be released from the intestine into the environment and may be transferred to other individuals, causing additional infections.

Contact precautions are instituted for residents with symptomatic C. difficile infection. Thorough hand washing with soap and water after caring for the resident reduces the risk of cross-transmission. Another control measure is to give the resident his or her own toilet facilities that will not be shared by other residents.

The C. difficile can survive in the environment (e.g., on floors, bed rails or around toilet seats) in its spore form for up to 6 months. Rigorously cleaning the environment removes C. difficile spores, and can help prevent transmission of the organism.[39] Cleaning equipment used for residents with C. difficile with a 1:10 dilution of sodium hypochlorite (nine parts water to one part bleach) will also reduce the spread of the organism. Once mixed, the solution is effective for 24 hours.

PREVENTING INFECTIONS RELATED TO THE USE OF SPECIFIC DEVICES

Intravascular catheters are used widely to provide vascular access, and are increasingly seen in nursing homes. While providing such access, they may increase the risk for local and systemic infections and additional complications such as septic thrombophlebitis.

Central venous catheters (CVCs) have also been associated with infectious complications. Other intravascular catheters such as dialysis catheters and implanted ports may be accessed multiple times per day, such as for hemodynamic measurements, or to obtain samples for laboratory analysis, thus increasing the risk of contamination and subsequent clinical infection. Limiting access to central venous catheters for only the primary purpose may help reduce the risk of infection.

Consistent use of appropriate infection control measures when caring for residents with vascular access catheters reduces the risk for catheter-related infections.[40] Surveillance consistently includes all residents with vascular access, including those with venous access and implanted ports such as peripherally inserted central catheter lines, and midline access catheters. Activities to reduce infection risk includes surveillance such as observation of insertion sites, routine dressing changes, use of appropriate PPE and hand hygiene during the care and treatment of residents with venous catheters, and review of the resident for clinical evidence of infection.[40] It is important that practices reflect the most current CDC guidelines.

[**Editor's Note:** See page 395 for endnotes pertaining to this section.]

INVESTIGATIVE PROTOCOL FOR INFECTION CONTROL

Objectives

- To determine if the facility has an infection prevention and control program that prevents, investigates, and controls infections in the facility, and determines appropriate procedures to be applied to a resident with an infection;

- To determine if the facility has a program that collects information regarding infections acquired in the facility, analyzes the information and develops a plan of action to prevent further infections;

- To determine if staff practices are consistent with current infection control principles and prevent cross-contamination (e.g., laundry and hand hygiene practices); and

- To determine whether staff with communicable disease or open lesions are prohibited, as appropriate, from direct contact with the resident.

Use

Use this protocol to investigate compliance at F441 for every initial certification and recertification survey. In addition, use this protocol on revisit or abbreviated surveys (complaint investigations) when indicated.

Procedures

The surveyor(s), throughout the survey, should conduct the following observations, interviews and record reviews. In addition, the surveyor(s) should also review the facility's infection control policies, procedures, as well as documentation of staff training, and as necessary, interview facility staff with responsibility for oversight of the infection prevention and control program.

1. Observations

Observe various disciplines (nursing, dietary, and housekeeping) to determine if they follow appropriate infection control practices and transmission based precaution procedures. Observe, for example, whether:

- Linens are handled, processed, transported, and stored to prevent contamination and the transmission of infection;

- Employees exhibit overt signs of illness or communicable disease that have the potential to transmit disease (e.g., cold symptoms, infected, open lesions on hands) and if present, whether they are prohibited from contact with the resident or the resident's food;

- Staff and visitors adhere to precautions and related processes, including the use of PPE;

- Precautions/accommodations are in place and followed (as recommended, e.g., gowns, singles rooms or adequate space between residents, exclusion from group activities, etc.) for residents with potentially transmissible infections;

- Staff utilize appropriate precautions when residents on special precautions are permitted out of their rooms,(e.g., mask on resident with TB in the halls, wound drainage contained); and

- Staff involved in the care and management of residents with special needs, e.g., urinary catheters (also note characteristics of urine, which may indicate potential infection), wound care, respiratory treatments, and residents on ventilators, receiving IVs, or with tracheotomies follow current accepted infection control standards of practice.

Also, observe residents for signs and symptoms of potential infection, such as:

- Elevated respiratory rate or labored breathing, coughing, congestion;

- Vomiting or loss of appetite, diarrhea;

- Skin rash, reddened or draining eyes, wound drainage; and

- Frequency/urgency of urination, malodorous urine.

Observe for cleaning and disinfecting to determine whether:

- Equipment in transmission based precaution rooms is either dedicated to that resident and appropriately cleaned or is thoroughly cleaned and disinfected between residents using appropriate agents and procedures;

- High touch surfaces in the environment are visibly soiled (i.e., contaminated) or have been cleaned and disinfected;

- Small non-disposable equipment such as glucose meters, scissors, and thermometers are cleaned and appropriately disinfected after each use for individual resident care;

- Single-use items (e.g., blood glucose lancet, other sharps) are properly disposed of after one use;

- Single resident use items (e.g., basins, bed pans) are maintained to be visibly clean for use, and are disposed of after use by a single resident;

- Resident dressings and supplies are properly stored to maintain their integrity, and soiled dressings and supplies are appropriately discarded; and

- Multiple use items (e.g., shower chairs, bedside scales, resident lifts, commodes, tubs) are properly cleaned/disinfected between each resident use.

Observe whether hand hygiene and use of gloves (when indicated) is in accordance with current standards. Hand hygiene should occur before and after putting on sterile gloves and after taking off all gloves during all resident care that requires the use of gloves. This includes:

- Medication administration (e.g., eye drops, sublinguals, and injections);

- Dressing changes that require the use of gloves (e.g., anticipated contact with body fluid, excretions, tissue and specimens);

- Insertion or removal of a catheter; and

- Any invasive procedure. Note the availability of gloves and the equipment and products to perform hand hygiene.

Note the availability of gloves and the equipment and products to perform hand hygiene.

Interview

During the resident review, interview the resident, family or responsible party to the extent possible to identify, as appropriate, whether they have received education and information about infection control practices, such as appropriate hand hygiene and any special precautions applicable to the resident.

Interview direct care staff to determine:

- Whether they are aware of and have reported any signs or symptoms exhibited by the resident that may be associated with an infection;

- Whether they are aware of and have been instructed on any special precautions that are applicable to any resident on transmission based precautions;

- Whether they are familiar with the indications for washing hands and/or using alcohol based products and understand the basis for the use of gloves and when they are to be removed;

- How staff know which residents are covered by transmission-based precautions; and

- Whether staff is aware of what specific actions are required for each type of transmission-based precautions.

Record Review

Review the resident's record to determine, for example:

- Whether the resident's record included an evaluation of the factors which may increase a resident's risk of infection (e.g., indwelling urinary catheters, intravenous catheters, and tracheostomy tubes), and if an infection is present, whether the resident's record reflects the identification of the infection, potential causes and contributing factors; and

- Whether the resident's plan of care identifies interventions (device management and isolation precaution measures) to prevent the transmission of infection.

Review the facility's record of incidents of infection and related corrective actions to help determine whether the facility is identifying, recording, and analyzing infections.

In order to investigate identified infection control concerns, review, as applicable, the facility's:

- Infection control policies to determine if they are consistent with current professional standards of practice and if the infection control policies are defined by department (e.g., dietary, nursing, laundry);

- Documentation of whether and how the infection prevention and control program collects, analyzes, and uses data and implements a program to guide all disciplines to prevent the spread of infections and identify infections in a standardized and systematic way;

- Policies regarding handling and processing soiled linens as well as handling, transporting, and storing clean linens;

- Applied preventive components of the infection prevention and control program in the care of individual residents;

- Policies, procedures, and documentation regarding identifying and prohibiting contact with residents or food by employees with open lesions or communicable diseases and addressing occupational communicable disease exposure and post-exposure follow up;

- Employee records to determine if employees receive initial and ongoing employee infection control training regarding critical elements of the infection control plan; and

- Documentation related to their review of the appropriateness and effectiveness of antibiotics for residents that are identified as receiving antibiotics.

Interview the Designated Infection Control Representative

If concerns are identified, (e.g., practices are not consistent with accepted principles of infection control or residents are exhibiting symptoms of infections, but have not been assessed or surveillance data are not available or being utilized) interview the facility staff members who are responsible for implementing and overseeing the infection prevention and control program. Investigate as appropriate, for example, whether:

- The facility identifies where infections are acquired (e.g., nursing home, hospital, or community);

- The infection prevention and control program includes any review, in addition to the medication regimen review, of whether antibiotic use in the nursing home is appropriate and effective;

- Staff training includes critical areas of infection control such as hand hygiene, areas for improvement from surveillance data, and appropriate use of protective equipment and isolation precautions; how staff are apprised of changes in policies and procedures;

- The facility collects, analyzes, and uses data related to infections, to identify and prevent the spread of infections and to adjust its infection prevention and control program,(e.g., policies and procedures) as appropriate;

- The program implements processes to identify and address infection control issues and to monitor staff hand hygiene and sterile technique, and the implementation and discontinuation of transmission-based or other isolation precautions and cohorting or separating, as applicable;

- The facility appropriately implements and discontinues transmission based precaution procedures, and communicates initiation and discontinuation of these transmission-based precaution policies across departments;

- The facility has in place effective means to identify individuals (residents, staff, visitors, volunteers, practitioners) with infections;

- The facility has policies and procedures addressing linen handling and how it monitors how linens are stored, transported, and processed to prevent the spread of infection;

- The infection prevention and control program identifies and addresses infection control issues, for example whether the facility's infection control practices are consistent with CDC recommendations; and

- The facility effectively identifies and prevents employees with a communicable disease or infected skin lesions from direct contact with residents or their food, if direct contact will transmit the disease.

DETERMINATION OF COMPLIANCE CRITERIA FOR COMPLIANCE

Synopsis of Regulation (F441)

Criteria for Compliance

The facility is in compliance with 42 CFR 483.65 Infection Control if:

- The infection prevention and control program demonstrates ongoing surveillance, recognition, investigation and control of infections to prevent the onset and the spread of infection, to the extent possible;

- The facility demonstrates practices to reduce the spread of infection and control outbreaks through transmission-based precautions (e.g., isolation precautions);

- The facility demonstrates practices and processes (e.g., intravenous catheter care, hand hygiene) consistent with infection prevention and prevention of cross-contamination;

- The facility demonstrates that it uses records of incidents to improve its infection control processes and outcomes by taking corrective action;

- The facility has processes and procedures to identify and prohibit employees with a communicable disease or infected skin lesions from direct contact with residents or their food, if direct contact will transmit the disease;

- The facility consistently demonstrates appropriate hand hygiene (e.g., hand washing) practices, after each direct resident contact as indicated by professional practice; and

- The facility demonstrates handling, storage, processing and transporting of linens so as to prevent the spread of infection.

If not, cite at Tag F441.

Noncompliance for F441

After completing the Investigative Protocol, analyze the data in order to determine whether noncompliance with the regulation exists. Noncompliance for Tag F441 may include, but is not limited to, failure to do one or more of the following:

- Develop an infection prevention and control program;

- Utilize infection precautions to minimize the transmission of infection;

- Identify and prohibit employees with a communicable disease from direct contact with a resident;

- Demonstrate proper hand hygiene;

- Properly dispose of soiled linens;

- Demonstrate the use of surveillance; or

- Adjust facility processes as needed to address a known infection risk.

Potential Tags for Additional Investigation

During the investigation of F441, the surveyor may have identified concerns with additional outcome, process, and/or structure requirements. The surveyor is cautioned to investigate these related requirements before determining whether non-compliance may be present. Examples of some related requirements that may be considered when non-compliance at F441 has been identified include the following:

- 42 CFR §483.20(b), F272, Comprehensive Assessments

    - If the infection or risks were present at the time of the required comprehensive assessment, determine whether the facility comprehensively assessed the resident's physical, mental, and psychosocial needs to identify the risks and/or to determine underlying causes (to the extent possible) of the resident's condition and the impact upon the resident's function, mood, and cognition.

- 42 CFR §483.20(b)*, F274, Significant Change Assessments *[**Editor's Note:** The regulation cited is incorrect. The correct regulation is §483.20(b)(2)(ii).]

    - If there was a significant change in the infection or risk to the resident's condition, determine whether the facility did a significant change comprehensive assessment within 14 days.

- 42 CFR §483.20(k)(1)(i), F279, Comprehensive Care Plan

    - Determine if the facility developed a care plan consistent with the resident's specific infection status, risks, needs, behaviors, and current standards of practice and included measurable objectives and timetables, and specific interventions/services to prevent the onset and/or transmission of infection.

- 42 CFR §483.20(k)(2)(iii), F280, Comprehensive Care Plan Revision

    - Determine whether staff reassessed the effectiveness of the interventions and review and revised the plan of care (with input from the resident or representative, to the extent possible), if necessary, to meet the needs of the resident.

- 42 CFR §483.25(l), F329, Unnecessary Drugs

    - Determine if the facility has reviewed with the prescriber the rationale for placing the resident on an antibiotic to which the organism seems to be resistant or when the resident remains on antibiotic therapy without adequate monitoring or appropriate indications, or for an excessive duration.

- 42 CFR §483.25(l)(2)(n)*, F334, Influenza and Pneumococcal Immunizations *[**Editor's Note:** The regulation cited is incorrect. The correct regulation is §483.25(n).]

    - Determine if the facility has systems in place to immunize residents against influenza and pneumococcal infections.

- 42 CFR §483.35(i)(2), F371, Sanitary Conditions

    - Determine if the facility has implemented processes to prevent infection transmission via food handling, storing and delivery systems.

- 42 CFR 483.75(f) (F498) Proficiency of Nurse Aides

    - Determine whether the nurse aides demonstrate the knowledge and skills regarding use of accepted infection control principles, e.g., hand hygiene, transmission barriers, signs and symptoms of infection to report to the nurse, etc.

V. DEFICIENCY CATEGORIZATION (PART IV, APPENDIX P)

Once the team has completed its investigation, analyzed the data, reviewed the regulatory requirements, and determined that noncompliance exists, the team must determine the severity of each deficiency, based on the resultant effect or potential for harm to the resident.

The key elements for severity determination for Tag F441 are as follows:

1. **Presence of harm/negative outcome(s) or potential for negative outcomes due to a failure of care and services.** Actual or potential harm/negative outcomes for F441 may include but are not limited to facility failure to:

   - Properly implement transmission based precautions when indicated resulting in an increase (or potential) of infections or communicable diseases;

   - Develop and implement corrective actions despite recording an increase in infections in the facility;

   - Recognize and act on an increase or trend in infections within the facility;

   - Prohibit employees with symptoms of active communicable infections from continuing to provide resident care or have direct contact with food;

   - Properly perform hand hygiene when entering and exiting the room of a resident on special precautions; and

   - Recognize and investigate a resident's complaints of rash and pruritis resulting in additional resident's requiring treatment for scabies.

2. **Degree of harm (actual or potential) related to the noncompliance.** Identify how the facility practices caused, resulted in, allowed, or contributed to the actual or potential for harm:

   - If harm has occurred, determine if the harm is at the level of serious injury, impairment, death, compromise, or discomfort; and

   - If harm has not yet occurred, determine how likely the potential is for serious injury, impairment, death, compromise or discomfort to occur to the resident.

3. **The immediacy of correction required.** Determine whether the noncompliance requires immediate correction in order to prevent serious injury, harm, impairment, or death to one or more residents.

The survey team must evaluate the harm or potential for harm based upon the following levels of severity for this tag. First, the team must rule out whether Severity Level 4, immediate jeopardy to a resident's health or safety exists by evaluating the deficient practice in relation to immediacy, culpability, and severity. (Follow the guidance in Appendix Q.)

Severity Level 4 Considerations: Immediate jeopardy to resident health or safety

Immediate jeopardy is a situation in which the facility's noncompliance:

   - With one or more requirements of participation has caused/resulted in, or is likely to cause, serious injury, harm, impairment, or death to a resident; and

   - Requires immediate correction as the facility either created the situation or allowed the situation to continue by failing to implement preventative or corrective measures.

     NOTE: The death or transfer of a resident who was harmed as a result of facility practices, does not remove a finding of immediate jeopardy. The facility is required to implement specific actions to correct the deficient practices which allowed or caused the immediate jeopardy.

Examples of negative outcomes that occurred or have the potential to occur at Severity Level 4 as a result of the facility's deficient practices may include:

- The facility failed to follow standard precautions during the performance of routine testing of blood sugars. The facility did not clean and disinfect the glucometers before or after use and/or did not use new glucometer lancets on residents who required blood sugar monitoring. This practice of not cleaning and disinfecting glucometers between every use and re-using glucometer lancets created an Immediate Jeopardy to resident health by potentially exposing residents to the spread of blood borne infections for multiple residents in the facility who required blood sugar testing.

- The facility failed to restrict a staff member with a documented open, draining and infected skin lesion that was colonized with MRSA from working without adequately covering the area, resulting in MSRA transmission and infection of one or more residents under that staff person's care.

- The facility failed to investigate, document surveillance of and try to contain an outbreak of gastrointestinal illness among residents; as a result, additional residents became ill with diarrheal illnesses.

   NOTE: If immediate jeopardy has been ruled out based upon the evidence, then evaluate whether actual harm that is not immediate jeopardy exists at Severity Level 3 or the potential for more than minimal harm at Level 2 exists.

Severity Level 3 Considerations: Actual Harm that is not Immediate Jeopardy

Level 3 indicates noncompliance that results in actual harm that is not immediate jeopardy. The negative outcome can include, but may not be limited to clinical compromise, decline, or the resident's inability to maintain and/or reach his/her highest practicable well-being.

Examples of avoidable actual resident outcomes that demonstrate severity at Level 3 may include, but are not limited to:

- The facility routinely sent urine cultures of asymptomatic residents with indwelling catheters, putting residents with positive cultures on antibiotics, resulting in two residents acquiring antibiotic-related colitis and significant weight loss.

- The facility failed to institute internal surveillance for adherence to hand washing procedures or pertinent reminders to staff regarding appropriate respiratory precautions during an influenza outbreak, resulting in additional cases of influenza in residents on another, previously unaffected unit or section of the facility.

   NOTE: If Severity Level 3 (actual harm that is not immediate jeopardy) has been ruled out based upon the evidence, then evaluate as to whether Severity Level 2 (no actual harm with the potential for more than minimal harm) exists.

Severity Level 2 Considerations: No Actual Harm with potential for more than minimal harm that is not Immediate Jeopardy

Level 2 indicates noncompliance that results in a resident outcome of no more than minimal discomfort and/or has the potential to compromise the resident's ability to maintain or reach his or her highest practicable level of well being. The potential exists for greater harm to occur if interventions are not provided.

For Level 2 severity, the resident was at risk for, or has experienced the presence of one or more outcome(s). Examples of avoidable outcomes include, but are not limited to:

- The facility failed to ensure that their staff demonstrates proper hand hygiene between residents to prevent the spread of infections. The staff administered medications to a resident via a gastric tube and while wearing the same gloves proceeded to administer oral medications to another resident. The staff did not remove the used gloves and wash or sanitize their hands between residents.

- The facility failed to implement a surveillance program including the investigation of infections or attempt to distinguish facility-acquired infections from community-acquired infections.

- The facility identified issues related to staff infection control practices, as part of its infection prevention and control program, but did not follow up to identify the cause, and institute measures to correct the problems.

Severity Level 1: No actual harm with potential for minimal harm

The failure of the facility to provide appropriate care and services for infection control practices places the resident at risk for more than minimal harm. Therefore, Severity Level 1 does not apply for this regulatory requirement.

[This page intentionally left blank]

F454 – F469

§483.70 — Physical Environment

F454

§483.70 Physical Environment

The facility must be designed, constructed, equipped, and maintained to protect the health and safety of residents, personnel and the public.

§483.70(a) Life Safety From Fire

§483.70(a)(1) Except as otherwise provided in this section –

§483.70(a)(1)(i) the facility must meet the applicable provisions of the 2000 edition of the Life Safety Code of the National Fire Protection Association. The Director of the Office of the Federal Register has approved the NFPA 101® 2000 edition of the Life Safety Code, issued January 14, 2000, for incorporation by reference in accordance with 5 U.S.C. 552(a) and 1 CFR Part 51. A copy of the Code is available for inspection at the CMS Information Resource Center, 7500 Security Boulevard, Baltimore, MD or at the National Archives and Records Administration (NARA). For information on the availability of this material at NARA, call 202-741-6030, or go to http://www.archives.gov/federal_register/code_of_federal_regulations/ibr_locations.html. Copies may be obtained from the National Fire Protection Association, 1 Batterymarch Park, Quincy, MA 02269. If any changes in this edition of the Code are incorporated by reference, CMS will publish notice in the *Federal Register* to announce the changes.

§483.70(a)(1)(ii) Chapter 19.3.6.3.2, exception number 2 of the adopted edition of the LSC does not apply to long-term care facilities.

§483.70(a)(2) After consideration of State survey agency findings, CMS may waive specific provisions of the Life Safety Code which, if rigidly applied, would result in unreasonable hardship upon the facility, but only if the waiver does not adversely affect the health and safety of the patients.

§483.70(a)(3) The provisions of the Life Safety Code do not apply in a State where CMS finds, in accordance with applicable provisions of sections 1819(d)(2)(B)(ii) and 1919(d)(2)(B)(ii) of the Act, that a fire and safety code imposed by State law adequately protects patients, residents and personnel in long term care facilities.

§483.70(a)(4) Beginning March 13, 2006, a long-term care facility must be in compliance with Chapter 19.2.9, Emergency Lighting.

§483.70(a)(5) Beginning March 13, 2006, Chapter 19.3.6.3.2, exception number 2 does not apply to long-term care facilities.

§483.70(a)(6) Notwithstanding any provisions of the 2000 edition of the Life Safety Code to the contrary, a long-term care facility may install alcohol-based hand rub dispensers in its facility if –

§483.70(a)(6)(i) Use of alcohol-based hand rub dispensers does not conflict with any State or local codes that prohibit or otherwise restrict the placement of alcohol-based hand rub dispensers in health care facilities;

§483.70(a)(6)(ii) The dispensers are installed in a manner that minimizes leaks and spills that could lead to falls;

[**Editor's Note:** §§483.70(a)(6)(iii) and (iv) were amended and §483.70(a)(6)(v) was added by *Federal Register*, Volume 71, Number 184, dated Friday, September 22, 2006. The changes are reflected in the text below.]

§483.70(a)(6)(iii) The dispensers are installed in a manner that adequately protects against inappropriate access;

§483.70(a)(6)(iv) The dispensers are installed in accordance with chapter 18.3.2.7 or chapter 19.3.2.7 of the 2000 edition of the Life Safety Code, as amended by NFPA Temporary Interim Amendment 00-1(101), issued by the Standards Council of the National Fire Protection Association on April 15, 2004. The Director of the Office of the Federal Register has approved NFPA temporary interim Amendment 00-1(101) for incorporation by reference in accordance with 5 U.S.C. 552(a) and 1 CFR part 51. A copy of the amendment is available for inspection at CMS Information Resource Center, 7500 Security Boulevard, Baltimore, MD and at the Office of the Federal Register, 800 North Capitol Street NW, Suite 700, Washington, DC. Copies may be obtained from the National Fire Protection Association, 1 Battery March Park, Quincy, MA 02269. If any additional changes are made to this amendment, CMS will publish notice in the Federal Register to announce the changes.

§483.70(a)(6)(v) The dispensers are maintained in accordance with dispenser manufacturer guidelines.

§483.70(a)(7) A long-term care facility must:

§483.70(a)(7)(i) Install, at least, battery-operated single station smoke alarms in accordance with the manufacturer's recommendations in resident sleeping rooms and common areas.

§483.70(a)(7)(ii) Have a program for inspection, testing, maintenance, and battery replacement that conforms to the manufacturer's recommendations and that verifies correct operation of the smoke alarms.

§483.70(a)(7)(iii) Exception:

§483.70(a)(7)(iii)(A) The facility has system-based smoke detectors in patient rooms and common areas that are installed, tested, and maintained in accordance with NFPA 72, *National Fire Alarm Code,* for system-based smoke detectors; or

§483.70(a)(7)(iii)(B) The facility is fully sprinklered in accordance with NFPA 13, *Standard for the Installation of Sprinkler Systems.*

[Editor's Note: §§483.70(a)(8)(i) and (ii) was added by *Federal Register*, Volume73, Number 157, dated Wednesday, August 13, 2008. The changes are reflected in the text below.]

§483.70(a)(8) A long term care facility must:

§483.70(a)(8)(i) Install an approved, supervised automatic sprinkler system in accordance with the 1999 edition of NFPA 13, *Standard for the Installation of Sprinkler Systems,* as incorporated by reference, throughout the building by August 13, 2013. The Director of the Office of the Federal Register has approved the NFPA 13 1999 edition of the *Standard for the Installation of Sprinkler Systems,* issued July 22, 1999 for incorporation by reference in accordance with 5 U.S.C. 552(a) and 1 CFR part 51. A copy of the Code is available for inspection at the CMS Information Resource Center, 7500 Security Boulevard, Baltimore, MD or at the National Archives and Records Administration (NARA). For information on the availability of this material at NARA, call 202–741–6030, or go to: http://www.archives.gov/federal_register/code_of_federal_regulations/ibr_locations.html. Copies may be obtained from the National Fire Protection Association, 1 Batterymarch Park, Quincy, MA 02269.

§483.70(a)(8)(ii) Test, inspect, and maintain an approved, supervised automatic sprinkler system in accordance with the 1998 edition of NFPA 25, *Standard for the Inspection, Testing, and Maintenance of Water-Based Fire Protection Systems,* as incorporated by reference. The Director of the Office of the Federal Register has approved the NFPA 25, *Standard for the Inspection, Testing, and Maintenance of Water- Based Fire Protection Systems,* 1998 edition, issued January 16, 1998 for incorporation by reference in accordance with 5 U.S.C. 552(a) and 1 CFR part 51. A copy of the Code is available for inspection at the CMS Information Resource Center, 7500 Security Boulevard, Baltimore, MD or at the National Archives and Records Administration (NARA). For information on the availability of this material at NARA, call 202–741–6030, or go to: http://www.archives.gov/federal_register/code_of_federal_regulations/ibr_locations.html. Copies may be obtained from the National Fire Protection Association, 1 Batterymarch Park, Quincy, MA 02269.

Interpretive Guidelines §483.70(a)

A waiver of specific provisions of the Life Safety Code is reviewed each time a facility is certified. The State fire authority will determine if the waiver continues to be justified, in that compliance with the requirement would result in an unreasonable hardship upon the facility and does not adversely affect the health and safety of residents or personnel. The State fire authority will forward its findings and recommendation as soon as possible to the State survey agency which will forward it to the CMS RO for a decision on granting a waiver.

Procedures §483.70(a)

The survey for safety from fire is normally conducted by the designated State fire authority. The State agency must establish a procedure for the State fire authority to notify them whether the facility is or is not in compliance with the requirement. If the survey team observes fire hazards or possible deficiencies in life safety from fire, they must notify the designated State fire authority or the RO.

F455

§483.70(b) Emergency Power

(1) An emergency electrical power system must supply power adequate at least for lighting all entrances and exits; equipment to maintain the fire detection, alarm, and extinguishing systems; and life support systems in the event the normal electrical supply is interrupted.

[This page intentionally left blank]

Interpretive Guidelines §483.70(b)(1)

"**Emergency electrical power system**" includes, at a minimum, battery-operated lighting for all entrances and exits, fire detection and alarm systems, and extinguishing systems.

An "**exit**" is defined as a means of egress which is lighted and has three components: an exit access (corridor leading to the exit), an exit (a door), and an exit discharge (door to the street or public way). We define an entrance as any door through which people enter the facility. Furthermore, when an entrance also serves as an exit, its components (exit access, exit, and exit discharge) must be lighted. A waiver of lighting required for both exits and entrances is not permitted.

Procedures §483.70(b)(1)

Review results of inspections by the designated State fire safety authority that the emergency power system has been tested periodically and is functioning in accordance with the Life Safety Code.

Check placement of lighting system to ensure proper coverage of the listed areas. Test all batteries to ensure they work.

Probes §483.70(b)(1)

Is emergency electrical service adequate?

Additional guidance is available in the National Fire Protection Association's Life Safety Code 99 and 101 (NFPA 99 and NFPA 101), 12-5.1.3 which is surveyed in Tags K105 and K106 of the Life Safety code survey.

§483.70(b)(2) When life support systems are used, the facility must provide emergency electrical power with an emergency generator (as defined in NFPA 99, Health Care Facilities) that is located on the premises.

Interpretive Guidelines §483.70(b)(2)

"**Life support systems**" is defined as one or more Electro-mechanical device(s) necessary to sustain life, without which the resident will have a likelihood of dying (e.g., ventilators suction machines if necessary to maintain an open airway). The determination of whether a piece of equipment is life support is a **medical determination** dependent upon the condition of the individual residents of the facility e.g. suction machine maybe required "life support equipment" in a facility, depending on the needs of its residents).

Procedures §483.70(b)(2)

If life support systems are used determine if there is a working emergency generator at the facility, A generator is not required if a facility does not use life support systems. Check that the emergency generator starts and transfers power under load conditions within 10 seconds after interruption of normal power. Where residents are on life support equipment, **do not test** transfer switches by shutting off the power unless there is an uninterruptible power supply available.

Probes §483.70(b)(2)

Is there a working generator if the facility is using life support systems?

---

§483.70(c) Space and Equipment

The facility must—

(1) Provide sufficient space and equipment in dining, health services, recreation, and program areas to enable staff to provide residents with needed services as required by these standards and as identified in each resident's plan of care; and

Intent §483.70(c)(1)

The intent of this regulation is to ensure that dining, health services, recreation, activities and programs areas are large enough to comfortably accommodate the needs of the residents who usually occupy this space.

Dining, health services, recreation, and program areas should be large enough to comfortably accommodate the persons who usually occupy that space, including the wheelchairs, walkers, and other ambulating aids used by the many residents who require more than standard movement spaces. "Sufficient space" means the resident can access the area, it is not functionally off-limits, and the resident's functioning is not restricted once access to the space is gained.

Program areas where resident groups engage in activities focused on manipulative skills and hand-eye coordination should have sufficient space for storage of their supplies and "works in progress."

Program areas where residents receive physical therapy should have sufficient space and equipment to meet the needs of the resident's therapy requirement.

Recreation/activities area means any area where residents can participate in those activities identified in their plan of care.

Procedures §483.70(c)(1)

In the use of space, consider if available space allows residents to pursue activities and receive health services and programs as identified in their care plan.

F456

§483.70(c)(2) Maintain all essential mechanical, electrical, and patient care equipment in safe operating condition.

Probes §483.70(c)(2)

Is essential equipment (e.g., boiler room equipment, nursing unit/medication room refrigerators, kitchen refrigerator/freezer and laundry equipment) in safe operating condition?

Is equipment maintained according to manufacturers recommendations.

---

§483.70(d) Resident Rooms

Resident rooms must be designed and equipped for adequate nursing care, comfort, and privacy of residents.

F457

§483.70(d)(1) Bedrooms must--

§483.70(d)(1)(i) Accommodate no more than four residents;
Interpretive Guidelines §483.70(d)(1)(i)

See §483.70(d)(3) regarding variations.

Probes §483.70(d)(1)(i)

Unless a variation has been applied for and approved under §483.70(d)(3), do the residents' bedrooms accommodate no more than four residents?

F458

§483.70(d)(1)(ii) Measure at least 80 square feet per resident in multiple resident bedrooms, and at least 100 square feet in single resident rooms;

Interpretive Guidelines §483.70(d)(1)(ii)

See §483.70(d)(3) regarding variations.

The measurement of the square footage should be based upon the useable living space of the room. Therefore, the minimum square footage in resident rooms should be measured based upon the floor's measurements exclusive of toilets and bath areas, closets, lockers, wardrobes, alcoves, or vestibules. However, if the height of the alcoves or vestibules reasonably provides useful living area, then the corresponding floor area may be included in the calculation.

The space occupied by movable wardrobes should be excluded from the useable square footage in a room unless it is an item of the resident's own choice and it is in addition to the individual closet space in the resident's room. Non-permanent items of the resident's own choice should have no effect in the calculation of useable living space.

Protrusions such as columns, radiators, ventilation systems for heating and/or cooling should be ignored in computing the useable square footage of the room if the area involved is minimal (e.g., a baseboard heating or air conditioning system or ductwork that does not protrude more than 6 to 8 inches from the wall, or a column that is not more than 6 to 8 inches on each side) and does not have an adverse effect on the resident's health and safety or does not impede the ability of any resident in that room to attain his or her highest practicable well-being. If these protrusions are not minimal they would be deducted from useable square footage computed in determining compliance with this requirement.

The swing or arc of any door which opens directly into the resident's room should not be excluded from the calculations of useable square footage in a room.

Procedures §483.70(d)(1)(ii)

The facility layout may give square footage measurements. Carry a tape measure and take measurements if the room appears small.

Probes §483.70(d)(1)(ii)

Unless a variation has been applied for and approved under §483.70(d)(3), are there at least 80 square feet per resident in multiple resident rooms and at least 100 square feet for single resident rooms?

F459

§483.70(d)(1)(iii) Have direct access to an exit corridor;

Interpretive Guidelines §483.70(d)(1)(iii)

There is no authority under current regulations to approve a variation to this requirement.
Additional guidance is available in the National Fire Protection Association's Life Safety Code 101 (NFPA 101), 12-2.5.1, which is Tag K41 of the Life Safety Code Survey.

F460

§483.70(d)(1)(iv) Be designed or equipped to assure full visual privacy for each resident;

Interpretive Guidelines §483.70(d)(1)(iv)

"**Full visual privacy**" means that residents have a means of completely withdrawing from public view while occupying their bed (e.g., curtain, moveable screens, private room).

The guidelines do not intend to limit the provisions of privacy to solely one or more curtains, movable screens or a private room. Facility operators are free to use other means to provide full visual privacy, with those means varying according to the needs and requests of residents. However, the requirement explicitly states that bedrooms must "be designed or equipped to assure full visual privacy for each resident." For example, a resident with a bed by the window cannot be required to remain out of his or her room while his/her roommate is having a dressing change. Room design or equipment must provide privacy. Surveyors will assess whether the means the facility is using to assure full visual privacy meets this requirement without negatively affecting any other resident rights.

Procedures §483.70(d)(1)(iv)

There are no provisions for physician statements to be used as a basis for variation of the requirements for full visual privacy.

Probes §483.70(d)(1)(iv)

Observe whether each resident selected for a comprehensive or focused review has a means to achieve full visual privacy.

§483.70(d)(1)(v) In facilities initially certified after March 31, 1992, except in private rooms, each bed must have ceiling suspended curtains, which extend around the bed to provide total visual privacy in combination with adjacent walls and curtains;

Interpretive Guidelines §483.70(d)(1)(v)

The term "**initially certified**" is defined as all newly certified nursing facilities (NFs) or SNFs as well as NFs and SNFs after March 31, 1992, which re-enter the Medicare or Medicaid programs, whether they voluntarily or involuntarily left the program.

It is not necessary for the bed to be accessible from both sides when the privacy curtain in pulled.

Additional guidance is available in the National Fire Protection Association's Life Safety Code 101 (NFPA 101), 31-1.4.1, 31-4.5, which is Tag K74 of the Life Safety Code Survey.

F461

(Rev. 48; Issued: 06-12-09; Effective/Implementation Date: 06-12-09)

§483.70(d)(1)(vi) Have at least one window to the outside; and

Interpretive Guidelines §483.70(d)(1)(vi)

A facility with resident room windows, as defined by Section 18.3.8 of the 2000 edition of the Life Safety Code, or that open to an atrium in accordance with Life Safety Code can meet this requirement for a window to the outside.

In addition to conforming with the Life Safety Code, this requirement was included to assist the resident's orientation to day and night, weather, and general awareness of space outside the facility. The facility is required to provide for a "safe, clean, comfortable and homelike environment" by deemphasizing the institutional character of the setting, to the extent possible. Windows are an important aspect in assuring the homelike environment of a facility. The allowable window sill height shall not exceed 36 inches. The window may be operable.

Probes §483.70(d)(1)(vi)

Is there at least one window to the outside?

§483.70(d)(1)(vii) Have a floor at or above grade level.

Interpretive Guidelines §483.70(d)(1)(vii)

"At or above grade level" means a room in which the room floor is at or above the surrounding exterior ground level.

Probes §483.70(d)(1)(vii)

Are the bedrooms at or above ground level?

---

§483.70(d)(2) The facility must provide each resident with--

(i)   A separate bed of proper size and height for the convenience of the resident;

(ii)   A clean, comfortable mattress;

(iii)   Bedding appropriate to the weather and climate; and

Probes: §483.70(d)(2)(i), (ii), and (iii)

Are mattresses clean and comfortable?

Is bedding appropriate to weather and climate?

§483.70(d)(2)(iv) Functional furniture appropriate to the resident's needs, and individual closet space in the resident's bedroom with clothes racks and shelves accessible to the resident.

§483.15(h)(4) Private closet space in each resident room, as specified in §483.70 (d)(2)(iv) of this part;

Interpretive Guidelines §483.70(d)(2)(iv) and §483.15(h)(4)

"Functional furniture appropriate to the residents' needs" means that the furniture in each resident's room contributes to the resident attaining or maintaining his or her highest practicable level of independence and well-being. In general, furnishings include a place to put clothing away in an organized manner that will let it remain clean, free of wrinkles, and accessible to the resident while protecting it from casual access by others; a place to put personal effects such as pictures and a bedside clock, and furniture suitable for the comfort of the resident and visitors (e.g., a chair).

For issues with arrangement of room furniture according to resident needs and preferences, see §483.15(e), Accommodation of Needs, Tag F246.

"Clothes racks and shelves accessible to the resident" means that residents can get to and reach their hanging clothing whenever they choose.

"Private closet space" means that each resident's clothing is kept separate from clothing of roommate(s).

The term "closet space" is not necessarily limited to a space installed into the wall. For some facilities without such installed closets, compliance may be attained through the use of storage furniture such as wardrobes. Out-of-season items may be stored in alternate locations outside the resident's room.

Probes §483.70(d)(2)(iv) and §483.15(h)(4)

Functional furniture: Is there functional furniture, appropriate to resident's needs?

Closet space: Is there individual closet space with accessible clothes racks and shelves? If the resident is able to use a closet, can the resident get to and reach her/his hanging clothing as well as items from shelves in the closet?

§483.70(d)(3) CMS, or in the case of a nursing facility the survey agency, may permit variations in requirements specified in paragraphs (d)(1)(i) and (ii) of this section relating to rooms in individual cases when the facility demonstrates in writing that the variations—

(i) Are in accordance with the special needs of the residents; and

(ii) Will not adversely affect residents' health and safety.

Interpretive Guidelines §483.70(d)(3)

A variation must be in accordance with the special needs of the residents and must not adversely affect the health or safety of residents. Facility hardship is not part of the basis for granting a variation. Since the special needs of residents may change periodically, or different residents may be transferred into a room that has been granted a variation, variations must be reviewed and considered for renewal whenever the facility is certified. If the needs of the residents within the room have not changed since the last annual inspection, the variance should continue if the facility so desires.

Interpretive Guidelines §483.70(d)(1)(i)

As residents are transferred or discharged from rooms with more than four residents, beds should be removed from the variance until the number of residents occupying the room does not exceed four.

F462

§483.70(e) Toilet Facilities

Each resident room must be equipped with or located near toilet facilities.

Interpretive Guidelines §483.70(e)

"Toilet facilities" is defined as a space that contains a lavatory and a toilet. If the resident's room is not equipped with an adjoining toilet facility, then "located near" means residents who are independent in the use of a toilet, including chairbound residents, can routinely use a toilet in the unit.

Probes §483.70(e)

Are resident rooms equipped with or located near toilet and bathing facilities?

F463

(Rev. 48; Issued: 06-12-09; Effective/Implementation Date: 06-12-09)

§483.70(f) Resident Call System

The nurses' station must be equipped to receive resident calls through a communication system from--

(1) Resident rooms; and

(2) Toilet and bathing facilities.

Intent §483.70(f)

The intent of this requirement is that residents, when in their rooms and toilet and bathing areas, have a means of directly contacting caregivers. In the case of an existing centralized nursing station, this communication may be through audible or visual signals and may include "wireless systems." In those cases in which a facility has moved to decentralized nurse/care team work areas, the intent may be met through other electronic systems that provide direct communication from the resident to the caregivers.

Interpretive Guidelines §483.70(f)

This requirement is met only if all portions of the system are functioning (e.g., system is not turned off at the nurses' station, the volume too low to be heard, the light above a room or rooms is not working), and calls are being answered. For wireless systems, compliance is met only if staff who answer resident calls, have functioning devices in their possession, and are answering resident calls.

Probes §483.70(f)

Is there a functioning communication system from rooms, toilets, and bathing facilities in which resident calls are received and answered by staff?

F464

§483.70(g) Dining and Resident Activities

The facility must provide one or more rooms designated for resident dining and activities.

These rooms must--

§483.70(g)(1) Be well lighted;

Interpretive Guidelines §483.70(g)(1)

"**Well lighted**" is defined as levels of illumination that are suitable to tasks performed by a resident.

Probes §483.70(g)(1)

Are there adequate and comfortable lighting levels?

Are illumination levels appropriate to tasks with little glare?

Does lighting support maintenance of independent functioning and task performance?

§483.70(g)(2) Be well ventilated, with nonsmoking areas identified;

Interpretive Guidelines §483.70(g)(2)

"**Well ventilated**" is defined as good air circulation, avoidance of drafts at floor level, and adequate smoke exhaust removal.

"**Nonsmoking areas identified**" is defined as signs posted in accordance with State law regulating indoor smoking policy and facility policy.

Probes §483.70(g)(2)

How well is the space ventilated?

Is there good air movement?

Are temperature, humidity, and odor levels all accepted?

Are non-smoking areas identified?

§483.70(g)(3) Be adequately furnished; and

Interpretive Guidelines §483.70(g)(3)

An "**adequately furnished**" dining area accommodates different residents' physical and social needs. An adequately furnished organized activities area accommodates the specific activities offered by the facility.

Probes §483.70(g)(3)

How adequate are furnishings?

Are furnishings structurally sound and functional (e.g., chairs of varying sizes to meet varying needs of residents, wheelchairs can fit under the dining room table)?

§483.70(g)(4) Have sufficient space to accommodate all activities.

Interpretive Guidelines §483.70(g)(4)

"**Sufficient space to accommodate all activities**" means that the space available is adaptable to a variety of uses and residents' needs.

Probes §483.70(g)(4)

How sufficient is space in dining, health services, recreation and program areas to accommodate all activities?

Are spaces adaptable for all intended uses?

Is resident access to space limited?

Do residents and staff have maximum flexibility in arranging furniture to accommodate residents who use walkers, wheelchairs, and other mobility aids?

Is there resident crowding?

F465

§483.70(h) Other Environmental Conditions

The facility must provide a safe, functional, sanitary, and comfortable environment for residents, staff and the public.

F466

The facility must--

§483.70(h)(1) Establish procedures to ensure that water is available to essential areas when there is a loss of normal water supply;

Interpretive Guidelines §483.70(h)(1)

The facility should have a written protocol which defines the source of water provisions for storing the water, both potable and non-potable, a method for distributing water, and a method for estimating the volume of water required.

Procedures §483.70(h)(1)

During the entrance conference, ask the administrator the facility's procedure to ensure water availability.

F467

§483.70(h)(2) Have adequate outside ventilation by means of windows, or mechanical ventilation, or a combination of the two;

Probes §483.70(h)(2)

How well is the space ventilated?

Is there good air movement?

Are temperature, humidity, and odor levels all acceptable?

F468

§483.70(h)(3) Equip corridors with firmly secured handrails on each side; and

Interpretive Guidelines §483.70(h)(3)

"**Secured handrails**" means handrails that are firmly affixed to the wall.

Probes §483.70(h)(3)

Are handrails secure?

F469

§483.70(h)(4) Maintain an effective pest control program so that the facility is free of pests and rodents.

Interpretive Guidelines §483.70(h)(4)

An **"effective pest control progra**m" is defined as measures to eradicate and contain common household pests (e.g., roaches, ants, mosquitoes, flies, mice, and rats).

Procedures §483.70(h)(4)

As part of the overall review of the facility, look for signs of vermin. Evidence of pest infestation in a particular space is an indicator of noncompliance.

Probes §483.70(h)(4)

Is area pest free?

F490 – F522

§483.75 — Administration

F490

§483.75 Administration

A facility must be administered in a manner that enables it to use its resources effectively and efficiently to attain or maintain the highest practicable physical, mental, and psychosocial well-being of each resident.

Procedures §483.75

If there is a deficiency in §483.13, Resident behavior and facility practices; §483.15, Quality of life; or §483.25, Quality of care, which has the scope and/or severity to be defined as substandard quality of care, fully review for compliance all the tags within this section (§483.75).

F491

§483.75(a) Licensure

A facility must be licensed under applicable State and local law.

Interpretive Guidelines §483.75(a)

Applicable licenses, permits, and approvals must be available to you for inspection upon request.

Procedures §483.75(a)

If there are problems with care provided or supervised by licensed personnel, verify applicable licenses, permits and approvals.

F492

§483.75(b) Compliance With Federal, State, and Local Laws and Professional Standards

The facility must operate and provide services in compliance with all applicable Federal, State, and local laws, regulations, and codes, and with accepted professional standards and principles that apply to professionals providing services in such a facility.

Intent §483.75(b)

The intent of this regulation is to ensure that a facility is in compliance with Federal, State, and local laws, regulations, and codes relating to health, safety, and sanitation.

Interpretive Guidelines §483.75(b)

The State is responsible for making decisions about whether there are violations of State laws and regulations. Licenses, permits and approvals of the facility must be available to you upon request. Current reports of inspections by State and/or local health authorities are on file, and notations are made of action taken by the facility to correct deficiencies.

§483.75(c) Relationship to Other HHS Regulations

In addition to compliance with the regulations set forth in this subpart, facilities are obliged to meet the applicable provisions of other HHS regulations, including but not limited to those pertaining to nondiscrimination on the basis of race, color, or national origin (45 CFR part 80); nondiscrimination on the basis of handicap (45 CFR part 84); nondiscrimination on the basis of age (45 CFR part 91); protection of human subjects of research (45 CFR part 46); and fraud and abuse (42 CFR part 455). Although these regulations are not in themselves considered requirements under this part, their violation may result in the termination or suspension of, or the refusal to grant or continue payment with Federal funds.

Procedures §483.75(b)

If resident/family interviews reveal possible problems with admission contracts, review these contracts for violations of requirements at §§483.10 and 483.12. As appropriate, refer problems to an ombudsman or other agencies, e.g., Office for Civil Rights.

Some State or local laws are more stringent than the Federal requirement on the same issue. Failure of the facility to meet a Federal, State or local law may be cited at this tag only when the authority having jurisdiction has **both** made a determination of noncompliance and has taken a final adverse action as a result.

Accepted professional standards and principles include the various practice acts and scope of practice regulations in each State, and current, commonly accepted health standards established by national organizations, boards and councils.

If interviews with residents suggest that the facility may have required deposits from Medicare residents at admission, review the facility's admissions documents.

Procedures §483.75(c)

If during the survey you identify problems relating to one or more of these requirements, which are under the purview of another Federal agency, forward the information to the RO, who will forward it to the appropriate Federal agency.

F493

§483.75(d) Governing Body

(1) The facility must have a governing body, or designated persons functioning as a governing body, that is legally responsible for establishing and implementing policies regarding the management and operation of the facility; and

(2) The governing body appoints the administrator who is--

   (i) Licensed by the State where licensing is required; and

   (ii) Responsible for the management of the facility.

Interpretive Guidelines §483.75(d)(2)(1) [**Editor's Note**: The regulation number cited should be §483.75(d)(2)(i).]

The administrator must be licensed where required by the State.

§483.75(e) Required Training of Nursing Aides

(Rev. 26; Issued: 08-17-07; Effective/Implementation Dates: 08-17-07)

(1) Definitions

"Licensed health professional" means a physician; physician assistant; nurse practitioner; physical, speech, or occupational therapist; physical or occupational therapy assistant; registered professional nurse; licensed practical nurse; or licensed or certified social worker.

"Nurse aide" means any individual providing nursing or nursing-related services to residents in a facility who is not a licensed health professional, a registered dietitian, or someone who volunteers to provide such services without pay. Nurse aides do not include those individuals who furnish services to residents only as paid feeding assistants as defined in §488.301 of this chapter. [**Editor's Note**: §483.75(e)(1) was amended by *Federal Register*, Volume 68, number 187, dated Friday, September 26, 2003. The changes are reflected in the text above.]

Nurse aides do not include those individuals who furnish services to residents only as paid feeding assistants as defined in §488.301 of this chapter.

Interpretive Guidelines §483.75(e)

Volunteers are not nurse aides and do not come under the nurse aide training provisions of these requirements. Unpaid students in nursing education programs who use facilities as clinical practice sites under the direct supervision of an RN are considered volunteers.

Private duty nurse aides who are not employed or utilized by the facility on a contract, per diem, leased or other basis, do not come under the nurse aide training provisions.

F494

§483.75(e)(2) General rule

A facility must not use any individual working in the facility as a nurse aide for more than 4 months, on a full-time basis, unless:

(i) That individual is competent to provide nursing and nursing related services; and

(ii)(A) That individual has completed a training and competency evaluation program, or a competency evaluation program approved by the State as meeting the requirements of §§483.151-483.154 of this part; or

(B) That individual has been deemed or determined competent as provided in §483.150(a) and (b).

§483.75(e)(3) Non-permanent employees

A facility must not use on a temporary, per diem, leased, or any basis other than a permanent employee any individual who does not meet the requirements in paragraphs (e)(2)(i) and (ii) of this section.

See Tag F495 for guidelines, probes, and procedures for §483.75(e)(2-4).

F495

(4) Competency

A facility must not use any individual who has worked less than 4 months as a nurse aide in that facility unless the individual--

(i) Is a full-time employee in a State-approved training and competency evaluation program;

(ii) Has demonstrated competence through satisfactory participation in a State-approved nurse aide training and competency evaluation program or competency evaluation program; or

(iii) Has been deemed or determined competent as provided in §483.150(a) and (b).

Interpretive Guidelines §483.75(e)(2 - 4)

Facilities may use, as nurse aides, any individuals who have successfully completed either a nurse aide training and competency evaluation program or a competency evaluation program. However, if an individual has not completed a program at the time of employment, a facility may **only** use that individual as a nurse aide if the individual is in a nurse aide training and competency evaluation program (**not a competency evaluation program alone**) and that individual is a permanent employee in his or her first four months of employment in the facility.

Facilities may not use non-permanent employees as nurse aides unless they have either completed a training and competency evaluation program, or a competency evaluation program.

Probes §483.75(e)(2 - 4)

During an extended or partial extended survey:

- Have all nurse aides completed a nurse aide training and competency evaluation program or a competency evaluation program? If not, are those nurse aides permanent employees enrolled in a training and competency evaluation program who have worked in the facility for 4 months or less?

- Ask nurse aides where they received their training, how long the training was and how long they have worked in the facility as a nurse aide.

During all surveys:

- If incorrect nurse aide work performance is observed during the survey, check to see if the nurse aide received training and licensed nurse supervision to correctly carry out the task.

A "**permanent employee**" is defined as any employee you expect to continue working on an ongoing basis.

Procedures §483.75(e)(2-4)

Review competency requirements for nurse aides if you identify potential deficient care practices in quality of care, resident rights, resident behavior and facility practice or quality of life which may be related to nurse aide competency. Is there evidence that the nurse aide has successfully completed the competency evaluation program, or has the individual been grandfathered in by the State?

If you identify deficient care practices by nurse aides who do not have evidence of having successfully completed a competency evaluation program, determine:

- If the aide is currently receiving training an a State approved Nurse Aide Training Program;

- If the aide is under the supervision of a licensed nurse; and

- If the aide has been trained and determined to be proficient for the tasks to which he or she is assigned. See §483.152 for specific training that the aide is to receive. This training includes:

- At least 16 hours of training in the following subjects **before** any direct contact with the resident:

   o   Communication and interpersonal skills;

   o   Infection control;

   o   Safety and emergency procedures, including the Heimlich Maneuver;

   o   Promoting resident's independence; and

   o   Respecting resident's rights.

- Basic nursing skills;

- Personal care skills;

- Mental health and social services of residents;

- Care of cognitively impaired residents;

- Basic restorative services; and

- Resident's rights.

F496

§483.75(e)(5) Registry verification

Before allowing an individual to serve as a nurse aide, a facility must receive registry verification that the individual has met competency evaluation requirements unless--

(i) The individual is a full-time employee in a training and competency evaluation program approved by the State; or

(ii)The individual can prove that he or she has recently successfully completed a training and competency evaluation program or competency evaluation program approved by the State and has not yet been included in the registry. Facilities must follow up to ensure that such an individual actually becomes registered.

§483.75(e)(6) Multi-State registry verification

Before allowing an individual to serve as a nurse aide, a facility must seek information from every State registry established under sections 1819(e)(2)(A) or 1919(e)(2)(A) of the Act the facility believes will include information on the individual.

§483.75(e)(7) Required retraining

If, since an individual's most recent completion of a training and competency evaluation program, there has been a continuous period of 24 consecutive months during none of which the individual provided nursing or nursing-related services for monetary compensation, the individual must complete a new training and competency evaluation program or a new competency evaluation program.

Interpretive Guidelines §483.75(e)(7)

If an individual does not wish to be retrained, the individual must establish that he or she performed nursing or nursing-related services for monetary compensation for at least one documented day (i.e., 8 consecutive hours) during the previous 24 months. The State is required to remove the individual's name from the registry if the services are not provided for monetary compensation during the 24-month period. Thus, in the absence of any evidence to the contrary, you can assume that the retraining requirement does not apply to an individual whose name appears on the registry.

F497

§483.75(e)(8) Regular In-Service Education

The facility must complete a performance review of every nurse aide at least once every 12 months, and must provide regular in-service education based on the outcome of these reviews. The in-service training must--

    (i) Be sufficient to ensure the continuing competence of nurse aides, but must be no less than 12 hours per year;

    (ii) Address areas of weakness as determined in nurse aides' performance reviews and may address the special needs of residents as determined by the facility staff; and

    (iii) For nurse aides providing services to individuals with cognitive impairments, also address the care of the cognitively impaired.

Interpretive Guidelines §483.75(e)(8)

The adequacy of the in-service education program is measured not only by documentation of hours of completed in-service education, but also by demonstrated competencies of nurse aide staff in consistently applying the interventions necessary to meet residents' needs.

If there has been deficient care practices identified during Phase 1 of the survey, review as appropriate training received by nurse aides in that corresponding subject area. For example, if the facility has deficiencies in infection control, review the infection control unit in the facility's inservice nurse aide training program.

Each nurse aide must have no less than twelve hours of in-service education per year. Calculate the date by which a nurse aide must receive annual in-service education by the employment date rather than the calendar year.

Probes §483.75(e)(8)

During an extended or partial extended survey, or during any survey in which nurse aide performance is questioned. (See §483.75(f).)

- Does the facility review the performance of its nurse aides?

- How has in-service education addressed areas of weakness identified in performance reviews, special resident needs, and needs of residents with cognitive impairments?

- How has in-service education addressed quality of care problems including those of special care needs and resident rights?

F498

§483.75(f) Proficiency of Nurse Aides

The facility must ensure that nurse aides are able to demonstrate competency in skills and techniques necessary to care for residents' needs, as identified through resident assessments, and described in the plan of care.

Interpretive Guidelines §483.75(f)

"Competency in skills and techniques necessary to care for residents' needs" includes competencies in areas such as communication and personal skills, basic nursing skills, personal care skills, mental health and social service needs, basic restorative services and resident rights.

Procedures §483.75(f)

During the Resident Review, observe nurse aides.

Probes §483.75(f)

Do nurse aides show competency in skills necessary to:

- Maintain or improve the resident's independent functioning, e.g.:

  o Performing range of motion exercises,

  o Assisting the resident to transfer from the bed to a wheelchair,

  o Reinforcing appropriate developmental behavior for persons with MR, or

  o Psychotherapeutic behavior for persons with MI;

- Observe and describe resident behavior and status and report to charge nurse;

- Follow instructions; and

- Carry out appropriate infection control precautions and safety procedures.

F499

§483.75(g) Staff Qualifications

(1) The facility must employ on a full-time, part-time or consultant basis those professionals necessary to carry out the provisions of these requirements.

(2) Professional staff must be licensed, certified, or registered in accordance with applicable State laws.

Procedures §483.75(g)

If there is reason to doubt the qualifications of temporary agency personnel working in the facility, check with the appropriate registry or professional licensing board.

F500

§483.75(h) Use of Outside Resources

(1) If the facility does not employ a qualified professional person to furnish a specific service to be provided by the facility, the facility must have that service furnished to residents by a person or agency outside the facility under an arrangement described in section 1861(w) of the Act or an agreement described in paragraph (h)(2) of this section.

(2) Arrangements as described in section 1861(w) of the Act or agreements pertaining to services furnished by outside resources must specify in writing that the facility assumes responsibility for--

(i) Obtaining services that meet professional standards and principles that apply to professionals providing services in such a facility; and

(ii) The timeliness of the services.

F501

§483.75(i) Medical Director

(1) The facility must designate a physician to serve as medical director.

(2) The medical director is responsible for--

(i) Implementation of resident care policies; and

(ii) The coordination of medical care in the facility.

INTENT:

The intent of this requirement is that:

- The facility has a licensed physician who serves as the medical director to coordinate medical care in the facility and provide clinical guidance and oversight regarding the implementation of resident care policies;

- The medical director collaborates with the facility leadership, staff, and other practitioners and consultants to help develop, implement and evaluate resident care policies and procedures that reflect current standards of practice; and

- The medical director helps the facility identify, evaluate, and address/resolve medical and clinical concerns and issues that:

  o   Affect resident care, medical care or quality of life; or

  o   Are related to the provision of services by physicians and other licensed health care practitioners.

NOTE: While many medical directors also serve as attending physicians, the roles and functions of a medical director are separate from those of an attending physician. The medical director's role involves the coordination of facility-wide medical care while the attending physician's role involves primary responsibility for the medical care of individual residents.[1]

DEFINITIONS

Definitions are provided to clarify terms related to the provision of medical director services.

o   "Attending Physician" refers to the physician who has the primary responsibility for the medical care of a resident.

o   "Current standards of practice" refers to approaches to care, procedures, techniques, treatments, etc., that are based on research and/or expert consensus and that are contained in current manuals, textbooks, or publications, or that are accepted, adopted or promulgated by recognized professional organizations or national accrediting bodies.

o   "Medical care" refers to the practice of medicine as consistent with State laws and regulations.

o   "Medical director" refers to a physician who oversees the medical care and other designated care and services in a health care organization or facility. Under these regulations, the medical director is responsible for coordinating medical care and helping to develop, implement and evaluate resident care policies and procedures that reflect current standards of practice.

o   "Resident care policies and procedures" – Resident care policies are the facility's overall goals, directives, and governing Statements that direct the delivery of care and services to residents. Resident care procedures describe the processes by which the facility provides care to residents that is consistent with current standards of practice and facility policies.

OVERVIEW

The medical director has an important leadership role in actively helping long term care facilities provide quality care. The regulation requires each facility to have a medical director who is responsible for the implementation of resident care policies and the coordination of medical care. These two roles provide the basis for the functions and tasks discussed in this guidance. The medical director's roles and functions require the physician serving in that capacity to be knowledgeable about current standards of practice in caring for long term care residents, and about how to coordinate and oversee related practitioners. As a clinician, the medical director plays a pivotal role in providing clinical leadership regarding application of current standards of practice for resident care and new or proposed treatments, practices, and approaches to care. The medical director's input promotes the attainment of optimal resident outcomes which may also be influenced by many other factors, such as resident characteristics and preferences, individual attending physician actions, and facility support. The 2001 Institute of Medicine report, "Improving the Quality of Long Term Care," urged facilities to give medical directors greater authority for medical services and care. The report states, "nursing homes should develop structures and processes that enable and require a more focused and dedicated medical staff responsible for patient care."[2]

The medical director is in a position, because of his/her roles and functions, to provide input to surveyors on physician issues, individual resident's clinical issues, and the facility's clinical practices. The text "Medical Direction in Long Term-Care"[3] asserts that:

"The Medical Director has an important role in helping the facility deal with regulatory and survey issues...the medical director can help ensure that appropriate systems exist to facilitate good medical care, establish and apply good monitoring systems and effective documentation and follow up of findings, and help improve physician compliance with regulations, including required visits. During and after the survey process, the medical director can clarify for the surveyors clinical questions or information about the care of specific residents, request surveyor clarification of citations on clinical care, attend the exit conference to demonstrate physician interest and help in understanding the nature and scope of the facility's deficiencies, and help the facility draft corrective actions."

Nationally accepted statements concerning the roles, responsibilities and functions of a medical director can be found at the American Medical Directors Association website at www.amda.com.

> **NOTE:** References to non-CMS sources or sites on the Internet are provided as a service and do not constitute or imply endorsement of these organizations or their programs by CMS or the U.S. Department of Health and Human Services. CMS is not responsible for the content of pages found at these sites. URL addresses were current as of the date of this publication.

MEDICAL DIRECTION

The facility is responsible for designating a medical director, who is currently licensed as a physician in the State(s) in which the facility(ies) he/she serves is (are) located. The facility may provide for this service through any of several methods, such as direct employment, contractual arrangements, or another type of agreement. Whatever the arrangement or method employed, the facility and the medical director should identify the expectations for how the medical director will work with the facility to effectively implement resident care policies and coordinate medical care.

> **NOTE:** While the roles of medical directors who work for multi-facility organizations with corporate or regional offices may vary for policy development, the medical directors, nonetheless, should be involved in facility level issues such as application of those policies to the care of the facility's residents.

Implementation of Resident Care Policies and Procedures

The facility is responsible for obtaining the medical director's ongoing guidance in the development and implementation of resident care policies, including review and revision of existing policies. The medical director's role involves collaborating with the facility regarding the policies and protocols that guide clinical decision making (for example, interpretation of clinical information, treatment selection, and monitoring of risks and benefits of interventions) by any of the following: facility staff; licensed physicians; nurse practitioners; physician assistants; clinical nurse specialists; licensed, certified, or registered health care professionals such as nurses, therapists, dieticians, pharmacists, social workers, and other health care workers.

The medical director has a key role in helping the facility to incorporate current standards of practice into resident care policies and procedures/guidelines to help assure that they address the needs of the residents. Although regulations do not require the medical director to sign the policies or procedures, the facility should be able to show that its development, review, and approval of resident care policies included the medical director's input.

This requirement does not imply that the medical director must carry out the policies and procedures or supervise staff performance directly, but rather must guide, approve, and help oversee the implementation of the policies and procedures. Examples of resident care policies include, but are not limited to:

- Admission policies and care practices that address the types of residents that may be admitted and retained based upon the ability of the facility to provide the services and care to meet their needs;

- The integrated delivery of care and services, such as medical, nursing, pharmacy, social, rehabilitative and dietary services, which includes clinical assessments, analysis of assessment findings, care planning including preventive care, care plan monitoring and modification, infection control (including isolation or special care), transfers to other settings, and discharge planning;

- The use and availability of ancillary services such as x-ray and laboratory;

- The availability, qualifications, and clinical functions of staff necessary to meet resident care needs;

- Resident formulation and facility implementation of advance directives (in accordance with State law) and end-of-life care;

- Provisions that enhance resident decision making, including choice regarding medical care options;

- Mechanisms for communicating and resolving issues related to medical care;

- Conduct of research, if allowed, within the facility;

- Provision of physician services, including (but not limited to):

  o Availability of physician services 24 hours a day in case of emergency;

  o Review of the resident's overall condition and program of care at each visit, including medications and treatments;

  o Documentation of progress notes with signatures;

  o Frequency of visits, as required;

  o Signing and dating all orders, such as medications, admission orders, and re-admission orders; and

  o Review of and response to consultant recommendations.

- Systems to ensure that other licensed practitioners (e.g., nurse practitioners) who may perform physician-delegated tasks act within the regulatory requirements and within the scope of practice as defined by State law; and

- Procedures and general clinical guidance for facility staff regarding when to contact a practitioner, including information that should be gathered prior to contacting the practitioner regarding a clinical issue/question or change in condition.

Coordination of Medical Care

The medical director is responsible for the coordination of medical care in the facility. The coordination of medical care means that the medical director helps the facility obtain and maintain timely and appropriate medical care that supports the healthcare needs of the residents, is consistent with current standards of practice, and helps the facility meet its regulatory requirements. In light of the extensive medical needs of the long term care population, physicians have an important role both in providing direct care and in influencing care quality. The medical director helps coordinate and evaluate the medical care within the facility by reviewing and evaluating aspects of physician care and practitioner services, and helping the facility identify, evaluate, and address health care issues related to the quality of care and quality of life of residents. "A medical director should establish a framework for physician participation, and physicians should believe that they are accountable for their actions and their care."[4]

The medical director addresses issues related to the coordination of medical care identified through the facility's quality assessment and assurance committee and quality assurance program, and other activities related to the coordination of care. This includes, but is not limited to, helping the facility:

- Ensure that residents have primary attending and backup physician coverage;

- Ensure that physician and health care practitioner services are available to help residents attain and maintain their highest practicable level of functioning, consistent with regulatory requirements;

- Develop a process to review basic physician and health care practitioner credentials (e.g., licensure and pertinent background);

- Address and resolve concerns and issues between the physicians, health care practitioners and facility staff; and

- Resolve issues related to continuity of care and transfer of medical information between the facility and other care settings.

Throughout this guidance, a response from a physician implies appropriate communication, review, and resident management, but does not imply that the physician must necessarily order tests or treatments recommended or requested by the staff, unless the physician agrees that those are medically valid and indicated.

In addition, other areas for medical director input to the facility may include:

- Facilitating feedback to physicians and other health care practitioners about their performance and practices;

- Reviewing individual resident cases as requested or as indicated;

- Reviewing consultant recommendations;

- Discussing and intervening (as appropriate) with a health care practitioner about medical care that is inconsistent with applicable current standards of care;

- Assuring that a system exists to monitor the performance of the health care practitioners;

- Guiding physicians regarding specific performance expectations;

- Identifying facility or practitioner educational and informational needs;

- Providing information to the facility practitioners from sources such as nationally recognized medical care societies and organizations where current clinical information can be obtained; and

- Helping educate and provide information to staff, practitioners, residents, families and others.

NOTE: This does not imply that the medical director must personally present educational programs.

[**Editor's Note:** See page 391 for endnotes pertaining to this section.]

Investigative Protocol

Medical Director

Objective

- To determine whether the facility has designated a licensed physician to serve as medical director; and

- To determine whether the medical director, in collaboration with the facility, coordinates medical care and the implementation of resident care policies.

Use

Use this protocol for all initial and extended surveys or, as indicated, during any other type of survey. Use this protocol if the survey team has identified:

- That the facility does not have a licensed physician serving as medical director; and/or

- That the facility has designated a licensed physician to serve as medical director; however, concerns or noncompliance identified indicate that:

  o The facility has failed to involve the medical director in his/her roles and functions related to coordination of medical care and/or the implementation of resident care policies; and/or

  o The medical director may not have performed his/her roles and functions related to coordination of medical care and/or the implementation of resident care policies.

Procedures

The investigation involves interviews, review of pertinent policies and procedures, and may involve additional review of resident care.

Provision of a Medical Director

Determine whether the medical director is available during the survey to respond to surveyor questions about resident care policies, medical care, and physician issues.

Interview the facility leadership (e.g., Administrator, Director of Nursing [DON], others as appropriate) about how it has identified and reviewed with the medical director his/her roles and functions as a medical director, including those related to coordination of medical care and the facility's clinical practices and care.

Interview the medical director about his/her understanding and performance of the medical director roles and functions, and about the extent of facility support for performing his/her roles and functions.

If the survey team has identified that the facility lacks a medical director, collect information from the facility administrator to:

- Determine the duration and possible reasons for this problem; and

- Identify what the facility has been doing to try to retain a medical director.

Facility/Medical Director Responsibility for Resident Care Policies

After identifying actual or potential noncompliance with the provision of resident care or medical care:

- Review related policies/procedures;

- Interview facility leadership (e.g., Administrator, DON) to determine how or if they involved the medical director in developing, reviewing, and implementing policies and procedures regarding clinical care of residents (especially where these involve medical and clinical issues; for example, management of causes of delirium, falling, and weight loss) to ensure that they are clinically valid and consistent with current standards of care;

- Interview the medical director regarding his/her input into:

  o Scope of services the facility has chosen to provide;

  o The facility's capacity to care for its residents with complex or special care needs, such as dialysis, hospice or end-of-life care, respiratory support with ventilators, intravenous medications/fluids, dementia and/or related conditions, or problematic behaviors or complex mood disorders;

  o The following areas of concern:

    – Appropriateness of care as it relates to clinical services (for example, following orders correctly, communicating important information to physicians in a timely fashion, etc.);

    – Processes for accurate assessment, care planning, treatment implementation, and monitoring of care and services to meet resident needs; and

    – The review and update of policies and procedures to reflect current standards of practice for resident care (e.g., pressure ulcer prevention and treatment and management of: incontinence, pain, fall risk, restraint reduction, and hydration risks) and quality of life.

Coordination of Medical Care/Physician Leadership

If the survey team has identified issues or concerns related to the provision of medical care:

- Interview appropriate facility staff and management as well as the medical director to determine what happens when a physician (or other healthcare practitioner) has a pattern of inadequate or inappropriate performance or acts contrary to established rules and procedures of the facility; for example, repeatedly late in making visits, fails to take time to discuss resident problems with staff, does not adequately address or document key medical issues when making resident visits, etc;

- If concerns are identified for any of the following physician services, determine how the facility obtained the medical director's input in evaluating and coordinating the provision of medical care:

  o Assuring that provisions are in place for physician services 24 hours a day and in case of emergency (§483.40(b));

  o Assuring that physicians visit residents, provide medical orders, and review a resident's medical condition as required (§483.40(b)&(c));

  o Assuring that other practitioners who may perform physician delegated tasks, act within the regulatory requirements and within their scope of practice as defined by State law (§483.40(e)&(f));

  o Clarifying that staff know when to contact the medical director; for example, if an attending or covering physician fails to respond to a facility's request to evaluate or discuss a resident with an acute change of condition;

o   Clarifying how the medical director is expected to respond when informed that the staff is having difficulty obtaining needed consultations or other medical services; or

o   Addressing other concerns between the attending physician and the facility, such as issues identified on medication regimen review, or the problematic use of restraints.

In addition, determine how the facility and medical director assure that physicians are informed of expectations and facility policies, and how the medical director reviews the medical care and provides guidance and feedback regarding practitioner performance, as necessary.

Regardless of whether the medical director is the physician member of the quality assurance committee, determine how the facility and medical director exchange information regarding the quality of resident care, medical care, and how the facility disseminates information from the committee to the medical director and attending physicians regarding clinical aspects of care and quality such as infection control, medication and pharmacy issues, incidents and accidents, and other emergency medical issues (§483.75(o)).

DETERMINATION OF COMPLIANCE (Task 6, Appendix P)

Synopsis of Regulation (F501)

This requirement has 3 aspects: Having a physician to serve as medical director, implementing resident care policies, and coordinating medical care. As with all other long term care requirements, the citation of a deficiency at F501, Medical Director, is a deficiency regarding the facility's failure to comply with this regulation. The facility is responsible for designating a physician to serve as medical director and is responsible for oversight of, and collaboration with, the medical director to implement resident care policies and to coordinate medical care.

Criteria for Compliance

The facility is in compliance if:

* They have designated a medical director who is a licensed physician;

* The physician is performing the functions of the position;

* The medical director provides input and helps the facility develop, review and implement resident care policies, based on current clinical standards; and

* The medical director assists the facility in the coordination of medical care and services in the facility.

If not, cite F501.

Noncompliance for F501

After completing the Investigative Protocol, analyze the data in order to determine whether or not noncompliance with the regulation exists. The survey team must identify whether the noncompliance cited at other tags relates to the medical director's roles and responsibilities. In order to cite at F501 when noncompliance has been identified at another tag, the team must demonstrate an association between the identified deficiency and a failure of medical direction. Noncompliance for F501 may include (but is not limited to) the **facility** failure to:

* Designate a licensed physician to serve as medical director; or

* Obtain the medical director's input for timely and ongoing development, review and approval of resident care policies;

Noncompliance for F501 may also include (but is not limited to) the **facility** and **medical director** failure to:

- Coordinate and evaluate the medical care within the facility, including the review and evaluation of aspects of physician care and practitioner services;

- Identify, evaluate, and address health care issues related to the quality of care and quality of life of residents;

- Assure that residents have primary attending and backup physician coverage;

- Assure that physician and health care practitioner services reflect current standards of care and are consistent with regulatory requirements;

- Address and resolve concerns and issues between the physicians, health care practitioners and facility staff;

- Resolve issues related to continuity of care and transfer of medical information between the facility and other care settings;

- Review individual resident cases, as warranted, to evaluate quality of care or quality of life concerns or other problematic situations and take appropriate steps to resolve the situation as necessary and as requested;

- Review, consider and/or act upon consultant recommendations that affect the facility's resident care policies and procedures or the care of an individual resident, when appropriate;

- Discuss and intervene (as appropriate) with the health care practitioner about medical care that is inconsistent with applicable current standards of care; or

- Assure that a system exists to monitor the performance and practices of the health care practitioners.

This does not presume that a facility's noncompliance with the requirements for the delivery of care necessarily reflects on the performance of the medical director.

V. DEFICIENCY CATEGORIZATION (*Part V, Appendix P) *[Editor's Note: The part number cited is incorrect. The correct part number is IV.]

Once the survey team has completed its investigation, analyzed the data, reviewed the regulatory requirements, and determined that noncompliance exists, the team must determine the severity of each deficiency, based on the resultant effect or potential for harm to the resident.

The key elements for severity determination for F501 are as follows:

1. **Vi. Presence of harm/negative outcome(s) or potential for negative outcomes because of lack of resident care policies and/or medical care.**

Deficient practices related to actual or potential harm/negative outcome for F501 may include but are not limited to:

- Lack of medical director involvement in the development, review and/or implementation of resident care policies that address the types of residents receiving care and services, such as a resident with end-stage renal disease, pressure ulcers, dementia, or that address practices such as restraint use;

- Lack of medical director involvement in coordinating medical care regarding problems with physician coverage or availability; or

- Lack of medical director response when the facility requests intervention with an attending physician regarding medical care of a resident.

2. **Degree of harm (actual or potential) related to the noncompliance.**

Identify how the facility practices caused, resulted in, allowed or contributed to the actual or potential for harm:

- If harm has occurred, determine if the harm is at the level of serious injury, impairment, death, compromise, or discomfort; and

- If harm has not yet occurred, determine the potential for serious injury, impairment, death, compromise, or discomfort to occur to the resident.

3. **The immediacy of correction required.**

Determine whether the noncompliance requires immediate correction in order to prevent serious injury, harm, impairment, or death to one or more residents.

The survey team must evaluate the harm or potential for harm based upon the following levels of severity for F501. First, the team must rule out whether Severity Level 4, Immediate Jeopardy, to a resident's health or safety exists by evaluating the deficient practice in relation to immediacy, culpability, and severity. (Follow the guidance in Appendix Q.)

Severity Level 4 Considerations: Immediate Jeopardy to Resident Health or Safety

Immediate Jeopardy is a situation in which the facility's noncompliance with one or more requirements of participation:

- Has allowed/caused/resulted in, or is likely to allow/cause /result in serious injury, harm, impairment, or death to a resident; and

- Requires immediate correction, as the facility either created the situation or allowed the situation to continue by failing to implement preventative or corrective measures.

NOTE: The death or transfer of a resident who was harmed or injured as a result of facility noncompliance does not remove a finding of immediate jeopardy. The facility is required to implement specific actions to correct the noncompliance which allowed or caused the immediate jeopardy.

In order to cite immediate jeopardy at this tag, the surveyor must be able to identify the relationship between noncompliance cited as immediate jeopardy at other regulatory tags and the failure of the medical care and systems associated with the roles and responsibilities of the medical director. **In order to select severity level 4 at F501, both of the following must be present:**

1. Findings of noncompliance at Severity Level 4 at another tag:

- Must have allowed, caused or resulted in, or is likely to allow, cause or result in serious injury, harm, impairment or death and require immediate correction. The findings of noncompliance associated with immediate jeopardy are written at tags that also show evidence of process failures with respect to the medical director's responsibilities; and

2. There is no medical director or the facility failed to involve the medical director in resident care policies or resident care or medical care as appropriate or the medical director had knowledge of a problem with care, or physician services, or lack of resident care policies and practices that meet current standards of practice and failed:

- To get involved or to intercede with the attending physician in order to facilitate and/or coordinate medical care; and/or

- To provide guidance and/or oversight for relevant resident care policies.

NOTE: If immediate jeopardy has been ruled out based upon the evidence, then evaluate whether actual harm that is not immediate jeopardy exists at Severity Level 3.

Severity Level 3 Considerations: Actual Harm that is not Immediate Jeopardy

Level 3 indicates noncompliance that results in actual harm, and may include, but is not limited to, clinical compromise, decline, or the resident's inability to maintain and/or reach his/her highest practicable well-being.

In order to cite actual harm at this tag, the surveyor must be able to identify a relationship between noncompliance cited at other regulatory tags and failure of medical care or processes and practices associated with roles and responsibilities of the medical director, such as:

1. Findings of noncompliance at Severity Level 3 at another tag must have caused actual harm:

    *   The findings of noncompliance associated with actual harm are written at tags that show evidence of process failures with respect to the medical director's responsibilities; and

2. There is no medical director or the facility failed to involve the medical director in resident care policies or resident care or medical care as appropriate or the medical director had knowledge of a problem with care, or physician services, or lack of resident care policies and practices that meet current standards of practice and failed:

    *   To get involved or intercede with the attending physician in order to facilitate and/or coordinate medical care (medical care and systems associated with roles and responsibilities of the medical director show evidence of breakdown); or

    *   To provide guidance and/or oversight for resident care policies.

NOTE: If Severity Level 3 (actual harm that is not immediate jeopardy) has been ruled out based upon the evidence, then evaluate as to whether Level 2 (no actual harm with the potential for more than minimal harm) exists.

Severity Level 2 Considerations: No Actual Harm with Potential for More than Minimal Harm that is not Immediate Jeopardy

In order to cite no actual harm with potential for more than minimal harm at this tag, the surveyor must be able to identify a relationship between noncompliance cited at other regulatory tags and the failure of medical care, processes and practices associated with roles and responsibilities of the medical director, such as:

1. Findings of noncompliance at Severity Level 2 at another tag:

    *   Must have caused no actual harm with potential for more than minimal harm (Level 2). Level 2 indicates noncompliance that results in a resident outcome of no more than minimal discomfort and/or has the potential to compromise the resident's ability to maintain or reach his or her highest practicable level of well being. The potential exists for greater harm to occur if interventions are not provided; and

2. There is no medical director or the facility failed to involve the medical director in resident care policies or resident care as appropriate or the medical director had knowledge of an issue with care or physician services, and failed:

    *   To get involved with or intercede with attending physicians in order to facilitate and/or coordinate medical care; or

    *   To provide guidance and/or oversight for resident care policies.

Severity Level 1 Considerations: No Actual Harm with Potential for Minimal Harm

In order to cite no actual harm with potential for minimal harm at this tag, the survey team must have identified that:

- There is no medical director; and

    - There are no negative resident outcomes that are the result of deficient practice; and

        - Medical care and systems associated with roles and responsibilities of the medical director are in place; and

        - There has been a relatively short duration of time without a medical director; and

        - The facility is actively seeking a new medical director.

F502

§483.75(j) Laboratory Services

(1) The facility must provide or obtain laboratory services to meet the needs of its residents. The facility is responsible for the quality and timeliness of the services.

Intent §483.75(j)(1)

The intent of this regulation is to assure that laboratory services are accurate and timely so that the utility of laboratory testing for diagnosis, treatment, prevention or assessment is maximized. The facility is responsible for quality and timely laboratory services whether or not services are provided by the facility or an outside agency.

Interpretive Guidelines §483.75(j)(1)

A "**laboratory service or test**" is defined as any examination or analysis of materials derived from the human body for purposes of providing information for the diagnosis, prevention, or treatment of any disease or impairment of, or the assessment of the health of human beings.

Services provided must be both accurate and timely. Timely means that laboratory tests are completed and results are provided to the facility (or resident's physician) within timeframes normal for appropriate intervention. All laboratories providing services for facility residents must meet applicable requirements of 42 CFR Part 493. The purpose of this requirement is to assist in assuring quality of laboratory services.

Procedures §483.75(j)(1)

Verify that laboratory services are provided to meet the needs of the residents. If a problem in quality of care leads you to suspect a problem in laboratory services, timeliness or quality, refer to the interpretive guidelines for laboratory testing found in Appendix C.

Probes §483.75(j)(1)

Are problems attributable to:

- An inability to order laboratory tests in a timely manner, including delays in transporting the resident to and from the source of service, if needed?

- A delay of treatment due to untimely receipt of lab results?

- A large lag time between an order for a test and the recording of the results that may have resulted in poor care?

F503

§483.75(j)(1)(i) **If the facility provides its own laboratory services, the services must meet the applicable requirements for laboratories specified in part 493 of this chapter.**

§483.75(j)(1)(ii) **If the facility provides blood bank and transfusion services, it must meet the applicable requirements for laboratories specified in Part 493 of this chapter.**

§483.75(j)(1)(iii) **If the laboratory chooses to refer specimens for testing to another laboratory, the referral laboratory must be certified in the appropriate specialties and subspecialties of services in accordance with the requirements of part 493 of this chapter.**

§483.75(j)(1)(iv) **If the facility does not provide laboratory services on site, it must have an agreement to obtain these services from a laboratory that meets the applicable requirements of part 493 of this chapter.**

Intent §483.75(j)(1)(i) - (iv)

The intent of this regulation is to assure that laboratory services, blood bank and transfusion services are obtained from an entity that meets the requirements of 42 CFR Part 493 in order to provide a standard of quality for laboratory and transfusion services. If the long term care facility does not provide laboratory services on site, there must be an agreement to obtain these services from a laboratory that meets the same requirements.

Interpretive Guidelines §483.75(j)(1)(i) - (iv)

If a facility provides its own laboratory services, the provisions of 42 CFR Part 493 apply.

The facility must have a Clinical Laboratory Improvement Amendments (CLIA) certificate appropriate for the level of testing performed. An application for a certificate of waiver may be made if the facility performs only those tests categorized as waived under CLIA.

Direct questions concerning the application of these requirements to your State laboratory consultant or the CMS RO.

Procedures §483.75(j)(1)(i) - (iv)

Determine if all laboratory services provided for the facility are provided by a laboratory that meets the requirements of 42 CFR Part 493.

The surveyor should determine if the facility has an arrangement in writing to assume responsibility for (a) obtaining services that meet professional standards and principles that apply to professionals providing services in such a facility; and (b) the timeliness of the services.

Probes §483.75(j)(1)(i) - (iv)

Are problems attributable to:

- Lack of an arrangement to provide or obtain clinical laboratory services from a source that meets the applicable conditions for coverage of the services?

- Delays in interpreting the results of laboratory tests?

F504

§483.75(j)(2) The facility must--

§483.75(j)(2)(i) Provide or obtain laboratory services only when ordered by the attending physician;

Intent §483.75(j)(2)(i)

The intent of this regulation is to assure that only medically necessary laboratory services are ordered.

Procedures §483.75(j)(2)(i)

Verify that all laboratory services received were ordered by the attending physician.

F505

§483.75(j)(2)(ii) Promptly notify the attending physician of the findings;

Intent §483.75(j)(2)(ii)

The intent of this regulation is to assure that the physician is notified of all lab results so that prompt, appropriate action may be taken if indicated for the resident's care.

Procedures §483.75(j)(2)(ii)

If you have reason to believe that a physician(s) may not have been notified of laboratory results in a timely manner, determine if the facility has a policy/procedure for routine notification of physician and if the procedure is implemented.

Probes §483.75(j)(2)(ii)

- Are any problems identified as relating to lack of prompt notification of the attending physician, contributing to delays in changing the course of treatment or care plan?

F506

§483.75(j)(2)(iii) Assist the resident in making transportation arrangements to and from the source of service, if the resident needs assistance; and

Intent §483.75(j)(2)(iii)

The intent of this regulation is to assure that residents are able to get to and receive necessary laboratory testing when the testing is conducted outside of the facility.

Probes §483.75(j)(2)(iii)

- Does the resident ever have to cancel lab service appointments due to difficulties with transportation?

F507

§483.75(j)(2)(iv) File in the resident's clinical record laboratory reports that are dated and contain the name and address of the testing laboratory.

Intent §483.75(j)(2)(iv)

The intent of this regulation is to assure that the laboratory performing the tests is Medicare approved, and that test results are accurate and are available for clinical management.

F508

§483.75(k) Radiology and Other Diagnostic Services

    (1) The facility must provide or obtain radiology and other diagnostic services to meet the needs of its residents. The facility is responsible for the quality and timeliness of the services.

Intent §483.75(k)(1)

The intent of this regulation is to assure that the resident receives quality radiologic and diagnostic services in a timely manner to meet his/her needs for diagnosis, treatment, and prevention.

Probes §483.75(k)(1)

If problems are identified in radiology or other diagnostic services, are problems attributable to:

- An inability to order radiological and diagnostic services in a timely manner, including delays in transporting the resident for these services?

- Delays in interpreting the results of x-rays and other tests?

- Lack of prompt notification, in writing, of test results to the attending physician, contributing to delays in changing care plans or the course of treatment?

F509

§483.75(k)(1)(i) If the facility provides its own diagnostic services, the services must meet the applicable conditions of participation for hospitals contained in §482.26 of this subchapter.

§483.75(k)(1)(ii) If the facility does not provide it's own diagnostic services, it must have an agreement to obtain these services from a provider or supplier that is approved to provide these services under Medicare.

F510

§483.75(k)(2) The Facility must--

    (i) Provide or obtain radiology and other diagnostic services only when ordered by the attending physician;

F511

§483.75(k)(2)(ii) Promptly notify the attending physician of the findings;

F512

§483.75(k)(2)(iii) Assist the resident in making transportation arrangements to and from the source of service, if the resident needs assistance; and

F513

§483.75(k)(2)(iv) File in the resident's clinical record signed and dated reports of x-ray and other diagnostic services.

F514

§483.75(l) Clinical Records

(1) The facility must maintain clinical records on each resident in accordance with accepted professional standards and practices that are--

(i) Complete;

(ii) Accurately documented;

(iii) Readily accessible; and

(iv) Systematically organized

Intent §483.75(l)(1)

To assure that the facility maintains accurate, complete and organized clinical information about each resident that is readily accessible for resident care.

Interpretive Guidelines §483.75(l)(1)

A complete clinical record contains an accurate and functional representation of the actual experience of the individual in the facility. It must contain enough information to show that the facility knows the status of the individual, has adequate plans of care, and provides sufficient evidence of the effects of the care provided. Documentation should provide a picture of the resident's progress, including response to treatment, change in condition, and changes in treatment.

The facility determines how frequently documentation of an individual's progress takes place apart from the annual comprehensive assessment, periodic reassessments when a significant change in status occurs, and quarterly monitoring assessments. Good practice indicates that for functional and behavioral objectives, the clinical record should document change toward achieving care plan goals. Thus, while there is no "right" frequency or format for "reporting" progress, there is a unique reporting schedule to chart each resident's progress in maintaining or improving functional abilities and mental and psychosocial status. Be more concerned with whether the staff has sufficient progress information to work with the resident and less with how often that information is gathered.

In cases in which facilities have created the option for an individual's record to be maintained by computer, rather than hard copy, electronic signatures are acceptable. In cases when such attestation is done on computer records, safeguards to prevent unauthorized access, and reconstruction of information must be in place. The following guideline is an example of how such a system may be set up:

- There is a written policy, at the health care facility, describing the attestation policy(ies) in force at the facility.

- The computer has built-in safeguards to minimize the possibility of fraud.

- Each person responsible for an attestation has an individualized identifier.

- The date and time is recorded from the computer's internal clock at the time of entry

- An entry is not to be changed after it has been recorded.

- The computer program controls what sections/areas any individual can access or enter data, based on the individual's personal identifier (and, therefore his/her level of professional qualifications).

Procedures §483.75(l)(1)

In reviewing sampled residents' clinical records:

- Is there enough record documentation for staff to conduct care programs and to revise the program, as necessary, to respond to the changing status of the resident as a result of interventions?

- How is the clinical record used in managing the resident's progress in maintaining or improving functional abilities and mental and psychosocial status?

§483.75(l)(5) the clinical record must contain--

(i) Sufficient information to identify the resident;

(ii) A record of the resident's assessments;

(iii) the plan of care and services provided;

(iv)The results of any preadmission screening conducted by the State; and

(v) progress notes.

F515

§483.75(l)(2) Clinical records must be retained for--

(i) The period of time required by State law; or

(ii) Five years from the date of discharge when there is no requirement in State law; or,

(iii) For a minor, three years after a resident reaches legal age under State law.

F516

§483.20(f)(5)

(5) Resident-identifiable information.

(i) A facility may not release information that is resident-identifiable to the public.

(ii) The facility may release information that is resident-identifiable to an agent only in accordance with a contract under which the agent agrees not to use or disclose the information except to the extent the facility itself is permitted to do so.

Interpretive Guidelines §483.20(f)(5)

Automated RAI data are part of a resident's clinical record and as such are protected from improper disclosure by facilities under current law. Facilities are required by §§1819(c)(1)(A)(iv) and 1919(c)(1)(A)(iv) of the Act and 42 CFR Part 483.75(l)(3) and (l)(4), to keep confidential all information contained in the resident's record and to maintain safeguards against the unauthorized use of a resident's clinical record information, regardless of the storage method of the records.

§483.75(l)(3) The facility must safeguard clinical record information against loss, destruction, or unauthorized use;

Intent §483.75(l)(3)

To maintain the safety and confidentiality of the resident's record.

Procedures §483.75(l)(3)

Determine through observations and interviews with staff, the policy and implementation of that policy, for maintaining confidentiality of residents' records.

Probes §483.75(1)(3)

- How does the facility ensure confidentiality of resident records/

- If there is a problem with confidentiality, is it systematic, that is, does the problem lie in the recordkeeping system, or with a staff person's use of records, e.g., leaving records in a place easily accessible to residents, visitors, or other unauthorized persons?

[**Editor's Note:** §483.75(l)(4) was moved by CMS in Transmittal 5, dated November 19, 2004. See Tag F164.]

[**Editor's Note:** §483.75(l)(5) was moved by CMS in Transmittal 5, dated November 19, 2004. See Tag F514.]

§483.75(m) Disaster and Emergency Preparedness

F517

§483.75(m)(1) The facility must have detailed written plans and procedures to meet all potential emergencies and disasters, such as fire, severe weather, and missing residents.

F518

§483.75(m)(2) The facilities must train all employees in emergency procedures when they begin to work in the facility, periodically review the procedures with existing staff, and carry out unannounced staff drills using those procedures.

Interpretive Guidelines §483.75(m)

The facility should tailor its disaster plan to its geographic location and the types of residents it serves. "Periodic review" is a judgment made by the facility based on its unique circumstances changes in physical plant or changes external to the facility can cause a review of the disaster review plan

The purpose of a "staff drill" is to test the efficiency, knowledge, and response of institutional personnel in the event of an emergency. Unannounced staff drills are directed at the responsiveness of staff, and care should be taken not to disturb or excite residents.

Procedures §483.75(m)

Review and disaster and emergence preparedness plan, including plans for natural or man made disasters.

Probes §483.75(m)

Ask two staff persons separately (e.g., nurse aide, housekeeper, maintenance person) and the charge nurse:

- If the fire alarm goes off, what do you do?

- If you discover that a resident missing, what do you do?

- What would you do if you discovered a fire in a resident's room?

- Where are fire alarms and fire extinguisher(s) located on this unit?

- How do you use the fire extinguisher?

NOTE: Also, construct probes relevant to a geographically specific natural emergencies (e.g., for areas prone to hurricanes, tornadoes, earthquakes, or floods, each of which may require a different response).

Are the answers to these questions correct (staff answers predict competency in assuring resident safety)?

F519

§483.75(n) Transfer Agreement

(1) In accordance with section 1861(1) of the Act, the facility (other than a nursing facility which is located in a State on an Indian reservation) must have in effect a written transfer agreement with one or more hospitals approved for participation under the Medicare and Medicaid programs that reasonably assures that—

(i) Residents will be transferred from the facility to the hospital, and ensured of timely admission to the hospital when transfer is medically appropriate, as determined by the attending physician; and

(ii) Medical and other information needed for care and treatment of residents, and , when the transferring facility deems it appropriate, for determining whether such residents can be adequately cared for in a less expensive setting than either the facility or the hospital, will be exchanged between the institutions

(2) The facility is considered to have a transfer agreement in effect if the facility has attempted in good faith to enter into an agreement with a hospital sufficiently close to the facility to make transfer feasible.

F520

(Rev. 19, Issued: 06-01-06, Effective/Implementation: 06-01-06)

483.75(o) Quality Assessment and Assurance

(1) A facility must maintain a quality assessment and assurance committee consisting of –

    (i)   The director of nursing services;

    (ii)   A physician designated by the facility; and

    (iii)   At least 3 other members of the facility's staff.

(2) The quality assessment and assurance committee –

    (i)   Meets at least quarterly to identify issues with respect to which quality assessment and assurance activities are necessary; and

    (ii)   Develops and implements appropriate plans of action to correct identified quality deficiencies.

(3) State or the Secretary may not require disclosure of the records of such committee except insofar as such disclosure is related to the compliance of such committee with the requirements of this section.

(4) Good faith attempts by the committee to identify and correct quality deficiencies will not be used as a basis for sanctions.

Intent: 483.75(o) Quality Assurance and Assessment

The intent of this requirement is that:

- The facility has an ongoing quality assessment and assurance (QAA) committee that includes designated key members and that meets at least quarterly; and

- The committee identifies quality deficiencies and develops and implements plans of action to correct these quality deficiencies, including monitoring the effect of implemented changes and making needed revisions to the action plans.

DEFINITIONS

Definitions are provided to clarify terms related to the requirement for a quality assessment and assurance committee.

- "Quality Assessment" is an evaluation of a process and/or outcomes of a process to determine if a defined standard of quality is being achieved.

- "Quality Assurance" is the organizational structure, processes, and procedures designed to ensure that care practices are consistently applied and the facility meets or exceeds an expected standard of quality. Quality assurance includes the implementation of principles of continuous quality improvement.

- "Quality Deficiencies" are potential markers of quality that the facility considers to be in need of investigating and which, after investigation, may or may not represent a deviation from quality that results in a potential or actual undesirable outcome. The term "quality deficiency" in this regulation is meant to describe a deficit or an area for improvement. This term is not synonymous with a deficiency cited by surveyors.

- "Quality Improvement (QI)" is an ongoing interdisciplinary process that is designed to improve the delivery of services and resident outcomes.

NOTE: Many facilities have changed their terminology for the QAA processes to "quality improvement (QI)." However, in these guidelines, we will continue to use the designation of QAA, as specified in the requirement. The elements are comparable regardless of the terminology.

OVERVIEW

QAA is a management process that is ongoing, multi-level, and facility-wide. It encompasses all managerial, administrative, clinical, and environmental services, as well as the performance of outside (contracted or arranged) providers and suppliers of care and services. Its purpose is continuous evaluation of facility systems with the objectives of:

- Keeping systems functioning satisfactorily and consistently including maintaining current practice standards;

- Preventing deviation from care processes from arising, to the extent possible;

- Discerning issues and concerns, if any, with facility systems and determining if issues/concerns are identified; and

- Correcting inappropriate care processes.

Several studies conducted under the auspices of the U.S. Department of Health and Human Services have examined quality of care and quality of life in nursing homes.[1,2] These studies have concluded that QAA committees provide an important point of accountability for ensuring both quality of care and quality of life in nursing homes. The QAA committees represent key internal mechanisms that allow nursing homes opportunities to deal with quality deficiencies in a confidential manner.

Resources are available that recommend processes and standards to develop and enhance quality improvement programs. Some Web site resources include:

- American Medical Directors Association (www.amda.com);

- American Health Care Association (www.ahca.org);

- American College of Physicians Quality Indicators for Assessing Care of Vulnerable Elders (www.acponline.org/sci-policy/acove/);

- American Geriatric Society (www.americangeriatrics.org);

- Agency for Healthcare Research and Quality (www.ahrq.gov);

- Medicare Quality Improvement Community (www.Medqic.org);

- American Association of Homes and Services for the Aging (www.aahsa.org); and

- The American Health Quality Association (www.ahqa.org).

NOTE: References to non-CMS sources or sites on the Internet are provided as a service and do not constitute or imply endorsement of these organizations or their programs by CMS or the U.S. Department of Health and Human Services. CMS is not responsible for the content of pages found at these sites. The URL addresses were current as of the date of this publication.

The guidance below includes sections that describe facility responsibilities to meet the various aspects of the QAA requirement, including:

- The composition of the QAA committee and the minimum frequency of committee meetings;

- The committee's monitoring of systems and identification of concerns with the quality of facility systems; and

- Modification and correction of facility systems, when needed, including monitoring the effect of action plans.

QAA COMMITTEE FUNCTIONS

Key aspects of the QAA requirements include the specifications that the facility must have a QAA committee, that this committee must include certain staff members, and that the committee must meet at least quarterly. The QAA committee is responsible for identifying whether quality deficiencies are present (potential or actual deviations from appropriate care processes or facility procedures) that require action. If there are quality deficiencies, the committee is responsible for developing plans of action to correct them and for monitoring the effect of these corrections. These functions of the QAA committee are described below.

Committee Composition and Frequency of Meetings

The regulation states that the QAA committee must include the director of nursing, a physician, and three other staff. These additional members may include:

- The administrator (facilities with effective QAA committees include members who have knowledge of facility systems and the authority to change those systems, including the administrator or assistant administrator due to their responsibility to manage the facility, and make changes to facility systems);

- The medical director (part of the medical director's responsibility (see F501)) is to guide the facility's development and implementation of resident care policies and coordination of medical care. If the medical director is not a committee member, exchange of information with the medical director enhances the functioning of the QAA committee);

- Staff with responsibility for direct resident care and services, such as nursing aides, therapists, staff nurses, social workers, activities staff members; and

- Staff with responsibility for the physical plant, such as maintenance, housekeeping, and laundry staff.

NOTE: Facilities may have a larger committee than required by the regulation. Consideration should be given as to how committee information is provided to consultants who may not be members of the committee, but whose responsibilities include oversight of departments or services.

Meetings of the QAA committee must be held at least quarterly or more often as the facility deems necessary to fulfill committee functions and operate effectively. The Committee should maintain a record of the dates of all meetings and the names/titles of those attending each meeting.

Identification of Quality Deficiencies

Facilities can collect and analyze data about their performance from various sources that may help them to identify quality deficiencies. These may include information from reports such as open and closed record audits, facility logs and tracking forms, incident reports, consultants' reports, and other reports as part of the QAA function. Quality deficiencies related to facility operations and practices are not only related to those that cause negative outcomes, but also may be directed toward enhancing quality of care and quality of life for residents. The committee responds to quality deficiencies and serves a preventative function by reviewing and improving systems.

Records of the committee meetings identifying quality deficiencies, by statute, may not be reviewed by surveyors unless the facility chooses to provide them. However, the documents the committee used to determine quality deficiencies are subject to review by the surveyors.

NOTE: A State or the Secretary may not require disclosure of the records of the QAA committee except insofar as such disclosure is related to the compliance of the QAA committee with the regulations.

If concerns, especially repeat survey deficiencies, have not been identified by the facility's QAA committee, this may be an indication that the committee is not performing the functions required by this regulation.

Development of Action Plans

In order to fulfill the regulatory mandate, the facility's QAA committee, having identified the root causes which led to their confirmed quality deficiencies, must develop appropriate corrective plans of action. Action plans may include, but are not limited to, the development or revision of clinical protocols based on current standards of practice, revision of policies and procedures, training for staff concerning changes, plans to purchase or repair equipment and/or improve the physical plant, and standards for evaluating staff performance.

Implementation of Action Plans and Correction of Identified Quality Deficiencies

The facility's action plans to address quality deficiencies may be implemented in a variety of ways, including: staff training and deployment of changes to procedures; monitoring and feedback mechanisms; and processes to revise plans that are not achieving or sustaining desired outcomes. The committee may delegate the implementation of action plans to various facility staff and/or outside consultants.

[**Editor's Note:** See page 391 for endnotes pertaining to this section.]

Investigative Protocol

Quality Assessment and Assurance

(Rev. 19, Issued: 06-01-06, Effective/Implementation: 06-01-06)

Objectives

- To determine if the facility has a QAA committee consisting of the director of nursing, a physician designated by the facility, and at least three other staff members; and

- To determine if the QAA committee:

    o   Meets at least quarterly (or more often, as necessary);

    o   Identifies quality deficiencies; and

    o   Develops and implements appropriate plans of action to address identified quality deficiencies.

Use

Use this protocol for all initial and standard surveys. Also, use it as necessary on revisits and abbreviated standard surveys (complaint investigations).

Procedures

During Offsite Survey Preparation (see Appendix P, Task 1), the survey team must review information about the facility prior to the survey. Sources include, at a minimum:

- Quality Measure/Quality Indicator Reports;

- The OSCAR 3 Report (includes a 4-year history of the facility's deficiencies from standard surveys, revisits, and complaint surveys). The survey team should determine if the facility has had repeat deficiencies as well as recent serious deficiencies (Levels F and H and above); and

- Information from the State ombudsman.

The regulation states that good faith attempts by the committee to identify and correct quality deficiencies will not be used as a basis for sanctions. The facility is not required to release the records of the QAA committee to the surveyors to review, and the facility is not required to disclose records of the QAA committee beyond those that demonstrate compliance with the regulation (F520). However the facility may choose such disclosure if it is the facility's only means of showing the composition and functioning of the QAA committee. If the facility has provided the records for surveyor review, this information may not be used to cite deficiencies unrelated to the QAA committee requirement. It is recommended that surveyors not review QAA records (if provided) until after they complete their investigations of other tags.

If the survey team's review of the QAA committee records reveals that the committee is making good faith efforts to identify quality deficiencies and to develop action plans to correct quality deficiencies, this requirement (F520) should not be cited. However, if the survey team had already independently (not through use of the records) identified noncompliance in the same areas as those that have been selected by the QAA committee, the team is expected to cite the noncompliance for the other requirements.

Throughout the survey, the survey team may become aware of other concerns regarding the delivery of care and services that may reflect that the QAA committee is not functioning in identifying ongoing and current quality deficiencies.

During the daily meetings, the team discusses concerns about facility compliance that they are identifying through observations, interviews, and record reviews. The information from the entrance conference about the composition and meetings of the QAA committee is reviewed and relayed to the team.

The team coordinator assigns a surveyor to obtain information from the person the facility has designated as responsible for the QAA committee. The surveyor should interview this designated person to determine:

- How the committee identifies current and ongoing issues for committee action. This could include how they monitor the provision of care and services on an ongoing basis, and how they ascertain from residents and/or their families information regarding the facility's provision of care and services, in addition to facility staff throughout the various departments, and outside consultants and/or suppliers and providers of care;

- The methods the committee uses to develop action plans; and

- How current action plans are being implemented, including: staff training; deployment of changes to procedures; monitoring and feedback mechanisms that have been established; and, for any plans that are not achieving or sustaining desired outcomes to correct the deficiencies, the process underway for revision to these plans.

The assigned surveyor should interview staff in various departments to determine if they know how to bring an issue to the attention of the QAA committee.

If, during the course of the survey, the survey team identifies noncompliance at a particular requirement, the assigned surveyor should interview the designated person responsible for the QAA committee to determine whether the committee knew of or should have known of the issues related to the noncompliance. The assigned surveyor should determine if the committee had considered the quality deficiency and if it was determined that an action plan was needed. If so, the surveyor determines whether the committee developed and implemented any action plans to address these concerns. The survey team should verify that the action plans that are described are actually implemented, and that staff are providing care and services according to the directives of these action plans.

DETERMINATION OF COMPLIANCE (Task 6, Appendix P)

NOTE: Although the literature of QAA and QI provides various definitions of the facility's achievement of quality, surveyors will need to determine the facility's compliance based on the language of this regulation.

Synopsis of Regulation (F520)

This requirement has two aspects: the facility must have a committee composed of certain key members that meets at least quarterly (or more often, as necessary); and the committee functions to develop and implement appropriate plans of actions to correct identified quality deficiencies.

Criteria for Compliance

The facility is in compliance if:

- It has a functioning QAA committee, consisting of the director of nursing, a physician, and at least three other staff members, that meets at least quarterly; and

- The committee:

    o   Identifies quality deficiencies; and

    o   Develops and implements appropriate plans of actions.

If not, cite F520.

Noncompliance for F520

After completing the investigative protocol, the survey team determines whether or not compliance with the regulation exists. Examples of noncompliance may include, but are not limited to, the following:

- Lack of a physician member of the committee;

- The committee met only twice during the previous year;

- The action plan to correct a quality deficiency regarding food temperatures was not being followed by staff in the dietary department, and food was not being served at proper temperatures; or

- An action plan was developed to correct a problem with inadequate assessment of root causes of falls. Staff did not implement the plan, and residents continued to experience serious falls.

- An action plan that was developed to correct the issue of resident falls did not take account of the root cause of the falls being overuse of sedative type medications. The plan was to increase the use of restraints which was an inappropriate action plan.

DEFICIENCY CATEGORIZATION (Part V*, Appendix P) *[Editor's Note: The part number cited is incorrect. The correct part number is IV.]

Once the survey team has determined that noncompliance exists, the team will select the appropriate level of severity for the deficiency using the guidance below.

The survey team must identify a relationship between noncompliance at other regulatory requirements and the facility's failure to have a functional QAA committee. The key elements for severity determination for F520 are as follows:

1. **Presence of harm/negative outcome(s) or potential for negative outcomes because of a failure of the QAA committee structure or function.**

   Actual or potential harm/negative outcome for F520 may include, but is not limited to:

   - Failure of the QAA committee to identify and implement an action plan to reduce of medication errors committed by agency staff, resulting in the noncompliance for medication errors based on the resident receiving the wrong medication, which resulted in the resident experiencing insulin shock; or

   - Failure of the QAA committee to develop an action plan to address assessment of the cause of a pattern of recent falls of several residents, resulting in noncompliance at the accident requirement based on several residents sustaining avoidable falls with bruises but no fractures.

2. **Degree of harm (actual or potential) related to the noncompliance.**

   Identify how the facility practices caused, resulted in, allowed, or contributed to the actual or potential for harm:

   - If harm has occurred, determine if the harm is at the level of serious injury, impairment, death, compromise, or discomfort; and

   - If harm has not yet occurred, determine how likely is the potential for serious injury, impairment, death, compromise, or discomfort to occur to the resident.

3. **The immediacy of correction required.**

   Determine whether the noncompliance requires immediate correction in order to prevent serious injury, harm, impairment, or death to one or more residents.

The survey team must evaluate the harm or potential for harm based upon the following levels of severity for Tag F520. First, the team must rule out whether Severity Level 4, Immediate Jeopardy to a resident's health or safety, exists by evaluating the deficient practice in relation to immediacy, culpability, and severity. (Follow the guidance in Appendix Q.)

Severity Level 4 Considerations: Immediate Jeopardy to Resident Health or Safety

Immediate Jeopardy is a situation in which the facility's noncompliance with one or more requirements of participation:

- Has caused, or is likely to cause, serious injury, harm, impairment, or death to a resident; and

- Requires immediate correction, as the facility either created the situation or allowed the situation to continue by failing to implement preventive or corrective measures.

NOTE: The death or transfer of a resident who was harmed or injured as a result of facility noncompliance does not remove a finding of immediate jeopardy. The facility is required to implement specific actions to correct the noncompliance which allowed or caused the immediate jeopardy.

In order to select Severity Level 4 for this regulation, the surveyor must be able to identify the relationship between the facility's noncompliance cited at Severity Level 4 at other regulatory tags, and the failure of the QAA Committee to function effectively. In order to select Severity Level 4 at F520, both of the following must be present:

- Deficiency(ies) has been cited at Severity Level 4 in other tags that are related to QAA committee failure; and

- The facility does not have a QAA committee, or the facility's QAA committee failed to develop and implement appropriate plans of action to correct identified quality deficiencies.

Severity Level 3: Actual Harm that is Not Immediate Jeopardy

In order to select Severity Level 3 for this regulation, the surveyor must be able to identify the relationship between the facility's noncompliance cited at Severity Level 3 at other regulatory tags, and the failure of the QAA Committee to function effectively. In order to select Severity Level 3 at F520, both of the following must be present:

- Deficiency(ies) has been cited at Severity Level 3 in other tags that are related to QAA committee failure; and

- The facility does not have a QAA committee, or the facility's QAA committee failed to develop and implement appropriate plans of action to correct identified quality deficiencies.

Severity Level 2: No Actual Harm with Potential for More than Minimal Harm that is Not Immediate Jeopardy

In order to select Severity Level 2 for this regulation, the surveyor must be able to identify the relationship between the facility's noncompliance cited at Severity Level 2 at other regulatory tags, and the failure of the QAA Committee to function effectively. In order to select Severity Level 2 at F520, both of the following must be present:

- Deficiency(ies) has been cited at Severity Level 2 in other tags that are related to QAA committee failure; and

- The facility does not have a QAA committee, or the facility's QAA committee failed to develop and implement appropriate plans of action to correct identified quality deficiencies.

Severity Level 1: No Actual Harm with Potential for Minimal Harm

Severity Level 1 should be selected if any of the following circumstances are present:

- The facility does not have a QAA committee, and there have been no other deficiencies cited above Severity Level 1; or

- The facility has a QAA committee that has failed to meet the regulatory specifications for the composition of the committee and/or the frequency of committee meetings, and there have been no deficiencies cited above Severity Level 1; or

- The facility's QAA committee meets regulatory specifications for committee membership and frequency of meetings, and deficiencies have been cited at Severity Level 1 in other tags. In order to select Severity Level 1 in this case, the surveyor must be able to identify the relationship between the facility's noncompliance cited at Severity Level 1 at other tags, and the failure of the QAA committee to function effectively.

F522

§483.75(p) Disclosure of Ownership

(1) The facility must comply with the disclosure requirements of §§420.206 and 455.104 of this chapter.

(2) The facility must provide written notice to the State agency responsible for licensing the facility at the time of change, if a change occurs in--

(i) Persons with an ownership or control interest, as defined in §§420.201 and 455.101 of this chapter;

(ii) The officers, directors, agents, or managing employees;

(iii) The corporation, association, or other company responsible for the management of the facility; or

(iv) The facility's administrator or director of nursing.

(3) The notice specified in the paragraph (p)(2) of this section must include the identity of each new individual or company.

§483.75(q) Required Training of Feeding Assistants

(Rev. 26; Issued: 08-17-07; Effective/Implementation Dates: 08-17-07)

A facility must not use any individual working in the facility as a paid feeding assistant unless that individual has successfully completed a State-approved training program for feeding assistants, as specified in §483.160 of this part.

Guidelines: §483.75(q)

Note: Refer to F373

ENDNOTES [*See Ftag F248, §483.15(f)*]

[1] Miller, M. E., Peckham, C. W., & Peckham, A. B. (1998). *Activities keep me going and going* (pp. 217-224). Lebanon, OH: Otterbein Homes.

[2] Alzheimer's Association (n.d.). *Activity based Alzheimer care: Building a therapeutic program.* Training presentation made 1998.

[3] Thomas, W.H. (2003). *Evolution of Eden.* In A. S. Weiner & J. L. Ronch (Eds.), Culture change in long-term care (pp. 146-157). New York: Haworth Press.

[4] Bowman, C. S. (2005). *Living Life to the Fullest: A match made in OBRA '87.* Milwaukee, WI: Action Pact, Inc.

[5] Glantz, C.G., & Richman, N. (2001). *Leisure activities. In Occupational therapy: Practice skills for physical dysfunction.* St Louis: Mosby.

[6] Glantz, C.G., & Richman, N. (1996). Evaluation and intervention for leisure activities, ROTE: Role of Occupational *Therapy for the Elderly* (2nd ed., p. 728). Bethesda, MD.: American Occupational Therapy Association.

[7] Glantz, C.G., & Richman, N. (1998). *Creative methods, materials and models for training trainers in alzheimer's education* (pp. 156-159). Riverwoods, IL: Glantz/Richman Rehabilitation Associates.

[8] Hellen, C. (1992). *Alzheimer's disease: Activity-focused care* (pp. 128-130). Boston, MA: Andover.

[9] American Occupatinal Therapy Association. (2002). *Occupational therapy practice framework: domain & process.* American Journal of Occupational Therapy, 56(6), 616-617. Bethesda, MD: American Occupational Therapy Association.

[10] Henderson, A., Cermak, S., Costner, W., Murray, E., Trombly, C., & Tickle-Gegnen, L. (1991). The issue is: *Occupational science is multidimensional.* American Journal of Occupational Therapy, 45, 370-372, Bethesda, MD: American Occupational Therapy Association.

[11] Pedretti, L.W. (1996). *Occupational performance: A model for practice in physical dysfunction.* In L.W. Pedretti (Ed.), Occupational therapy: Practice skills for physical dysfunction (4th ed., pp. 3-11). St. Louis: Mosby-Year Book

[12] Christenson, M.A. (1996). *Environmental design, modification, and adaptation, ROTE: Role of occupational therapy for the elderly* (2nd ed., pp. 380-408). Bethesda, MD: American Occupational·Therapy Association.

[13] Coppard, B.M., Higgins, T., & Harvey, K.D. (2004). *Working with elders who have orthopedic conditions.* In S. Byers-Connon, H.L. Lohman, and R.L. Padilla (Eds.), *Occupational therapy with elders: Strategies for the COTA* (2nd ed., p. 293). St. Louis, MO: Elservier Mosby.

[14] Glantz, C.G., & Richman, N. (1992). *Activity programming for the resident with mental illness* (pp. 53-76). Riverwoods, IL: Glantz/Richman Rehabilitation Associates.

[15] Day, K., & Calkins, M.P. (2002). *Design and dementia.* In R. B. Bechtel & A. Churchman (Eds.), Handbook of environmental psychology (pp. 374-393). New York: Wiley.

[16] Barrick, A.L., Rader, J., Hoeffer, B., & Sloane, P. (2002). *Bathing without a battle: Personal care of individuals with dementia* (p. 4). New York: Springer.

ENDNOTES [*See Ftag F314, §483.25(c)*]

(For more information on the references below, visit the CMS Sharing Innovations in Quality website: www.cms.hhs.gov/medicaid/survey-cert/siqhome.asp.

[1] Cuddigan, J., Ayello, E.A., Sussman, C., & Baranoski, S. (Eds.). (2001). *Pressure Ulcers in America: Prevalence, Incidence, and Implications for the Future.* National Pressure Ulcer Advisory Panel Monograph (pp. 181). Reston, VA: NPUAP.

[2] Gardner, S.E. & Frantz, R.A. (2003). Wound Bioburden. In Baranoski, S. & Ayello, E.A. (Eds.), *Wound Care Essentials: Practice Principles.* Philadelphia, PA: Lippincott, Williams, & Wilkins.

[3] Ayello, E.A. & Cuddigan, J.E. (2004). *Debridement: Controlling the Necrotic/Cellular Burden. Advances in Skin and Wound Care,* 17(2), 66-75.

[4] Bergstrom N., Bennett, M.A., Carlson, C.E., et al. (1994). *Treatment of Pressure Ulcers in Adults* (Publication 95-0652). Clinical Practice Guideline, 15, Rockville, MD: U.S. Department of Health and Human Services, Agency for Health Care Policy and Research.

[5] Thompson, P.D. & Smith, D.J. (1994). *What is Infection?* American Journal of Surgery, 167, 7-11.

[6] Ayello, E.A., Baranoski, S., Kerstein, M.D., & Cuddigan, J. (2003). *Wound Debridement.* In Baranoski. S. & Ayello, E.A. (Eds.) *Wound Care Essentials: Practice Principles.* Philadelphia, PA: Lippincott Williams & Wilkins

[7] Bergstrom, N., et al. (1994). *Clinical Practice Guideline,* 15.

[8] Ayello & Cuddigan. (2004). *Advances in Skin and Wound Care,* 66-75.

[9] Sherman, R.A. (1998). *Maggot Debridement in Modern Medicine. Infections in Medicine,* 15(9), 651-656.

[10] Piper, B. (2000). *Mechanical Forces: Pressure, Shear, and Friction.* In Bryant, R.A. (Ed.) *Acute and Chronic Wounds. Nursing Management* (2nd ed., pp. 221-264). St.Louis, MO: Mosby.

[11] Kosiak, M. (1961). *Etiology of Decubitus Ulcers.* Archives of Physical Medicine and Rehabilitation, 42, 19-29.

[12] *Frequently Asked Questions: Pressure Ulcer Staging and Assessment, Question 202* (2000, July 28). Retrieved July 1, 2004 from http://www.npuap.org/archive/stagingdefinition.htm.

[13] Lyder, C., Yu C., Emerling, J., Empleo-Frazier, O., Mangat, R., Stevenson, D. & McKay, J. (1999). *Evaluating the Predictive Validity of the Braden Scale for Pressure Ulcer Risk in Blacks and Latino/Hispanic Elders.* Applied Nursing Research, 12, 60-68.

[14] Lyder, C. (2003). *Pressure Ulcer Prevention and Management.* Journal of the American Medical Association, 289, 223-226.

[15] Fuhrer M., Garber S., Rintola D., Clearman R., Hart K. (1993). *Pressure Ulcers in Community-resident persons with spinal cord injury: Prevalence and Risk Factors.* Archives of Physical Medicine Rehabilitation, 74, 1172-1177.

[16] Cuddigan, Ayello, Sussman, & Baranoski S. (Eds.). (2001). *NPUAP Monograph,* 153.

[17] Ayello, E.A., Braden, B. (May-June 2002). *How and Why to do Pressure Ulcer Risk Assessment. Advances in Skin and Wound Care,* 15(3), 125-32.

[18] Bergstrom, N. & Braden, B.A. (1992). *A Prospective Study of Pressure Sore Risk Among Institutionalized Elderly.* Journal of the American Geriatric Society, 40(8), 747-758.

[19] Gosnell S.J. (1973). *An Assessment Tool to Identify Pressure Sores.* Nursing Research, 22(1), 55-59.

[20] Bergstrom, N., Braden, B., Kemp, M., Champagne, M., Ruby, E. (1998). *Predicting Pressure Ulcer Risk: A Multistate Study of the Predictive Validity of the Braden Scale.* Nursing Research, 47(5), 261-269.

[21] Bergstrom N. & Braden, B.A. (1992). Journal of the American Geriatric Society, 747-758.

[22] Braden, B. (2001). *Risk Assessment in Pressure Ulcer Prevention.* In Krasner, D.L., Rodeheaver, G.T., Sibbeald, R.G. (Eds.) *Chronic Wound Care: A Clinical Source Book for Healthcare Professionals* (3rd ed., pp. 641-651). Wayne, PA: HMP Communications Pub.

[23] Ayello, E.A., Baranoski, S., Lyder, C.H., Cuddigan, J. (2003). *Pressure Ulcers.* In Baranoski S. & Ayello, E.A. (Eds.) *Wound Care Essentials: Practice Principles* (pp. 245). Philadelphia, PA: Lippincott Williams & Wilkins.

[24] Cuddigan, J., Ayello, E.A., Sussman, C., & Baranoski, S. (Eds.). (2001). *NPUAP Monograph,* 27 & 168.

[25] Ferguson, R., O'Connor, P., Crabtree, B., Batchelor A., Mitchell J., Coppola, D. (1993). *Serum Albumin and Pre-albumin as Predictors of Hospitalized Elderly Nursing Home Patients.* Journal of the American Geriatric Society, 41, 545-549.

[26] Covinsky, K.E., Covinsky, K.H., Palmer, R.M., & Sehgal, A.R. (2002). *Serum Albumin Concentration and Clinical Assessments of Nutritional Status in Hospitalized Older People: Different Sides of Different Coins?* Journal of the American Geriatric Society, 50, 631-637.

[27] Maklebust, J. & Sieggreen, M. (2001). *Pressure Ulcers: Guidelines for Prevention and Management* (3rd ed., pp. 49). Springhouse, PA: Springhouse.

[28] Lyder, C. (1997). *Perineal Dermatitis in the Elderly: A Critical Review of the Literature.* Journal of Gerontological Nursing, 23(12), 5-10.

[29] Bergstrom N., et al. (1994). *Clinical Practice Guideline,* 15.

[30] Agency for Health Care Policy and Research (AHCPR). (1992). *Pressure Ulcers in Adults: Prediction and Prevention* (Publication 92-0050). Clinical Practice Guideline, 3.

[31] Wound Ostomy Continence Nurses Society. (2003). *Guidelines for Prevention and Management of Pressure Ulcers* (pp. 12). Glenview, IL: Author.

[32] Kloth, L.C. & McCulloch, J.M. (Eds.) (2002). *Prevention and Treatment of Pressure Ulcer. Wound Healing: Alternatives in Management* (3rd ed., pp. 434-438). Philadelphia: FA Davis Company.

[33] Jones, V., Bale, S., & Harding, K. (2003). *Acute and Chronic Wound Healing.* In Baranoski, S. & Ayello, E.A. (Eds.), *Wound Care Essentials: Practice Principles* (pp. 72-73). Philadelphia, PA: Lippincott Williams & Wilkins.

[34] Cuddigan, J., Ayello, E.A., Sussman, C., & Baranoski, S. (Eds.) (2001). *NPUAP Monograph,*181.

[35] Morrison, M.J. (Ed.). (2001). *The Prevention and Treatment of Pressure Ulcers.* London: Mosby.

[36] Bullen, E.C., Longaker, M.T., Updike, D.L., Benton, R., Ladin, D., Hou, Z., & Howard, E.W. (1996). *Tissue inhibitor of metalloproteinases-1 is decreased and activated gelatinases are increased in chronic wounds.* Journal of Investigative Dermatology, 106(2), 335-341.

[37] Ayello, E.A. & Cuddigan, J. (2003). *Jump start the healing process.* Nursing Made Incredibly Easy! 1(2), 18-26.

[38] Bergstrom N., et al. (1994). *Clinical Practice Guideline,* 15.

[39] Gardner, S.E., Frantz, R.A., & Doebbeling, B.N. (2001). *The Validity of the Clinical Signs and Symptoms Used to Identify Localized Chronic Wound Infection.* Wound Repair and Regeneration, 9, 178-186.

[40] Gardner, S.E. & Frantz, R.A. (2001). *A Tool to Assess Clinical Signs and Symptoms of Localized Chronic Wound Infection:* Development and Reliability. Ostomy/Wound Management, 47(1), 40-47.

[41] Cutting, K.F. & Harding, K.G. (1994). *Criteria for Identifying Wound Infection.* Journal of Wound Care, 3(4), 198-201.

[42] Bergstrom N., et al. (1994). *Clinical Practice Guideline,* 15.

[43] American Geriatric Society. (2002). *American Geriatric Society Guideline: The Management of Persistent Pain in Older Persons.* Journal of American Geriatric Society, 50(6), S205-S224.

[44] Gomez, S., Osborn, C., Watkins, T. & Hegstrom, S. (2002). *Caregivers team up to manage chronic pain.* Provider, 28(4), 51-58.

[45] Dallam, L.E., Barkauskas, C., Ayello, E.A., & Baranoski, S. (2003). *Pain Management and Wounds.* In Baranoski, S. & Ayello, E.A. (Eds.). *Wound Care Essentials: Practice Principles* (pp. 223-224). Philadelphia, PA: Lippincott Williams & Wilkins.

[46] Ayello, E.A., Baranoski, S., Lyder, C.H., & Cuddigan, J. (2003). *Pressure Ulcers.* In Baranoski, S. & Ayello, E.A. *Wound Care Essentials: Practice Principles* (pp. 257). Philadelphia, PA: Lippincott Williams & Wilkins.

[47] Schultz, G.S., Sibbald, R.G., Falanga, V., Ayello, E.A., Dowsett, C., Harding, K., Romanelli, M., Stacey, M.C., Teot, L., Vanscheidt, W. (2003). *Wound Bed Preparation: A systematic Approach to Wound Management.* Wound Repair Regeneration, 11,1-28.

[48] Association for Professionals in Infection Control and Epidemiology, Inc. (March/April 2001). *Position Statement: Clean vs. Sterile: Management of Chronic Wounds.* Retrieved July 6, 2004 from www.apic.org resource center.

[49] Black, J.M. & Black, S.B. (2003). *Complex Wounds.* In Baranoski, S. & Ayello, E.A. (Eds.). *Wound Care Essentials: Practice Principles* (pp. 372) Philadelphia, PA: Lippincott Williams & Wilkins.

[50] Bergstrom N., et al. (1994). *Clinical Practice Guideline,* 15.

[51] Adapted from American Society of Consultant Pharmacists (ASCP) Guidelines for Assessing the Quality of Drug Regimen Review in Long-Term Care Facilities.

ENDNOTES [*See Ftag F329, §483.25(l)*]

[52] Tobias, DE & Sey, M. (2001). General and psychotherapeutic medication use in 328 nursing facilities: A year 2000 national survey. *The Consultant Pharmacist*, 15, pp. 34-42.

[53] Briesacher, B.A., Limcangco, M.R., Simoni-Wastila, L., Doshi, J.A., Levens, S.R., Shea, D.G., & Stuart, B. (2005). *The quality of antipsychotic drug prescribing in nursing homes.* Archives of Internal Medicine, 165, pp. 1280-1285.

[54] Ray, W.A., Taylor, J.A., Meador, K.G., Lichtenstein, M.J., Griffin, M.R., Fought, R., Adams, M.L., & Blazer, D.G. (1993). *Reducing antipsychotic drug use in nursing homes.* A controlled trial of provider education. Archives of Internal Medicine, 153(6), pp. 713-21.

[55] Gurwitz, J.H., Field, T.S., Judge, J., Rochon, P., Harrold, L.R., Cadoret, C., Lee, M., White, K., LaPrino, J., Erramuspe-Mainard, J., DeFlorio, M., Gavendo, L., Auger, J., & Bates, D.W. (2005). *Incidence of adverse drug consequences in two large academic long-term care facilities.* American Journal of Medicine, 118, pp. 251-258.

[56] Gurwitz, J.H., Field, T.S., Avorn, J., McCormick, D., Jain, S., Eckler, M., Benser, M., Edmondson, A.C., & Bates, D.W. (2000). *Incidence and preventability of adverse drug events in nursing homes.* American Journal of Medicine, 109, pp. 87-94.

[57] Gurwitz, J.H., Field, T.S., Avorn, J., McCormick, D., Jain, S., Eckler, M., Benser, M., Edmondson, A.C., & Bates, D.W. (2000). *Incidence and preventability of adverse drug events in nursing homes.* American Journal of Medicine, 109, pp. 87-94.

[58] Field T.S., Gurwitz J.H., Avorn J., McCormick, D., Shailavi, J., Eckler, M., Benser, M., & Bates, D.W. (2001). *Risk factors for adverse drug events among nursing home residents.* Archives of Internal Medicine, 161, pp. 1629-34.

[59] Denham, M.J. (1990). *Adverse drug reactions.* British Medical Bulletin, 46, pp. 53-62.

[60] Rosen's Emergency Medicine: *Concepts and Clinical Practice,* 5th ed., (2002). Marx, J.A., Hockberger, R.S., Walls, R.M., Adams, J., Barkin, R.M., Danzl, D.F., Gausche-Hill, M., Hamilton, G.C., Ling, L.J., & Newton, E. (Eds.). St Louis: Mosby, Inc., p. 1469.

[61] Tune, L. Carr, S., Hoag, E. & Cooper, T. (1992). *Anticholinergic effects of drugs commonly prescribed for the elderly: Potential means for assessing risk of delirium.* American Journal of Psychiatry, 149, pp. 1393-1394.

[62] Tune, L.E. (2000). *Serum anticholinergic activity levels and delirium in the elderly.* Seminars in Clinical Neuropsychiatry, 5, pp. 149-153.

[63] Gurwitz, J.H., Field, T.S., Avorn, J., McCormick, D., Jain, S., Eckler, M., Benser, M., Edmondson, A.C., & Bates, D.W. (2000). *Incidence and preventability of adverse drug events in nursing homes.* American Journal of Medicine, 109, pp. 87-94.

[64] Gurwitz, J.H., Field, T.S., Judge, J., Rochon, P., Harrold, L.R., Cadoret, C., Lee, M., White, K., LaPrino, J., Erramuspe-Mainard, J., DeFlorio, M., Gavendo, L., Auger, J., & Bates, D.W. (2005). *Incidence of adverse drug consequences in two large academic long-term care facilities.* American Journal of Medicine, 118, pp. 251-258.

[65] Adapted from American Society of Consultant Pharmacists (ASCP) *Guidelines for Assessing the Quality of Drug Regimen Review in Long-Term Care Facilities.*

[66] Adapted from Hepler, C.D., & Strand, L.M., (1990). *Opportunities and responsibilities in pharmaceutical care.* American Journal of Hospital Pharmacy, 47, pp.533-543.

[67] Adapted from Top 10 Dangerous Drug Interactions in Long-Term Care presented by the Multidisciplinary Medication Management Project, a collaborative initiative of the American Society of Consultant Pharmacists (ASCP) and the American Medical Directors Association (AMDA).

SOM, Appendix PP, Guidance to Surveyors

ENDNOTES [*See Ftag F315, §483.25(d)(1) and §483.25(d)(2)*]

[1]Geurrero, P. & Sinert, R. (November 18, 2004). *Urinary Incontinence.* Retrieved November 29, 2004 from E-Medicine. Website: www.emedicine.com/emerg/topic791.htm.

[2]Delafuente, J.C. & Stewart, R.B. (Eds.). (1995). *Therapeutics in the Elderly* (2nd ed., pp. 471). Cincinnati, OH: Harvey Whitney Books..

[3]Newman, D.K. (2002). *Managing and Treating Urinary Incontinence* (pp.106-107). Baltimore, MD: Health Professions Press.

[4]Newman, D.K. (2002). *Managing and Treating Urinary Incontinence.*

[5]Ouslander, J.G., Schnelle, J.F., Uman, G., Fingold, S., Nigam, J.G., Tuico, E., et al. (1995). *Predictors of Successful Prompted Voiding Among Incontinent Nursing Home Residents.* Journal of the American Medical Association, 273(17), 1366-1370.

[6]Armstrong, E.P. & Ferguson, T.A. (1998). *Urinary Incontinence: Healthcare Resource Consumption in Veteran Affair Medical Centers.* Veteran's Health System Journal, October, 37-42.

[7]Byers, P.H., Ryan, P.A., Regan, M.B., Shields, A., & Carta, S.G. (1995). *Effects of Incontinence Care Cleansing Regimens on Skin Integrity. Continence Care,* 22(4), 187-192.

[8]Niël-Weise BS, van den Broek PJ. *Urinary catheter policies for long-term bladder drainage.* The Cochrane Database of Systematic Reviews 2005, Issue 1. Art. No.: CD004201. DOI: 10.1002/14651858.CD004201.pub2.

[9]Maki, D.G. & Tambyah, P.A. (2001). *Engineering out the Risk of Infection with Urinary Catheters. Emerging Infectious Diseases,* 7(2), 342-347.

[10]Grahn, D., Norman, D.C., White, M.L., Cantrell, M. & Thomas, T.T. (1985). *Validity of Urinary Catheter Specimen for Diagnosis of Urinary Tract Infection in the Elderly.* Archives of Internal Medicine, 145,1858.

[11]Nicolle, L.E. (1999). *Urinary Tract Infections in the Elderly.* In W.R.Hazzard, J.P. Blass., W.H. Ettinger,, J.B. Halter & J.G. Ouslander (Eds.), *Principles of Geriatric Medicine and Gerontology* (4th ed., pp.823-833). New York: McGraw-Hill.

[12]Nicolle, L.E. & SHEA Long-term Care Committee. (2001). *Urinary tract Infections in Long-Term Care Facilities. Infection Control Hospital Epidemiology,* 22, 167-175.

[13]McGreer, A., Campbell, B., Emori, T.G., Hierholzer, W.J., Jackson, M.M., Nicolle, L.E., et al. (1991). *Definitions of Infections for Surveillance in Long Term Care Facilities.* American Journal of Infection Control, 19(1), 1-7.

[14]AMDA: *Common Infections in the Long-term Care Setting.* Clinical practice guideline Adapted from Bentley DW, Bradley S, High K, et al. Practice guideline for evaluation of fever and infection in long-term care facilities. Guidelines from the Infectious Diseases Society of America. J Am Med Dir Assoc 2001; 2(5): 246-258.

[15]Ouslander, J.G., Osterweil, D., Morley, J. (1997). *Medical Care in the Nursing Home.* (2nd ed., pp.303-307). New York: McGraw-Hill.

[16]Nicolle, L.E. (1997). *Asymptomatic Bacteriuria in the Elderly.* Infectious Disease Clinics of North America, 11, 647-62.

REFERENCES [*See Ftag F501, §483.75(i)*]

[1]Pattee JJ, Otteson OJ. (1991). *Medical direction in the nursing home* (p.5). Minneapolis, MN: Northridge Press.

[2]Institute of Medicine (2001). *Improving The Quality Of Long-Term Care* (pp. 201). Washington, DC: National Academy Press.

[3]Levenson, S.A. (1993). Medical Direction In Long-Term Care. *A Guidebook For The Future* (2nd ed., pp. 135). Durham, NC: Carolina Academic Press.

[4]Levenson, SA. *Medical Director and Attending Physicians Policy and Procedure Manual for Long-term Care.* Dayton, Ohio: MED-PASS. 2005.

ENDNOTES [*See Ftag F520, §483.75(o)*]

[1] Institute of Medicine (2001). *Improving the Quality of Long-Term Care.* Washington, DC: National Academy Press.

[2] Office of Inspector General (2003) Quality Assurance Committees in Nursing Homes, Baltimore, MD: U.S. Department of Health and Human Services (OEI-01-01-00090).

ENDNOTES (*See Ftag F323, 483.25(h)*)

[1] Centers for Medicare & Medicaid Services. (December 2002 revised June 2006). Revised Long-Term Care Facility Resident Assessment Instrument User's Manual. Version 2.0, 3-146.

[2] Pizzi, L.T., Goldfarb, N.I., Nash, D.B. (2002). Promoting a culture of safety. In: K.G. Shojania, B.W. Duncan, K.M. McDonald , & R.M. Wachter (Eds.), Evidence Report/Technology Assessment, No. 43. Making Health Care Safer: A Critical Analysis of Patient Safety Practices. Rockville, MD: Agency for Healthcare Research and Quality. Retrieved February 9, 2004 from <http://www.ahrq.gov/clinic/ptsafety/chap40.htm>.

[3] Singer, S.J., Gaba, D.M., Geppert, J.J., et al. (2003). The culture of safety: Results of an organization-wide survey in 15 California hospitals. Qual Saf Health Care, 12, 112-118.

[4] American Geriatrics Society, British Geriatrics Society American Academy of Orthopedic Surgeons Panel on Falls Prevention. (2001). Guideline for the prevention of falls in older persons. J Am Geriatr Soc, 49, 664–672.

[5] Boltz, M. (2003). Litigation Issues Related To Wandering and Elopement. The John A. Hartford Foundation Institute for Geriatric Nursing, New York University, The Steinhardt School of Education, Division of Nursing. Retrieved November 30, 2005 from http://www.hartfordign.org/resources/special topics/spectopics.html>

[6] Agency for Toxic Substances & Disease Registry web site at http://www.atsdr.cdc.gov/toxpro2.html.

[7] US Dept. of Labor, Occupational Safety and Health Standards, 29 CFR 1910.1200 (g)(1) and (2)

[8] Katcher, L.K. (1981). Scald Burns from Hot Tap Water. Journal of Am Med Assoc., 246(11), 1219-1222.

[9] Moritz, A.R., Henriques F.C. Jr. (1947). Studies of Thermal Injury: II. The Relative Importance of Time and Surface Temperatures in the Causation of Cutaneous Burns. Am J Pathology, 23, 695-720.

[10] US Dept. of Health and Human Services. Centers for Disease Control and Prevention. (June 12, 2003). Emergency Preparedness & Response. Burns. Retrieved November 8, 2005 from <http://www.bt.cdc.gov/masstrauma/burns.asp>

[11] Electrical Safety Foundation International. Plug into Electrical Safety. Retrieved February 9, 2004 from <http://www.nesf.org/index.html>.

[12] US Dept. of Health and Human Services. Food and Drug Administration. (December 12, 1995). Public Health Advisory: Hazards Associated with the Use of Electric Heating Pads.

[13] Tideiksaar, R. (1998). Falls in Older Persons: Prevention and Management (2nd Edition). Baltimore, MD: Health Profession Press.

[14] Warren, M. (2001), Occupational Therapy Practice Guidelines for Adults with Low Vision, The American Occupational Therapy Association, Inc.

[15] Taylor, J.A., Brown, A.K., Meredith, S., Ray, W.A. (2002). The fall reduction program: a comprehensive program for reduction of falls and injuries in long-term care residents. Nashville, TN: Department of Preventive Medicine, Vanderbilt University School of Medicine.

[16] US Dept. of Veterans Affairs, Office of Occupational Safety and Health. (January. 2003). Safe Patient Movement and Handling Guide.

[17] US Dept. of Health and Human Services. Food and Drug Administration. (July 15, 1992). FDA Safety Alert: Potential Hazards with Restraint Devices.

[18] US Dept. of Health and Human Services. Food and Drug Administration. (August 23, 1995). FDA Safety Alert: Entrapment Hazards with Hospital Bed Side Rails.

[19] US Dept. of Health and Human Services, Food and Drug Administration, Hospital Bed Safety Workgroup. (April 2003), Clinical Guidance For the Assessment and Implementation of Bed Rails In Hospitals, Long Term Care Facilities, and Home Care Settings. Retrieved November 11, 2005 from http://www.fda.gov/cdrh/beds/.

[20] Miles, S. (June 2002). Death between bedrails and air pressured mattresses. J Am Geriatr Soc, 50(6), 1124-5.

NOTE: References to non-CMS/HHS sources or sites on the Internet included above or later in this document are provided as a service and do not constitute or imply endorsement of these organizations or their programs by CMS or the U.S. Department of Health and Human Services. CMS is not responsible for the content of pages found at these sites. URL addresses were current as of the date of this publication.

ENDNOTES (*See Ftag F325, 483.25(i)*)

[1] Vella, C., & Kravitz, L. (2002). Sarcopenia: The mystery of muscle loss. IDEA Personal Trainer, 13(4), 30-35

[2] Thomas, D.R. (2002). Distinguishing starvation from cachexia. Clinics of Geriatric Medicine, 18(4), 883-892.

[3] VanItallie, T.B. (2003). Frailty in the elderly: Contributions of sarcopenia and visceral protein depletion. Metabolism, 52(10), Supplement 2 (October), 22-26.

[4] Morley, J.E., & Thomas, D. R. (Eds). (2007) Geriatric Nutrition. Boca Raton: CRC Press

[5] Bouras, E.P., Lange, S.M., & Scolapio, J.S. (2001). Rational approach to patients with unintentional weight loss. Mayo Clinic Proceedings, 76(9), 923-929.

[6] Kieselhorst, K.J., Skates, J., & Pritchett, E. (2005). American Dietetic Association: Standards of practice in nutrition care and updated standards of professional performance. Journal of the American Dietetic Association, 105(4), 641-645.

[7] Lacey, K. & Pritchett, E. (2003). Nutrition care process and model: ADA adopts road map to quality care and outcomes management. Journal of the American Dietetic Association, 103(8), 1061-1072.

[8] Walker, G. (Ed.) (2005). Pocket Guide for Nutrition Assessment. Chicago, IL: Consulting Dietitians in Healthcare Facilities.

[9] Thomas D.R., Tariq, S.H., Makhdomm S., Haddad R., & Moinuddin A. (2003). Physician misdiagnosis of dehydration in older adults. Journal of the American Medical Directors Association, 4(5), 251–254.

[10] Wilson, M.G., Thomas, D.R., Rubenstein, L.Z., Chibnall, J.T., Anderson, S., Baxi, A., Diebold, M., & Morley, J.E. (2005). Appetite assessment: Simple appetite questionnaire predicts weight loss in community-dwelling adults and nursing home residents. American Journal of Clinical Nutrition, 82(5), 1074-1081.

[11] Chouinard, J. (2000). Dysphagia in Alzheimer 's disease: A review. Journal of Nutrition, Health and Aging, 4(4), 214-217.

[12] Pronsky ZM, Crowe JP, Young VSL, Elbe D, Epstein S. Food-medication interactions, 14th Edition. Food Medications Interactions 2006.

[13] Sullivan, D.H. (2001). What do the serum proteins tell us about our elderly patients? Journal of Gerontology Series A: Biological Sciences and Medical Sciences, 56(2), M71-M74.

[14] Covinsky, K.E., Covinsky, M.H., Palmer, R.M., & Sehgal, A.R. (2002). Serum albumin concentration and clinical assessments of nutritional status in hospitalized older people: Diferent sides of different coins? Journal of the American Geriatrics Society, 50(4) 631- 637

[15] American Dietetic Association. (2005). Position of the American Dietetic Association: Liberalization of the diet prescription improves quality of life for older adults in long-term care. Journal of the American Dietetic Association, 105, 1955-1965.

[16] Mathus-Vliegen, E.M. (2004). Old age, malnutrition, and pressure sores: An ill -fated alliance. Journals of Gerontology Series A: Biological Sciences & Medical Sciences, 59(4), M355-M360.

[17] Alzheimer's Association. (2006). Eating, Retrieved July 27, 2006 from http://www.alz.org/living_with_Alzheimers_eating.asp

[18] Groher, M.E. & McKaig, T.N. (1995). Dysphagia and dietary levels in skilled nursing facilities. Journal of the American Geriatric Society, 43(5), 528-532.

[19] Kikawada, M., Iwamoto, T., & Takasaki, M. (2005). Aspiration and infection in the elderly. Drugs Aging, 22(2), 115-130.

[20] Loeb, M.B., Becker, M., Eady, A., & Walker-Dilks, C. (2003). Interventions to prevent aspiration pneumonia in older adults: A systematic review. Journal of the American Geriatrics Society, 51(7), 1018-1022.

[21] Feinberg, M.J., Knebl, J., & Tully, J. (1996). Prandial aspiration and pneumonia in an elderly population followed over 3 years. Dysphagia, 11(2), 104-109.

[22] Mamun, K., & Lim, J. (2005). Role of nasogastric tube in preventing aspiration pneumonia in patients with dysphagia. Singapore Medical Journal, 46(11), 627-631.

[23] Pronsky ZM, Crowe JP, Young VSL, Elbe D, Epstein S. Food-medication Interactions, 14th Edition. Food Medications Interactions 2006.

[24] Thomas, D.R. (2006). Guidelines for the use of orexigenic drugs in long-term care. Nutrition in Clinical Practice, 21(1), 82-87.

[25] Dasgupta, M., Binns, M.A., & Rochon, P.A. (2000). Subcutaneous fluid infusion in along-term care setting. Journal of the American Geriatric Society, 48(7), 795-799.

[26] Thomas D.R. (2006). Guidelines for the use of orexigenic drugs in long-term care. Nutrition in Clinical Practice, Vol. 21(1) 82-87

[27] Grant, M.D. & Rudberg, M.A., & Brody J.A. (1998). Gastrostomy placement and mortality among hospitalized Medicare beneficiaries. Journal of the American Medical Association, 279, 1973-1976.

ENDNOTES *(See Ftag F371, 483.35(i))*

[1] The Partnership for Food Safety and Education. (2006). Food Safety Glossary. Retrieved September 25, 2006 from htp:/www.fightbac.org/content/view/15/22/.

[2] The Partnership for Food Safety and Education. (2006). Food Safety Glossary. htp:/www.cdc.gov/mmwr/preview/mmwrhtml/ss4901 a1.htm

[3] Mead, P.S., Slutsker, L., Dietz, V., McCaig, L.F., Bresee, J.S., Shapiro, C., Grifin, P.M., & Tauxe, R.V. (1999). Food-related illness and death in the United States. Emerging Infectious Diseases, 5(5), 607-625.

[4] Hedberg, C.W., Smith, S.J., Kirkland, E., Radke, V., Jones, T.F., Selman, C.A., & EHSNET Working Group. (2006). Systematic environmental evaluations to identify food safety differences between outbreak and non-outbreak restaurants. Journal of Food Protection, 69(9).

[5] Centers for Disease Control and Prevention Outbreak Surveillance Data. (2006). Annual Listing of Foodborne Disease Outbreaks, United States, 1990-2004. Retrieved September 25, 2006 from htp:/www.cdc.gov/foodborneoutbreaks/outbreak_data.htm

[6] U.S. Department of Health and Human Services, Public Health Service, Food and Drug Administration. (2005). Code (p. 48).

[7] International Association of Food Protection. (1999). Procedures to Investigate Foodborne Illness (5th edition). Des Moines, IA: Author. [Prepared by the Committee on Communicable Diseases Affecting Man.]

[8] U.S. Department of Health and Human Services, Public Health Service, Food and Drug Administration. (2005). Food Code (p. 43).

[9] U.S. Department of Health and Human Services, Public Health Service, Food and Drug Administration. (2005). Food Code (pp. 43-45).

[10] U.S. Department of Health and Human Services, Public Health Service, Food and Drug Administration. (2005). Food Code (p.-66).

[11] U.S. Department of Health and Human Services, Public Health Service, Food and Drug Administration. (2005). Food Code (pp. 103-104; 123).

[12] U.S. Department of Health and Human Services, Public Health Service, Food and Drug Administration. (2005). Food Code (p. 11 4).

Endnotes for Pain Management (*See Ftag F309, 483.25*)

[1] Definitions Related to the Use of Opioids for the Treatment of Pain: Consensus document from the American Academy of Pain Medicine, the American Pain Society, and the American Society of Addiction Medicine, 2001. Document available at www.painmed.org, www.ampainsoc.org and www.asam.org.

[2] Lussier, D., Huskey, A.G., & Portenoy, R.K. (2004). Adjuvant analgesics in cancer pain management. The Oncologist, 9, 571-591.

[3] National Center for Complementary and Alternative Medicine. (2002). What is complementary and alternative medicine? NCCAM Publication, No. D156. Retrieved 3/06/06 from www.nccam.nih.gov.

[4] American Medical Directors Association. (2003). Clinical Practice Guideline: Pain Management in the Long Term Care Setting. AMDA. Columbia: MD. Retrieved 3/06/06 from www.amda.com.

[5] The Federation of State Medical Boards. (2004). Model Policy for the Use of Controlled Substances for the Treatment of Pain. Retrieved 3/06/06 from http://www.fsmb.org/pdf/2004_grpol_controlled_substances.pdf.

[6] American Geriatrics Society: AGS Panel on Persistent Pain in Older Persons. (2002). Clinical Practice Guidelines: The management of persistent pain in older persons. Journal of the American Geriatrics Society, 50, S205-S224.

[7] Yong, H.H., Gibson, S.J., De L Home, D.J., & Hleme, R.D. (2001). Development of a pain attitudes questionnaire to assess stoicism and cautiousness for possible age differences [Electronic version]. The Journals of Gerontology, 56, 279-284.

[8] Jones, K., Fink, R., Clark, L., Hutt, E., Vijor, C. & Mellis, K. (2005). Nursing Home Resident Barriers to Effective Pain Management: Why Nursing Home Residents May Not Seek Pain Medication. Journal of the American Medical Directors Association, 6(1): 10-17.

[9] Cohen-Mansfield J. (2006). Pain Assessment in Noncommunicative Elderly Persons – PAINE. Clinical Journal of Pain. July/August; 22(6): 569-575.

[10] Won, A.B., Lapane, K.L., Vallow, S., Schein, J., Morris, J.N., & Lipsitz L.A. (2004). Persistent nonmalignant pain and analgesic prescribing patterns in elderly nursing home residents. Journal of the American Geriatrics Society, 52, 867-876.

[11] Teno, J.M., Weitzen, S., Wetle, T., & Mor, V. (2001). Persistent pain in nursing home residents. Journal of the American Medical Association, 285, 2081.

[12] Cohen-Mansfield J. (2005). Self-report of pain in nursing home residents with dementia: a comparison of assessments. American Journal of Pain Management, 15, 128-139.

[13] Pautex S., Michon A., Guedira M., Emond, H., Le Lous, P., Samaras, D., Michel, JP, Herrmann, F., Giannakopoulos, P., Gold, G. (2006). Pain in severe dementia: self-assessment of observational scales? Journal of American Geriatric Society, 54(7), 1040-5.

[14] Ferrell BA, Ferrell BR, Rivera L. (1995). Pain in cognitively impaired nursing home patients. Journal of Pain and Symptom Management, 10, 591-8.

[15] Chibnall, J.T., Tait, R.C., Harman, B. (2005). Effect of acetaminophen on behavior, well-being, and psychotropic medication use in nursing home residents with moderate-to-severe dementia. Journal of the American Geriatrics Society, 53(11), 1921-1929.

[16] World Union of Wound Healing Societies. (2006). Principles of best practice: Minimising pain at wound dressing-related procedures: A consensus document. World Council of Enterostomal Therapists Journal, 26(2), 26-38.

[17] Cohen-Mansfield, J. & Lipson, S. (2002). Pain in cognitively impaired nursing home residents: How well are physicians diagnosing it? Journal of the American Geriatrics Society, 50, 1039-1044.

[18] Cohen-Mansfield, J. & Lipson, S. (2002). The underdetection of pain of dental etiology in persons with dementia. American Journal of Alzheimer's Disease and Other Dementias, 17(4), 249-253.

[19] Herr, K., Bjoro, K, & Decker, S. (2006). Tools for the assessment of pain in nonverbal older adults with dementia: A state-of-the-science review. Journal of Pain and Symptom Management, 31(2), 170-192.

[20] Lin, Wen-Chieh; Lum, Terry Y.; Mehr, David R.; Kane, Robert L. (2006). Measuring Pain Presence and Intensity in Nursing Home Residents. Journal of the American Medical Directors Association, 7(3), 147-153.

[21] Cohen-Mansfield, J. & Creedon, M. (2002). Nursing staff members' perceptions of pain indicators in persons with severe dementia. The Clinical Journal of Pain, 18(1), 64-73.

[22] Ferrell, B.A. (1995). Pain evaluation and management in the nursing home. Annals of Internal Medicine, 123, 681-687.

[23] World Health Organization (WHO) pain ladder: www.who.int/cancer/palliative/painladder/en

[24] American Medical Directors Association (AMDA) Clinical Practice Guideline "Pain Management in the Long-Term Care Setting" (2003) at: www.amda.com/tools/guidelines.cfm

[25] Bernstein, C., Lateef, B., Fine, P.G. Interventional Pain Management Procedures in Older Patients. In: Gibson S, Weiner D, eds. Pain in Older Persons. IASP Press, Seattle, 2005.

ENDNOTES (*See Ftag F441, 483.65*)

[1] Siegel, J.D., Rhinehart, E., Jackson, M., Chiarello, L., and the Healthcare Infection Control Practices Advisory Committee. (2007 June). *2007 Guideline for Isolation Precautions: Preventing transmission of infectious agents in healthcare settings*. Pp. 71. Accessed December 10, 2008 from http://www.cdc.gov/ncidod/dhqp/pdf/isolation2007.pdf

[2] Centers for Disease Control and Prevention (CDC). (2002). *Guideline for hand hygiene in health-care settings: recommendations of the Healthcare Infection Control Practices Advisory Committee and the HICPAC/SHEA/APIC/IDSA Hand Hygiene Task Force*. MMWR 2002; 51 (No.RR-16). pp. 3. Accessed December 10, 2008 from http://www.cdc.gov/mmwr/PDF/rr/rr5116.pdf

[3] Siegel, J.D., Rhinehart, E., Jackson, M., Chiarello, L., and the Healthcare Infection Control Practices Advisory Committee. (2007 June). *2007 Guideline for Isolation Precautions: Preventing transmission of infectious agents in healthcare settings*. Pp. 71. Accessed December 10, 2008 from http://www.cdc.gov/ncidod/dhqp/pdf/isolation2007.pdf

[4] Siegel, J.D., Rhinehart, E., Jackson, M., Chiarello, L., and the Healthcare Infection Control Practices Advisory Committee. (2007 June). *2007 Guideline for Isolation Precautions: Preventing transmission of infectious agents in healthcare settings*. Pp. 70. Accessed December 10, 2008 from http://www.cdc.gov/ncidod/dhqp/pdf/isolation2007.pdf

[5] Siegel, J.D., Rhinehart, E., Jackson, M., and Chiarello, L. (2006). *Management of multidrug-resistant organisms in healthcare settings, 2006*. Pp. 5. Accessed December 8, 2008 from http://www.cdc.gov/ncidod/dhqp/pdf/ar/mdroGuideline2006.pdf

[6] American Medical Directors Association (AMDA). (2006). *Clinical practice guideline; managing common infections in the assisted living setting*. Assisted Living Consult, Jan/Feb 2006: Pp.31

[7] Siegel, J.D., Rhinehart, E., Jackson, M., Chiarello, L., and the Healthcare Infection Control Practices Advisory Committee. (2007 June). *2007 Guideline for Isolation Precautions: Preventing transmission of infectious agents in healthcare settings*. Pp. 66. Accessed December 10, 2008 from http://www.cdc.gov/ncidod/dhqp/pdf/isolation2007.pdf

[8] Nicolle, L.E., Strausbaugh, L.J., and Garibaldi, R.A. (1996, Jan.). *Infections and antibiotic resistance in nursing homes. Clinical Microbiology Reviews*. 9(1): 1-17

[9] Richards, C. (2002). *Infections in residents of long-term facilities*. J AM Geriatr Soc 2002; 50. Pp.676.

[10] Smith, P.W., Bennett, G., Bradley, S., Drinka, P., Lautenbach, E., Marx, J., Mody, L., Nicolle, L., and Stevenson, K. (2008). *SHEA/APIC Guideline: infection prevention and control in the long-term care facility. Infect Control Hosp Epidemiology* 29(9): Pp.795

[11] Smith, P.W., Bennett, G., Bradley, S., Drinka, P., Lautenbach, E., Marx, J., Mody, L., Nicolle, L., and Stevenson, K. (2008). *SHEA/APIC Guideline: infection prevention and control in the long-term care facility. Infect Control Hosp Epidemiology* 29(9): Pp.803.

[12] Siegel, J.D., Rhinehart, E., Jackson, M., Chiarello, L., and the Healthcare Infection Control Practices Advisory Committee. (2007 June). *2007 Guideline for Isolation Precautions: Preventing transmission of infectious agents in healthcare settings*. Pp. 78. Accessed December 10, 2008 from http://www.cdc.gov/ncidod/dhqp/pdf/isolation2007.pdf

[13] Sehulster, L.M., Chinn, R.Y.W., Arduino, M.J., Carpenter, J., Donlan, R., Ashford, D., Besser, R., Fields, B., McNeil, M.M., Whitney, C., Wong, S., Juranek, D., and Cleveland, J. (2003). *Guidelines for environmental infection control in health-care facilities: Recommendations from CDC and the Healthcare Infection Control Practices Advisory Committee (HICPAC)*. Accessed December 10, 2008 from http://www.cdc.gov/ncidod/dhqp/pdf/guidelines/Enviro_guide_03.pdf

[14] Siegel, J.D., Rhinehart, E., Jackson, M., Chiarello, L., and the Healthcare Infection Control Practices Advisory Committee. (2007 June). *2007 Guideline for Isolation Precautions: Preventing transmission of infectious agents in healthcare settings*. Pp. 79. Accessed December 10, 2008 from http://www.cdc.gov/ncidod/dhqp/pdf/isolation2007.pdf

[15] Siegel, J.D., Rhinehart, E., Jackson, M., Chiarello, L., and the Healthcare Infection Control Practices Advisory Committee. (2007 June). *2007 Guideline for Isolation Precautions: Preventing transmission of infectious agents in healthcare settings*. Accessed December 10, 2008 from http://www.cdc.gov/ncidod/dhqp/pdf/isolation2007.pdf

[16] Siegel, J.D., Rhinehart, E., Jackson, M., Chiarello, L., and the Healthcare Infection Control Practices Advisory Committee. (2007 June). *2007 Guideline for Isolation Precautions: Preventing transmission of infectious agents in healthcare settings*. Accessed December 10, 2008 from http://www.cdc.gov/ncidod/dhqp/pdf/isolation2007.pdf

[17] Centers for Disease Control and Prevention (CDC). (2008, March). *Injection Safety FAQs for Providers.* Accessed December 10, 2008 from http://www.cdc.gov/ncidod/dhqp/injectionSafetyFAQs.html#Q11

[18] Smith, P.W., Bennett, G., Bradley, S., Drinka, P., Lautenbach, E., Marx, J., Mody, L., Nicolle, L., and Stevenson, K. (2008). *SHEA/APIC Guideline: infection prevention and control in the long-term care facility. Infect Control Hosp Epidemiology* 29(9): 785-814.

[19] Siegel, J.D., Rhinehart, E., Jackson, M., Chiarello, L., and the Healthcare Infection Control Practices Advisory Committee. (2007 June). *2007 Guideline for Isolation Precautions: Preventing transmission of infectious agents in healthcare settings.* Pp. 48. Accessed December 10, 2008 from http://www.cdc.gov/ncidod/dhqp/pdf/isolation2007.pdf

[20] Sehulster, L.M., Chinn, R.Y.W., Arduino, M.J., Carpenter, J., Donlan, R., Ashford, D., Besser, R., Fields, B., McNeil, M.M., Whitney, C., Wong, S., Juranek, D., and Cleveland, J. (2003). *Guidelines for environmental infection control in health-care facilities. Recommendations from CDC and the Healthcare Infection Control Practices Advisory Committee (HICPAC).* Accessed December 10, 2008 from http://www.cdc.gov/ncidod/dhqp/pdf/guidelines/Enviro_guide_03.pdf

[21] Kim, K.H., Fekety, R., Batts, D.H.,Brown, D., Cudmore, M., Silva, J. Jr., and Waters, D. (1981, Jan. 1). *Isolation of Clostridium Difficile from the environment and contacts of residents with antibiotic-associated colitis. Journal of Infectious Disease.* 143:1. Pp.42-50.

[22] Centers for Disease Control and Prevention, (CDC). (2008, July 8). *Hepatitis B FAQs for healthcare professionals.* Accessed December 16, 2008 from http://www.cdc.gov/print.do?url=http%3A//www.cdc.gov/hepatitis/HBV/HBVfaq.htm%23overview

[23] Centers for Disease Control and Prevention (CDC). (2007, February 15). *Preventing seasonal flu.* Accessed December 16, 2008 from http://www.cdc.gov/flu/about/qa/preventing.htm

[24] Siegel, J.D., Rhinehart, E., Jackson, M., Chiarello, L., and the Healthcare Infection Control Practices Advisory Committee. (2007 June). *2007 Guideline for Isolation Precautions: Preventing transmission of infectious agents in healthcare settings.* Pp.61. Accessed December 10, 2008 from http://www.cdc.gov/ncidod/dhqp/pdf/isolation2007.pdf

[25] U.S. Department of Health and Human Services, Public Health Service, Food and Drug Administration (FDA). *(2005). Food Code.* Pp. 43.

[26] U.S. Department of Health and Human Services, Public Health Service, Food and Drug Administration (FDA). *(2005). Food Code.* Pp.44

[27] Siegel, J.D., Rhinehart, E., Jackson, M., Chiarello, L., and the Healthcare Infection Control Practices Advisory Committee. (2007 June). *2007 Guideline for Isolation Precautions: Preventing transmission of infectious agents in healthcare settings.* Accessed December10, 2008 from http://www.cdc.gov/ncidod/dhqp/pdf/isolation2007.pdf

[28] Siegel, J.D., Rhinehart, E., Jackson, M., Chiarello, L., and the Healthcare Infection Control Practices Advisory Committee. (2007 June). *2007 Guideline for Isolation Precautions: Preventing transmission of infectious agents in healthcare settings.* Accessed December 10, 2008 from http://www.cdc.gov/ncidod/dhqp/pdf/isolation2007.pdf

[29] Siegel, J.D., Rhinehart, E., Jackson, M., Chiarello, L., and the Healthcare Infection Control Practices Advisory Committee. (2007 June). *2007 Guideline for Isolation Precautions: Preventing transmission of infectious agents in healthcare settings.* Pp. 53. Accessed December10, 2008 from http://www.cdc.gov/ncidod/dhqp/pdf/isolation2007.pdf

[30] Hall, C.B., Douglas, Jr., R.G., Schnabal, K.C., and Geinan, J.M. (1981, Sep.). *Infectivity of respiratory syncytial virus by various routes of inoculation.* Infection and Immunity. 33(3). Pp.782.

[31] Siegel, J.D., Rhinehart, E., Jackson, M., Chiarello, L., and the Healthcare Infection Control Practices Advisory Committee. (2007 June). *2007 Guideline for Isolation Precautions: Preventing transmission of infectious agents in healthcare settings.* Pp. 17. Accessed December 10, 2008 from http://www.cdc.gov/ncidod/dhqp/pdf/isolation2007.pdf

[32] Sehulster, L.M., Chinn, R.Y.W., Arduino, M.J., Carpenter, J., Donlan, R., Ashford, D., Besser, R., Fields, B., McNeil, M.M., Whitney, C., Wong, S., Juranek, D., and Cleveland, J. (2003). *Guidelines for environmental infection control in health-care facilities. Recommendations from CDC and the Healthcare Infection Control Practices Advisory Committee (HICPAC).* Pp.139. Accessed December 10, 2008 from http://www.cdc.gov/ncidod/dhqp/pdf/guidelines/Enviro_guide_03.pdf

[33] Sehulster, L.M., Chinn, R.Y.W., Arduino, M.J., Carpenter, J., Donlan, R., Ashford, D., Besser, R., Fields, B., McNeil, M.M., Whitney, C., Wong, S., Juranek, D., and Cleveland, J. (2003). *Guidelines for environmental infection control in health-care facilities. Recommendations from CDC and the Healthcare Infection Control Practices Advisory Committee (HICPAC).* Pp.139. Accessed December 10, 2008 from http://www.cdc.gov/ncidod/dhqp/pdf/guidelines/Enviro_guide_03.pdf

[34] Sehulster, L.M., Chinn, R.Y.W., Arduino, M.J., Carpenter, J., Donlan, R., Ashford, D., Besser, R., Fields, B., McNeil, M.M., Whitney, C., Wong, S., Juranek, D., and Cleveland, J. (2003). *Guidelines for environmental infection control in health-care facilities. Recommendations from CDC and the Healthcare Infection Control Practices Advisory Committee (HICPAC).* Pp. 139. Accessed December 10, 2008 from http://www.cdc.gov/ncidod/dhqp/pdf/guidelines/Enviro_guide_03.pdf

[35] Sehulster, L.M., Chinn, R.Y.W., Arduino, M.J., Carpenter, J., Donlan, R., Ashford, D., Besser, R., Fields, B., McNeil, M.M., Whitney, C., Wong, S., Juranek, D., and Cleveland, J. (2003). *Guidelines for environmental infection control in health-care facilities. Recommendations from CDC and the Healthcare Infection Control Practices Advisory Committee (HICPAC).* Pp. 140. Accessed December 10, 2008 from http://www.cdc.gov/ncidod/dhqp/pdf/guidelines/Enviro_guide_03.pdf

[36] American Medical Directors Association (AMDA). (2006). *Clinical practice guideline; managing common infections in the assisted living setting. Assisted Living Consult*, Jan/Feb 2006: Pp.31

[37] American Medical Directors Association (AMDA). (2001). *Critical Issues in Infection Control, Focusing on VRE and MRSA in LTC Setting.*

[38] Williams, R.E.O. (1963). *Healthy carriage of Staphylococcus aureus: its prevalence and importance.* Bacterial Rev. 1963; 27:56-71

[39] Mayfield, J.L., Leet, T., Miller, J., and Mundy, L.M. (2000, Oct. 25). *Environmental control to reduce transmission of Clostridium Difficile. Clinical Infectious Disease.* 2000;31. Pp.998

[40] Morbidity and Mortality Weekly Report. (2002, August). *Guidelines for the Prevention of Intravascular Catheter-Related Infections Vol. 51, RR-10.* Centers for Disease Control and Prevention (CDC).

[This page intentionally left blank]

The Facility Guide to OBRA Regulations, and the Long Term Care Survey Process

- Survey Protocols (SOM, Appendix P)
  - Guidance to Surveyors (SOM, Appendix PP)
  - CMS Survey Process Forms

Chapter 3

**Exhibits - CMS Survey Process Forms
for Long-Term Care Facilities**

Sources

CMS Publication # 100-07, Appendix P, *State Operations Manual*, Transmittal # 9, dated August 5, 2005

www.cms.hhs.gov/manuals/107_som/som107c09_exhibitstoc.asp

The Facility Guide to OBRA Regulations and the Long-Term Care Survey Process

Exhibits - CMS Survey Process Forms for Long-Term Care Facilities

Table of Contents

[This page intentionally left blank]

DEPARTMENT OF HEALTH AND HUMAN SERVICES
CENTERS FOR MEDICARE & MEDICAID SERVICES

Exhibit 85

LONG TERM CARE FACILITY APPLICATION FOR MEDICARE AND MEDICAID

Standard Survey

From: F1 ☐☐☐☐☐☐ To: F2 ☐☐☐☐☐☐
　　　 MM　DD　YY　　　　 MM　DD　YY

Extended Survey

From: F3 ☐☐☐☐☐☐ To: F4 ☐☐☐☐☐☐
　　　 MM　DD　YY　　　　 MM　DD　YY

Name of Facility		Provider Number	Fiscal Year Ending: F5 ☐☐☐☐☐☐ MM DD YY
Street Address	City	County	State　Zip Code

Telephone Number: F6　　　　　　State/County Code: F7　　　　State/Region Code: F8

A. F9 ☐☐

　01 Skilled Nursing Facility (SNF) - Medicare Participation
　02 Nursing Facility (NF) - Medicaid Participation
　03 SNF/NF - Medicare/Medicaid

B. Is this facility hospital based? F10 Yes ☐ No ☐

　If yes, indicate Hospital Provider Number: F11 ☐☐☐☐☐☐☐

Ownership: F12 ☐☐

For Profit	**NonProfit**	**Government**	
01 Individual	04 Church Related	07 State	10 City/County
02 Partnership	05 Nonprofit Corporation	08 County	11 Hospital District
03 Corporation	06 Other Nonprofit	09 City	12 Federal

Owned or leased by Multi-Facility Organization:　F13　Yes ☐ No ☐

Name of Multi-Facility Organization:　F14

Dedicated Special Care Units (show number of beds for all that apply)

　F15 ☐☐ AIDS　　　　　　　　　　F16 ☐☐ Alzheimer's Disease
　F17 ☐☐ Dialysis　　　　　　　　　F18 ☐☐ Disabled Children/Young Adults
　F19 ☐☐ Head Trauma　　　　　　　F20 ☐☐ Hospice
　F21 ☐☐ Huntington's Disease　　　　F22 ☐☐ Ventilator/Respiratory Care
　F23 ☐☐ Other Specialized Rehabilitation

Does the facility currently have an organized residents group?	F24 Yes ☐	No ☐
Does the facility currently have an organized group of family members of residents?	F25 Yes ☐	No ☐
Does the facility conduct experimental research?	F26 Yes ☐	No ☐
Is the facility part of a continuing care retirement community (CCRC)?	F27 Yes ☐	No ☐

If the facility currently has a staffing waiver, indicate the type(s) of waiver(s) by writing in the date(s) of last approval.　Indicate the number of hours waived for each type of waiver granted.　If the facility does not have a waiver, write NA in the blanks.

　Waiver of seven day RN requirement.　　　　Date: F28 ☐☐☐☐☐☐ Hours waived per week: F29 _____
　Waiver of 24 hr licensed nursing requirement.　Date: F30 ☐☐☐☐☐☐ Hours waived per week: F31 _____
　　　　　　　　　　　　　　　　　　　　　　　MM　DD　YY

Does the facility currently have an approved Nurse Aide Training and Competency Evaluation Program?　F32 Yes ☐ No ☐

FACILITY STAFFING

	Tag Number	A Services Provided			B Full - Time Staff (hours)	C Part - Time Staff (hours)	D Contract (hours)
		1	2	3			
Administration	F33						
Physician Services	F34						
Medical Director	F35						
Other Physician	F36						
Physician Extender	F37						
Nursing Services	F38						
RN Director of Nurses	F39						
Nurses with Admin. Duties	F40						
Registered Nurses	F41						
Licensed Practical/Licensed Vocational Nurses	F42						
Certified Nurse Aides	F43						
Nurse Aides in Training	F44						
Medication Aides/Technicians	F45						
Pharmacists	F46						
Dietary Services	F47						
Dietitian	F48						
Food Service Workers	F49						
Therapeutic Services	F50						
Occupational Therapists	F51						
Occupational Therapy Assistants	F52						
Occupational Therapy Aides	F53						
Physical Therapists	F54						
Physical Therapists Assistants	F55						
Physical Therapy Aides	F56						
Speech/Language Pathologist	F57						
Therapeutic Recreation Specialist	F58						
Qualified Activities Professional	F59						
Other Activities Staff	F60						
Qualified Social Workers	F61						
Other Social Services	F62						
Dentists	F63						
Podiatrists	F64						
Mental Health Services	F65						
Vocational Services	F66						
Clinical Laboratory Services	F67						
Diagnostic X-ray Services	F68						
Administration and Storage of Blood	F69						
Housekeeping Services	F70						
Other	F71						

Name of Person Completing Form	Time
Signature	Date

GENERAL INSTRUCTIONS AND DEFINITIONS

(use with CMS-671 Long Term Care Facility Application for Medicare and Medicaid)

This Form is to be Completed by the Facility

For the purpose of this form "the facility" equals certified beds (i.e., Medicare and/or Medicaid certified beds).

Standard Survey - LEAVE BLANK - Survey team will complete
Extended Survey - LEAVE BLANK - Survey team will complete

INSTRUCTIONS AND DEFINITIONS

Name of Facility - Use the official name of the facility for business and mailing purposes. This includes components or units of a larger institution.

Provider Number - Leave blank on initial certifications. On all recertifications, insert the facility's assigned six-digit provider code.

Street Address - Street name and number refers to physical location, not mailing address, if two addresses differ.

City - Rural addresses should include the city of the nearest post office.

County - County refers to parish name in Louisiana and township name where appropriate in the New England States.

State - For U.S. possessions and trust territories, name is included in lieu of the State.

Zip Code - Zip Code refers to the "Zip-plus-four" code, if available, otherwise the standard Zip Code.

Telephone Number - Include the area code.

State/County Code - LEAVE BLANK - State Survey Office will complete.

State/Region Code - LEAVE BLANK - State Survey Office will complete.

Block F9 - Enter either 01 (SNF), 02 (NF), or 03 (SNF/NF).

Block F10 - If the facility is under administrative control of a hospital, check "yes," otherwise check "no."

Block F11 - The hospital provider number is the hospital's assigned six-digit Medicare provider number.

Block F12 - Identify the type of organization that controls and operates the facility. Enter the code as identified for that organization (e.g., for a for profit facility owned by an individual, enter 01 in the F12 block; a facility owned by a city government would be entered as 09 in the F12 block).

Definitions to determine ownership are:

FOR PROFIT - If operated under private commercial ownership, indicate whether owned by individual, partnership, or corporation.

NONPROFIT - If operated under voluntary or other nonprofit auspices, indicate whether church related, nonprofit corporation or other nonprofit.

GOVERNMENT - If operated by a governmental entity, indicate whether State, City, Hospital District, County, City/County or Federal Government.

Block F13 - Check "yes" if the facility is owned or leased by a multi-facility organization, otherwise check "no." A Multi-Facility Organization is an organization that owns two or more long term care facilities. The owner may be an individual or a corporation. Leasing of facilities by corporate chains is included in this definition.

Block F14 - If applicable, enter the name of the multi-facility organization. Use the name of the corporate ownership of the multi-facility organization (e.g., if the name of the facility is Soft Breezes Home and the name of the multi-facility organization that owns Soft Breezes is XYZ Enterprises, enter XYZ Enterprises).

Block F15-F23 - Enter the number of beds in the facility's Dedicated Special Care Units. These are units with a specific number of beds, identified and dedicated by the facility for residents with specific needs/diagnoses. They need not be certified or recognized by regulatory authorities. For example, a SNF admits a large number of residents with head injuries. They have set aside 8 beds on the north wing, staffed with specifically trained personnel. Show "8" in F19.

Block F24 - Check "yes" if the facility currently has an organized residents' group, i.e., a group(s) that meets regularly to discuss and offer suggestions about facility policies and procedures affecting residents' care, treatment, and quality of life; to support each other; to plan resident and family activities; to participate in educational activities or for any other purposes; otherwise check "no".

Block F25 - Check "yes" if the facility currently has an organized group of family members of residents, i.e., a group(s) that meets regularly to discuss and offer suggestions about facility policies and procedures affecting residents' care, treatment, and quality of life; to support each other, to plan resident and family activities; to participate in educational activities or for any other purpose; otherwise check "no."

GENERAL INSTRUCTIONS AND DEFINITIONS

Exhibit 85
(continued)

(use with CMS-671 Long Term Care Facility Application for Medicare and Medicaid)

Block F26 - Check "yes" if the facility conducts experimental research; otherwise check "no." Experimental research means using residents to develop and test clinical treatments, such as a new drug or therapy, that involves treatment and control groups. For example, a clinical trial of a new drug would be experimental research.

Block F27 - Check "yes" if the facility is part of a continuing care retirement community (CCRC); otherwise check "no." A CCRC is any facility which operates under State regulation as a continuing care retirement community.

Block F28-F31 - If the facility has been granted a nurse staffing waiver by CMS or the State Agency in accordance with the provisions at 42 CFR 483.30(c) or (d), enter the last approval date of the waiver(s) and report the number of hours being waived for each type of waiver approval.

Block F32 - Check "yes" if the facility has a State approved Nurse Aide Training and Competency Evaluation Program; otherwise check "no."

FACILITY STAFFING

GENERAL INSTRUCTIONS

This form requires you to identify whether certain services are provided and to specify the number of hours worked providing those services. Column A requires you to enter "yes" or "no" about whether the services are provided onsite to residents, onsite to nonresidents, and offsite to residents. Columns B-D requires you to enter the specific number of hours worked providing the service. To complete this section, base your calculations on the staff hours worked in the most recent complete pay period. If the pay period is more than 2 weeks, use the last 14 days. For example, if this survey begins on a Tuesday, staff hours are counted for the previous complete pay period.

Definition of Hours Worked - Hours are reported rounded to the nearest whole hour. Do not count hours paid for any type of leave or non-work related absence from the facility. If the service is provided, but has not been provided in the 2-week pay period, check the service in Column A, but leave B, C or D blank. If an individual provides service in more than one capacity, separate out the hours in each service performed. For example, if a staff person has worked a total of 80 hours in the pay period but has worked as an activity aide and as a Certified Nurse Aide, separately count the hours worked as a CNA and hours worked as an activity aide to reflect but not to exceed the total hours worked within the pay period.

Completion of Form

Column A - Services Provided - Enter Y (yes), N (no) under each sub-column. For areas that are blocked out, do not provide the information.

Column A-1 - Refers to those services provided onsite to residents, either by employees or contractors.

Column A-2 - Refers to those services provided onsite to non-resident

Column A-3 - Refers to those services provided to residents offsite/or not routinely provided onsite.

Column B - Full-time staff, C - Part-time staff, and D - Contract- Record hours worked for each field of full-time staff, part-time staff, and contract staff (do not include meal breaks of a half an hour or more). Full-time is defined as 35 or more hours worked per week. Part-time is anything less than 35 hours per week. Contract includes individuals under contract (e.g., a physical therapist) as well as organizations under contract (e.g., an agency to provide nurses). If an organization is under contract, calculate hours worked for the individuals provided. Lines blocked out (e.g., Physician services, Clinical labs) do not have hours worked recorded.

REMINDER - Use a 2-week period to calculate hours worked.

DEFINITION OF SERVICES

Administration - The administrative staff responsible for facility management such as the administrator, assistant administrator, unit managers and other staff in the individual departments, such as: Health Information Specialists (RRA/ARTI), clerical, etc. who do not perform services described below. Do not include the food service supervisor, housekeeping services supervisor, or facility engineer.

Physician Services - Any service performed by a physician at the facility, except services performed by a resident's personal physician.

Medical Director - A physician designated as responsible for implementation of resident care policies and coordination of medical care in the facility.

Other Physician - A salaried physician, other than the medical director, who supervises the care of residents when the attending physician is unavailable, and/or a physician(s) available to provide emergency services 24 hours a day.

Physician Extender - A nurse practitioner, clinical nurse specialist, or physician assistant who performs physician delegated services.

Nursing Services - Coordination, implementation, monitoring and management of resident care plans. Includes provision of personal care services, monitoring resident responsiveness to environment, range-of-motion exercises, application of sterile dressings, skin care, naso-gastric tubes, intravenous fluids, catheterization, administration of medications, etc.

GENERAL INSTRUCTIONS AND DEFINITIONS

Exhibit 85
(continued)

(use with CMS-671 Long Term Care Facility Application for Medicare and Medicaid)

Director of Nursing - Professional registered nurse(s) administratively responsible for managing and supervising nursing services within the facility. Do not additionally reflect these hours in any other category.

Nurses with Administrative Duties - Nurses (RN, LPN, LVN) who, as either a facility employee or contractor, perform the Resident Assessment Instrument function in the facility and do not perform direct care functions. Also include other nurses whose principal duties are spent conducting administrative functions. For example, the Assistant Director of Nursing is conducting educational/in-service, or other duties which are not considered to be direct care giving. Facilities with an RN waiver who do not have an RN as DON report all administrative nursing hours in this category.

Registered Nurses - Those persons licensed to practice as registered nurses in the State where the facility is located. Includes geriatric nurse practitioners and clinical nurse specialists who primarily perform nursing, not physician-delegated tasks. Do not include Registered Nurses' hours reported elsewhere.

Licensed Practical/Vocational Nurses - Those persons licensed to practice as licensed practical/vocational nurses in the State where the facility is located. Do not include those hours of LPN/LVNs reported elsewhere.

Certified Nurse Aides - Individuals who have completed a State approved training and competency evaluation program, or competency evaluation program approved by the State, or have been determined competent as provided in 483.150(a) and (3) and who are providing nursing or nursing-related services to residents. Do not include volunteers.

Nurse Aides in Training - Individuals who are in the first 4 months of employment and who are receiving training in a State approved Nurse Aide training and competency evaluation program and are providing nursing or nursing-related services for which they have been trained and are under the supervision of a licensed or registered nurse. Do not include volunteers.

Medication Aides/Technicians - Individuals, other than a licensed professional, who fulfill the State requirement for approval to administer medications to residents.

Pharmacists - The licensed pharmacist(s) who a facility is required to use for various purposes, including providing consultation on pharmacy services, establishing a system of records of controlled drugs, overseeing records and reconciling controlled drugs, and/or performing a monthly drug regimen review for each resident.

Dietary Services - All activities related to the provision of a nourishing, palatable, well-balanced diet that meets the daily nutritional and special dietary needs of each resident.

Dietitian - A person(s), employed full, part-time or on a consultant basis, who is either registered by the Commission of Dietetic Registration of the American Dietetic Association, or is qualified to be a dietitian on the basis of experience in identification of dietary needs, planning and implementation of dietary programs.

Food Service Workers - Persons (excluding the dietitian) who carry out the functions of the dietary service (e.g., prepare and cook food, serve food, wash dishes). Includes the food services supervisor.

Therapeutic Services - Services, other than medical and nursing, provided by professionals or their assistants, to enhance the residents' functional abilities and/or quality of life.

Occupational Therapists - Persons licensed/registered as occupational therapists according to State law in the State in which the facility is located. Include OTs who spend less than 50 percent of their time as activities therapists.

Occupational Therapy Assistants - Person(s) who, in accord with State law, have licenses/certification and specialized training to assist a licensed/certified/registered Occupational Therapist (OT) to carry out the OT's comprehensive plan of care, without the direct supervision of the therapist. Include OT Assistants who spend less than 50 percent of their time as Activities Therapists.

Occupational Therapy Aides - Person(s) who have specialized training to assist an OT to carry out the OT's comprehensive plan of care under the direct supervision of the therapist, in accord with State law.

Physical Therapists - Persons licensed/registered as physical therapists, according to State law where the facility is located.

Physical Therapy Assistants - Person(s) who in accord with State law, have licenses/certification and specialized training to assist a licensed/certified/registered Physical Therapist (PT) to carry out the PT's comprehensive plan of care, without the direct supervision of the PT.

Physical Therapy Aides - Person(s) who, have specialized training to assist a PT to carry out the PT's comprehensive plan of care under the direct supervision of the therapist, in accord with State law.

Speech-Language Pathologists - Persons licensed/registered, according to State law where the facility is located, to provide speech therapy and related services (e.g., teaching a resident to swallow).

Exhibit 85
(continued)

GENERAL INSTRUCTIONS AND DEFINITIONS
(use with CMS-671 Long Term Care Facility Application for Medicare and Medicaid)

Therapeutic Recreation Specialist - Person(s) who, in accordance with State law, are licensed/registered and are eligible for certification as a therapeutic recreation specialist by a recognized accrediting body.

Qualified Activities Professional - Person(s) who meet the definition of activities professional at 483.15(f)(2)(i)(A) and (B) or 483.15(f)(2)(ii) or (iii) or (iv) and who are providing an on-going program of activities designed to meet residents' interests and physical, mental or psychosocial needs. Do not include hours reported as Therapeutic Recreation Specialist, Occupational Therapist, OT Assistant, or other categories listed above.

Other Activities Staff - Persons providing an on-going program of activities designed to meet residents' needs and interests. Do not include volunteers or hours reported elsewhere.

Qualified Social Worker(s) - Person licensed to practice social work in the State where the facility is located, or if licensure is not required, persons with a bachelor's degree in social work, a bachelor's degree in a human services field including but not limited to sociology, special education, rehabilitation counseling and psychology, and one year of supervised social work experience in a health care setting working directly with elderly individuals.

Other Social Services Staff - Person(s) other than the qualified social worker who are involved in providing medical social services to residents. Do not include volunteers.

Dentists - Persons licensed as dentists, according to State law where the facility is located, to provide routine and emergency dental services.

Podiatrists - Persons licensed/registered as podiatrists, according to State law where the facility is located, to provide podiatric care.

Mental Health Services - Staff (excluding those included under therapeutic services) who provide programs of services targeted to residents' mental, emotional, psychological, or psychiatric well-being and which are intended to:

- Diagnose, describe, or evaluate a resident's mental or emotional status;
- Prevent deviations from mental or emotional well-being from developing; or
- Treat the resident according to a planned regimen to assist him/her in regaining, maintaining, or increasing emotional abilities to function

Among the specific services included are psychotherapy and counseling; and administration and monitoring of psychotropic medications targeted to a psychiatric diagnosis.

Vocational Services - Evaluation and training aimed at assisting the resident to enter, re-enter, or maintain employment in the labor force, including training for jobs in integrated settings (i.e., those which have both disabled and nondisabled workers) as well as in special settings such as sheltered workshops.

Clinical Laboratory Services - Entities that provide laboratory services and are approved by Medicare as independent laboratories or hospitals.

Diagnostic X-ray Services - Radiology services, ordered by a physician, for diagnosis of a disease or other medical condition.

Administration and Storage of Blood Services - Blood bank and transfusion services.

Housekeeping Services - Services, including those of the maintenance department, necessary to maintain the environment. Includes equipment kept in a clean, safe, functioning and sanitary condition. Includes housekeeping services supervisor and facility engineer.

Other - Record total hours worked for all personnel not already recorded, (e.g., if a librarian works 10 hours and a laundry worker works 10 hours, record 00020 in Column C).

Department of Health and Human Services
Centers for Medicare & Medicaid Services

Exhibit 264

RESIDENT CENSUS AND CONDITIONS OF RESIDENTS

Provider No.	Medicare		Medicaid		Other		Total Residents	
		F75		F76		F77		F78

ADL	Independent	Assist of One or Two Staff	Dependent
Bathing	F79	F80	F81
Dressing	F82	F83	F84
Transferring	F85	F86	F87
Toilet Use	F88	F89	F90
Eating	F91	F92	F93

A. Bowel/Bladder Status

F94_____ With indwelling or external catheter

F95 Of total number of residents with catheters, _____ were present on admission.

F96_____ Occasionally or frequently incontinent of bladder

F97_____ Occasionally or frequently incontinent of bowel

F98_____ On individually written bladder training program

F99_____ On individually written bowel training program

B. Mobility

F100_____ Bedfast all or most of time

F101_____ In chair all or most of time

F102_____ Independently ambulatory

F103_____ Ambulation with assistance or assistive device

F104_____ Physically restrained

F105 Of total number of residents restrained, _____ were admitted with orders for restraints.

F106_____ With contractures

F107 Of total number of residents with contractures, _____ had contractures on admission.

C. Mental Status

F108_____ With mental retardation

F109_____ With documented signs and symptoms of depression

F110_____ With documented psychiatric diagnosis (exclude dementias and depression)

F111_____ Dementia: multi-infarct, senile, Alzheimer's type, or other than Alzheimer's type

F112_____ With behavioral symptoms

F113 Of the total number of residents with behavioral symptoms, the total number receiving a behavior management program_____ .

F114_____ Receiving health rehabilitative services for MI/MR

D. Skin Integrity

F115_____ With pressure sores (exclude Stage I)

F116 Of the total number of residents with pressure sores excluding Stage I, how many residents had pressure sores on admission?_____ .

F117_____ Receiving preventive skin care

F118_____ With rashes

FORM CMS-672 (10/98)

RESIDENT CENSUS AND CONDITIONS OF RESIDENTS

E. Special Care

F119 _____ Receiving hospice care benefit

F120 _____ Receiving radiation therapy

F121 _____ Receiving chemotherapy

F122 _____ Receiving dialysis

F123 _____ Receiving intravenous therapy, parenteral nutrition, nutrition, and/or blood transfusion

F124 _____ Receiving respiratory treatment

F125 _____ Receiving tracheostomy care

F126 _____ Receiving ostomy care

F127 _____ Receiving suctioning

F128 _____ Receiving injections (exclude vitamin B12 injections)

F129 _____ Receiving tube feedings

F130 _____ Receiving mechanically altered diets including pureed and all chopped food (not only meat)

F131 _____ Receiving specialized rehabilitative services (Physical therapy, speech-language therapy, occupational therapy)

F132 _____ Assistive devices while eating

F. Medications

F133 _____ Receiving any psychoactive medication

   F134 _____ Receiving antipsychotic medications

   F135 _____ Receiving antianxiety medications

   F136 _____ Receiving antidepressant medications

   F137 _____ Receiving hypnotic medications

F138 _____ Receiving antibiotics

F139 _____ On pain management program

G. Other

F140 _____ With unplanned significant weight loss/gain

F141 _____ Who do not communicate in the dominant language of the facility (include those who use sign language)

F142 _____ Who use non-oral communication devices

F143 _____ With advance directives

F144 _____ Received influenza immunization

F145 _____ Received pneumococcal vaccine

I certify that this information is accurate to the best of my knowledge.

Signature of Person Completing the Form	Title	Date

TO BE COMPLETED BY SURVEY TEAM

F146 Was ombudsman office notified prior to survey?   Yes ☐   No ☐

F147 Was ombudsman present during any portion of the survey?   Yes ☐   No ☐

F148 Medication error rate _____ %

RESIDENT CENSUS AND CONDITIONS OF RESIDENTS
(use with Form CMS 672)

Exhibit 264
(continued)

GENERAL INSTRUCTIONS
THIS FORM IS TO BE COMPLETED BY THE FACILITY AND REPRESENTS THE CURRENT
CONDITION OF RESIDENTS AT THE TIME OF COMPLETION

There is not a federal requirement for automation of the 672 form. The facility may continue to complete the 672 with manual methods. The facility may use the MDS data to start the 672 form, but must verify all information, and in some cases, re-code the item responses to meet the intent of the 672 to represent current resident status according to the definitions of the 672. Since the census is designed to be a representation of the facility during the survey, it does not directly correspond to the MDS in every item.

For the purpose of this form "the facility" equals certified beds (i.e., Medicare and/or Medicaid certified beds).

For the purpose of this form "residents" means residents in certified beds regardless of payor source.

Following the definition of each field, the related MDS 2.0 codes and instructions will be noted within square brackets ([ ]).

Where coding refers to the admission assessment, use the first assessment done after the most recent admission or readmission event.

Complete each item by specifying the number of residents characterized by each category. If no residents fall into a category enter a "0."

INSTRUCTIONS AND DEFINITIONS

Provider No. - Enter the facility's assigned provider number. Leave blank for initial certifications.

Block F75 - Enter the number of facility residents, whose primary payer is Medicare. [code manually]

Block F76 - Enter the number of facility residents, whose primary payer is Medicaid. [code manually]

Block F77 - Enter the number of facility residents, whose primary payer is neither Medicare nor Medicaid. [code manually]

Block F78 - Enter the number of total residents for whom a bed is maintained, on the day the survey begins, including those temporarily away in a hospital or on leave. [Total residents in nursing facility or on bedhold]

ADLS (F79 - F93)

To determine resident status, unless otherwise noted, consider the resident's condition for the 7 days prior to the survey. [Horizontal totals must equal the number in F78; Manually re-code all "8" responses.]

Bathing (F79 - F81)

The process of bathing the body (excluding back and shampooing hair). This includes a full-body bath/shower, sponge bath, and transfer into and out of tub or shower. [F79: G2A = 0; F80: G2A = 1, 2, 3; F81: G2A = 4]

Many facilities routinely provide "setup" assistance to all residents such as drawing water for a tub bath or laying out bathing materials. If this is the case and the resident requires no other assistance, count the resident as independent.

ADLS (F79 - F93) - continued

Dressing (F82 - F84)

How the resident puts on, fastens, and takes off all items of street clothing, including donning or removing prostheses (e.g., braces and artificial limbs). [F82: G1Ag = 0; F83: G1Ag = 1, 2, 3; F84: G1Ag = 4]

Many facilities routinely set out clothes for all residents. If this is the case and this is the only assistance the resident receives, count the resident as independent. However, if a resident receives assistance with donning a brace, elastic stocking, a prothesis and so on, securing fasteners, or putting a garment on, count the resident as needing the assistance of 1 or 2 staff.

Transferring (F85 - F87)

How the resident moves between surfaces, such as to and from the bed, chair, wheelchair or to and from a standing position. (EXCLUDE transfers to and from the bath or toilet). [F85: G1Ab = 0; F86: G1Ab = 1, 2, 3; F87: G1Ab = 4]

Many facilities routinely provide "setup" assistance to all residents, such as handing the equipment (e.g., sliding board) to the resident. If this is the case and is the only assistance required, count the resident as independent.

Toilet Use (F88 - F90)

How the resident uses the toilet room (or bedpan, bedside commode, or urinal). How resident transfers on and off toilet, cleans self after elimination, changes sanitary napkins, ostomy, external catheters, and adjust clothing prior to and after using toilet. If all that is done for the resident is to open a package (e.g., a clean sanitary pad), count the resident as independent. [F88: G1Ai = 0; F89: G1Ai = 1, 2, 3; F90: G1Ai = 4]

ADLS (F79 - F93) - continued

Eating (F91 - F93)

How resident eats and drinks regardless of skill. Many facilities routinely provide "setup" activities, such as opening containers, buttering bread, and organizing the tray; if this is the case and is the extent of assistance, count this resident as independent. [F91: G1Ah = 0; F92: G1Ah = 1, 2, 3; F93: G1Ah = 4]

A. BOWEL/BLADDER STATUS (F94 - F99)

F94 - With an indwelling or an external catheter - The number of residents whose urinary bladder is constantly drained by a catheter (e.g., a Foley catheter, a suprapubic catheter) or who wears an appliance that is applied over the penis and connected to a drainage bag to collect urine from the bladder (e.g., a Texas catheter). [H3c or d = check]

F95 - Of the total number of residents with catheters - The number of residents who had a catheter present on admission. For a resident readmitted from a hospital with a catheter, count this resident as admitted with a catheter. [H3c or d = check and A8a = 1 or A8b = 1 or 5]

F96 - Occasionally or frequently incontinent of bladder - The number of residents who have an incontinent episode two or more times per week. Do not include residents with an indwelling or external catheter. [H1b = 2, 3 or 4 and H3c and d are not = check]

F97 - Occasionally or frequently incontinent of bowel - The number of residents who have a loss of bowel control two or more times per week. [H1a = 2, 3 or 4]

F98 - On individually written bladder training program - The number of residents with a detailed plan of care to assist the resident to gain and maintain bladder control (e.g., pelvic floor exercises). Count all residents on training programs including those who are incontinent. [H3b = check]

F99 - On individually written bowel training program - The number of residents with a detailed plan of care to assist the resident to gain and maintain bowel control (e.g., use of diet, fluids, and regular schedule for bowel movements). Count all residents on training programs including those who are incontinent. [code manually]

B. MOBILITY (F100 - F107)

[Total for F100 - F103 should = F78; Algorithm to force mutual exclusivity: Test for each resident. If F100 = 1 then add 1 to F100, and go to the next resident; If F101 = 1 then add 1 to F101 and go to the next resident; If F103 = 1 then add 1 to F103 and go to the next resident; If F102 = 1 then add 1 and go to the next resident.]

F100 - Bedfast all or most of time - The number of residents who were in bed or recliner 22 hours or more per day in the past 7 days. Includes bedfast with bathroom privileges. [G6a = check and G5d is not = check]

F101 - In chair all or most of time - The number of residents who depend on a chair for mobility. Includes those residents who can stand with assistance to pivot from bed to wheelchair or to otherwise transfer. The resident cannot take steps without extensive or constant weight-bearing support from others and is not bedfast all or most of the time. [G5d = check]

B. MOBILITY (F100 - F107) continued

F102 - Independently ambulatory - The number of residents who require no help or oversight; or help or oversight was provided only 1 or 2 times during the past 7 days. Do not include residents who use a cane, walker or crutch. [G1ac = 0 and G1Ad = 0 and G5a is not = check]

F103 - Ambulation with assistance or assistive devices - The number of residents who required oversight, cueing, physical assistance or who used a cane, walker, crutch. Count the use of lower leg splints, orthotics, and braces as assistive devices. [G1Ac or d = 1, 2 or 3 or G5a = check]

F104 - Physically restrained - The number of residents whose freedom of movement and/or normal access to his/her body is restricted by any manual method or physical or mechanical device, material or equipment that is attached or adjacent to his/her body and cannot be easily removed by the resident. [Any P4c, d or e = 1 or 2]

F105 - Of total number of restrained residents, number admitted or readmitted with an order for restraint. [Code manually when criteria for F104 is met and P4c, d or e = 1 or 2 and A8a = 1 or A8b = 1 or 5]

F106 - With contractures - The number of residents that have a restriction of full passive range of motion of any joint due to deformity, disuse, pain, etc. Includes loss of range of motion in fingers, wrists, elbows, shoulders, hips, knees and ankles. [Any G4Aa, b, c, d, e or f = 1 or 2]

F107- Of total of residents with contractures, the number who had a contracture(s) on admission. [Code when criteria for F106 is met on admission or readmission assessment and A8a = 1 or A8b = 1 or 5.]

C. MENTAL STATUS (F108 - F114)

F108 - With mental retardation - Identify the total number of residents in all of the categories of developmental disability regardless of severity, as determined by the State Mental Health or State Mental Retardation Authorities. [Any AB10b, c, e or f = check]

F109 - With documented signs and symptoms of depression - The total number of residents with documented signs and symptoms of depression as defined by MDS (Mood and Behavior Section). [I1ee = check or E1a, e, l or m > 0]

F110 - With documented psychiatric diagnosis (exclude dementias and depression) - The number of residents with primary or secondary psychiatric diagnosis including:

- Schizophrenia
- Schizo-affective disorder
- Schizophreniform disorder
- Delusional disorder
- Psychotic mood disorders (including mania and depression with psychotic features, acute psychotic episodes, brief reactive psychosis, and atypical psychosis). [I1dd, ff, or gg = check. Code manually for other psychiatric diagnoses listed here.]

F111 - Dementia: Multi-infarct, senile, Alzheimer's type, or other than Alzheimer's type - The number of residents with a primary or secondary diagnosis of dementia or organic mental syndrome including multi-infarct, senile type, Alzheimer's type, or other than Alzheimer's type. [I1q or u = check]

Exhibit 264
(continued)

Chapter 3

C. MENTAL STATUS (F108 - F114) continued

F112 - With behavioral symptoms - The number of residents with one or more of the following symptoms: wandering, verbally abusive, physically abusive, socially inappropriate/disruptive, resistive to care. (See MDS Section (Mood and Behavioral Patterns)). [Any E4Aa, b, c, d or e = 1, 2 or 3]

F113 - Of the total number with behavioral symptoms, the number receiving a behavior management program. The number of residents with behavior symptoms who are receiving an individualized care plan/program designed to address behavioral symptoms (as listed above). [Manually code when criteria for F112 is met and P2a = check and P2c or d = check]

F114 - Receiving health rehabilitative services for MI/MR - The number of residents for whom the facility is providing health rehabilitative services for MI/MR as defined at 483.45(a). [Use item for Residents who meet F108 or F110, then code manually]

D. SKIN INTEGRITY (F115- F118)

F115 - With pressure sores - The number of residents with ischemic ulcerations and/or necrosis of tissues overlying a bony prominence (exclude Stage I). [Any M1b, c or d > 0 or M2a > 1 code for first assessment after latest admission or re-admission]

F116 - Of the total number of residents with pressure sores excluding Stage I, the number who had pressure sores on admission or who were readmitted with a new pressure sore (exclude Stage I). [Code when criteria for field 115 are met and A8a = 1 or A8b = 1 or 5.]

F117 - Receiving preventive skin care - The number of residents receiving non-routine skin care provided according to a physician's order, and/or included in the resident's comprehensive plan of care (e.g., hydrocortisone ointment to areas of dermatitis three times a day, granulex sprays, etc.) [Any M5a, b, c, d, e, f, g, h, or i = check]

F118 - With rashes - Enter the number of residents who have rashes which may or may not be treated with any medication or special baths, etc. (e.g., but not limited to antifungals, cortisteroids, emollients, dipherydramines or scabiciduls, etc.) [M4d = check]

E. SPECIAL CARE (F119 - F132)

F119 - Receiving hospice care - Number of residents who have elected or are currently receiving the hospice benefit. [P1ao = check]

F120 - Receiving radiation therapy - The number of residents who are under a treatment plan involving radiation therapy. [P1ah = check]

F121 - Receiving chemotherapy - The number of residents under a specific treatment plan involving chemotherapy. [P1aa = check]

F122 - Receiving dialysis - The number of residents receiving hemodialysis or peritoneal dialysis either within the facility or offsite. [P1ab = check]

F123 - Receiving intravenous therapy, IV nutritional feedings and/or blood transfusion - The number of residents receiving fluids, medications, all or most of their nutritional requirements and/or blood and blood products administered intravenously. [K5a = check or P1ac = check or P1ak = check]

E. SPECIAL CARE (F119 - F132) continued

F124 - Receiving respiratory treatment - The number of residents receiving treatment by the use of respirators/ventilators, oxygen, IPPB or other inhalation therapy, pulmonary toilet, humidifiers, and other methods to treat conditions of the respiratory tract. This does not include residents receiving tracheotomy care or respiratory suctioning. [P1ag = check or P1al = check or P1bdA > 0]

F125 - Receiving tracheotomy care - The number of residents receiving care involved in maintenance of the airway, the stoma and surrounding skin, and dressings/coverings for the stoma. [P1aj = check]

F126 - Receiving ostomy care - The number of residents receiving care for a colostomy, ileostomy, uretrostomy, or other ostomy of the intestinal and/or urinary tract. DO NOT include tracheotomy. [P1af = check]

F127 - Receiving suctioning - The number of residents that require use of a mechanical device which provides suction to remove secretions from the respiratory tract via the mouth, nasal passage, or tracheotomy stoma. [P1ai = check]

F128 - Receiving injections - The number of residents that have received one or more injections within the past 7 days. (Exclude injections of Vitamin B12.) [Review residents for whom O3 = 1, 2, 3, 4, 5, 6 or 7. Omit from count any resident whose only injection currently is B12.]

F129 - Receiving tube feeding - The number of residents who receive all or most of their nutritional requirements via a feeding tube that delivers food/nutritional substances directly into the GI system (e.g., naso-gastric tube, gastrostomy tube). [K5b = check]

F130 - Receiving mechanically altered diets - The number of residents receiving a mechanically altered diet including pureed and/or chopped foods (not only meat). [K5c = check]

F131 - Receiving rehabilitative services - The number of residents receiving care designed to improve functional ability provided by, or under the direction of a rehabilitation professional (physical therapist, occupational therapist, speech-language pathologist. (Exclude health rehab. for MI/MR.) [P1baA or P1bbA or P1bcA > 0]

F132 - Assistive devices with eating - The number of residents who are using devices to maintain independence and to provide comfort when eating (i.e., plates with guards, large handled flatware, large handle mugs, extend hand flatware, etc.) [K5g = check]

F. MEDICATIONS (F133 - F139)

F133 - Receiving psychoactive drugs - The number of residents that receive drugs classified as anti-depressants, anti-anxiety, sedative and hypnotics, and anti-psychotics. [Any O4a, b, c or d = 1, 2, 3, 4, 5, 6 or 7]

Use the following lists to assist you in determining the number of residents receiving psychoactive drugs. These lists are not meant to be all inclusive, therefore, a resident receiving a psychoactive drug not on this list, should be counted under F133 and any other drug category that applies - F134, F135, F136, and/or F137.

F. MEDICATIONS (F133 - F139) continued

F134 - Receiving antipsychotic medications [O4a = 1, 2, 3, 4, 5, 6 or 7]

Clorazil (Clozapine)
Haldol (Haloperidol)
Haldol Decanoate (Haloperiodal Deconate)
Inapsine (Droperidol)
Loxitane (Loxapine)
Mellaril (Thioridazine)
Moban (Molindone)
Navane (Theothixene)
Olazapine (Zyprexa)
Orap (Pimozide)
Prolixin, Deconate (Fluphenazine Deconate)

Prolixin, Permitil (Fluphenazine)
Quetiapine (Seroquel)
Risperdal (Risperidone)
Serentil (Mesoridazine)
Sparine (Promazine)
Stelazine (Trifluoperazine)
Taractan (Chlorprothixene)
Thorazine (Chlorpromazine)
Tindel (Acetophenazine)
Trilafon (Perphenazine)

F135 - Receiving Anti-anxiety medications [O4b = 1, 2, 3, 4, 5, 6 or 7]

Ativan (Lorazepam)
Centrax (Prazepam)
Klonopin (Clonazepam)
Librium (Chlordiazepoxide)
Paxipam (Halazepam)

Serax (Oxazepam)
Valium (Diazepam)
Vistaril, Atarax (Hydroxyzine)
Xanax (Alprazolam)

F136 - Receiving Antidepressant medications [O4c = 1, 2, 3, 4, 5, 6 or 7]

Asendin (Amoxapine)
Aventyl, Pamelor (Nortriptyline)
Bupropion (Wellbutrin)
Desyrel (Trazodone)
Effexor (Venlafaxine)
Elavil (Amtriptyline)
Lithonate, Lithane (Lithium)
Ludiomil (Maprotiline)
Marplan (Isocarboxazid)
Nardil (Phenelzine)
Nefazodone (Serzone)
Norpramin (Desipramine)

Parnate (Tranylcypromine)
Paroxetine (Paxil)
Prozac (Fluoxetine)
Sertraline (Zoloft)
Sinequan (Doxepin)
Tofranil (Imipramine)
Vivactil (Protriptyline)

F137 - Receiving hypnotic medications [O4d = 1, 2, 3, 4, 5, 6 or 7]

Dalmane (Flurazepam)
Estazolam (ProSom)
Halcion (Triazolam)

Quazepam (Doral)
Restoril (Temazepam)
Zolpidem (Ambien)

F138 - Receiving antibiotics - The number of residents receiving sulfonamides, antibiotics, etc., either for prophylaxis or treatment. [Code manually]

F139 - On a pain management program - The number of residents with a specific plan for control of difficult to manage or intractable pain, which may include self medication pumps or regularly scheduled administration of medication alone or in combination with alternative approaches (e.g., massages, heat, etc.). [Code manually when any J3a, b, c, d, e, f, g, h, i or j = check]

G. OTHER RESIDENT CHARACTERISTICS (F140-F146)

F140 - With unplanned or significant weight loss/gain - The number of residents who have experienced gain or loss of 5% in one month or 10% over six months. [K3a or K3b = 1 and K5h is not = check]

F141 - Who do not communicate in the dominant language at the facility - The number of residents who only express themselves in a language not dominant at the facility (e.g., this would include residents who speak only Spanish, but the majority of staff that care for the residents speak only English). [code manually]

F142 - Who use non-oral communication devices (e.g., picture board, computers, sign-language). [Any C3b, c, d, e, or f = check]

F143 - Who have advanced directives (living will/durable power of attorney). The number of residents who have advanced directives, such as a living will or durable power of attorney for health care, recognized under state law and relating to the provisions of care when the individual is incapacitated. [Any A10a, b, c, f, g, or h = check]

F144 - Received influenza immunization - The number of residents known to have received the influenza immunization within the last 12 months. [code manually]

F145 - Received pneumococcal vaccine - The number of residents known to have received the pneumococcal vaccine. [code manually]

F146 - Ombudsman notice -LEAVE BLANK. This will be completed by survey team. Indicate yes or no whether Ombudsman office was notified prior to survey.

F147 - LEAVE BLANK. This will be completed by the survey team. Indicate whether Ombudsman was present at any time during the survey, 1 (yes) or 2 (no).

F148 - Medication error rate - LEAVE BLANK. This will be completed by the survey team.

DEPARTMENT OF HEALTH AND HUMAN SERVICES
CENTERS FOR MEDICARE & MEDICAID SERVICES

Exhibit 87

EXTENDED/PARTIAL EXTENDED SURVEY WORKSHEET

Facility	Standard or Abbreviated Survey Dates
	___/___/___ to ___/___/___ Mo Day Yr Mo Day Yr
Provider No.	Extended/Partial Extended Survey Dates
	___/___/___ to ___/___/___ Mo Day Yr Mo Day Yr

☐ **Extended Survey**: Substandard care determined during Standard Survey resulting in Extended Survey.

☐ **Partial Extended Survey**: Substandard care determined during Abbreviated Survey resulting in Partial Extended Survey.

Check all requirements not met that resulted in the Extended or Partial Extended Survey.

☐ **483.13**   ☐ **483.15**   ☐ **483.25**

Document observations from extended/partial extended survey

Tag/Concern	

FORM CMS-673 (7/95)

(continued on back)

SOM, Exhibits - CMS Survey Process Forms

(Revised August 2007)

Document observations from extended/partial extended survey (continued)

Tag/Concern	

MEDICATION PASS WORKSHEET

Exhibit 88

Provider Number	Surveyor Name	Date	Error Rate

Instructions: 1. Observe Pass for 20-25 opportunities for error. If one or more errors is found observe another 20-25 opportunities for error. 2. Record your observation of each opportunity for error. 3. Compare your record with physican orders. 4. Calculate and note error rate.

Deficiency Formulas:

1. One or more Significant Errors = Deficiency

2. $\dfrac{\text{Significant Error} + \text{Non-Significant Error}}{\text{Doses given} + \text{Doses ordered but not given}} \times 100 \geq 5\% = \text{Deficiency}$

Identifier	Pour	Pass	Record
Resident's Full Name	Drug Prescription Name, Dose and Form	Observation of Administration	Drug Order Written As *(when different from observation)*

MEDICATION PASS WORKSHEET

Identifier	Pour	Pass	Record
Resident's Full Name	Drug Prescription Name, Dose and Form	Observation of Administration	Drug Order Written As *(when different from observation)*

DEPARTMENT OF HEALTH AND HUMAN SERVICES
CENTERS FOR MEDICARE & MEDICAID SERVICES

Exhibit 89

OFFSITE SURVEY PREPARATION WORKSHEET

Facility Name:_____   **Ombudsman Name/Number:**_____

Facility Address:_____   **Ombudsman Contact Date:**_____

Provider Number:_____   **Offsite Review Date:**_____

Total Beds:_____   **Survey Begin Date:**_____

List potential facility areas of concern and any potential residents to be reviewed during the survey. List any current compliants to be investigated onsite.

_____

_____

_____

_____

_____

_____

_____

_____

_____

_____

_____

_____

_____

_____

_____

_____

_____

_____

_____

Surveyors/Discipline (list Team Coordinator first):

_____

_____

_____

_____

_____

FORM CMS-801 (7/95)

[This page intentionally left blank]

DEPARTMENT OF HEALTH AND HUMAN SERVICES
CENTERS FOR MEDICARE & MEDICAID SERVICES

Roster/Sample Matrix - Exhibit 265

Offsite _____ Phase I _____ Phase 2 _____ Prov. # _____

Review | **For Surveyor Use** | **Resident Characteristics**

Total Sample:
Phase 1 _____
Phase 2 _____
Individual Interview (I) _____
Family Interview (F) _____
Closed Record (CL) _____
Comprehensive (C) _____
Focused Review (F) _____

#	Heading
	Resident Number
	Resident Room
	Surveyor Assigned
	Resident Name
	Interview: Indiv/Fam
	Closed Rec/Compr/Focus
1	Privacy/Dignity Issues
2	Social Services
3	Choices
4	Abuse/Neglect
5	Clean/Comfort/Homelike
6	Falls/Fx/Abras/Bruise
7	Behavior Symp/Depression
8	9 or more Meds
9	Cognitive Impairment
10	Incont/Toilet Program (Elimination)
11	Catheter
12	Fecal Impaction
13	UTI/Inf Control/Antibio
14	Wt/Nutr/Swallow/Denture (Nutrition)
15	Tube Feeding
16	Dehydration
17	Bedfast Residents (Phys. Funct)
18	ADL Decline/Concern
19	ROM/Contract/Position
20	Psychoactive Meds
21	Physical Restraints (Q of Life)
22	Activities
23	Pressure Sores/Ulcers
24	Pain/Comfort
25	Language/Communication
26	Vision/Hearing/Devices
27	Specialized Rehab
28	Assistive Devices
29	Hospice
30	Dialysis
31	O$_2$/Respiratory
32	Admit/Trans/Disch
33	MR/MI (Non-Dementia)
34	
35	

Form CMS-802 (7/99)

[This page intentionally left blank]

EXHIBIT 266
Rev. 9, 08/05/2005

ROSTER/SAMPLE MATRIX PROVIDER INSTRUCTIONS
(use with FORM CMS-802)

The Roster/Sample Matrix form (CMS-802) is used by the facility to list all current residents (including residents on bedhold) and to note pertinent care categories. **The facility completes the following: resident name, resident room, and columns 6–33, which are described below.** All remaining columns are for Surveyor Use Only.

There is not a federal requirement for automation of Form CMS-802. The facility may continue manual coding of Form CMS-802. The facility may use MDS data to provide a "worksheet" of the form, but must amend item responses as necessary to represent current resident status on the first day of the survey. The MDS crosswalk items below are provided as a reference point, but the form is to be completed using the time frames and other specific instructions below. The information required on the Provider Instructions is not based on the Quality Measures/Indicators.

For each resident mark all columns that are pertinent.

6. **Falls/Fx/Abrasions/Bruises** – If the resident currently has abrasions, bruises, skin tears; has fallen within the past 30 days; or has had a fracture within the last 180 days.
   - Mark A if the resident has abrasions, skin tears or bruises, Fx for fractures and F for fallen.
   Crosswalk:
   If M4a checked or M4f checked, then 802 - 6 = A.
   If I1m checked or I1p checked or J4c checked or J4d checked, then 802 - 6 = Fx.
   If J4a checked, then 802 - 6 F.

7. **Behavioral Symptoms/Depression** – If the resident has behavioral symptoms or symptoms of depression, as listed in the MDS, mark this column.
   - Mark B for behavior and D for depression.
   Crosswalk:
   If E4A a, b, c, d or e are greater than 0, then 802 - 7 = B.
   If E5 = 2, then 802 - 7 = B.
   If E1a, b, c, d, e, f, g, h, i, j, k, l, m, n, o, p are greater than 0, then 802 - 7 = D.
   If E2 = 2, then 802 - 7 = D.
   If E3 = 2, then 802 - 7 = D.
   If I1ee checked, then 802 - 7 = D.

8. **9 or More Medications** – If the resident is using 9 or more medications, check this column.
   Crosswalk:
   If O1 is greater than 8, then 802 - 8 = checked.

9. **Cognitive Impairment** – If the resident is cognitively impaired, check this column.
   Crosswalk:
   If B5a, b, c, d, e or f are greater than 0, then 802 - 9 = checked.
   If B2a or b = 1, then 802 - 9 = checked.
   If B4 is greater than 1, then 802 - 9 = checked.

10. **Incontinence/Toileting Programs** – If the resident is incontinent of bladder, mark I. If the resident is on a bladder training program, mark T.

Crosswalk:
If H1b = 3 or 4, then 802 - 10 = I.
If H4 = 2 then 802 - 10 = I.
If H3b checked, then 802 - 10 = T.

11. **Catheter** – If the resident has an indwelling urinary catheter, check this column.
   Crosswalk:
   If H3d checked, then 802 - 11 = checked.

12. **Fecal Impaction** – If the resident has had fecal impaction within the last 90 days, check this column. Note: MDS item H2d only includes the past 14 days.
   Crosswalk:
   If H2d checked, then 802 - 12 = checked.

13. **UTI/Infection Control/Antibiotics** – If the resident has an infection or is on antibiotics, check this column.
   Crosswalk:
   Consider I2a, b, c, d, e, f, g, h, i, j, k, l checked or M6b checked, then 802 - 13 = checked, but amend this information to show the resident's condition on the day of the survey.

14. **Weight Change/Nutrition/Swallowing/Dentures** – If the resident has had an unintended weight loss/gain of 5% in one month or 10% in six months, has had chronic insidious weight loss or is at nutritional risk, mark this column. If the resident is in a restorative dining program, has chewing or swallowing problems that may affect dietary intake, or has dentures, mark this column.
   - Mark W for weight change, S for chewing or swallowing problems, D for dentures, and R for restorative dining program.
   Crosswalk:
   If J1a checked, then 802 - 14 = W.
   If K3a = 1, then 802 - 14 = W.
   If K3b = 1, then 802- 14 = W.
   If K1b checked, then 802 - 14 = S.

ROSTER/SAMPLE MATRIX PROVIDER INSTRUCTIONS
(use with FORM CMS-802)

If K1a checked, then 802 - 14 = S.
If L1b = check, then 802 - 14 = D.
If P3h is greater than 0, then 802 - 14 = R.
Note: MDS items for weight change do not differentiate between planned and unintended changes. Code only unintended changes.
No crosswalk is available for chronic insidious weight loss or nutritional risk. Insidious weight loss is a slow, steady, and persistent weight loss over time that when reviewed in the aggregate is clinically significant. Code manually with a W for either.

15. **Tube Feedings** – If the resident has a feeding tube, check this column.
Crosswalk:
If K5b checked, then 802 - 15 = checked.

16. **Dehydration** – If the resident has problems with dehydration, check this column.
Crosswalk:
If J1c or d checked, then 802 - 16 = checked.
Also consider I3 = 276.5.

17. **Bedfast Residents** – If the resident is bedfast, check this column.
Crosswalk:
If G6a checked then, 802 - 17 = checked.

18. **ADL Decline/Concern** – If the resident has shown a decline in ADL areas check this column.
Crosswalk:
If G9 = 2, then 802 - 18 = checked.

19. **ROM/Contractures/Positioning** – If the resident has functional limitations in range of motion, check this column.
Crosswalk:
Use codes below as reference, then determine if functional limitation in range of motion is present.
If G4Aa, b, c, d, e or f are greater than 0, then 802 - 19 = checked.

20. **Psychoactive Meds** – If the resident receives any psychoactive medications, mark this column.
• Mark P for antipsychotic, A for antianxiety, D for antidepressant, and H for hypnotic.
Crosswalk:
If O4a is greater than 0, then 802 - 20 = P.
If O4b is greater than 0, then 802 - 20 = A.
If O4c is greater than 0, then 802 - 20 = D.
If O4d is greater than 0, then 802 - 20 = H.

21. **Physical Restraints** – If the resident has a physical restraint, check this column.
• Mark N for non-siderail devices and S for siderails.
Crosswalk:
If P4 c, d, or e are greater than 0, then 802 - 21 = N.
If P4a or b are greater than 0 and G6b not checked, then 802 - 21 = S.

22. **Activities** – If the resident has little or no activity or has indicated a desire for change in type or extent of activity, check this column.
Crosswalk:
If N2 is greater than 1, then 802 - 22 = checked.
If N5a or b are greater than 1, then 802 - 22 = checked.

23. **Pressure Sores/Ulcers** – If the resident has a stage 2, 3 or 4 pressure sore(s), check this column.
Crosswalk:
If M2a is greater than 1, then 802 - 23 = checked.

24. **Pain/Comfort** – If the resident needs pain or comfort measures or is on a pain management program check this column.
Crosswalk:
If J2a = 2, then 802 - 24 = checked.
If J2b = 3, then 802 - 24 = checked.
No crosswalk is available for pain management program. Code manually.

25. **Language/Communication** – Enter a code in this item if the resident uses a language other than the dominant language of the facility or exhibits difficulty communicating his/her needs. This must be individually determined. In some facilities the predominant language is other than English, such as Spanish, Navajo, or French.
• Mark L if resident uses a language other than the dominant language of the facility. (If a resident uses American Sign Language, consider this a different language and mark L.) Mark C if the resident has communication difficulties.
Crosswalk:
For Dominant Language, AB8a must be individually determined, based on the predominant language spoken within the facility. If the resident's primary language is different, then 802 - 25 = L.
If C3d, e or f checked, then 802 - 25 = C.
If C4 = 2 or 3, then 802 - 25 = C.
If C5 = 1 or 2, then 802 - 25 = C.
If I1r checked, then 802 - 25 = C.

Exhibit 266 (Cont.)

Chapter 3

ROSTER/SAMPLE MATRIX PROVIDER INSTRUCTIONS
(use with FORM CMS-802)

26. Vision/Hearing/Devices – If the resident has significant impairment of vision or hearing, or uses devices to aid vision or hearing, mark this column.
   - Mark V for visual impairment, H for hearing impairment, and D for use of devices (glasses or hearing aids).

Crosswalk:
If D1 is greater than 1, then 802 - 26 = V.
If D2a or b checked, then 802 - 26 = V.
If C1 = 2 or 3, then 802 - 26 = H.
If D3 = 1, then 802 - 26 = D.
If C2 a or b is checked, then 802 - 26 = D.

27. Specialized Rehab – If the resident is receiving specialized rehabilitative services, mark the following:
   S   for speech/language therapy
   O   for occupational therapy
   P   for physical therapy
   H   for health rehabilitative services for MI/MR

Crosswalk:
If P1bAa is greater than 0, then 802 - 27 = S.
If P1bAb is greater than 0, then 802 - 27 = 0.
If P1bAc is greater than 0, then 802 - 27 = P.
If P1bAe is greater than 0, then 802 - 27 = H.
There is no code for services for mental retardation.
Code manually as H.

28. Assistive Devices – If the resident uses special devices to assist with eating or mobility (e.g., tables, utensils, hand splints, canes, crutches, etc.) and other assistive devices, check this column.

Crosswalk:
If K5g checked, then 802 - 28 = checked.
If G5a checked, then 802 - 28 = checked.
If G6e checked, then 802 - 28 = checked.
If P3c is greater than 0, then 802 - 28 = checked.

29. Hospice – If the resident is receiving Hospice Care, check this column.

Crosswalk:
If P1ao checked, then 802 - 29 = checked.

30. Dialysis – If the resident is receiving dialysis, check this column.

Crosswalk:
If P1 ab checked, then 802 - 30 = checked.

31. Oxygen/Respiratory Care – If the resident has a tracheotomy, ventilator, resident needs suctioning, or is receiving oxygen therapy, etc., check this column.

Crosswalk:
At item P1a, if g, i, j or l checked, then 802 - 31 = checked.
If P1bAd is greater than 0, then 802 - 31 = checked.

32. Adm./Transfer/Discharge – Enter a code in this column if the resident was admitted within the past 30 days or is scheduled to be transferred or discharged within the next 30 days.
   - Mark A for an admission. Code for first assessment after initial admission or readmission after discharge without expectation of return. Mark T for a transfer and D for a discharge.

Crosswalk:
If today's date minus AB1 is less than or equal to 30 days, then 802 - 32 = A.
No codes are available for transfer and discharge anticipated. Code manually.

33. MR/MI (Non Dementia) – Enter a code in this column if the resident has a diagnosis of mental retardation or mental illness.
   - Mark MR for mental retardation or MI for mental illness not classified as dementia.

Crosswalk:
If AB10 b, e or f checked, then 802 - 33 = MR.
If I1 dd ee, ff or gg checked, then 802 - 33 = MI.

[This page intentionally left blank]

DEPARTMENT OF HEALTH AND HUMAN SERVICES
CENTERS FOR MEDICARE & MEDICAID SERVICES

EXHIBIT 267
Rev. 9, 08/05/2005

ROSTER/SAMPLE MATRIX INSTRUCTIONS FOR SURVEYORS
(use with FORM CMS-802)

The Roster/Sample Matrix (CMS-802) is a tool for selecting the resident sample and may be used for recording information from the tour. When using the form to identify the resident sample, indicate by a check whether this CMS-802 is being used for the sample from Offsite, Phase 1 or Phase 2. The horizontal rows list residents chosen for review (or residents encountered during the tour) and indicate the characteristics/concerns identified for each resident.

Use the resident sample selection table to identify the number of residents required in the sample.

In the vertical columns under the heading **Review,** code the Interview: Individual /Family column with **'I'** for each resident receiving a Resident Interview or with **'F'** for any non-interviewable resident receiving a Family Interview/Observation. **Code** the Closed Record/Comprehensive/Focused Review column with **'CL'** for a closed record review, **'C'** for a resident chosen for a comprehensive review or **'F'** for a resident chosen for a focused review.

Use the vertical columns numbered 1 through 35 to check the characteristics for each resident, as appropriate. The bolded language in columns 6 through 23 corresponds to fields in the Facility Quality Measure/Indicator (QM/QI) Report. Some columns capture language from more than one QM/QI, as well as non-indicator characteristics; e.g., QM/QI's 1.1 and 1.2 and residents with abrasions and bruises in column 6; QM/QI's 2.1, 2.2 and 2.3 in column 7; QM/QI's 5.1 and 5.3 in column 10 and QM/QI's 10.1, 10.2, and 10.3 in column 20.

During each portion of the survey (Offsite, Phase I, Phase 2) highlight the vertical columns for each characteristic identified as a potential facility concern.

Resident Number – Number each line sequentially down the rows continuing the numbering sequence for any additional pages needed. These numbers may be used as resident identifiers for the sample.

Resident Room – Identify room no. for the resident listed.

Surveyor Assigned – List initials or surveyor number of surveyor assigned to review each resident.

Resident Name – List the name of the resident.

COLUMNS 6–35: Highlight each column that is an area of concern. For each resident entered on the roster/sample matrix, check all columns that pertain to the resident according to the Offsite and Sample Selection Tasks of the Survey. The term QM/QI Report refers to the Resident Level/Quality Measure/Indicator Reports.

1. **Privacy/Dignity** – Concerns about residents' right to privacy (accommodations, written and telephone communication, visitation, personal care) or concerns that the facility does not maintain or enhance residents' dignity.

2. **Social Services** – Concerns about medically related social services; e.g., interpersonal relationships, grief, clothing.

3. **Choices** – Concerns about residents' ability to exercise their rights as citizens; freedom from coercion, discrimination or reprisal; self determination and participation; choice of care and schedule, etc.

4. **Abuse/Neglect** – Concerns about resident abuse, neglect or misappropriation of resident property, or how the facility responds to allegations of abuse, neglect or misappropriation of resident property.

5. **Clean/Comfortable/Homelike** – Concerns about the facility environment including cleanliness, lighting levels, temperature, comfortable sound levels, or homelike environment and the residents ability to use their personal belongings and individualize their room to the extent possible.

6. **Falls/Fractures/Abrasions/Bruises** (QM/QI 1.1, 1.2) – Concerns about residents with bruises, skin tear, abrasions, history of accidents or incidence of a new fracture or a fall or QM/QI Report indicates accidents or falls.

7. **Behavioral Symptoms/Depression** (QM/QI 2.1, 2.2, and 2.3) – Concerns about incidence or prevalence of resident behaviors that need to be addressed by the facility (e.g., verbal or physical outbursts, withdrawing/isolation) or residents indicated on the QM/QI Report as having behavioral symptoms affecting others or symptoms of depression with or without antidepressant therapy.

8. **9 or more Medications** (QM/QI 3.1) – Residents identified during the tour or on the QM/QI Report as using 9 or more medications.

9. **Cognitive Impairment** (QM/QI 4.1) – Concerns for residents with cognitive impairment or residents identified as becoming cognitively impaired on the QM/QI Report.

10. **Incontinence/Toileting Programs** (QM/QI 5.1 and 5.3) – Concerns related to resident incontinence and facility toileting programs including residents identified as such on the QM/QI Report.

11. **Catheter** (QM/QI 5.2) – Concerns related to catheter use in the facility or residents identified on the QM/QI Report.

12. **Fecal Impaction** (QM/QI 5.4) – Concerns related to management of constipation or residents having a fecal impaction as identified on the QM/QI Report. *This condition is considered a sentinel event.*

EXHIBIT 267

ROSTER/SAMPLE MATRIX INSTRUCTIONS FOR SURVEYORS

13. **UTI/Infection Control/Antibiotics** (QM/QI 6.1) – Concerns about presence or prevalence of resident infections, facility infection control practices, residents receiving antibiotics, or residents identified as having a UTI on the QM/QI Report.

14. **Weight Change/Nutrition/Swallowing/Dentures** (QM/QI 7.1) – Concerns about residents with nutritional needs, chewing or swallowing problems that may affect intake (including the use of dentures), experiencing significant or chronic insidious unintended weight change, being on a restorative dining program or residents identified on the QM/QI Report as having a weight loss.

15. **Tube Feedings** (QM/QI 7.2) – Concerns related to residents having a feeding tube or identified on the QM/QI Report as having a feeding tube.

16. **Dehydration** (QM/QI 7.3) – Concerns about residents who show signs or symptoms or have risk factors for dehydration or who are identified on the QM/QI Report as having dehydration. *This condition is considered a sentinel event.*

17. **Bedfast Residents** (QM/QI 9.2) – Concerns about residents identified on the QM/QI Report or observed to be spend most time in bed or chair.

18. **ADL Decline/Concern** (QM/QI 9.1 and 9.3) – Concern that resident receives appropriate treatment and services to maintain or improve ability or concerns about residents identified on the QM/QI Report as having an ADL decline.

19. **ROM/Contractures/Positioning** (QM/QI 9.4) – Concerns about the occurrence, prevention or treatment of contractures. Concerns with staff provision or lack of provision of splints, ROM, the appropriate positioning of residents or residents identified on the QM/QI Report as having a decline in ROM.

20. **Psychoactive Meds** (QM/QI 10.1, 10.2 and 10.3) – Concerns about the use of psychoactive medications or residents identified on QM/QI Report with antipsychotic use in the absence of psychotic or related conditions or use of antianxiety or hypnotic medications.

21. **Physical Restraints** (QM/QI 11.1) – Concerns about the use of physical restraints or residents identified on the QM/QI Report as physically restrained daily (excluding side rails).

22. **Activities** (QM/QI 11.2) – Concerns about activities meeting cultural needs, interests, preferences, etc. of residents or residents identified on the QM/QI Report as having little or no activity.

23. **Pressure Sores/Ulcers** (QM/QI 12.1 and 12.2) (QM/QI 13.3 for PAC residents) – Concerns about the occurrence, assessment, prevention or treatment of pressure ulcers or other necessary skin care or residents identified on the QI Report as having stage 1–4 pressure ulcers. *Residents who flag at low risk for this QM/QI are considered to have a sentinel event.*

24. **Pain/Comfort** (QM/QI 8.1 and for PAC residents 13.2) – Concerns about timely assessment and intervention with residents needing pain or comfort measures or who are on a pain management program.

25. **Language/Communication** – Concerns about the facility assisting those residents with communication difficulties to communicate at their highest practicable level or residents identified as speaking other than the dominant language of the facility.

26. **Vision/Hearing/Devices** – Concerns about the facility assisting those residents with visual or hearing impairments to function at their highest practicable level including those residents who have glasses or hearing aids.

27. **Specialized Rehab** – Concerns about the facility's provision or lack of provision of Specialized Rehabilitative Services including:
    • Physical therapy
    • Speech/language pathology
    • Occupational therapy
    • Health rehabilitative services for MI/MR

28. **Assistive Devices** – Concerns about the need for, absence of or use of special devices to assist residents in eating (e.g., tables, utensils, hand splints, etc.) or concerns about any other assistive devices (e.g., canes, crutches, etc.).

29. **Hospice** – Concerns for residents who have elected the hospice benefit, whether the resident lives in the facility or is temporarily receiving inpatient services or respite care.

30. **Dialysis** – Concern about care and coordination of services for residents receiving hemo or peritoneal dialysis either in the facility or at another site.

31. **Oxygen/Respiratory Care** – Concerns about care provided to residents with tracheotomies or ventilators, residents needing suctioning, and residents receiving oxygen, etc.

32. **Adm./Transfer/Discharge** – Concerns about care/tx for residents recently admitted. Concerns about resident preparation and procedures for transfer or discharge.

33. **MR/MI(NonDementia)** – Concerns related to the care and treatment of residents with mental retardation or mental illness.

34–35. Note any other concerns; e.g., residents who are comatose or have special care areas (e.g., prosthesis, side rails, ostomy, injection, special foot care and IV's, including total parenteral nutrition) that may be of concern in the column. If during the Offsite prep, concerns arise about the accuracy of the MDS, enter MDS accuracy as a concern. Also add concerns with delirium (QM/QI 13.1) in these fields.

DEPARTMENT OF HEALTH AND HUMAN SERVICES
CENTERS FOR MEDICARE & MEDICAID SERVICES

Exhibit 91

GENERAL OBSERVATIONS OF THE FACILITY

Facility Name:_____   Surveyor Name:_____

Provider Number:_____   Surveyor Number:_____ Discipline:_____

Observation Dates: From _____ To _____

Instructions: Use the questions below to focus your observations of the facility. Include all locations used by residents (units, hallways, dining rooms, lounges, activity and therapy rooms, bathing areas, and resident smoking areas). Also check other areas that affect the residents, such as storage and utility areas. Initial that there are no concerns or note concerns and your follow-up in the space provided. Begin your observations as soon as possible after entering the facility and continue throughout the survey. **Note:** These tags are not all inclusive.

LIST ANY POTENTIAL CONCERNS FROM OFFSITE SURVEY PREPARATION. _____

1. HANDRAILS: Do corridors have handrails? Are handrails affixed to walls, intact, and free of splinters? (F468)

2. ODORS: Is the facility free of objectionable *odors*? Are resident areas well *ventilated*? Especially observe activity areas and the dining room during activities and lunch, when the residents are using them. Are nonsmoking areas smoke free? Do smoking areas provide good quality of life for residents who smoke? (F252)

3. CLEANLINESS: How *clean* is the environment (walls, floors, drapes, furniture)? (F252)

4. PESTS: Is the facility *pest free*? (F469)

5. LINEN: Is the linen processed, transported, stored and handled properly to *prevent the spread of infection*? (F445*)

6. HAZARDS: Is the facility as free of *accident hazards* as possible? Are water temperatures safe and comfortable? Are housekeeping/hazards, compounds, and other chemicals stored to prevent resident access? (F252, 323)

7. CALL SYSTEM: Is there a functioning *call system* in bathing areas and resident toilets in common areas? (F463)

8. SPACE: Do the *space and furnishings* in dining and activity areas appear sufficient to accommodate all activities? (F464)

9. FURNISHINGS: Are dining and activity rooms *adequately furnished*? (F464)

10. DRUG STORAGE: Are *drugs* and biologicals *stored properly* (locked and at appropriate temperatures)? (F432)

11. EQUIPMENT: Is the resident equipment in common areas *sanitary, orderly, and in good repair*? (Equipment in therapy rooms, bathing rooms, activity areas, etc.) Are equipment and supplies appropriately stored and handled in clean and dirty utility areas (sterile supplies, thermometer, etc.)? (F253)

12. EQUIPMENT CONDITION: [*Excluding* the kitchen] Is *essential equipment* in safe and effective operating condition (e.g. boiler room equipment, nursing unit/medication room equipment, unit refrigerators, laundry equipment, therapy equipment)? (F456)

13. SURVEY POSTED: Are *survey results* readily accessible to residents? Are the survey results or a notice concerning survey results posted? (F167)

14. INFORMATION POSTED: Is information about Medicare, Medicaid and contacting advocacy agencies posted? (F156)

15. POSITIONING: Is correct posture and comfortable positioning and assistance being provided to residents who need assistance-especially check residents who are dining or participating in activities? (F246, 311, 318)

16. EMERGENCY: Are staff *prepared for an emergency or disaster?* Ask two staff and a charge nurse to describe what they do in emergencies (include staff from different shifts). Evaluate the responses to determine their correctness and preparedness. (F518)

17. EMERGENCY POWER: Is there *emergency power?* Are staff aware of outlets, if any, powered by emergency source? (F455)

18. WASTE: Is waste contained in properly maintained (no breaks) cans, dumpsters or compactors with covers? (F454, 371)

THERE ARE NO IDENTIFIED CONCERNS FOR THESE REQUIREMENTS (Init.)_____

Document concerns and follow-up on back of page: FORM CMS-803 (7-95)

*[Editor's Note: The tag number stated is incorrect. The correct tag number is F441.]

Exhibit 91
(continued)

GENERAL OBSERVATIONS OF THE FACILITY

Tag / Concerns	Source*	Surveyor Notes (including date/time)

*Source: O=Observation, RR=Record Review, I=Interview

FORM CMS-803 (7-95)

DEPARTMENT OF HEALTH AND HUMAN SERVICES
CENTERS FOR MEDICARE & MEDICAID SERVICES

Exhibit 92

KITCHEN/FOOD SERVICE OBSERVATION

Facility Name:_____   Surveyor Name:_____

Provider Number:_____   Surveyor Number:_____ Discipline:_____

Observation Dates/Times:_____

Instructions: Use the questions below to focus your observations of the kitchen and the facility's storage, preparation, distribution and service of food to residents. Initial that there are no identifiable concerns or note concerns and follow-up in the space provided. All questions relate to the requirement to prevent the contamination of food and the spread of food-borne illness. (F371 This tag is not all inclusive.)

LIST ANY POTENTIAL CONCERNS FROM OFFSITE SURVEY PREPARATION: _____
_____

FOOD STORAGE

1. Are the refrigerator and freezer shelves and floors clean and free of spillage, and foods free of slime and mold?
2. Is the freezer temperature 0 degrees F or below and refrigerator 41 degrees F or below (allow 2-3 degrees variance)? Do not check during meal preparation.
3. Are refrigerated foods covered, dated, labeled, and shelved to allow air circulation?
4. Are foods stored correctly (e.g., cooked foods over raw meat in refrigerator, egg and egg rich foods refrigerated)?
5. Is dry storage maintained in a manner to prevent rodent/pest infestation?

FOOD PREPARATION

6. Are cracked eggs being used only in foods that are thoroughly cooked, such as baked goods or casseroles?
7. Are frozen raw meats and poultry thawed in the refrigerator or in cold, running water? Are cooked foods cooled down safely?
8. Are food contact surfaces and utensils cleaned to prevent cross-contamination and food-borne illness?

FOOD SERVICE/SANITATION

9. Are hot foods maintained at 140 degrees F or above and cold foods maintained at 41 degrees F or below when served from tray line?
10. Are food trays, dinnerware, and utensils clean and in good condition?
11. Are the foods covered until served? Is food protected from contamination during transportation and distribution?
12. Are employees washing hands before and after handling food, using clean utensils when necessary and following infection control practices?
13. Are food preparation equipment, dishes and utensils effectively sanitized to destroy potential food borne illness? Is dishwasher's hot water wash 140 degrees F and rinse cycle 180 degrees F or chemical sanitation per manufacturers instructions followed?
14. Is facility following correct manual dishwashing procedures (i.e., 3 compartment sink, correct water temperature, chemical concentration, and immersion time)?

NOTE: If any nutritional concerns have been identified (such as weight loss) by observation, interviews or record review, check portion sizes and how that type of food is prepared (see guidelines at 483.35). If any concerns are identified regarding meals that are not consistent in quality see guidance at Task 5B and at 483.35.

LADLES: 1/4 C = *2oz.*, 1/2C = *4oz.*, 3/4C = *6oz.*, 1C = *8oz.*
SCOOPS: #6 = *2/3C*, #8 = *1/2C.*, #10 = *2/5C.*, #12 = *1/3C.*, #16 = *1/4C.*

THERE ARE NO IDENTIFIED CONCERNS FOR THESE REQUIREMENTS: (Init.)_____

Document concerns and follow-up on back of page.

Exhibit 92
(continued)

KITCHEN/FOOD SERVICE OBSERVATION

Tag / Concerns	Source*	Surveyor Notes (including date/time)

*Source: O=Observation, RR=Record Review, I=Interview

SOM, Exhibits - CMS Survey Process Forms

(Revised August 2007)

DEPARTMENT OF HEALTH AND HUMAN SERVICES
CENTERS FOR MEDICARE & MEDICAID SERVICES

Exhibit 93

RESIDENT REVIEW WORKSHEET

Facility Name:_____ Resident Name:_____

Provider Number:_____ Resident Identifier:_____

Surveyor Name:_____ Birthdate: _____ Unit:_____ Rm #:_____

Surveyor Number:_____ Discipline:_____ Orig. Admission Date:_____ Readmission Date:_____

Survey Date:_____

Payment Source: Admission: _____

Current: _____

Diagnosis:_____

Interviewable: Yes ☐ No ☐ Type of Review: Comprehensive ☐ Focused ☐ Closed Record ☐

Selected for Individual Interview: Yes ☐ No ☐

Selected for Family Interview and Observation of Non-Interviewable Resident: Yes ☐ No ☐

Focus/Care Areas: _____

Instructions: Any regulatory areas related to the sampled resident's needs are to be included in this review.
- Initial that each section was reviewed if there are no concerns. ● If there are concerns, document your investigation.
- Document all pertinent resident observations and information from resident, staff, family interviews and record reviews for every resident in the sample.

SECTION A: RESIDENT ROOM REVIEW: Evaluate if appropriate requirements are met in each of the following areas, including the accommodation of needs:

- Adequate accommodations are made for resident privacy, including bed curtains.
- Call bells are functioning and accessible to residents.
- Resident is able to use his/her bathroom without difficulty.
- Adequate space exists for providing care to residents.
- Resident with physical limitations (e.g. walker, wheelchair) is able to move around his/her room.
- Environment is homelike, comfortable and attractive; accommodations are made for resident personal items and his/her modifications.
- Bedding, bath linens and closet space is adequate for resident needs.
- Resident care equipment is clean and in good repair.
- Room is safe and comfortable in the following areas: temperature, water temperature, sound level and lighting.

THERE ARE NO IDENTIFIED CONCERNS FOR THESE REQUIREMENTS (Init.)_____
Document concerns and follow-up on Surveyor Notes sheet page 4:

SECTION B: RESIDENT DAILY LIFE REVIEW: Evaluate if appropriate requirements are met in each of the following areas:

- Resident appears well groomed and reasonably attractive (e.g. clean clothes, neat hair, free from facial hair).
- Staff treats residents respectfully and listens to resident requests. Note staff interaction with both communicative and non-communicative residents.
- Staff is responsive to resident requests and call bells.
- Residents are free from unexplained physical injuries and there are no signs of resident abuse. (e.g. residents do not appear frightened around certain staff members.)
- Facility activities program meets resident's individually assessed needs and preferences.
- Medically related social services are identified and provided when appropriate.
- Restraints are used only when medically necessary. (see 483.13(a))
- Resident is assisted with dining when necessary.

THERE ARE NO IDENTIFIED CONCERNS FOR THESE REQUIREMENTS (Init.)_____
Document concerns and follow-up on Surveyor Notes sheet page 4:

Exhibit 93
(continued)

RESIDENT REVIEW WORKSHEET
(continued)

SECTION C: ASSESSMENT OF DRUG THERAPIES

Review all the over-the-counter and prescribed medications taken by the resident during the last 7 days.

- Evaluate drug therapy for indications/reasons, side effects, dose, review of therapy/monitoring, and evidence of unnecessary medications including antipsychotic drugs.
- Correlate drug therapy with resident's clinical condition
- If you note concerns with drug therapy, review the pharmacist's report. See if the physician or facility has responded to recommendations or concerns.

THERE ARE NO IDENTIFIED CONCERNS FOR THESE REQUIREMENTS (Init.)_____

Medications/Dose/Schedule	Medications/Dose/Schedule	Medications/Dose/Schedule

Document concerns and follow-up on page 4.

SECTION D: RAI/CARE REVIEW SHEET (*Includes both MDS and use of RAPS*):

Reason for the most current RAI: Annual ☐ Initial ☐ Significant Change ☐

Date of Most Recent RAI_____ Date of Comparison/Quarterly RAI_____

- For a *comprehensive review* complete a review of all care areas specific to the resident, all ADL functional areas, cognitive status, and MDS categories triggering a RAP.
- For a *focused review:*
  Phase I: Complete a review of those requirements appropriate to focus and care areas specific to the resident.
  Phase II: Complete a review of requirements appropriate to focus areas.
- **For both *comprehensive* and *focused reviews* record only the applicable sections and relevant factors about the clinical status indicating an impairment or changes between reviews.**
- If the current RAI is less than 9 months old, scan and compare with the previous RAI and most recent quarterly review.
- If the RAI is 9 months or older, compare the current RAI with the most recent quarterly review.
- Note any differences for the applicable areas being reviewed.
- Review the RAP summary and care planning.
- Look for implementation of the care plan as appropriate to the comprehensive or focused review.
- Note specifically the effects of care or lack of care.
- If the resident declined or failed to improve relative to expectations, determine if this was avoidable or unavoidable.
- For *closed records, complete a review* of the applicable areas of concern.
- Use the additional MDS item blocks on page 3 to document other sections or additional concerns.
- *Dining observation:* If there are concerns with weight loss or other nutritional issues, observe resident dining and review adequacy of meals served and menus.

THERE ARE NO IDENTIFIED CONCERNS FOR THESE REQUIREMENTS (Init.)_____

Document concerns and follow-up on page 4.

RESIDENT REVIEW WORKSHEET
(continued)

MDS Items	RAI Status/Comparison	Care Plan Y/N	Notes/Dates/Times/Source and Tag: Observations and Interview for resident and implementation of care plan and TX, including accuracy, completeness, and how information from use of RAPs is incorporated into the resident's care. Outcome: improve/failure to improve/same/decline. If a decline or failure to improve occurred, was it avoidable or unavoidable?
Cognitive/ Decisionmaking			
Mood/Behavior/ Psychosocial			
Transfer			
Ambulation			
Dressing			
Eating			
Hygiene/Bathing			
ROM Limits			
Bowel			
Bladder			
Activities			

FORM CMS-805 (7-95)

Exhibit 93
(continued)

RESIDENT REVIEW WORKSHEET
(continued)

Tag / Concerns	Source*	Surveyor Notes *(including date/time)*

*Source: O=Observation, RR=Record Review, I=Interview

DEPARTMENT OF HEALTH AND HUMAN SERVICES
CENTERS FOR MEDICARE & MEDICAID SERVICES

Exhibit 94

QUALITY OF LIFE ASSESSMENT
RESIDENT INTERVIEW

Facility Name:_____ Resident Name:_____

Provider Number:_____ Resident Identifier:_____

Surveyor Name: _____ Interview Dates/Times: _____

Surveyor Number: _____ Discipline:_____

Instructions:

For question 1, if you are meeting with the resident in a location away from the resident's room, visit the room before the interview and note anything about the room that you want to discuss. For question 7, review the RAI to determine the ADL capabilities of this resident.

Introduce yourself and explain the survey process and the purpose of the interview using the following concepts. It is not necessary to use the exact wording.

"[Name of facility] is inspected by a team from the [Name of State Survey Agency] periodically to assure that all residents receive good care. While we are here, we make a lot of observations, review the nursing home's records, and talk to residents to help us understand what it's like to live in this nursing home. We appreciate your taking the time to talk to us."

"We ask certain questions because we want to know whether you have a say in decisions affecting your nursing and medical care, your schedule and the services you receive at this facility. We want to know how you feel about your life here and whether the facility has made efforts to accommodate your preferences."

"If it is all right with you, I'd like to meet with you again later. That will give you time to think things over and to provide additional information later."

In asking the following questions, it is not necessary to use the exact wording. However, <u>do</u> use complete questions, not one-word probes.

Get the resident to talk about actual situations and examples by using open-ended probes, such as: "Can you tell me more about that?" or "How is that done here?" Avoid asking leading questions which suggest a certain response.

If a resident gives a response to any question that indicates there may be a concern with facility services, probe to determine if the resident has communicated the problem to facility staff and what their response was.

1. ROOM: (F177, 201, 207, 242, 250, 252, 256, 257)

A good approach for initiating this discussion is to make a comment about something you have noticed about the resident's room, for example, "I notice that you have a lot of plants in your room."

Please tell me about your room and how you feel about it.

Do you enjoy spending time in your room?

Is there enough light for you?

Is the room temperature comfortable?

Have you lived in a different room in the facility?
 (If yes) **What was the reason for the room change?**

Did you have a choice about changing rooms?

Where was your other room? What was it like?

Is there anything you would like to change about your room?
 (If yes) **Have you talked to the facility about this? How did they respond?**

RESIDENT INTERVIEW

2. ENVIRONMENT: (F252, 258)

I realize that being in a nursing home is not like being in your own home, but do staff here try to make this facility seem homelike?

We've already talked about your room. How about other places you use, like the activities room and dining room? Do they seem homelike to you?

Is there anything that would make this facility more comfortable for you?

Is it generally quiet or noisy here?

What about at night?

Is the facility usually clean and free of bad smells?

3. PRIVACY: (F164, 174)

Are you a person who likes to have privacy sometimes?

Are you able to have privacy when you want it?

Do staff and other residents respect your privacy?

Do you have a private place to meet with visitors?

(If no phone in the room) Where do you make phone calls?

Do you have privacy when you are on the phone?

(If the resident indicates any problems with privacy, probe for specific examples. Ask if they talked to staff and what was their response.)

4. FOOD (F365)

Tell me about the food here.

Do you have any restrictions on your diet?

How does your food taste?

Are you served foods that you like to eat?

Are your hot and cold foods served at a temperature you like?

Have you ever refused to eat something served to you?

 (If yes) Did the facility offer you something else to eat?

 (If the resident refused a food and did not get a substitute)

Did you ask for another food? What was the facility's response?

5. ACTIVITIES (F242, 248)

How do you find out about the activities that are going on?

Are there activities available on the weekends?

Do you participate in activities?

 (If yes) What kinds of activities do you participate in?

 (If resident participates) Do you enjoy these activities?

(If resident does not participate, probe to find out why not.)

Is there some activity that you would like to do that is not available here?

 (If yes) Which activity would you like to attend?

 Have you talked to anybody about this? What was the response?

RESIDENT INTERVIEW

---

6. STAFF: (F223, 241)

Tell me how you feel about the staff members at this facility. Do they treat you with respect?

Do you feel they know something about you as a person?

Are they usually willing to take the time to listen when you want to talk about something personal or a problem you are having?

Do they make efforts to resolve your problems?

Has any resident or staff member ever physically harmed you?

Has any resident or staff member ever taken anything belonging to you without permission?
  (If yes) Can you tell me who did this?

Has a staff member ever yelled or sworn at you?
  (If yes) Please describe what happened.
  Can you tell me who did this? Did you report this to someone?
  (If yes) How did they respond?

---

7. ADLs: (F216, 311, 312)

(Tailor this question to what you have observed and what is noted in the MDS about ADL capabilities of this resident.) For example: **"I see that your care plan calls for you to dress with a little help from staff." How is that working for you?**

Do you feel that you get help when you need it?

Do staff encourge you to do as much as you can for yourself?

---

8. DECISIONS: (F154, 242, 280)

Here at this facility, are you involved in making choices about your daily activities?

Are you involved in making decisions about your nursing care and medical treatment?

(If not, probe to determine what these choices and decisions are, and relate this information to necessary restrictions that are part of the resident's plan of care.)

Do you participate in meetings where staff plan your activities and daily medical and nursing care?

If you are unhappy with something, or if you want to change something about your care or your daily schedule, how do you let the facility know?

Do you feel the staff members listen to your requests and respond appropriately?

If the staff are unable to accommodate one of your requests, do they provide a reasonable explanation of why they cannot honor the request?

Can you choose how you spend the day?

Have you ever refused care or treatment (such as a bath or certain medication)?
  (If yes) What happened then?

Exhibit 94
(continued)

RESIDENT INTERVIEW

9. *MEDICAL SERVICES:* (F156, 163, 164, 250, 411, 412)

Who is your physician?

Did you choose your physician yourself?
(If no, probe for details about who selected the physician and why the resident did not do it).

Are you satisfied with the care provided by your physician?

Can you see your doctor if you need to?

Do you see your physician here or at the office?
(If they say here) **Where in the facility does your doctor see you?**

Do you have privacy when you are examined by your physician?
(If they say they go to the office) **How do you get to the office?**

Do facility staff help you make doctor's appointments and help you obtain transportation?

Can you get to see a dentist, podiatrist, or other specialist if you need to?

10. **(Write here any special items not already discussed that you have noted about this resident or about the facility that you would like to discuss with the resident.)**

_____

_____

_____

_____

_____

11. **Is there anything else you would like to talk about regarding your life here?**

_____

_____

_____

_____

_____

_____

_____

_____

_____

Thank the resident. Review your notes from this interview and determine if there are any concerns you need to investigate further. Share any problems you have found with the team so they may keep them in mind during the remainder of the survey.

DEPARTMENT OF HEALTH AND HUMAN SERVICES
CENTERS FOR MEDICARE & MEDICAID SERVICES

Exhibit 94

(continued)

QUALITY OF LIFE ASSESSMENT
GROUP INTERVIEW

Facility Name:_____   Surveyor Name: _____

Provider Number:_____   Surveyor Number: _____

Interview Dates/Times:_____   Discipline: _____

Residents Attending:_____   _____

_____   _____

_____   _____

_____   _____

Instructions:

Introduce yourself to the group and explain the survey process and the purpose of the interview using the following concepts. It is not necessary to use the exact wording.

"[Name of facility] is inspected by a team from the [Name of State Survey Agency] periodically as one part of a process in which we evaluate the quality of life and quality of care in this facility.

While we are here, we make observations, look over the facility's records, and talk to residents about life in this facility.

We appreciate you taking the time to talk to us.

We would like to ask you several questions about life in the facility and the interactions of residents and staff."

1. RULES: (F151, 242, 243)

Tell me about the rules in this facility.
For instance, rules about what time residents go to bed at night and get up in the morning?
Are there any other facility rules you would like to discuss?

Do you as a group have input into the rules of this facility?
Does the facility listen to your suggestions?

2. PRIVACY: (F164, 174)

Can you meet privately with your visitors?
Can you make a telephone call without other people overhearing your conversation?

Does the facility make an effort to assure that privacy rights are respected for all residents?

Exhibit 94
(continued)

GROUP INTERVIEW

3. *ACTIVITIES:* (F242, 248)

Activities programs are supposed to meet your interests and needs. Do you feel the activities here do that?
(If no, probe for specifics.)

Do you participate in the activities here?

Do you enjoy them?

Are there enough help and supplies available so that everyone who wants to can participate?

Do you as a group have input into the selection of the activities that are offered?

How does the facility respond to your suggestions?

Is there anything about the activities program that you would like to talk about?

Outside of the formal activity programs, are there opportunities for you to socialize with other residents?

Are there places you can go when you want to be with other residents?

(If answers are negative) Why do you think that occurs?

4. *PERSONAL PROPERTY:* (F252)

Can residents have their own belongings here if they choose to do so?

What about their own furniture?

How are your personal belongings treated here?

Does the facility make efforts to prevent loss, theft, or destruction of personal property?

Have any of your belongings ever been missing?

(If anyone answers yes) Did you talk to a staff member about this? What was their response?

5. *RIGHTS* (F151, 153, 156, 167, 168, 170, 280)

How do residents here find out about their rights — such as voting, making a living will, getting what you need here?

Are you invited to meetings in which staff plan your nursing care, medical treatment and activities?

Do you know that you can see a copy of the facility's latest survey inspection results?

Where is that report kept here?

Do you know how to contact an advocacy agency such as the ombudsman office?

Do you know you can look at your medical record?

Have any of you asked to see your record? What was the facility's response?

Has anyone from the facility staff talked to you about these things?

Tell me about the mail delivery system here.
Is mail delivery prompt? Does your mail arrive unopened daily?

6. *DIGNITY:* (F223, 241)

How do staff members treat the residents here, not just yourselves, but others who can't speak for themselves?

Do you feel the staff here treat residents with respect and dignity?

Do they try to accommodate residents' wishes where possible?

(If answers are negative) Please describe instances in which the facility did not treat you or another resident with dignity. Did you talk to anyone on the staff about this? How did they respond?

GROUP INTERVIEW

---

7. *ABUSE AND NEGLECT:* (F223)

Are you aware of any instances in which a resident
was abused or neglected?

Are you aware of any instances in which a resident
had property taken from them by a staff member
without permission?
(If yes) Tell me about it. How did you find out about
it?

Are there enough staff here to take care of everyone?
(If no) Tell me more about that.

We are willing to discuss any incidents that you know of
in private if you would prefer. If so, just stop me or one
of the other surveyors anytime, and we'll listen to you.

---

8. *COSTS:* (F156, 207)

Are residents here informed by the facility about which
items and services are paid by Medicare or Medicaid
and which ones you must pay for?

If there was any change in these items that you must
pay for, were you informed?

Are you aware of any changes in the care any resident has
received after they went from paying for their care to
Medicaid paying?
(If answers suggest the possibility of Medicaid discrimination, probe for specific instances of differences in care.)

---

9. *BUILDING:* (F256, 257, 258, 463, 465, 483)

I'd like to ask a few questions about the building,
including both your bedroom and other rooms you
use such as the dining room and activities room.

Is the air temperature comfortable for you?

Is there good air circulation or does it get stuffy in
these rooms?

What do you think about the noise level here? Is it
generally quiet or noisy? How about at night?

Do you have the right amount of lighting in your room to
read or do whatever you want to do?

How is the lighting in the dining rooms and activity
rooms?

Do you ever see insects or rodents here?
(If yes) Tell me about it.

---

10. *FOOD:* (F364, 365, 367)

The next questions are about the food here.

Is the flavor and appearance of your food satisfactory?

Outside of the dietary restrictions some of you may
have, do you receive food here that you like to eat?

If you have ever refused to eat a particular food, did
the facility provide you with something else to eat?
(If no, probe for specifics.)

Is the temperature of your hot and cold foods
appropriate?

Are the meats tender enough?

About what time do you receive your breakfast, lunch,
and dinner?

Are the meals generally on time or late?

What are you offered for a bedtime snack?

If you ever had a concern about your food, did you tell the
staff? What was their response?

Exhibit 94
(continued)

GROUP INTERVIEW

11. COUNCIL: (F243)

(If you are speaking with a resident council)

Does the facility help you with arrangements for council meetings?

Do they make sure you have space to meet?

Can you have meetings without any staff present if you wish?

How does the council communicate its concerns to the facility?

How does the administrator respond to the council's concerns?

If the facility cannot accommodate a council request, do they give you a reasonable explanation?

12. GRIEVANCES: (F165, 166)

Have any of you or the group as a whole ever voiced a grievance to the facility?

How did staff react to this?

Did they resolve the problem?

Do you feel free to make complaints to staff?

If not, why not (probe for specific examples)?

13. Identify here any issues you would like to discuss with the group that have not been covered in the questions above.

_____

_____

_____

_____

_____

14. Is there anything else about life here in the facility that you would like to discuss?

_____

_____

_____

_____

_____

_____

_____

_____

Thank the group for their time. After the interview, follow up on any concerns that need further investigation. Document your follow up on Resident Review or Surveyor Notes Worksheets. Share these concerns with the team.

DEPARTMENT OF HEALTH AND HUMAN SERVICES
CENTERS FOR MEDICARE & MEDICAID SERVICES

Exhibit 94
(continued)

QUALITY OF LIFE ASSESSMENT
FAMILY INTERVIEW

Facility Name:_____   Resident Name: _____

Provider Number:_____   Resident Identifier: _____

Surveyor Name: _____   Person Interviewed:_____

Surveyor Number: _____ Discipline:_____   Relationship to Resident: _____

Method of Contact: In person ☐ Phone ☐   Interview Dates/Times: _____

Instructions:

This interview is intended to be conducted with a person (family, friend or guardian) who is the one acting on behalf of the resident and authorizing care. Prior to the interview, complete as many questions as you can through review of the resident assessment, care plan and any activities or social service assessment.

Adapt these questions and probes as necessary to make them applicable to this resident.

Introduce yourself and explain the survey process and the purpose of the interview using the following concepts. It is not necessary to use the exact wording.

"[Name of facility] is inspected by a team from the [Name of State Survey Agency] periodically to assure that residents receive quality care. While we are here, we make observations, review the nursing home's records, and talk to residents and family members or friends who can help us understand what it's like to live in this nursing home. We appreciate your taking the time to talk to us.

"We ask these questions because we want to know about your opportunity for involvement in decisions about _____'s care and schedule, your views on services he/she receives here, and in general, what you think of the facility. We want to know if the facility has obtained information about _____'s past and current preferences in order to provide the highest quality of care. We also want to find out about the admission process and what the facility discussed with you about costs and payment for _____'s stay here.

Question 1 below screens the family member to see if she/he knows the resident well enough to complete the rest of the interview. Based on answers to question 1, decide whether you can complete the interview, complete it partially if the family member knows some things, or conclude the interview. If you decide you must conclude this interview, ask a general question that lets the family member say what they wish to say about the facility such as: "Is there anything you would like to tell me about this facility and how your relative is treated?".

---

1. (Ask about the nature and extent of the relationship between interviewee and resident both prior to and during nursing home residence):

With whom did your relative/friend live before coming to the nursing home? (If the resident did not live with this person) About how often did you see her/him?

How often do the resident and you see each other now?

Are you familiar with _____'s preferences and daily routines when he/she was more independent and more able to make choices and express preferences? (If the resident has had a lifelong disability, ask about choice and preferences prior to moving to this facility. Adapt question 2 and 3 also.)

Exhibit 94
(continued)

FAMILY INTERVIEW

To the extent that the interviewee is knowledgeable about the resident's past life, ask the following:

---

2. I have some questions about _____'s life-style and preferences when she/he was more independent and able to express preferences. Would you tell me about:

Did he/she enjoy any particular activities or hobbies?
Was she/he social or more solitary;
Types of social and recreational activities;

Eating habits, food likes and dislikes;
Sleeping habits, alertness at different times of the day;
Religious/spiritual activities;
Work, whether in or out of the home;
Things that gave him/her pleasure.

---

3. The next questions are about the resident's lifelong general personality. How would you describe:

General manner; for example, was she/he thought to be quiet, happy, argumentative, etc.?
How she/he generally adapted to change, prior to the current disability. How, for example, did the resident react to moving to a new residence, to losing a loved one, and to other changing life situations?

Characteristic ways of talking— was she/he talkative or usually quiet, likely to express herself/himself or not?

---

4. Have any of the preferences and personality characteristics that you told me about changed, either due to a change in her/his condition or due to relocation to this facility?

Have her/his daily routines and activities changed in a substantial way since moving here?
(If yes) Please describe these differences.

FAMILY INTERVIEW

5. **(For all the items below: If the family member describes any problems, probe for specific information. Ask if they have talked to staff, and what was the facility's response. If the resident's payment source changed from private pay or Medicare to Medicaid, inquire if there were any changes in any of the following after the payment source changed.)**

Please share with me your observations, either positive things or concerns, about all of the following items. If you have no information about these issues that is OK.

Meals and snacks (F242, 310, 365, 366, 367)
Routines and activities (F242, 245, 248)
Visitor policies and hours, privacy for visits when
 desired (F164, 172)
Care by nursing home staff (F241, 309-312)

Noise level of the facility (F258)
Privacy when receiving care (F164)
Transfers (F177, 201, 203-207)
Security and personal property (F159, 223, 252)
Cleanliness and odor (F252-254)

6. **Did you participate in the admission process?**
 (If yes) Were you told anything about using Medicare or Medicaid to pay for _____ 's stay here?
 (If yes) What did they tell you?
(If resident's care is being paid by Medicaid) Were you asked to pay for any extras above the Medicaid rate?
 (If yes) What were these? Did you have a choice about receiving these services?
When your relative/friend moved here, did the facility ask you to pay out of your savings or your relative's savings?
(F156, 208)

7. **Are you the person who would be notified if _____ 's condition changed. (If yes) Have you been notified when there have been changes in your relative's condition? Are you involved in _____ 's care planning? (F157)**

8. **"Is there anything else that I have not asked that is important to understand about _____ 's everyday life here?"**

When finished: "Thank you for your help. You will be able to examine a copy of the results of this survey in about _____ days."

DEPARTMENT OF HEALTH AND HUMAN SERVICES
CENTERS FOR MEDICARE & MEDICAID SERVICES

Exhibit 94
(continued)

QUALITY OF LIFE ASSESSMENT
OBSERVATION OF NON-INTERVIEWABLE RESIDENT

1. Special items to observe: _____

_____

_____

2. RESIDENT AND ENVIRONMENT:

Physical condition of resident (comfort, positioning, etc.) (F246)

Appearance (grooming and attire) (F241)

Physical environment (comfort, safety, privacy, infection control, stimulation, personal belongings, homelike) (F164, 246, 252, 441, 444, 459)

Level of assistance received. Note instances of too much or too little and resulting problem —(e.g., violation of dignity). (F241, 309-312)

Privacy afforded when care is given (F164)

Use of restraints and/or other restrictions on behavior (F221)

Do staff intervene to assist resident if there is a problem and the resident tries to indicate this? (F312)

3. DAILY LIFE:

The agreement of the daily schedule and activities with assessed interests and functional level (Note during activities if cues/prompts and adapted equipment are provided as needed and according to care plan.) (F242, 255)

Restriction of choices that the resident can make (e.g., resident reaching out for a drink or pushing away food or medication and facility response.) (F155, 242)

Consistency of TV or radio being on or off with assessed interests (F242, 280)

4. INTERACTIONS WITH OTHERS:

Do staff individualize their interactions with this resident, based on her/his preferences, capabilities, and special needs? (F241, 246)

What is the resident's response to staff interactions? (smiling, attempting to communicate, distressed, anxious, etc.) (F241, 246)

Do staff try to communicate in a reassuring way? (Note staff tone of voice and use of speech.) While staff are giving care do they include resident in conversation or do staff talk to each other as if resident is not there? (F241, 223)

Evidence of a roommate problem that could be addressed by the facility. (F250)

Consistency of opportunities for socializing with regard to assessed interests and functional level (Note time and situations when isolated.) (F174, 242, 248, 250)

Location of resident: segregated in some way, in a special unit, or fully integrated with other residents (Note any adverse consequences for resident.) (F223)

Use the Resident Review or Surveyor Notes Worksheet to follow-up on any concerns. Share any concerns with the team.

Exhibit 95

DEPARTMENT OF HEALTH AND HUMAN SERVICES
CENTERS FOR MEDICARE & MEDICAID SERVICES

SURVEYOR NOTES WORKSHEET

Facility Name: _____   Surveyor Name: _____

Provider Number: _____   Surveyor Number: _____ Discipline: _____

Observation Dates: From _____ To _____

TAG/CONCERNS	DOCUMENTATION

FORM CMS-807 (7/95)

SURVEYOR NOTES WORKSHEET

Exhibit 95
(continued)

TAG/CONCERNS	DOCUMENTATION

OSCAR Report 3
History Facility Profile

Facility

Provider #:
Phone Number:
Participation Date: 11/28/1969

Type Action: Recertification
Type Ownership: For Profit - Corporation

Total Certified Beds: 83

18	18/19	19	ICF/MR
	83		

State's Region Code: 001
Compliance Status: Facility Meets Requirements Based on an Acceptable Plan of Correction

Facility Beds
Total: 83
Certified: 83

LTC Admission/Suspension Dates

Admission Suspended:
Suspension Rescinded:

Resident Census on 10/03/2001

Total: 73
Medicare: 6
Medicaid: 61
Other: 6

Current Survey Revisit Dates – 12/13/2001 11/21/2001

Program Requirements		Prior 3 Survey 05/1998	S/S Code	Prior 2 Survey 04/1999	S/S Code	Prior 1 Survey 07/2000	S/S Code	Current Survey 10/03/2001	S/S Code	Plan/Date Of Correct
F0159 – Facility Management of RES Funds	REQ	X	D			X	C			
F0164 – Personal Privacy/Confidentiality of Records	REQ			X	D					
F0167 – Survey Results Readily Accessible to Residents	REQ					X	D	X C	C	11/21/2001
F0221 – Right to be Free from Physical Restraints Not REQ	REQ			X	G					
F0224 – Facility Prohibits Abuse, Neglect	REQ	X	D	X	D	X	D	X C	D	11/21/2001
F0225 – Not Employ Persons Guilty of Abuse	REQ			X	D	X	D			
F0241 – Dignity	REQ					X	D			
F0248 – Activity Program Meets Individual Needs	REQ	X	D	X	D	X	D			
F0250 – Medically Related Social Services	REQ	X	B							
F0252 – Safe/Clean/Comfortable/Homelike Environment	REQ					X	C			
F0253 – Housekeeping & Maintenance Services	REQ									
F0272 – Comprehensive Assessments	REQ	X	E	X	E					
F0274 – Assessment After a Significant Change	REQ	X	D	X	D	X	D	X C	D	11/21/2001
F0278 – Accuracy of Assessments/Coord w/Professionals	REQ	X	D	X	D					
F0279 – Develop Comprehensive Care Plans	REQ			X	H					
F0281 – Services Provided Meet Professional Standards	REQ	X	E	X	D					
F0282 – Services by Qualified Persons in Accordance with Care Plan	REQ							X C	D	12/13/2001
F0310 – ADLS Do Not Decline Unless Unavoidable	REQ			X	D			X C	D	11/21/2001
F0312 – ADL Care Provided for Dependent Residents	REQ	X	G	X	G			X C	D	11/21/2001
F0314 – Proper Treatment to Prevent/Heal Pressure Sores	REQ									
F0316 – Appropriate Treatment for Incontinent Residents	REQ	X	E	X	D	X	D			
F0318 – Range of Motion Treatment & Services	REQ									
F0322 – Proper Care & Services for Residents with NG Tube	REQ	X	D	X	G	X	G	X C	D	11/21/2001
F0324 – Supervision/Devices to Prevent Accidents	REQ			X	D			X C	G	11/21/2001
F0325 – RES Maintain Nutritional Status Unless Unavoidable	REQ									
F0327 – Facility Provides Sufficient Fluid Intake	REQ	X	D							

C = Date of Correction   N = No Date Given   P = Plan of Correction   X = Deficient
COP = Condition   REQ = Requirement   R = Refused to Correct   W = Waived

Run Date of Report: 07/03/2003

Last File Update: 07/02/2003

Exhibit 96
(continued)

OSCAR Report 3
History Facility Profile

Facility

Provider #:

Program Requirements		Prior 3 Survey 05/1998	S/S Code	Prior 2 Survey 04/1999	S/S Code	Prior 1 Survey 07/2000	S/S Code	Current Survey 10/03/2001	S/S Code	Plan/Date Of Correct
F0329 – Drug Regimen is Free from Unnecessary Drugs	REQ	X	G							
F0332 – Medication Error Rates of 5% or More	REQ	X	E							
F0353 – Sufficient Nursing Staff on a 24-Hour Basis	REQ			X	F	X	F			
F0364 – Food Properly Prepared, Palatable, Etc.	REQ					X	C			
F0367 – Therapeutic Diet Prescribed by Physician	REQ					X	D			
F0371 – Store/Prepare/Distribute Food Under Sanitary Conditions	REQ	X	C	X	C	X	F			
F0426 – Facility Provides Pharmaceutical Services	REQ					X	D			
F0432 – Drugs Stored in Locked Compartments/Under Proper Tem	REQ			X	D				D	11/21/2001
F0441 – Facility Establishes Infection Control Program	REQ					X	D	X	C	11/21/2001
F0444 – Wash Hands When Indicated	REQ							X C		
F0445 – Handle Linens to Prevent Spread of Infection	REQ							X C		
F0465 – Environment is Safe/Functional/Sanitary/Comfortable	REQ			X	F					
F0466 – Procedures to Ensure Water Availability	REQ			X	C					
F0493 – Governing Body Appoints Admin; Manages Facility	REQ			X	F					
F0514 – Clinical Records Meet Professional Standards	REQ			X	D					

Edition of LSC Applied

LSC Deficiencies – Building Number 01	85 Exist Prior 3 Survey 05/1998	85 Exist Prior 2 Survey 04/1999	85 Exist Prior 1 Survey 07/2000	85 Exist Current Survey 10/09/2001	Plan/Date Of Correct
K0012 – Construction Type	X				
K0017 – Corridor Walls	X	X			
K0025 – Smoke Partition Construction	X	X	X	X C	11/20/2001
K0029 – Hazardous Areas – Separation	X	X	X		
K0038 – Exit Access		X			
K0046 – Emergency Lighting	X	X		X C	11/20/2001
K0047 – Exit Signs		X			
K0048 – Evacuation Plan		X			
K0050 – Fire Drills	X	X	X	X C	11/20/2001
K0051 – Fire Alarm System		X		X C	11/20/2001
K0052 – Testing of Fire Alarm		X			
K0056 – Automatic Sprinkler System		X			
K0062 – Sprinkler System Maintenance		X			
K0066 – Smoking Regulations	X	X			
K0067 – Ventilating Equipment	X	X			
K0069 – Cooking Equipment	X	X			
K0072 – Furnishing and Decorations	X	X			
K0076 – Medical Gas System	X	X		X C	11/20/2001
K0130 - Other	X	X		X C	11/20/2001

C = Date of Correction   N = No Date Given   P = Plan of Correction   R = Refused to Correct   W = Waived   F = Fses   X = Deficient

COP = Condition   REQ = Requirement

Run Date of Report: 07/03/2003   Last File Update: 07/02/2003

OSCAR Report 3
Full Facility Profile

Facility

Provider #:
Phone Number:
Participation Date: 07/01/1967

Type Action: Recertification

Type Ownership: For Profit - Corporation

State's Region Code: 001
Compliance Status: Facility Meets Requirements Based on an Acceptable Plan of Correction

Resident Census on 10/09/2001

Total:	73
Medicare:	6
Medicaid:	61
Other:	6

Survey Dates From: 10/01/2001 To: 10/03/2001
Extended Survey Dates From: To:
Date Provider Signed POC: 10/22/2001   11/21/2001
Revisit Dates: 12/13/2001   11/21/2001

LTC Admission/Suspension Dates

Admission Suspended:
Suspension Rescinded:

Total Certified Beds: 83

18	18/19	19	ICF/MR
	83		

Program Requirements

S/S Code	Tag #	Requirement	Plan/Date of Correction	Status of Deficiency	State #	State %	Region #	Region %	Nation #	Nation %

And Percent of Facilities
Not Meeting Requirement – After 09/30/1990

S/S Code	Tag #	Requirement	Plan/Date of Correction	Status of Deficiency	State #	State %	Region #	Region %	Nation #	Nation %
C	F0167	Survey Results Readily Accessible to Residents	11/21/2001	Deficiency Corrected	4	2.3	56	3.3	371	3.7
D	F0225	Not Employ Persons Guilty of Abuse	11/21/2001	Deficiency Corrected	22	13.0	190	11.3	1132	11.4
D	F0274	Assessment After a Significant Change	11/21/2001	Deficiency Corrected	17	10.0	95	5.6	401	4.0
D	F0282	Services by Qualified Persons in Accordance with Care Plan	12/13/2001	Deficiency Corrected	67	39.6	260	15.5	1040	10.4
D	F0310	ADLs Do Not Decline Unless Unavoidable	11/21/2001	Deficiency Corrected	1	0.5	24	1.4	124	1.2
D	F0312	ADL Care Provided for Dependent Residents	11/21/2001	Deficiency Corrected	51	30.1	214	12.8	1172	11.8
D	F0322	Proper Care & Services for Resident with NG Tube	11/21/2001	Deficiency Corrected	18	10.6	141	8.4	564	5.6
G	F0324	Supervision/Devices to Prevent Accidents	11/21/2001	Deficiency Corrected	20	11.8	233	13.9	1896	19.1
D	F0444	Wash Hands when Indicated	11/21/2001	Deficiency Corrected	33	19.5	152	9.1	820	8.2
C	F0445	Handle Linens to Prevent Spread of Infection	11/21/2001	Deficiency Corrected	6	3.5	55	3.2	297	2.9

Building Characteristics

LSC Compliance Status   Facility Meets Requirements Based on an Acceptable POC

Building Number	Type of Building	Edition of LSC Applied
01	Building	85 Exist

Survey Dates From: 10/01/2001 To: 10/03/2001
Extended Survey Dates From: To:
Date Provider Signed POC: 10/29/2001
Revisit Dates: 11/20/2001

LSC Deficiencies

And Percent of Facilities
Not Meeting Requirement – After 09/30/1990

Building Number	Tag #	Requirement	Plan/Date Of Correction	Status of Deficiency	State #	State %	Region #	Region %	Nation #	Nation %

Run Date of Report: 07/03/2003

Last File Update: 07/02/2003

OSCAR Report 4
Full Facility Profile

Facility   Provider #:

Survey Dates From: 10/01/2001 To: 10/03/2001
Extended Survey Dates From: To:
Date Provider Signed POC: 10/29/2001
Revisit Dates: 11/20/2001

LSC Deficiencies

Building Number	Tag #	Requirement	Plan/Date of Correction	Status of Deficiency	# And Percent of Facilities Not Meeting Requirement – After 09/30/1990					
					State		Region		Nation	
					#	%	#	%	#	%
01	K0025	Smoke Partition Construction	11/20/2001	Deficiency Corrected	35	20.7	147	8.8	1057	10.6
01	K0046	Emergency Lighting	11/20/2001	Deficiency Corrected	10	5.9	87	5.2	589	5.9
01	K0050	Fire Drills	11/20/2001	Deficiency Corrected	56	33.1	186	11.1	764	7.6
01	K0051	Fire Alarm System	11/20/2001	Deficiency Corrected	44	26.0	155	9.2	589	5.9
01	K0076	Medical Gas System	11/20/2001	Deficiency Corrected	38	22.4	143	8.5	738	7.4
01	K0130	Other	11/20/2001	Deficiency Corrected	49	28.9	230	13.7	1379	13.8

Run Date of Report: 07/03/2003

Last File Update: 07/02/2003

OSCAR Report 4
Full Facility Profile

Facility

Provider #:

Resident Characteristics

	Facility #	Facility %	State %	Region %	Nation %
F075 Number of Residents Who Are Medicare Beneficiaries.	6	8.2	10.9	12.6	11.1
F076 Number of Residents Who Are Medicaid Recipients.	61	83.5	72.7	71.7	67.6
F077 Number of Residents Not Medicare or Medicaid Beneficiaries.	6	8.2	16.3	15.6	21.1
F078 Total Number of Residents/Clients.	73	100.0	100.0	100.0	100.0
F079 Bathing – Number of Independent Residents.	2	2.7	4.0	3.8	4.3
F080 Bathing – Number of Residents Assisted by Staff.	36	49.3	52.8	51.6	56.1
F081 Bathing – Number of Residents Dependent on Staff.	35	47.9	43.0	44.4	39.5
F082 Dressing – Number of Independent Residents.	8	10.9	10.8	9.6	11.2
F083 Dressing – Number of Residents Assisted by Staff.	30	41.0	54.4	53.5	56.2
F084 Dressing – Number of Residents Dependent on Staff.	35	47.9	34.6	36.7	32.5
F085 Transferring – Number of Independent Residents.	21	28.7	24.4	21.5	23.4
F086 Transferring – Number of Residents Assisted by Staff.	23	31.5	42.8	46.0	49.2
F087 Transferring – Number of Residents Dependent on Staff.	29	39.7	32.6	32.4	27.2
F088 Toilet Use – Number of Independent Residents.	19	26.0	20.0	16.7	18.4
F089 Toilet Use – Number of Residents Assisted by Staff.	22	30.1	39.0	41.2	46.4
F090 Toilet Use – Number of Residents Dependent on Staff.	32	43.8	40.8	42.0	35.0
F091 Eating – Number of Independent Residents.	21	28.7	48.9	46.1	48.3
F092 Eating – Number of Residents Assisted by Staff.	27	36.9	26.5	30.5	32.3
F093 Eating – Number of Residents Dependent on Staff.	25	34.2	24.4	23.3	19.2
F094 Continence – Number of Residents with Indwelling or External Catheter.	6	8.2	5.2	6.2	6.3
F095 Number of Residents with Catheters Present on Admission.	4	5.4	4.0	4.3	4.4

Run Date of Report: 07/03/2003

Last File Update: 07/02/2003

Exhibit 96
(continued)

OSCAR Report 4
Full Facility Profile

Provider #:

Facility

Resident Characteristics

	Facility #	Facility %	State %	Region %	Nation %
F096	Continence – Number of Residents Occasionally or Frequently Incontinent of Bladder.	30	41.0	56.7	57.6	56.3
F097	Continence – Number of Residents Occasionally or Frequently Incontinent of Bowel.	35	47.9	51.2	52.6	46.5
F098	Continence – Number of Residents on Individually Written Bladder Training Program.	4	5.4	10.0	5.8	6.0
F099	Continence – Number of Residents on Individually Written Bowel Training Program.	4	5.4	7.2	4.0	3.7
F100	Mobility – Number of Residents Who Are Bedfast Most or All of the Time.	1	1.3	8.2	6.6	4.0
F101	Mobility – Number of Residents in Chairs Most or All of the Time.	57	78.0	55.6	57.6	56.9
F102	Mobility – Number of Independently Ambulatory Residents.	1	1.3	11.8	11.4	13.2
F103	Mobility – Number of Residents Needing Assistance or Assistive Device for Ambulation.	14	19.1	27.1	27.0	30.8
F104	Mobility – Number of Physically Restrained Residents.	11	15.0	4.4	9.4	8.8
F105	Mobility – Number of Residents Admitted with Orders for Restraints.	0	0.0	0.4	1.3	2.0
F106	Mobility – Number of Residents with Contractures.	19	26.0	31.3	31.5	31.1
F107	Mobility – Number of Residents with Contractures at Time of Admission.	17	23.2	20.1	17.8	19.3
F108	Mental Status – Number of Residents with Mental Retardation.	3	4.1	4.5	2.9	2.6
F109	Mental Status – Number of Residents with Documented Signs and Symptoms of Depression.	36	49.3	39.7	40.7	41.6
F110	Mental Status – Number of Residents with Documented Psychiatric Diagnosis (Excluding Dementias and Depression.)	7	9.5	18.6	18.2	17.5
F111	Mental Status – Number of Residents with Dementia: Multi-Infarct, Senile, Alzheimer's Type, or Other Than Alzheimer's Type.	20	27.3	53.8	48.3	46.0

Run Date of Report: 07/03/2003

Last File Update: 07/02/2003

SOM, Exhibits - CMS Survey Process Forms

(Revised August 2007)

Exhibit 96
(continued)

OSCAR Report 4
Full Facility Profile

Provider #:

Facility

Resident Characteristics

	Facility #	%	State %	Region %	Nation %
F112 Mental Status – Number of Residents with Behavioral Symptoms.	2	2.7	26.0	29.0	30.5
F113 Mental Status – Number of Residents with Behavioral Symptoms Receiving a Behavior Management Program.	1	1.3	18.0	12.3	13.6
F114 Mental Status – Number of Residents Receiving Health Rehabilitative Services for MI/MR.	0	0.0	4.3	3.0	3.1
F115 Skin Integrity – Number of Residents with Pressure Sores, Excluding Stage 1.	3	4.1	5.5	7.4	7.2
F116 Skin Integrity – Number of Residents with Pressure Sores on Admission.	0	0.0	3.3	3.9	3.7
F117 Number of Residents Receiving Preventive Skin Care.	4	5.4	77.8	74.9	69.6
F118 Skin Integrity – Number of Residents with Skin Rashes.	2	2.7	3.7	4.8	5.3
F119 Special Care – Number of Residents Receiving Hospice Care Benefit.	1	1.3	2.7	2.7	2.0
F120 Special Care – Number of Residents Receiving Radiation Therapy.	0	0.0	0.0	0.1	0.1
F121 Special Care – Number of Residents Receiving Chemotherapy.	0	0.0	0.1	0.2	0.4
F122 Special Care – Number of Residents Receiving Dialysis.	0	0.0	0.9	1.4	1.2
F123 Number of Residents Receiving Intravenous Therapy, Parenteral Nutrition, and/or Blood Transfusions.	0	0.0	0.6	1.3	1.3
F124 Special Care – Number of Residents Receiving Respiratory Treatment.	4	5.4	8.4	9.7	9.7
F125 Special Care – Number of Residents Receiving Tracheostomy Care.	0	0.0	0.2	0.6	0.9
F126 Special Care – Number of Residents Receiving Ostomy Care.	6	8.2	6.5	5.4	4.3
F127 Special Care – Number of Residents Receiving Suctioning.	0	0.0	1.1	1.3	1.4
F128 Special Care – Number of Residents Receiving Injections.	17	23.2	14.1	15.1	13.8

Last File Update: 07/02/2003

Run Date of Report: 07/03/2003

Exhibit 96
(continued)

OSCAR Report 4
Full Facility Profile

Provider #:

Resident Characteristics

Facility		Facility #	Facility %	State %	Region %	Nation %
F129	Special Care – Number of Residents Receiving Tube Feedings.	4	5.4	11.1	9.4	6.9
F130	Special Care – Number of Residents Receiving Mechanically Altered Diets Including Purced and All Chopped Food.	38	52.0	39.9	39.7	35.9
F131	Special Care – Number of Residents Receiving Specialized Rehabilitative Services.	21	28.7	13.2	16.1	15.6
F132	Special Care – Number of Residents Using Assistive Devices While Eating.	15	20.5	5.4	5.4	8.0
F133	Medications – Number of Residents Receiving Psychoactive Drugs.	48	65.7	60.1	60.1	58.8
F134	Medications – Number of Residents Receiving Antipsychotic Medications.	29	39.7	23.1	25.6	24.5
F135	Medications – Number of Residents Receiving Antianxiety Medications.	5	6.8	15.8	18.6	15.3
F136	Medications – Number of Residents Receiving Antidepressant Medications.	34	46.5	44.5	40.9	40.6
F137	Medications – Number of Residents Receiving Hypnotic Medications.	0	0.0	4.1	6.6	4.8
F138	Medications – Number of Residents Receiving Antibiotics.	8	10.9	7.0	8.2	7.6
F139	Medications – Number of Residents on Pain Management Program.	12	16.4	23.1	17.9	21.9
F140	Other – Number of Residents with Unplanned Significant Weight Loss/Gain.	1	1.3	8.5	8.3	7.6
F141	Other – Number of Residents Who Do Not Communicate in Dominant Language of Facility, Including Those Who Use Sign Language.	0	0.0	0.3	1.6	2.8
F142	Other – Number of Residents Who Use Non-Oral Communication Devices.	0	0.0	2.8	3.3	3.7

Run Date of Report: 07/03/2003

Last File Update: 07/02/2003

Exhibit 96
(continued)

OSCAR Report 4
Full Facility Profile

Facility

Provider #:

Resident Characteristics

		Facility		State	Region	Nation
		#	%	%	%	%
F143	Other – Number of Residents with Advance Directives.	48	65.7	42.3	53.3	61.6
F144	The Number of Residents Who Received Influenza Immunizations.	51	69.8	56.8	53.9	63.8
F145	The Number of Residents Who Received Pneumococcal Vaccine.	0	0.0	23.3	24.2	34.4

Last File Update: 07/02/2003

Run Date of Report: 07/03/2003

[This page intentionally left blank]

DEPARTMENT OF HEALTH AND HUMAN SERVICES
CENTERS FOR MEDICARE & MEDICAID SERVICES

CMS Form "A"

STATEMENT OF ISOLATED DEFICIENCIES WHICH CAUSE NO HARM WITH ONLY A POTENTIAL FOR MINIMAL HARM FOR SNFs AND NFs

	PROVIDER #	DATE SURVEY COMPLETE:
NAME OF FACILITY	STREET ADDRESS, CITY, STATE, ZIP CODE	

ID PREFIX TAG	SUMMARY STATEMENT OF DEFICIENCIES

The findings entered above are disclosable 14 days after such information is made available to the facility.

If continuation sheet Page _____ of _____

SOM, Exhibits - CMS Survey Process Forms

[This page intentionally left blank]

DEPARTMENT OF HEALTH AND HUMAN SERVICES
CENTERS FOR MEDICARE & MEDICAID SERVICES

Exhibit 7

FORM APPROVED
OMB NO. 0938 0391

STATEMENT OF DEFICIENCIES AND PLAN OF CORRECTION	(X1) PROVIDERS/SUPPLIER/CLIA IDENTIFICATION NUMBER:	(X2) MULTIPLE CONSTRUCTION A. BUILDING _____ B. WING _____	(X3) DATE SURVEY COMPLETED

NAME OF FACILITY   STREET ADDRESS, CITY, STATE, ZIP CODE

(X4) ID PREFIX TAG	SUMMARY STATEMENT OF DEFICIENCIES (EACH DEFICIENCY SHOULD BE PRECEDED BY FULL REGULATORY OR LSC IDENTIFYING INFORMATION)	ID PREFIX TAG	PLAN OF CORRECTION (EACH CORRECTIVE ACTION SHOULD BE CROSS-REFERRED TO THE APPROPRIATE DEFICIENCY)	(X5) COMPLETION DATE

Any deficiency statement ending with an asterisk (*) denotes a deficiency which the institution may be excused from correcting providing it is determined that other safeguards provide sufficient protection to the patients. *(See reverse for further instructions.)* Except for nursing homes, the findings stated above are disclosable 90 days following the date of survey whether or not a plan of correction is provided. For nursing homes, the above findings and plans of correction are disclosable 14 days following the date these documents are made available to the facility. If deficiencies are cited, an approved plan of correction is requisite to continued program participation.

LABORATORY DIRECTOR'S OR PROVIDER/SUPPLIER REPRESENTATIVE'S SIGNATURE   TITLE   (X6) DATE

FORM CMS-2567 (02/99) Previous Versions Obsolete   If continuation sheet Page _____ of _____

Exhibit 7
(continued)

INSTRUCTIONS FOR COMPLETION OF THE STATEMENT OF DEFICIENCIES AND PLAN OF CORRECTION (CMS-2567)

I. **PURPOSE**

This document contains a listing of deficiencies cited by the surveying State Agency (SA) or Regional Office (RO) as requiring correction. The Summary Statement of Deficiencies is based on the surveyors' professional knowledge and interpretation of Medicare and/or Medicaid or Clinical Laboratory Improvement Amendments requirements.

II. **FORM COMPLETION**

Name and Address of Facility – Indicate the name and address of the facility identified on the official certification record. When surveying multiple sites under one identification number, identify the site where a deficiency exists in the text of the deficiency under the Summary Statement of Deficiencies column.

Prefix Identification Tag – Each cited deficiency and corrective action should be preceded by the prefix identification tag (as shown to the left of the regulation in the State Operations Manual or survey report form). For example, a deficiency in Patient Test Management (493.1107) would be preceded by the appropriate D-Tag in the 3000 series. A deficiency cited in the Life Safety Code provision 2-1 (construction) would be preceded by K8. Place this appropriate identification tag in the column labeled ID Prefix Tag.

III. **Summary Statement of Deficiencies** – Each cited deficiency should be followed by full identifying information, e.g., 493.1107(a). Each Life Safety Code deficiency should be followed by the referenced citation from the Life Safety Code and the provision number shown on the survey report form.

IV. **Plan of Correction** – In the column Plan of Correction, the statements should reflect the facility's plan for corrective action and the anticipated time of correction (an explicit date must be shown). If the action has been completed when the form is returned, the plan should indicate the date completed. The date indicated for completion of the corrective action must be appropriate to the level of deficiency(ies).

V. **Waivers** – Waivers of other than Life Safety Code deficiencies in hospitals are by regulations specifically restricted to the RN waiver as provided in section 1861(e)(5) of the Social Security Act. The long term care regulations provide for waiver of the regulations for nursing, patient room size and number of beds per room. The regulations provide for variance of the number of beds per room for intermediate care facilities for the mentally retarded. Any other deficiency must be covered by an acceptable plan of correction. The waiver principle cannot be invoked in any other area than specified by regulation.

VI. **Waiver Asterisk(*)** – The footnote pertaining to the marking by asterisk of recommended waivers presumes an understanding that the use of waivers is specifically restricted to the regulatory items. In any event, when the asterisk is used after a deficiency statements, the CMS Regional Office should indicate in the right hand column opposite the deficiency whether or not the recommended waiver has been accepted.

VII. **Signature** – This form should be signed and dated by the provider or supplier representative or the laboratory director. The original, with the facility's proposed corrective action, must be returned to the appropriate surveying agency (SA or RO) within 10 days of receipt. Please maintain a copy for your records.

According to the Paperwork Reduction Act of 1995, no persons are required to a collection of information unless it displays a valid OMB control number for this information is 0938-0391. The time required to complete this information collection is estimated to average 15 minutes per response, including the time to review instructions, search existing data resources, gather the data needed, and complete and review the information collection. If you have any comments concerning the accuracy of the time estimate(s) or suggestions for improving this form, please write to: CMS, Attn: PRA Reports Clearance Officer, 7500 Security Boulevard, Baltimore, Maryland 21244-1850.

STANDARD and ABBREVIATED SURVEYS PROCESS

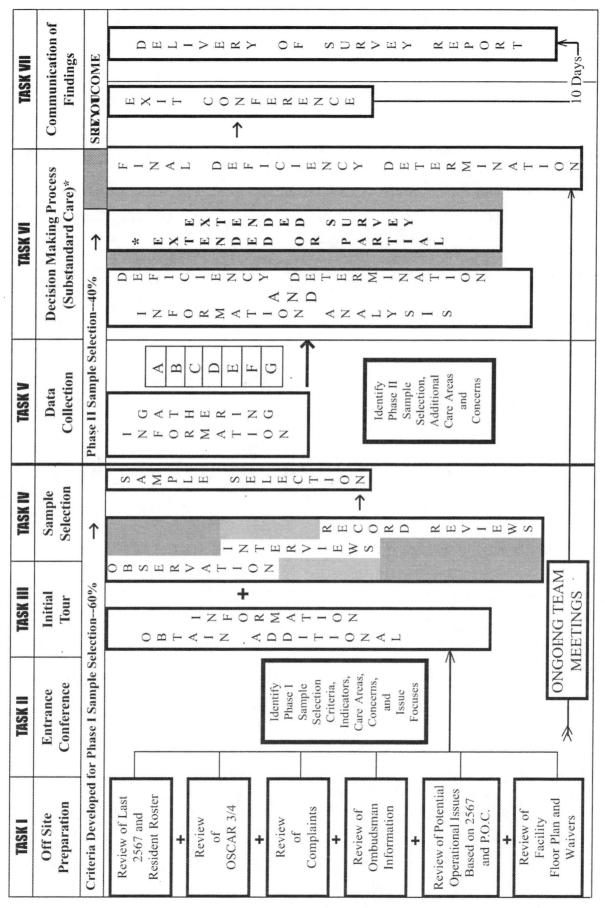

[This page intentionally left blank]

EXHIBIT 268
Rev. 9, 08/05/2005

Facility Characteristics Report

Page 1 of 1

Facility Name	LISA01
City/State	SACRAMENTO,CA
Provider Number	855134
Login/Internal ID	LISA01/1234

Run Date	04/21/05 09:55:36
Report Period	09/01/04 - 02/28/05
Comparison Group	07/01/04 - 12/31/04
Report Version Number	1.07

	Facility			Comparison Group	
	Num	**Denom**	**Observed Percent**	**State Average**	**National Average**
Gender					
Male	9	46	19.6%	33.0%	31.3%
Female	37	46	80.4%	67.0%	68.7%
Age					
<25 years old	0	46	0.0%	0.3%	0.5%
25-54 years old	0	46	0.0%	9.0%	5.8%
55-64 years old	0	46	0.0%	7.4%	6.7%
65-74 years old	4	46	8.7%	12.6%	13.3%
75-84 years old	24	46	52.2%	30.6%	32.7%
85+ years old	18	46	39.1%	40.0%	40.9%
Payment Source (all that apply)					
Medicaid per diem	0	46	0.0%	45.0%	44.7%
Medicare per diem	0	46	0.0%	28.4%	30.3%
Medicare ancillary Part A	37	46	80.4%	15.1%	18.2%
Medicare ancillary Part B	0	46	0.0%	6.0%	8.4%
Self or family pays for full per diem	9	46	19.6%	20.0%	15.1%
Medicaid resident liability or Medicare co-payment	0	46	0.0%	5.4%	10.6%
Private insurance per diem (including co-payment)	1	46	2.2%	10.7%	10.4%
All other per diem	0	46	0.0%	2.1%	3.2%
Diagnostic Characteristics					
Psychiatric diagnosis	0	46	0.0%	18.1%	13.1%
Mental retardation	0	46	0.0%	2.0%	2.7%
Hospice	0	46	0.0%	2.7%	3.2%
Type of Assessment					
Admission assessment	37	46	80.4%	30.7%	31.2%
Annual assessment	1	46	2.2%	11.6%	10.9%
Significant change in status assessment	0	46	0.0%	7.5%	8.4%
Significant correction of prior full assessment	0	46	0.0%	0.0%	0.0%
Quarterly assessment	8	46	17.4%	50.2%	49.4%
Significant correction of prior quarterly assessment	0	46	0.0%	0.0%	0.0%
All other assessment types	0	46	0.0%	0.0%	0.0%
Stability of Conditions					
Conditions/disease make resident unstable	8	46	17.4%	42.5%	41.8%
Acute episode or chronic flareup	36	46	78.3%	17.3%	17.1%
End-stage disease, 6 or fewer months to live	0	46	0.0%	2.0%	2.8%
Discharge Potential					
No discharge potential	8	46	17.4%	66.6%	65.7%
Discharge potential within 30 days	32	46	69.6%	9.5%	10.6%
Discharge potential 30-90 days	2	46	4.3%	5.1%	5.5%
Uncertain discharge potential	4	46	8.7%	17.9%	17.4%

[This page intentionally left blank]

EXHIBIT 269
Rev. 9, 08/05/2005

Facility Quality Measure/Indicator Report

Page 1 of 2

Facility Name	LISA01	Run Date	05/20/05 16:01:28
City/State	SACRAMENTO,CA	Report Period	09/01/04 - 02/28/05
Provider Number	855134	Comparison Group	07/01/04 - 12/31/04
Login/Internal ID	LISA01/1234	Report Version Number	1.07

Measure ID	Domain/Measure Description	Num	Denom	Observed Percent	Adjusted Percent	State Average	National Average	State Percentile
Chronic Care Measures								
	Accidents							
1.1	Incidence of new fractures	1	109	0.9%	-	1.9%	2.1%	29
1.2	Prevalence of falls	5	109	4.6%	-	12.3%	12.9%	8
	Behavior/Emotional Patterns							
2.1	Residents who have become more depressed or anxious	9	109	8.3%	-	16.1%	15.7%	23
2.2	Prevalence of behavior symptoms affecting others: Overall	16	106	15.1%	-	23.3%	18.9%	26
2.2-HI	Prevalence of behavior symptoms affecting others: High risk	15	86	17.4%	-	26.1%	22.1%	29
2.2-LO	Prevalence of behavior symptoms affecting others: Low risk	1	20	5.0%	-	8.7%	8.1%	49
2.3	Prevalence of symptoms of depression without antidepressant therapy	0	106	0.0%	-	6.7%	5.3%	0
	Clinical Management							
3.1	Use of 9 or more different medications	76	109	69.7%	-	56.2%	60.2%	84
	Cognitive Patterns							
4.1	Incidence of cognitive impairment	1	22	4.5%	-	15.0%	12.3%	23
	Elimination/Incontinence							
5.1	Low-risk residents who lost control of their bowels or bladder	42	67	62.7%	-	47.1%	46.8%	88
5.2	Residents who have/had a catheter inserted and left in their bladder	7	109	6.4%	5.8%	5.2%	7.7%	62
5.3	Prevalence of occasional or frequent bladder or bowel incontinence without a toileting plan	32	33	97.0%	-	54.9%	44.2%	85
5.4	Prevalence of fecal impaction	0	109	0.0%	-	0.2%	0.1%	0
	Infection Control							
6.1	Residents with a urinary tract infection	8	109	7.3%	-	8.5%	9.5%	44
	Nutrition/Eating							
7.1	Residents who lose too much weight	6	90	6.7%	-	10.9%	10.0%	21
7.2	Prevalence of tube feeding	24	109	22.0%	-	9.0%	7.2%	96 *
7.3	Prevalence of dehydration	2	109	1.8%	-	0.5%	0.4%	93 *
	Pain Management							
8.1	Residents who have moderate to severe pain	13	109	11.9%	9.4%	9.8%	7.8%	61
	Physical Functioning							
9.1	Residents whose need for help with daily activities has increased	6	77	7.8%	-	15.6%	17.5%	16
9.2	Residents who spend most of their time in bed or in a chair	29	106	27.4%	-	8.1%	5.5%	98 *
9.3	Residents whose ability to move in and around their room got worse	6	52	11.5%	10.1%	14.0%	15.7%	33
9.4	Incidence of decline in ROM	4	105	3.8%	-	8.1%	8.5%	27

Note: Dashes represent a value that could not be computed

EXHIBIT 269 (Cont.)

Facility Quality Measure/Indicator Report

Page 2 of 2

Facility Name LISA01
City/State SACRAMENTO,CA
Provider Number 855134
Login/Internal ID LISA01/1234

Run Date 05/20/05 16:01:28
Report Period 09/01/04 - 02/28/05
Comparison Group 07/01/04 - 12/31/04
Report Version Number 1.07

| | | Facility | | | | Comparison Group | | |
| | | | | Observed | Adjusted | State | National | State |
Measure ID	Domain/Measure Description	Num	Denom	Percent	Percent	Average	Average	Percentile
Chronic Care Measures								
	Psychotropic Drug Use							
10.1	Prevalence of antipsychotic use, in the absence of psychotic or related conditions: Overall	18	100	18.0%	-	26.7%	22.0%	20
10.1-HI	Prevalence of antipsychotic use, in the absence of psychotic or related conditions: High risk	7	11	63.6%	-	47.7%	46.0%	83
10.1-LO	Prevalence of antipsychotic use, in the absence of psychotic or related conditions: Low risk	11	86	12.8%	-	22.2%	18.1%	18
10.2	Prevalence of antianxiety/hypnotic use	20	100	20.0%	-	18.6%	18.8%	58
10.3	Prevalence of hypnotic use more than two times in last week	3	109	2.8%	-	3.8%	4.1%	47
	Quality of Life							
11.1	Residents who were physically restrained	8	109	7.3%	-	9.8%	7.1%	40
11.2	Prevalence of little or no activity	65	106	61.3%	-	10.5%	9.2%	99 *
	Skin Care							
12.1	High-risk residents with pressure ulcers	13	75	17.3%	-	17.1%	15.2%	58
12.2	Low-risk residents with pressure ulcers	1	34	2.9%	-	2.9%	3.4%	64 *
Post-Acute Care(PAC) Measures								
13.1	Short-stay residents with delirium	5	86	5.8%	5.2%	4.8%	3.4%	69
13.2	Short-stay residents who had moderate to severe pain	44	86	51.2%	-	23.5%	23.7%	92 *
13.3	Short-stay residents with pressure ulcers	20	83	24.1%	23.4%	19.7%	18.8%	67

Note: Dashes represent a value that could not be computed

EXHIBIT 270
Rev. 9, 08/05/2005

Resident Level Quality Measure/Indicator Report: Chronic Care Sample

Facility Name	LISA01
City/State	SACRAMENTO,CA
Provider Number	855134
Login/Internal ID	LISA01/1234

Run Date	05/21/05 10:06:04
Report Period	09/01/04 - 02/28/05
Report Version Number	1.07
	Page 1 of 10

Resident Int Id	Resident Name	AABa	Accid: NewFract	Accid: Falls	Behav: Depression	Behav: Problem Behavior Hi	Behav: Problem Behavior Lo	Behav: Dprs No Tx	Clin: 9+ Meds	Cog: Cog Impair	Elim: Bw/Blad Incnt Lo	Elim: Cath Insert	Elim: Incnt No TP	Elim: Fecal Impct	Infct: UTIs	Nutr: Wt Loss	Nutr: Tube Feed	Nutr: Dhyd	Pain: Mod/Sevr Pain	Pain: ADL Help Incrs	Phys: Most Time Chair	Phys: Move Ability Wrse	Phys: Decln ROM	Psych: Psychotic w/o Condition Hi	Psych: Psychotic w/o Condition Lo	Psych: Anti-anx/Hpnot	Psych: Hpnot 2x Week	Qual: Phys Rstrn	Qual: Little Activ	Skin: Pressure Ulcers Hi	Skin: Pressure Ulcers Lo	Count
Active Residents																																
999999	DOE, JANE	05		X					X		X				X														X			5
999999	DOE, JANE	01		X					X							X			X													4
999999	DOE, JOHN	05									X																					1
999999	DOE, JANE	05		X					X				X																X			4
999999	DOE, JOHN	01		X					X				X				X									X				X		6
999999	DOE, JANE	01		X							X					X			X							X						4
999999	DOE, JANE	01		X		X			X				X			X			X													5
999999	DOE, JOHN	05				X			X		X	X									X											4
999999	DOE, JANE	05				X			X			X	X			X			X		X											5
999999	DOE, JANE	05		X					X		X		X			X					X			X					X	X		6
999999	DOE, JOHN	01							X			X				X	X		X		X	X				X	X		X	X		9
999999	DOE, JANE	05															X				X								X			3
999999	DOE, JOHN	05							X				X								X					X			X			5
999999	DOE, JANE	01		X		X			X												X	X				X	X	X				6
999999	DOE, JOHN	02																											X			3
999999	DOE, JANE	01							X			X							X						X				X			7
999999	DOE, JOHN	01																															0
999999	DOE, JANE	02																							X							3
999999	DOE, JANE	05				X			X								X				X				X	X			X			5
999999	DOE, JOHN	05							X								X				X					X			X	X		5
999999	DOE, JANE	05															X				X								X		X	3
999999	DOE, JOHN	05							X								X				X								X		X	5
999999	DOE, JOHN	05															X								X				X			3

Note: X=triggered, blank=not triggered or excluded.

EXHIBIT 270 (Cont.)

Resident Level Quality Measure/Indicator Report: Post Acute Care Sample Page 1 of 1

Facility Name LISA01
City/State SACRAMENTO,CA
Provider Number 855134
Login/Internal ID LISA01/1234

Run Date 05/09/05 16:18:49
Report Period 09/01/04 - 02/28/05
Report Version Number 1.07

Resident Int Id	Resident Name	Delrm	Mod/Sevr Pain	Press Ulcer	Count
Active Residents					
999999	DOE, JANE				0
999999	DOE, JANE				0
999999	DOE, JANE				0
999999	DOE, JOHN				0
Discharged Residents					
999999	DOE, JANE				0
999999	DOE, JANE				0
999999	DOE, JOHN	X			1
999999	DOE, JANE			X	1
999999	DOE, JOHN				0
999999	DOE, JOHN				0
999999	DOE, JOHN				0
999999	DOE, JANE				0
999999	DOE, JANE				0
999999	DOE, JANE		X		1
999999	DOE, JANE				0
999999	DOE, JANE				0
999999	DOE, JOHN				0
999999	DOE, JANE	X			1
999999	DOE, JANE		X		1
999999	DOE, JOHN		X		1

Note: X=triggered, blank=not triggered or excluded.

Exhibit 74

Chapter 3

Department of Health and Human Services
Centers for Medicare & Medicaid Services

Form Approved
CMS No 0938-0583

Survey Team Composition and Workload Report

Public reporting burden for this collection of information is estimated to average 10 minutes per response, including time for reviewing instructions, searching existing data sources, gathering and maintaining data needed, and completing and reviewing the collection of information. Send comments regarding this burden estimate or any other aspect of this collection of information, including suggestions for reducing the burden to Office of Federal Management, CMS, P.O. Box 26684, Baltimore, MD 21207 and to the Office of Management and Budget, paperwork reduction project (0938-0583), Washington, DC 20503.

Provider/Supplier Number	Provider/Supplier Name

Type of Survey *(select all that apply)*

A   Complaint Investigation
B   Dumping Investigation
C   Federal Monitoring
D   Follow-up Visit

E   Initial Certification
F   Inspection of Care
G   Validation
H   Life Safety Code

I   Recertification
J   Sanctions/Hearings
K   State License
L   CHOW
M   Other

Extent of Survey *(select all that apply)*

A   Routine/Standard Survey (all providers/suppliers)
B   Extended Survey (HHA or Long Term Care Facility)
C   Partial Extended Survey
D   Other Survey

Survey Team and Workload Data

Please enter the workload information for each surveyor. Use the surveyor's identification number.

Surveyor ID Number (A)	First Date Arrived (B)	Last Date Departed (C)	Pre-survey Preparation Hours (D)	On-site Hours 12am-8am (E)	On-site Hours 8am-4pm (F)	On-site Hours 6pm-12am (G)	Travel Hours (H)	Off-site Report Preparation Hours (I)
Team Leader ID 1.								
2.								
3.								
4.								
5.								
6.								
7.								
8.								
9.								
10.								

Total Supervisory Review Hours..

Total Clerical/Data Entry Hours...

Was Statement of Deficiencies given to the provider on-site at completion of the survey?............................... ☐ yes ☐ no

Form CMS-670 (12-91)

If the survey is more than one day, and if you perform survey work after you leave the facility **but before you have completed the survey**, (e.g., the survey is conducted Monday and Tuesday and you work at your motel on Monday night) include this as on-site work only if it is activity that normally would be done at the facility (e.g., determination of deficiencies). Enter these hours per surveyor in the appropriate time band(s).

If you write the formal Statement of Deficiencies or the survey report on-site, include this time as on-site time, not in off-site report preparation.

Travel Hours (H) - Document the total time traveling to and from the facility, excluding meal stops. If surveyors meet at the office and proceed from there, the starting time is the time they leave the office. If, however, surveyors leave their residences, travel toward the facility, and meet on the way to the facility, travel time should be no longer than the time required to travel from the primary duty station to the facility.

If, on completion of one survey, travel is made directly to another facility, travel hours should be shared between the two facilities (i.e., to report two hours of travel from your office or residence for Facility A and Facility B, report one hour travel for Facility A and one hour travel for Facility B)

Off-site Report Preparation Hours (I) - Enter the time necessary for all the activities performed to produce a report. Include the time spent discussing the survey activities during supervisory review, and the time spent to rewrite the report after supervisory review.

If you investigate a complaint or conduct a followup visit by phone or letter, include in this section the time to conduct these activities. Fill out a separate HCFA-670 each time these activities occur, whether or not this work is performed onsite or from the office via phone or letter.

Likewise, include in this column the total number of off-site hours spent with all sanction, appeal, and change-of-ownership activities.

Total Supervisory Review Hours - Include all time spent in review of the survey team's decisions. If supervisory personnel make the deficiency determination, include the time spent reviewing data and making the deficiency determination.

Total Clerical/Data Entry Hours - Enter the number of clerical and/or data entry hours involved in the survey. Clerical duties include, but are not limited to, typing, transcribing, filing, retrieving from files, and travel arrangements. Data entry includes all direct entry or survey data.

Do not inlcude survey team time spent in formulating and typing the report directly from notes. Include that activity in Off-site Report Preparation Hours.

Was Statement of Deficiencies given to the provider on-site at completion of the survey? - Enter the letter Y or N in the block provided to indicate if the formal Statement of Deficiencies was given to the provider/supplier on-site at the completion of the survey.

CMS-670 Survey Team Composition and Workload Report

This form provides information on resource utilization applicable to survey activity in all Medicare and/or Medicaid provider/supplier types and CLIA laboratories. (HCFA CO's system will compute the appropriate share of time spent on Medicare/Medicaid and/or licensure inspections based on the annual rate negotiated between the ROs and the State Agencies.)

Provider/Supplier Number - Leave this item blank on all initial certifications. The RO assigns the Federal identification numbers for all new providers and suppliers of health services. On subsequent actions such as resurveys, followups, and life safety code surveys, insert the facility's assigned 6 or 10 digit provider/supplier number.

Provider/Supplier Name - Enter the provider or supplier name in the space provided.

Type of Survey - Using the letters to the right of the blocks, enter the type(s) of survey being conducted. More than one entry may apply.

Extent of Survey - Using the letters to the right of the blocks, enter the extent(s) of the survey being conducted. More than one entry may apply. For example, for HHAs, it is possible that a survey would include a standard, extended, and partial extended survey.

Surveyor Identification (ID) Number (A) - Enter, on the lines provided, the unique 5-digit ID number of each surveyor participation in the survey. If you do not know your ID number, contact your State or Regional Office Training Coordinator.
First Date Arrived (B) - Enter the date(s) (MMDDYY) each surveyor on the team arrived at the provider/supplier.

Exhibit 74 (continued)

Last Date Departed (C) - Enter the final date(s) (MMDDYY) each surveyor on the team departed the provider/supplier. For example, if a surveyor arrived on Monday to begin the survey, left the facility Tuesday on another assignment but returned to finish on Thursday, Thursday would be shown as the Last Date Departed.

Pre-survey Preparation Hours (D) - Enter the number of hours each surveyor spent in preparing for the survey. This includes telephone calls, conferences pertaining to the survey, file retrieval, analyzing the individual facility profile, copying and organizing material. Record hours to the nearest decimal quarter hour, e.g., two hours and ten minutes would be reported as 2.25 hours.

On-Site Hours (E), (F), and (G) - Enter each surveyor's **working hours** spent on-site, within the time bands specified. Report the hours, as outlined above, to the nearest decimal quarter hour. Do not include meal times as working hours in these columns unless, during meals, you perform survey activities that would otherwise be performed during other times on-site.

[This page intentionally left blank]

EXHIBIT 271
Rev. 9, 08/05/2005

QM/QI Reports Technical Specifications: Version 1.0

Introduction

The measures contained on the Quality Measure/Indicator (QM/QI) Reports are calculated in two major steps. In the first step, two samples of assessments are selected: a chronic care sample and a post-acute care (PAC) sample. In the second step, logic is applied to the two samples of assessments to produce the chronic care and PAC measures. The purpose of this document is to describe the technical details that are involved in these two steps.

This document is divided into three major sections. The first section describes the logic that is used to calculate each of the measures on the QM/QI Reports. The second and third sections describe the criteria that are used to select the assessment records for the chronic care and post-acute care resident samples.

Calculation Logic

The table below[1] lists all of the measures that are on the QM/QI Reports and describes the logic that is used to calculate each measure. The table contains three columns:

- Measure description
- Measure specifications
- Covariates/Risk adjustment

The contents of these columns are described below.

Measure Description Column

- **Measure number.** Each measure is assigned a number that corresponds to the numbering in the QM/QI Reports.
- **Measure description.** This is a brief description of the measure.
- **Source.** The QM/QI Reports combine the publicly reported Quality Measures (QMs) and the CHSRA Quality Indicator (QI) measures. For QM measures, the "source" indicates "QM" and lists the abbreviation that has been assigned to the measure. For the QI measures, the "source" says QInn where "nn" is a number that corresponds to the measure's number on the prior CHSRA QI reports. For example, "QI01" refers to QI #1.

---

[1] This table is based upon information presented in two documents: (1) *National Nursing Home Quality Measures User's Manual, November, 2004 (v1.2)*, and (2) *Facility Guide for the Nursing Home Quality Indicators, September 28, 1999*.

EXHIBIT 271 (Cont.)
QM/QI Reports Technical Specifications: Version 1.0

- **QI Replaced.** Several CHSRA QI measures were replaced by corresponding QM measures. For these measures, a "QI Replaced" entry indicates the number for the QI measure that has been replaced.

Measure Specifications Column

- **Numerator.** The numerator entry gives the logic used to determine whether a resident triggers the QM (if the resident is included in the numerator for the QM rate in the facility).
- **Denominator.** The denominator entry defines whether a resident has the necessary records available to be a candidate for the QM (inclusion of the resident in the denominator for the QM rate for the facility).
- **Exclusions.** The exclusions entry provides clinical conditions and missing data conditions that preclude a resident from consideration for the QM. An excluded resident is excluded from both the numerator and denominator of the QM rate for the facility.
- **Technical comments.** These comments provide additional technical details pertaining to the QM numerator, denominator, and exclusions. Examples of the type of information provided include specific details for calculating scale scores, definition of missing data values for an MDS item, and selection of the value for an MDS item that may come from different assessments for a resident.

Covariates/Risk Adjustment Column

- **Covariates.** The "Covariates" entry defines the calculation logic for covariates. Covariates are always prevalence indicators with a value of 1 if the condition is present and a value of 0 if the condition is not present.
- **High Risk/Low Risk.** A "High Risk" entry defines the calculation logic for a resident who is high risk for the measure. A "Low Risk" entry defines a resident who is low risk.
- **Technical comments.** In some cases, technical comments are provided to define measures or scales that are used to calculate covariates or risk groups.

Notes regarding interpreting the specifications table

- The symbol [t] indicates a target assessment, and [t-1] indicates a prior assessment.
- An MDS item has missing data if that item has an "unable to determine" response (dash in the MDS record), if that item has been skipped (blank), or if that item is not active on the assessment.
- In lists of ICD-9 codes, an asterisk (*) indicates that any value meets the requirements. For example, a code listed as 295.** indicates that any code starting with "295." meets the requirements. In this case the last 2 digits are ignored.

EXHIBIT 271 (Cont.)
QM/QI Reports Technical Specifications: Version 1.0

Measure Description	Measure Specifications	Covariates/Risk Adjustment
	Chronic Care Measures	
Accidents		
1.1 Incidence of new fractures Source: QI01	**Numerator:** Residents with new fractures on target assessment. New fracture defined as: 1. New hip fracture (J4c[t]) is checked on target assessment and J4c[t-1] is not checked on prior assessment) *OR* 2. Other new fractures (J4d[t]) is checked on target assessment and J4d[t-1] is not checked on prior assessment) **Denominator:** All residents with a valid target assessment and a valid prior assessment who did not have fractures on the prior assessment (J4c[t-1] is not checked and J4d[t-1] is not checked). **Exclusions:** Residents satisfying any of the following conditions: 1. The measure did not trigger (resident not included in the numerator) and there is missing data on J4c or J4d on either the target or prior assessment (J4c[t], J4d[t], J4c[t-1], or J4d[t-1] is missing).	
1.2 Prevalence of falls Source: QI02	**Numerator:** Residents who had falls within the past 30 days (J4a is checked on the target assessment). **Denominator:** All residents with a valid target assessment. **Exclusions:** Residents satisfying any of the following conditions: 1. The target assessment is an admission (AA8a = 01) assessment. 2. J4a has missing data on the target assessment.	

EXHIBIT 271 (Cont.)
QM/QI Reports Technical Specifications: Version 1.0

Measure Description	Measure Specifications	Covariates/Risk Adjustment
Behavior/Emotional Patterns		
2.1 Residents who have become more depressed or anxious **Source: QM CMOD03**	*Numerator:* Residents whose Mood Scale scores are greater on target assessment relative to prior assessment (Mood Scale [t] > Mood Scale [t-1]). [The Mood Scale is defined in the Technical Comments.] *Denominator:* All residents with a valid target assessment and a valid prior assessment. *Exclusions:* Residents satisfying any of the following conditions: 1. The Mood Scale score is missing on the target assessment [t]. 2. The Mood Scale score is missing on the prior assessment [t-1] and the Mood Scale score indicates symptoms present on the target assessment (Mood Scale [t] >0). 3. The Mood Scale score is at a maximum (value 8) on the prior assessment. 4. The resident is comatose (B1 = 1) or comatose status is unknown (B1 = missing) on the target assessment. *Technical Comments* *Mood Scale Definition:* Mood Scale score is defined as the count of the number of the following eight conditions that are satisfied (range 0 through 8) on the target assessment. The mood scale has a missing value if any of the MDS items in the following eight conditions has missing data. 1. Any verbal expression of distress (E1a>0, E1c>0, E1e>0, E1f>0, E1g>0, or E1h>0). 2. Shows signs of crying, tearfulness (E1m>0). 3. Motor agitation (E1n>0). 4. Leaves food uneaten (K4c=checked) on target or last full assessment. The K4c value from the last full assessment is only considered if the target assessment is a quarterly assessment and the state quarterly assessment does not include K4c. 5. Repetitive health complaints (E1h>0).	

EXHIBIT 271 (Cont.)
QM/QI Reports Technical Specifications: Version 1.0

Measure Description	Measure Specifications	Covariates/Risk Adjustment
2.2 Prevalence of behavior symptoms affecting others **2.2-HI High risk** **2.2-LO Low risk** **Source:** QI03	6. Repetitive/recurrent verbalizations (E1a>0, E1c>0, or E1g>0). 7. Negative statements (E1a>0, E1e>0, or E1f>0). 8. Mood symptoms not easily altered (E2=2). ***Numerator:*** Residents with behavioral symptoms affecting others on target assessment. Behavioral symptoms affecting others: Verbally abusive (E4bA >0); OR physically abusive (E4cA > 0); OR socially inappropriate /disruptive behavior (E4dA > 0). ***Denominator:*** All residents with a valid target assessment. ***Exclusions:*** Residents satisfying any of the following conditions: 1. The target assessment is an admission (AA8a = 01) assessment. 2. The measure did not trigger (resident not included in the numerator) and there is missing data on E4bA, E4cA, or E4dA. 3. The resident does not qualify as high risk and B2a, B4, I1ff or I1gg has missing data—i.e., the risk group is unknown. ***Note:*** Three separate measures are defined: (1) for all residents (overall), (2) for residents defined as high risk, and (3) for residents defined as low risk. The only difference between the three measures is the denominator definition and use of exclusions as follows: ***Denominator for overall:*** All residents with a valid target assessment with only the first 2 exclusions applied. ***Denominator for high risk:*** All residents with a valid target assessment who are defined as high risk, with all 3 exclusions applied. ***Denominator for low risk:*** All residents with a valid target assessment who are defined as low risk, with all 3 exclusions applied.	***High Risk:*** Presence of Cognitive Impairment (see technical note, below) on the target assessment. OR Psychotic disorders (I3a-I3e = ICD-9 295.**-295.**, 297.**-298.** or I1gg schizophrenia is checked) on the target assessment or on the most recent full assessment. The I3a-I3e values from both the target assessment and the last full assessment are always considered. The I1gg value from the last full assessment is only considered if the target assessment is a quarterly assessment and the state quarterly assessment does not include I1gg. OR Manic-depressive (I3 a-I3e =ICD-9 296.**-296.** or I1ff is checked) on the target assessment or on the most recent full assessment. The I3a-I3e values from both the target assessment and the last full assessment are always considered. The I1ff value from the last full assessment is only considered if the target assessment is a quarterly assessment and the state quarterly assessment does not include I1ff. ***Low Risk:*** All other residents that are not high risk.

EXHIBIT 271 (Cont.)
QM/QI Reports Technical Specifications: Version 1.0

Measure Description	Measure Specifications	Covariates/Risk Adjustment
2.3 Prevalence of symptoms of depression without antidepressant therapy Source: QI05	**Numerator:** Residents with symptoms of depression (see technical comments, below) and no antidepressant therapy (O4c=0) on the target assessment. **Denominator:** All residents with a valid target assessment. **Exclusions:** Residents satisfying any of the following conditions: 1. The target assessment is an admission (AA8a = 01) assessment. 2. The measure did not trigger (resident not included in the numerator) and the following 2 conditions are both satisfied: (a) there is missing data on any of the following items: B1, E1a, E1g, E1j, E1n, E1o, E1p, E2, E4eA, K3a, N1a, N1b, N1c, N1d, or O4c and (b) the measure could have triggered if there had been no missing data. **Technical Comments** **Symptoms of Depression Definition.** Sad mood (E2 = 1 or 2) and at least 2 of the following other symptoms of functional depression: 1. **Symptom 1 distress** (E1a = 1 or 2: resident made negative statements); 2. **Symptom 2 agitation or withdrawal** (E1n = 1 or 2: repetitive physical movements, or E4eA = 1, 2, or 3: resists care, or E1o = 1 or 2: withdrawal from activity, or E1p = 1 or 2: reduced social activity); 3. **Symptom 3 wake with unpleasant mood** (E1j = 1 or 2), **or not awake most of the day** (N1d is checked), **or awake 1 period of the day or less and not comatose** (N1a+N1b +N1c <= 1 and B1 = 0);	**Technical Comments** **Cognitive Impairment Definition.** Resident has impairment in daily decision making ability (B4 >0) and has short term memory problems (B2a=1).

EXHIBIT 271 (Cont.)
QM/QI Reports Technical Specifications: Version 1.0

Measure Description	Measure Specifications	Covariates/Risk Adjustment
	4. **Symptom 4** suicidal or has recurrent thoughts of death (E1g = 1 or 2); 5. **Symptom 5** weight loss (K3a = 1).	
Clinical Management		
3.1 Use of 9 or more different medications Source: QI06	*Numerator:* Residents who received 9 or more different medications on target assessment: O1 (number of medications) >= 9. *Denominator:* All residents with a valid target assessment. *Exclusions:* Residents satisfying any of the following conditions: 1. The target assessment is an admission (AA8a = 01) assessment. 2. O1 has missing data on the target assessment.	
Cognitive Patterns		
4.1 Incidence of cognitive impairment Source: QI07	*Numerator:* Residents who were cognitively impaired on the target assessment and who were not cognitively impaired on the prior assessment (see technical comment below for definition of cognitive impairment). *Denominator:* Residents with a valid target assessment and a valid prior assessment who were not cognitively impaired on the prior assessment. *Exclusions:* Residents satisfying the following condition: 1. The measure did not trigger (resident not included in the numerator) and there is missing data on B4 or B2a on target or prior assessment (B4[t], B2a[t], B4[t-1], or B2a[t-1] is missing). *Technical Comments* *Cognitive Impairment Definition.* Resident has any impairment in daily decision making ability (B4 >0) and has short term memory problems (B2a=1).	

EXHIBIT 271 (Cont.)
QM/QI Reports Technical Specifications: Version 1.0

Measure Description	Measure Specifications	Covariates/Risk Adjustment
Elimination/Incontinence		

5.1 Low-risk residents who lost control of their bowels or bladder
 	
Source: QM CCNT06
 	
QI Replaced: QI08 Low Risk
	Numerator: Residents who were frequently incontinent or fully incontinent on the target assessment (H1a = 3 or 4, or H1b = 3 or 4).
	
	Denominator: All residents with a valid target assessment and not qualifying as high risk.
	
	Exclusions:
	
	1. Residents who qualify as high risk are excluded from the denominator:
	
	   a. Severe cognitive impairment on the target assessment as indicated by B4 = 3 AND B2a = 1; OR
	
	   b. Totally dependent in mobility ADLs on the target assessment: G1aA = 4 or 8 AND G1bA = 4 or 8 AND G1eA = 4 or 8.
	
	2. Residents satisfying any of the following conditions are also excluded from the risk group:
	
	   a. The target assessment is an admission (AA8a = 01) assessment.
	
	   b. The QM did not trigger (resident is not included in the QM numerator) AND the value of H1a or H1b is missing on the target assessment.
	
	   c. The resident is comatose (B1 = 1) or comatose status is unknown (B1 = missing) on the target assessment.
	
	   d. The resident has an indwelling catheter (H3d = checked) or indwelling catheter status is unknown (H3d = missing) on the target assessment.
	
	   e. The resident has an ostomy (H3i = checked) or ostomy status is unknown (H3i = missing) on the target assessment.
	
	   f. The resident does not qualify as high risk and either of the cognitive impairment items (B2a or B4) are missing on the target assessment.	

EXHIBIT 271 (Cont.)
QM/QI Reports Technical Specifications: Version 1.0

Measure Description	Measure Specifications	Covariates/Risk Adjustment
	g. The resident does not qualify as high risk and any of the mobility ADLs (G1aA, G1bA and G1eA) is missing on the target assessment.	
5.2 Residents who have/had a catheter inserted and left in their bladder Source: QM CCAT02 QI Replaced: QI10	*Numerator:* Residents with indwelling catheters on target assessment (H3d = checked). *Denominator:* All residents with a valid target assessment. *Exclusions:* Residents satisfying any of the following conditions: 1. The target assessment is an admission (AA8a = 01) assessment. 2. H3d is missing on the target assessment.	*Covariates:* 1. Indicator of bowel incontinence on the prior assessment: Covariate = 1 if H1a = 4 Covariate = 0 if H1a = 0,1,2, or 3 2. Indicator of pressure sores on the prior assessment: Covariate = 1 if M2a = 3 or 4 Covariate = 0 if M2a = 0, 1 or 2
5.3 Prevalence of occasional or frequent bladder or bowel incontinence without a toileting plan Source: QI09	*Numerator:* Residents with no scheduled toileting plan and no bladder retraining program (neither H3a nor H3b is checked) on the target assessment and either or both of the following conditions on the target assessment: 1. Occasional or frequent bladder incontinence (H1b = 2 or 3), OR 2. Bowel incontinence (H1a = 2 or 3). *Denominator:* Residents with frequent incontinence or occasionally incontinent in either bladder (H1b = 2 or 3) or bowel (H1a = 2 or 3) on target assessment. *Exclusions:* Residents satisfying any of the following conditions: 1. The target assessment is an admission (AA8a = 01) assessment. 2. The measure did not trigger (resident not included in the numerator) and there is missing data on any of the following: H3a, H3b, H1a, H1b.	

EXHIBIT 271 (Cont.)
QM/QI Reports Technical Specifications: Version 1.0

Measure Description	Measure Specifications	Covariates/Risk Adjustment
5.4 Prevalence of fecal impaction Source: QI11	*Numerator:* Residents with fecal impaction (H2d is checked) on the most recent assessment. *Denominator:* All residents with a valid target assessment. *Exclusions:* Residents satisfying any of the following conditions: 1. The target assessment is an admission (AA8a = 01) assessment. 2. H2d is missing on the target assessment.	
Infection Control		
6.1 Residents with a urinary tract infection Source: QM CCNT04 QI Replaced: QI12	*Numerator:* Residents with urinary tract infection on target assessment (I2j = checked). *Denominator:* All residents with a valid target assessment. *Exclusions:* Residents satisfying any of the following conditions: 1. The target assessment is an admission (AA8a = 01) assessment. 2. I2j is missing on the target assessment.	
Nutrition/Eating		
7.1 Residents who lose too much weight Source: QM CWLS01 QI Replaced: QI13	*Numerator:* Residents who have experienced weight loss (K3a=1) of 5 percent of more in the last 30 days or 10 percent or more in the last 6 months. *Denominator:* All residents with a valid target assessment. *Exclusions:* Residents satisfying any of the following conditions: 1. The target assessment is an admission (AA8a = 01) assessment. 2. K3a is missing on the target assessment. 3. The resident is receiving hospice care (P1ao = checked) or hospice status is unknown (P1ao = missing) on the target assessment or the most recent full assessment. The P1ao value from the last full assessment is only considered if the target assessment is a quarterly assessment and the state quarterly assessment does not include P1ao.	

EXHIBIT 271 (Cont.)
QM/QI Reports Technical Specifications: Version 1.0

Measure Description	Measure Specifications	Covariates/Risk Adjustment
7.2 Prevalence of tube feeding Source: QI14	***Numerator:*** Residents with tube feeding (K5b is checked) on target assessment. ***Denominator:*** All residents with a valid target assessment. ***Exclusions:*** Residents satisfying any of the following conditions: 1. The target assessment is an admission (AA8a = 01) assessment. 2. K5b is missing on the target assessment.	
7.3 Prevalence of dehydration Source: QI15	***Numerator:*** Residents with dehydration: output exceeds input (J1c is checked) on the target assessment or I3a-I3e =. ICD-9 276.5 on the target assessment. ***Denominator:*** All residents with a valid target assessment. ***Exclusions:*** Residents satisfying any of the following conditions: 1. The target assessment is an admission (AA8a = 01) assessment. 2. J1c is missing on the target assessment.	
Pain Management		
8.1 Residents who have moderate to severe pain Source: QM CPAI0X	***Numerator:*** Residents with moderate pain at least daily (J2a=2 AND J2b=2) OR horrible/excruciating pain at any frequency (J2b=3) on the target assessment. ***Denominator:*** All residents with a valid target assessment. ***Exclusions:*** Residents satisfying any of the following conditions: 1. The target assessment is an admission (AA8a = 01) assessment. 2. Either J2a or J2b is missing on the target assessment. 3. The values of J2a and J2b are inconsistent on the target assessment. J2a and J2b are inconsistent if either (a) J2a = 0 and J2b is not blank, or (b) J2a >0 and J2b = blank.	***Covariates:*** 1. Indicator of independence or modified independence in daily decision making on the prior assessment: Covariate = 1 if B4 = 0 or 1. Covariate = 0 if B4 = 2 or 3.

EXHIBIT 271 (Cont.)
QM/QI Reports Technical Specifications: Version 1.0

Measure Description	Measure Specifications	Covariates/Risk Adjustment
Physical Functioning		
9.1 Residents whose need for help with daily activities has increased **Source: QM CADL01** **QI Replaced: QI17**	***Numerator:*** Residents with worsening (increasing MDS item score) in Late-Loss ADL self performance at target relative to prior assessment. Residents meet the definition of Late-Loss ADL worsening when at least two of the following are true: 1. Bed mobility – [Level at target assessment (G1aA[t]) – [Level at previous assessment (G1aA[t-1])]] > 0, or 2. Transfer – [Level at target assessment (G1bA[t]) – [Level at previous assessment (G1bA[t-1])]] > 0, or 3. Eating – [Level at target assessment (G1hA[t]) – [Level at previous assessment (G1hA[t-1])]] > 0, or 4. Toileting – [Level at target assessment (G1iA[t]) – [Level at previous assessment (G1iA[t-1])]] > 0, OR at least one of the following is true: 1. Bed mobility – [Level at target assessment (G1aA[t]) – [Level at previous assessment (G1aA[t-1])]] > 1, or 2. Transfer – [Level at target assessment (G1bA[t]) – [Level at previous assessment (G1bA[t-1])]] > 1, or 3. Eating – [Level at target assessment (G1hA[t]) – [Level at previous assessment (G1hA[t-1])]] > 1, or 4. Toileting – [Level at target assessment (G1iA[t]) – [Level at previous assessment (G1iA[t-1])]] > 1. ***Denominator:*** All residents with a valid target and a valid prior assessment. ***Exclusions:*** Residents meeting any of the following conditions: 1. None of the four Late-Loss ADLs (G1aA, G1bA, G1hA, and G1iA) can show decline because each of the four have a value of 4 (total dependence) or a value of 8 (activity did not occur) on the prior assessment [t-1]. 2. The QM did not trigger (resident not included in the numerator) AND there is missing data on any one of the four Late-Loss ADLs	

SOM, Exhibits - CMS Survey Process Forms

(Revised August 2007)

EXHIBIT 271 (Cont.)
QM/QI Reports Technical Specifications: Version 1.0

Measure Description	Measure Specifications	Covariates/Risk Adjustment
	(G1aA), G1bA, G1hA, or G1iA) on the target assessment [t] or prior assessment [t-1]. 3. The resident is comatose (B1 = 1) or comatose status is unknown (B1 = missing) on the target assessment. 4. The resident has end-stage disease (J5c = checked) or end-stage disease status unknown (J5c = missing) on the target assessment. 5. The resident is receiving hospice care (P1ao = checked) or hospice status is unknown (P1ao = missing) on the target assessment or the most recent full assessment. The P1ao value from the last full assessment is only considered if the target assessment is a quarterly assessment and the state quarterly assessment does not include P1ao.	
9.2 Residents who spend most of their time in a bed or in a chair **Source: QM CBFT01** **QI Replaced: QI16**	*Numerator:* Residents who are bedfast (G6a is checked) on target assessment. *Denominator:* All residents with a valid target assessment. *Exclusions:* Residents meeting any of the following conditions: 1. The target assessment is an admission (AA8a = 01) assessment. 2. G6a is missing on the target assessment. 3. The resident is comatose (B1=1), or comatose status is unknown (B1= missing) on the target assessment.	

9.3 Residents whose ability to move in and around their room got worse
 	
 Source: QM CMOB01
	Numerator: Residents whose value for locomotion self performance is greater at target relative to prior assessment (G1eA[t]>G1eA[t- 1]).
	
	 Denominator: All residents with a valid target assessment and a valid prior assessment.
	
	 Exclusions: Residents satisfying any of the following conditions:
	
	 1. The G1eA value is missing on the target assessment [t].
	 2. The G1eA value is missing on the prior assessment [t-1] and the G1eA value shows some dependence on the target assessment (G1eA[t]>0).
	 3. The G1eA value on the prior assessment is 4 (total dependence)
		Covariates:
		
		 1. Indicator of recent falls on the prior assessment:
		
		    Covariate = 1 if J4a checked or J4b checked
		    Covariate = 0 if J4a not checked AND J4b not checked
		
		 2. Indicator of extensive support or more dependence in eating on the prior assessment:

EXHIBIT 271 (Cont.)
QM/QI Reports Technical Specifications: Version 1.0

Measure Description	Measure Specifications	Covariates/Risk Adjustment
	or 8 (activity did not occur).	Covariate = 1 if G1hA = 3,4, or 8
	4. The resident is comatose (B1 = 1) or comatose status is unknown (B1 = missing) on the target assessment.	Covariate = 0 if G1hA = 0,1, or 2
	5. The resident has end-stage disease (J5c = checked) or end-stage disease status is unknown (J5c = missing) on the target assessment.	3. Indicator of extensive support or more dependence in toileting on the prior assessment:
	6. The resident is receiving hospice care (P1ao = checked) or hospice status is unknown(P1ao = missing) on the target assessment or the most recent full assessment. The P1ao value from the last full assessment is only considered if the target assessment is a quarterly assessment and the state quarterly assessment does not include P1ao.	Covariate = 1 if G1iA = 3,4, or 8 Covariate = 0 if G1iA = 0,1, or 2
9.4 Incidence of decline in ROM Source: Ql18	*Numerator:* Residents with increases in functional limitation in ROM between prior and target assessments. Functional limitation in ROM is defined as the sum of items G4aA through G4f A: G4aA + G4bA + G4cA + G4dA + G4eA + G4fA, as follows: SUM(G4aA..G4fA)[t] = functional limitation in ROM on target assessment, and SUM(G4aA..G4fA)[t-1] = functional limitation in ROM on prior assessment. Resident triggers if: SUM(G4aA..G4fA)[t] > SUM(G4aA..G4fA)[t-1] *Denominator:* All residents with a valid target assessment and a valid prior assessment. *Exclusions:* Residents satisfying any of the following conditions: 1. Residents with maximal loss of ROM on prior assessment: SUM(G4aA..G4fA)[t-1]=12. 2. Residents with missing data on either the target or prior assessment on any of the following items: G4aA, G4bA, G4cA, G4dA, G4eA, or G4fA.	

EXHIBIT 271 (Cont.)
QM/QI Reports Technical Specifications: Version 1.0

Measure Description	Measure Specifications	Covariates/Risk Adjustment
Psychotropic Drug Use		

10.1 Prevalence of antipsychotic use, in the absence of psychotic or related conditions
 	
10.1-HI High risk
10.1-LO Low risk
 	
Source: QI19
	Numerator: Residents receiving anti-psychotics (O4a >= 1) on target assessment
	
	Denominator: All residents on target assessment, except those with psychotic or related conditions (see exclusion).
	
	Exclusions: Residents satisfying any of the following conditions:
	
	1. The target assessment is an admission (AA8a = 01) assessment.
	2. Residents with one or more of the following psychotic or related conditions on the target assessment or on the most recent full assessment. The I3a-I3e values from both the target assessment and the last full assessment are always considered. The I1gg value from the last full assessment is only considered if the target assessment is a quarterly assessment and the state quarterly assessment does not include I1gg.
	  a. I3a-I3e ICD-9 = 295.** - 295.**, 297.** - 298.**, or
	  b. I1gg schizophrenia is checked, or
	  c. Tourette's (I3a-I3e ICD-9 =307.23), or
	  d. Huntington's (I3a-I3e ICD-9 =333.4 or 333.40).
	3. Residents with hallucinations (J1i is checked) on the target assessment.
	4. Residents who do not trigger the measure (are not included in the numerator) and who have missing data on any of the following items: O4a, I1gg, or J1i.
	5. Residents who are not high risk and the following 2 conditions are both satisfied: (a) there is missing data on any of the following items: B2a, B4, E4bA, E4cA, or E4dA and (b) high risk could have resulted if there had been no missing data.
	
	Note: Three separate measures are defined, one for all residents (overall), one for residents defined as high risk, and one for residents defined as low risk. The only difference between the two measures is the denominator definition and use of exclusions as follows:
	
	Denominator for overall: All residents with a valid target
		High risk: Cognitive Impairment AND Behavior Problems on target assessment (see technical comments below for definitions).
		
		Low Risk: All other residents that are not high risk.
		
		Technical Comments
		
		Cognitive impairment definition. Any impairment in daily decision making ability (B4 >0) AND has short term memory problems (B2a=1).
		
		Behavior problems definition. Behavior problems. defined as one or more of the following less than daily or daily: verbally abusive (E4bA > 0), physically abusive (E4cA > 0), or socially inappropriate/disruptive behavior (E4dA > 0).

EXHIBIT 271 (Cont.)
QM/QI Reports Technical Specifications: Version 1.0

Measure Description	Measure Specifications	Covariates/Risk Adjustment
	assessment except those with psychotic or related conditions, with only the first 4 exclusions applied. ***Denominator for high risk:*** All residents with a valid target assessment who are defined as high risk except those with psychotic or related conditions, with all 5 exclusions applied. ***Denominator for low risk:*** All residents with a valid target assessment who are defined as low risk except those with psychotic or related conditions, with all 5 exclusions applied.	

10.2 Prevalence of antianxiety/hypnotic use
 	
Source: QI20
	Numerator: Residents who received antianxiety or hypnotics (O4b or O4d >= 1) on target assessment.
	
	Denominator: All residents on target assessment, except those with psychotic or related conditions (see exclusion).
	
	Exclusions: Residents satisfying any of the following conditions:
	
	1. The target assessment is an admission (AA8a = 01) assessment.
	2. Residents with one or more of the following psychotic disorders on the target assessment or on the most recent full assessment The I3a-I3e values from both the target assessment and the last full assessment are always considered. The I1gg value from the last full assessment is only considered if the target assessment is a quarterly assessment and the state quarterly assessment does not include I1gg.
	   a. I3a-I3e ICD-9 = 295.** - 295.**, 297.** - 298.**, or
	   b. I1gg schizophrenia is checked, or
	   c. Tourette's (I3a-I3e ICD-9 =307.23), or
	   d. Huntington's (I3a-I3e ICD-9 =333.4 or 333.40)
	3. Residents with hallucinations (J1i is checked) on the target assessment.
	4. Residents who do not trigger the measure (are not included in the numerator) and who have missing data on any of the following items: O4b, O4d, I1gg, or J1i.	

EXHIBIT 271 (Cont.)
QM/QI Reports Technical Specifications: Version 1.0

Measure Description	Measure Specifications	Covariates/Risk Adjustment
10.3 Prevalence of hypnotic use more than two times in last week Source: QI21	*Numerator:* Residents who received hypnotics more than 2 times in last week (O4d > 2) on the target assessment. *Denominator:* All residents with a valid target assessment. *Exclusions:* Residents satisfying any of the following conditions: 1. The target assessment is an admission (AA8a = 01) assessment. 2. O4d is missing on the target assessment.	
Quality of Life		
11.1 Residents who were physically restrained Source: QM CRES01 QI Replaced: QI22	*Numerator:* Residents who were physically restrained daily (P4c or P4d or P4e = 2) on target assessment. *Denominator:* All residents with a valid target assessment. *Exclusions:* Residents satisfying any of the following conditions: 1. The target assessment is an admission (AA8a = 01) assessment. 2. The QM did not trigger (resident is not included in the QM numerator) AND the value of P4c or P4d or P4e is missing on the target assessment.	
11.2 Prevalence of little or no activity Source: QI23	*Numerator:* Residents with little or no activity (N2 = 2 or 3) on the target assessment. *Denominator:* All residents with a valid target assessment. *Exclusions:* Residents satisfying any of the following conditions: 1. The target assessment is an admission (AA8a = 01) assessment. 2. The resident is comatose (B1=1). 3. N2 or B1 is missing on the target assessment.	

EXHIBIT 271 (Cont.)
QM/QI Reports Technical Specifications: Version 1.0

Measure Description	Measure Specifications	Covariates/Risk Adjustment
Skin Care		
12.1 High-risk residents with pressure ulcers Source: QM CPRU02 QI Replaced: QI24 High Risk	**Numerator:** Residents with pressure sores (Stage 1-4) on target assessment (M2a >0 OR I3a-I3e = ICD-9 707.0*) who are defined as high risk (see denominator definition). **Denominator:** All residents with a valid target assessment and any one of the following high-risk criteria: 1. Impaired in bed mobility or transfer on the target assessment as indicated by G1aA = 3, 4, or 8 OR G1bA = 3, 4, or 8. 2. Comatose on the target assessment as indicated by B1 = 1. 3. Suffer malnutrition on the target assessment as indicated by I3a through I3e = 260, 261, 262, 263.0, 263.1, 263.2, 263.8, or 263.9. **Exclusions:** Residents satisfying any of the following conditions are excluded: 1. The target assessment is an admission (AA8a = 01) assessment. 2. The QM did not trigger (resident is not included in the QM numerator) AND the value of M2a is missing on the target assessment.	
12.2 Low-risk residents with pressure ulcers Source: QM CPRU03 QI Replaced: QI24 Low Risk	**Numerator:** Residents with pressure sores (Stage 1-4) on target assessment (M2a >0 OR I3a-I3e = ICD-9 707.0*) who are defined as low risk (see denominator definition). **Denominator:** All residents with a valid target assessment who are defined as low risk. "Low risk" residents are those who do not qualify as high risk as defined in denominator definition for measure 12.1 above. **Exclusions:** Residents satisfying any of the following conditions are excluded from all risk groups (high and low): 1. The target assessment is an admission (AA8a = 01) assessment. 2. The QM did not trigger (resident is not included in the QM numerator) AND the value of M2a is missing on the target assessment.	

SOM, Exhibits - CMS Survey Process Forms

EXHIBIT 271 (Cont.)
QM/QI Reports Technical Specifications: Version 1.0

Measure Description	Measure Specifications	Covariates/Risk Adjustment
	3. The resident does not qualify as high-risk AND the value of G1aA or G1bA is missing on the target assessment. 4. The resident does not qualify as high-risk AND the value of B1 is missing on the target assessment.	

Post-Acute Care (PAC) Measures

Measure Description	Measure Specifications	Covariates/Risk Adjustment

13.1 Short-stay residents with delirium
 	
Source: QM PAC-DEL0X
	Numerator: Short-stay residents at SNF PPS 14-day assessment with at least one symptom of delirium that represents a departure from usual functioning (at least one B5a through B5f = 2).
	
	Denominator: All patients with a valid SNF PPS 14-day assessment (AA8b = 7).
	
	Exclusions: Patients satisfying any of the following conditions:
	
	1. Patients who are comatose (B1 = 1) or comatose status is unknown (B1 = missing) on the SNF PPS 14-day assessment.
	2. Patients with end-stage disease (J5c = checked) or end-stage disease status is unknown (J5c = missing) on the SNF PPS 14-day assessment.
	3. Patients who are receiving hospice care (P1ao = checked) or hospice status is unknown (P1ao = missing) on the SNF PPS 14-day assessment.
	4. The QM did not trigger (patient not included in the numerator) AND there is a missing value on any of the items B5a through B5f on the SNF PPS 14-day assessment.
		Covariates:
		
		1. Indicator of NO prior residential history preceding the current SNF stay for the patient:
		
		Covariate = 1 if there is NO prior residential history indicated by the following condition being satisfied:
		
		  a. There is a recent admission assessment (AA8a = 01) AND AB5a through AB5e are not checked (value 0) and AB5f is checked (value 1).
		
		Covariate = 0 if there is prior residential history indicated by either of the following conditions being satisfied:
		
		  a. There is a recent admission assessment (AA8a = 01) AND any of the items AB5a through AB5e are checked (value 1) OR AB5f is not checked (value 0).
		  b. There is no recent admission assessment (AA8a = 01).

13.2 Short-stay residents who had moderate to severe pain **Source: QM PAC-PAI0X**	**Numerator:** Short-stay residents at SNF PPS 14-day assessment with moderate pain at least daily (J2a = 2 and J2b = 2) OR horrible/excruciating pain at any frequency (J2b = 3). **Denominator:** All patients with valid SNF PPS 14-day assessment (AA8b	

EXHIBIT 271 (Cont.)
QM/QI Reports Technical Specifications: Version 1.0

Measure Description	Measure Specifications	Covariates/Risk Adjustment
	= 7). ***Exclusions:*** Patients satisfying any of the following conditions: 1. Either J2a or J2b is missing on the 14-day assessment. 2. The values of J2a and J2b are inconsistent on the 14-day assessment. J2a and J2b are inconsistent if either (a) J2a = 0 and J2b is not blank, or (b) J2a >0 and J2b = blank.	

13.3 Short-stay residents with pressure ulcers
 	
Source: QM PAC-PRU0X
	Numerator: Short-stay residents at SNF PPS 14-day assessment who satisfy either of the following conditions:
	
	1. On the SNF PPS 5-day assessment, the patient had no pressure sores (M2a[t-1] = 0) AND, on the SNF PPS 14-day assessment, the patient has at least a Stage 1 pressure sore (M2a[t] = 1,2,3, or 4).
	2. On the SNF PPS 5-day assessment, the patient had a pressure sore (M2a[t-1] = 1,2,3, or 4) AND on the SNF PPS 14-day assessment, pressure sores worsened or failed to improve (M2a[t]>= M2a[t-1]).
	
	Denominator: All patients with a valid SNF PPS 14-day assessment (AA8b = 7) AND a valid preceding SNF PPS 5-day assessment (AA8b = 1).
	
	Exclusions: Patients satisfying any of the following conditions:
	
	1. M2a is missing on the 14-day assessment [t].
	2. M2a is missing on the 5-day assessment [t-1] and M2a shows presence of pressure sores on the 14-day assessment (M2a = 1,2,3, or 4).
		Covariates:
		
		1. Indicator of history of resolved pressure sore on the SNF PPS 5-day assessment:
		
		    Covariate = 1 if M3 = 1
		    Covariate = 0 if M3 = 0
		
		2. Indicator of requiring limited or more assistance in bed mobility on the SNF PPS 5-day assessment:
		
		    Covariate = 1 if G1aA = 2,3,4, or 8
		    Covariate = 0 if G1aA =0 or 1
		
		3. Indicator of bowel incontinence at least one/week on the SNF PPS 5-day assessment:
		
		    Covariate = 1 if H1a = 2,3, or 4
		    Covariate = 0 if H1a = 0 or 1
		
		4. Indicator of diabetes or peripheral vascular disease on the SNF PPS 5-day assessment:
		
		    Covariate = 1 if I1a checked (value 1) OR I1j checked (value 1)

SOM, Exhibits - CMS Survey Process Forms

(Revised August 2007)

EXHIBIT 271 (Cont.)
QM/QI Reports Technical Specifications: Version 1.0

Measure Description	Measure Specifications	Covariates/Risk Adjustment
		Covariate = 0 if I1a not checked (value 0) AND I1j not checked (value 0).
		5. Indicator of Low Body Mass Index (BMI) on the SNF PPS 5- day assessment:
		Covariate = 1 if BMI >= 12 AND <= 19 Covariate = 0 if BMI > 19 AND <= 40
		Where: BMI = weight (kg)/height^2 (m^2) = ((K2b*0.45)/(K2a*.0254)^2)
		(Note: An implausible BMI value <12 or >40 will be treated as a missing value on this covariate.)

EXHIBIT 271 (Cont.)
QM/QI Reports Technical Specifications: Version 1.0
Selection of the Chronic Care Sample

The chronic care measure calculation sample involves selection of residents with a target assessment in the target period. For a selected resident, three different assessment records are then selected: target assessment, prior assessment and most recent full assessment.

Assessment Selected		Chronic Care Measure Selection Specifications
Target Assessment	Selection period	The QM/QI reports use a default 6 month target period, however the user can change this period if desired.
	Qualifying Reasons for Assessment (AA8a/AA8b)	01/*, 02/*, 03/*, 04/*, 05/*, 10/* (* indicates any value accepted)
	Selection Logic	Latest assessment with qualifying reasons for assessment and assessment reference date (A3a) within selection period.
	Rationale	Select a normal (OBRA) assessment from the target quarter. Normal OBRA assessments that are coupled with a PPS assessment (item AA8b = 1,2,3,4,5,7, or 8) are still selected. Selection ignores whether an assessment is also a PPS assessment or not.
Prior Assessment	Selection period	46 to 165 days before the target assessment
	Qualifying Reasons for Assessment (AA8a/AA8b)	01/*, 02/*, 03/*, 04/*, 05/*, 10/* (* indicates any value accepted)
	Selection Logic	Latest assessment with qualifying reasons for assessment and assessment reference date (A3a) in the window of 46 days to 165 days preceding the target assessment reference date (A3a).
	Rationale	Select a normal (OBRA) assessment in the 4-month window ending 46 days before the target assessment. This window insures that the gap between the prior and target assessment will not be small (gaps of 45 days or less are excluded). A 4-month window is employed to allow sufficient time to find an OBRA assessment. OBRA assessments are required every 3 months. A grace month has been added to yield a window of 4 months to account for late assessments. In the last half of 2000, scheduled OBRA assessments were late about 8 percent of the time. A relative window based on the assessment reference date (A3a) of the target assessment is used to accommodate cases in which scheduled assessments are performed early or a significant change occurs. Normal OBRA assessments that are coupled with a PPS assessment (item AA8b = 1,2,3,4,5,7, or 8) are still selected. Selection ignores whether an assessment is also a PPS assessment or not.

EXHIBIT 271 (Cont.)
QM/QI Reports Technical Specifications: Version 1.0

Assessment Selected		Chronic Care Measure Selection Specifications
Most Recent Full Assessment	**Selection period**	Most recent 18.5 months preceding target assessment
	Qualifying Reasons for Assessment (AA8a/AA8b)	01/*, 02/*, 03/*, 04/* (* indicates any value accepted)
	Selection Logic	Latest assessment with qualifying reasons for assessment and assessment reference date (A3a) in the 18.5-month (or 562- day) period preceding the target assessment reference date (A3a).
	Rationale	Select a normal (OBRA) full assessment. Normal OBRA full assessments that are coupled with a PPS assessment (item AA8b = 1,2,3,4,5,7, or 8) are still selected. Selection ignores whether a full assessment is also a PPS assessment or not. If the target assessment is a quarterly assessment, it will at times be necessary to carry -forward items (not available on the quarterly assessment) from the most recent full assessment to that target assessment. The most recent full assessment will be used to carry forward values to a target quarterly assessment, but only if the most recent full assessment is in the 395 day period (approximately 13 months) preceding the target assessment reference date (A3a). A 13-month look-back period is employed to allow sufficient time to find an earlier OBRA full assessment. OBRA full assessments are required every 12 months. A grace month has been added to yield a look-back period of 13 months to account for late full assessments. If the prior assessment is a quarterly assessment, it will at times be necessary to carry -forward items (not available on the quarterly assessment) from the most recent full assessment to that prior assessment. The most recent full assessment will be used to carry forward values to a prior quarterly assessment, but only if the most recent full assessment is in the 395 day period (approximately 13 months) preceding the prior assessment reference date (A3a). A 13-month look-back period is employed to allow sufficient time to find an earlier OBRA full assessment. OBRA full assessments are required every 12 months. A grace month has been added to yield a look-back period of 13 months to account for late full assessments.

EXHIBIT 271 (Cont.)
QM/QI Reports Technical Specifications: Version 1.0
Selection of the Post-acute Care Sample

The post-acute measure calculation sample involves selection of residents with a 14-day SNF PPS assessment in the target period. If a resident has more than one 14-day assessment in the target period, then the latest 14-day assessment is selected. The appropriate 5-day assessment preceding the 14-day assessment is also selected, if available. One additional record is also selected, that record being the most recent admission assessment on the same date or before the selected 14-day assessment.

Assessment Selected		Post-acute Care Measure Selection Specifications
14-Day PPS Assessment	Selection period	The QM/QI reports use a default 6 month target period, however the user can change this period if desired.
	Qualifying Reasons for Assessment (AA8a/AA8b)	*/7 (*indicates any value accepted)
	Selection Logic	Select the latest 14-day assessment (*/7) with assessment reference date (A3a) in the selection period
	Rationale	If there are multiple qualifying assessments, the latest assessment is selected.
5-Day PPS Assessment	Selection period	The interval from 3 to 18 days before the selected 14-day assessment.
	Qualifying Reasons for Assessment (AA8a/AA8b)	*/1 (* indicates any value accepted)
	Selection Logic	Latest 5-day assessment with assessment reference date A3a) in the selection period for the same resident and facility.
	Rationale	Select a 5-day assessment (AA8b = 1) in the selection window preceding the selected 14-day assessment. The selection window (3 to 18 days prior to the 14-day assessment) allows for the 5-day to be completed on day 1 through day 8 of the stay and the 14-day to be completed on day 11 through day 19 of the stay, according to the SNF PPS assessment requirements. These requirements indicate that the gap between the 2 assessments should have a minimum of 3 and a maximum of 18 days. If there is more than one qualifying 5-day assessment in the selection window, then select the latest one.
Recent MDS Admission Assessment	Selection period	50-day period ending with the date of the selected 14-day assessment.
	Qualifying Reasons for Assessment (AA8a/AA8b)	01/* (* indicates any value accepted)
	Selection Logic	Select the latest admission assessment with assessment reference date (A3a) in the selection period.